SURVEYING

An Introduction to Engineering Measurements

PRENTICE-HALL
CIVIL ENGINEERING AND ENGINEERING MECHANICS SERIES
N. M. Newmark, Editor

SURVEYING

An Introduction to
Engineering Measurements

by Raymond

ADRIAN R. LEGAULT, 1909–
Professor of Civil Engineering, University of Nebraska

HOWARD M. McMASTER
Assistant Professor of Civil Engineering, University of Nebraska

RALPH R. MARLETTE
Assistant Professor of Civil Engineering, University of Nebraska

Prentice-Hall, Inc., Englewood Cliffs, N. J.

J

LIBRARY OF CONGRESS CATALOG CARD NUMBER: 56-12159

First printing..................October, 1956
Second printing..................June, 1957

PRINTED IN THE UNITED STATES OF AMERICA
87910

PREFACE

The first course in surveying, normally taken by engineering students early in their training period, should aid in developing the ability to visualize, to think logically, to plan, to work carefully and accurately, and to arrange the product of these efforts in a neat and orderly manner for record or presentation.

Surveying, unlike many of the subjects offered in the first two years of an engineering course, involves a combination of theory and practice—the engineering method. It has been our aim to stress these concepts in this book, intended for use in beginning courses in surveying. In addition, the importance of the art of mensuration in the field of engineering is emphasized.

In Part I we introduce the subject of surveying. Some historical background is given and the importance of the course as preliminary engineering training is stressed. Consideration has also been given to developing attitudes and thought processes which are important in continuing an engineering education. Here, as throughout the book, the thought of making the material interesting as well as informative has been uppermost in our minds.

In Part II the primary operations, namely the measurement of distance, direction, and elevation, have each been discussed separately. Where possible we have included several methods available for making each type of measurement.

Part III is concerned with the application of those principles, procedures, and techniques explained in Parts I and II.

In presenting the material in Parts II and III we emphasize the logic of all concepts and operations and the importance of choosing methods in terms of the results required.

We believe that fieldwork should constitute a substantial portion of any course in elementary surveying. However, since the facilities and time allocation for such work vary considerably at different institutions, no attempt has been made to present field exercises as such. Rather, the emphasis has been placed on explaining field procedures, techniques, and note keeping. Thus, the beginning student can make the best use of his time in the field on any type of exercise which might be assigned.

The opportunity is taken here to acknowledge with sincere appreciation the cooperation of all individuals, companies, and government organizations who have very kindly furnished illustrative material.

Gratitude is expressed to Mr. W. H. Boulter and his associates of the Keuffel and Esser Company for their review of the material on optical tooling.

A. R. L.

H. M. M.

R. R. M.

Lincoln, Nebraska

CONTENTS

I. The Engineer and Surveying

Part I

THE ENGINEER AND SURVEYING

Chapter 1

~~~~~~

SURVEYING: ITS USE TO THE ENGINEER

SURVEYING has as its purpose the determination of the dimensions and contour of any part of the earth. Establishing the relative position of points at or near the earth's surface requires both linear and angular measurements.

The application of surveying requires skill as well as a knowledge of mathematics, physics, and to some extent, astronomy.

The principles and practices of surveying have been connected with engineering throughout history. In our present civilization this connection has become more definite and at the same time broader than it has ever been. An introduction to some of these principles is desirable as a part of the training of any engineer, regardless of his later specialization.

1-1. The development of units of measure. The art of measuring is fundamental in many engineering operations in all fields. It forms the base upon which surveying rests.

The development of measuring techniques and units of measure parallel the development of civilization itself, for there has always been a need for measurement. Primitive man used night and day and the cycle of the four seasons as measures of time.

Units of linear measure were first adopted as the dimensions of various parts of a man's body. For example, a *digit* was the width of a man's middle finger. A *nail* was the width of the thumb nail and was considered the same as a digit. A *palm* was the breadth of the open hand. A *cubit* was the length from the point of the elbow to the tip of the middle finger. Other units of linear measure with which we are more familiar today were:

3

Foot: Distance from the back of a man's heel to the tip of his great toe.

Pace: Distance from the heel of one foot to the toe of the other as the feet are planted in taking a normal step.

Double pace or stride: Distance from the point at which one heel touches the ground to where the same heel again touches the ground as a man walks.

Fathom: Distance between the tips of the middle fingers when the arms are fully outstretched.

Standards of measure such as these were, of course, variable. As a need for more precise definition became apparent, some of the units were standardized according to the measurements of a chief, a ruler, or perhaps a favorite slave. This later standardization by statute has resulted in many of our present-day values. For example, an early measure of length known as the *cubit of a man*, represented by the height of a man standing erect, was later standardized as 72 inches. This length also became the standard for the fathom.

An early measure of area was based upon the amount of seed necessary to plant a given piece of land. Later the unit of land measure became the amount which could be plowed by a man with a yoke of oxen in one day. A *furrow long* (furlong) was the distance the oxen could plow before they were stopped to "blow." This distance was taken as forty lengths of the pole or goad used in driving the oxen, and was eventually standardized as one-eighth mile. The length of the ox goad was taken as sixteen and one-half feet and became known as the *pole, perch,* or *rod.* The width of a strip of land which could be plowed in one day was designated as four ox goads. A strip of land 40 rods long and 4 rods wide was legalized in England by the statutes of King Edward I as an acre. The designation doubtless came from the Anglo-Saxon *aecer*, a plowed or seeded field. It will be noted that the acre by these definitions contains 160 square rods or 43,560 square feet. This is the relationship in use in the United States today.

In angular measurement the use of 360 units for the basic subdivision of the circumference of a circle may be based on the knowledge that the earth completes one cycle of its orbit around the sun in a year and that the Chaldeans first divided the year into twelve months of thirty days each. The combination of the two would provide a basis for dividing any circumference into 360 equal parts.

1-2. The development of surveying instruments. The development of surveying instruments has been gradual, evolving in part from instruments used in astronomy.

About 4,000 B.C. the Chaldeans used a device called a *merchet* for measuring time and meridian. It consisted of a slotted palm leaf through which to sight and a bracket from which a plumb-bob was suspended. A line was projected by sighting through the slot and past the plumb-bob string.

Fig. 1-1. A group of Egyptians surveying. Original mural said to date from about 1,500 B.C. (From Bettmann Archive)

Babylonian tablets estimated to date from about 2,500 B.C. show primitive maps. The gathering of data for these maps must have involved the use of surveying instruments and methods. There is also evidence that the Egyptians used ropes or cords for measuring distances. Figure 1-1 shows a group of Egyptian "surveyors" at work. This scene is from a mural dating from about 1,500 B.C.

Archaeologists have learned that the foundations of the pyramids are almost horizontal, indicating that some device must have been used to define the horizontal when these structures were built. It is believed that the Assyrians and Egyptians used a triangular frame with a plumb line suspended from its apex to determine the horizontal. Figure 1-2 shows how one of these might have looked.

In the seventh century B.C. the height of pyramids was determined by means of a measuring pole, shadows, and a recognition of the

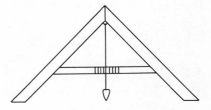

Fig. 1-2. Surveying instrument used by early Assyrians and Egyptians.

relationship between similar triangles.

During the rise of the Roman empire, cities, roads, and military camps were laid out on a system of rectangular coordinates. One type of instrument used, called the *groma*, has been described as a staff which supported two cross-arms attached at right angles to each other. Plumb-bobs, hung from each end of the cross thus formed, served to establish straight lines and lines at right angles to each other. The Greeks apparently used a similar instrument called the *Grecian star*, and there is evidence that the Assyrians also used a similar device much earlier.

By about 200 B.C. astronomy had become relatively systematized and the *astrolabe*, an instrument for measuring angles, had been introduced.

At the beginning of the Christian Era, Heron of Alexandria, a Greek mathematician, perfected a device called the *dioptra*, similar to instruments in use earlier. It consisted essentially of a copper tube supported on a standard and capable of being rotated in both a horizontal and a vertical plane. The copper tube was bent upward on both ends to accommodate vertical glass tubes. The assembly of tubes, when filled with water, provided a means of leveling and of measuring vertical angles. Leveling staves used with the dioptra were similar to the level rods in use today.

For measuring horizontal angles the tubes of the dioptra were replaced by a flat, circular disc graduated in degrees. An arm containing sighting apertures at either end could be rotated to any desired position on the disc.

Various instruments, including other types of plumb-bob levels, geometric squares, quadrants, and leveling staves, were developed prior to and during the Middle Ages.

During the Renaissance the development of surveying instruments and practices was stimulated by developments which included:

1. Disintegration of the feudal system which meant need for land subdivision and the establishment of ownership boundaries for the many smaller parcels of land.
2. The need for charts and maps as new lands were discovered and explored.
3. The development of artillery which created a need for instruments and methods to improve accuracy of fire, as well as the need for new types of fortifications for defense against artillery.
4. The need for more accurate instruments for astronomical observations as the science of astronomy and disagreements among astronomers grew.

The forerunner of our modern instruments for taping distances was the *Gunter's chain* invented by Sir Edmund Gunter in 1620. Use of the *plane table* began at approximately the same time. Both of these instruments are described later in the book.

The *wye level* in a form similar to its present one came into use during the middle of the eighteenth century, one hundred years after the tube bubble was invented. One reason for the delay may have been the erratic nature of the early bubbles because the inside of the tube was not ground on an arc nor smoothly finished.

In the 16th century the *surveyor's compass* came into wide use, followed about a century later by the telescope. These instruments led eventually to the development of the early 19th century models of the present-day *transit*.

From the 19th century until the present the improvements in the engineer's transit and level have been gradual. While there have been improvements, no basic changes were made until comparatively recent times. Among the most significant instrument changes are the *micrometer vernier, optical vernier, split bubble, tilting level,* and *self-leveling level*. The continuing improvement in optical techniques has been responsible for much of this development.

Modern surveying instruments are described in later chapters.

1-3. Surveying and the engineer. A knowledge of surveying is advantageous in many phases of engineering and provides excellent training in the ability to visualize, to think logically, and to pursue the "engineering approach." Engineers find that their duties often require direct or indirect application of the principles of surveying. In addition, the conscientious completion of an elementary surveying course will provide worthwhile general experience and develop desirable traits and habits because:

1. The nature of the subject with its related field measurements is such that it will help to develop habits of industry, accuracy, and reliability.
2. Experience in planning and working with others is provided in the fieldwork which is necessarily performed by groups responsible as a unit for the satisfactory completion of an assigned task.
3. Some of the computations are relatively long; practice in completing them will promote a feeling of self-confidence, and, in addition, habits of care, neatness, and continual checking will be developed.

All of these attributes will add to the professional stature and competence of any engineer. Those who hope to become engineers should begin to acquire them early.

Chapter 2

SURVEYING AS APPLIED TO ENGINEERING

THE PART played by surveying in early engineering work is not entirely known. However, it is logical to assume that it has always played an important part. For example, the property lines of the ancient Egyptians had to be continually re-established after each seasonal flooding in the Nile Valley. A reference to indicate that property surveys were made in Biblical times is found in Deuteronomy 19:14, "Thou shalt not remove thy neighbor's landmark, which they of old time have set in thine inheritance. . . ." Similar references are made in other books of the Old Testament. The pyramids were not only oriented with respect to the pole star, but have definite dimensions and plan. It is likely that the canal systems of the ancients were laid out by field surveys prior to construction. The draining of Lake Fucino by the Romans under Claudius I in about 50 A.D. required a tunnel between three and four miles in length. The tunneling was accomplished by simultaneous operations from forty shafts located at intervals throughout the entire length. Certainly surveying and engineering were necessary here.

Today, surveying instruments and methods are used at some point in nearly every engineering undertaking. Often the basic principles of surveying find application in all of the stages of a project from initial planning to final completion. Although surveying is more closely associated with construction projects and other work commonly classed as civil engineering, it still applies in other branches of engineering. For example, modern industry makes use of principles learned in surveying to set machines and machine foundations, to assemble aircraft, large generators, and other machines, and in the general layout of piping assemblies, conveyors, and the like. See Chapter 16.

2-1. Plane and geodetic surveying. Before discussing the applications of surveying it is necessary to recognize and define the two major categories into which it is divided, *plane* and *geodetic surveying.*

The term *plane surveying* is used to designate work where the distances or areas involved are small enough so that the curvature of the earth can be neglected without significant error. That is, in plane surveying the portion of the earth being surveyed is considered to be a plane.

It cannot be specifically stated how large an area must be before it becomes necessary to consider curvature of the earth. This will depend upon the degree of accuracy required in the work. In the subdivision of public lands, curvature is considered in running all four boundaries of tracts which are approximately 24 miles on a side. Only the east and west boundaries of townships, which are approximately 6 miles on a side, are run on the basis of the earth having a curved surface.

In the vertical plane the curved line defining the earth's surface deviates from any horizontal tangent at a rate which varies as the square of the distance from the point of tangency. A discussion of the consideration given this fact will be found in the chapter on measuring elevations.

Geodetic surveying requires the correction of the straight lines of sight through surveying instruments so that the points established will fall on the surface of a spheroid which represents very closely the true shape of the earth. The triangulation of the United States, for example, is computed on the surface known as Clark's spheroid of 1866. According to Clark the dimensions of the earth are:

Equatorial radius ... 6,378,206.4 meters
Polar semi-axis...... 6,356,583.8 meters
Based on a meter of 3.28086933 feet

Geodetic methods are often utilized to provide a framework covering a large area of the earth's surface. A number of points of known location and elevation are established in order to give a basis for smaller surveys, perhaps carried on as plane surveys.

Most geodetic surveys are made by governmental agencies such as the U. S. Coast and Geodetic Survey, which has established a network of points over the country, precisely located with respect to position and elevation. Such points provide an official basis for subsequent surveys, both geodetic and plane.

By geodetic methods, in the most precise work, distance can be measured with errors of less than one unit in one million; the accumulative error in leveling across the United States amounts to only about 0.5 foot of elevation.

Engineering surveys generally use plane surveying with occasional modifications being made that take into consideration the earth's shape. Some of the classes of surveys commonly made will be discussed next.

2-2. Land surveys. Land surveys are made to establish boundaries and provide records and maps which show the proper location and subdivision of lands in any specified area. The term *cadastral surveying* is sometimes used to designate this type of work. When the work is primarily concerned with property within a city it is commonly called *city surveying*.

In making land surveys it is usually necessary to relocate markers or monuments legally established by original surveys. This is done by examining records of the previous survey and retracing what was done. Many times either the records are incomplete or the original corners or monuments cannot be found. It is then necessary to re-establish them according to recognized methods, referring to whatever information is available. Individual or corporate property owners are concerned in this type of survey; often the material gathered in the survey is comprised of evidence in the form of legal descriptions for property deeds in litigation.

Figure 2-1 shows a portion of a property ownership plat. In Figure 2-2 is shown a section of a power line right-of-way map.

2-3. Topographic surveys. The basic purpose for the topographic survey is to gather data from which a map, showing both the natural and man-made features of the terrain, may be made. When the map shows only the plan (trees, water, buildings, etc. in a two-dimensional relationship) it is usually designated as a *planimetric* map. If the complete map also shows the relationships in the third dimension (elevation) as well, it is called a *topographic* map.

A topographic survey, and the resultant topographic map, provides a valuable tool for many engineering operations. From the beginning of the survey to the completion of the map, planning, logic, and comprehensive approach are used to attain a desired result.

Difference in elevation, the third dimension on the plane sheet

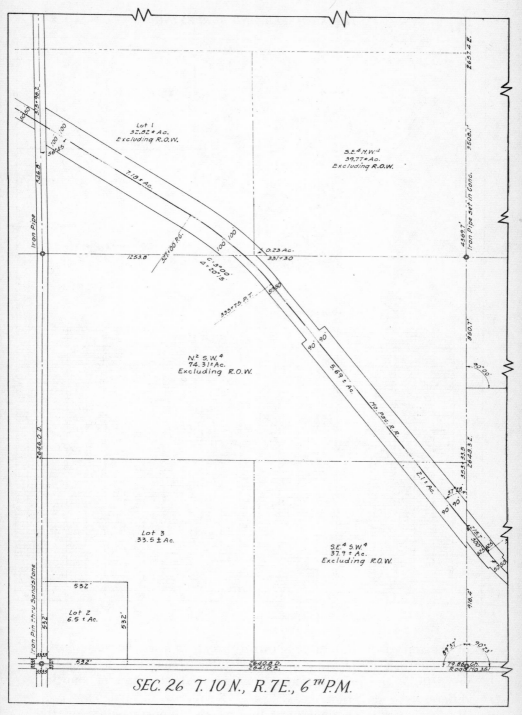

Fig. 2-1. Portion of ownership plat of several pieces of property.

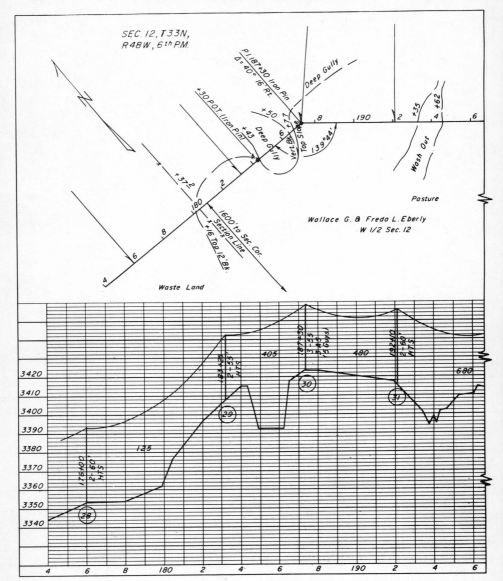

Fig. 2-2. Portion of power line R–O–W map.

of the topographic map, is shown by *contour lines, hachure marks,* or sometimes by shading or color combinations. The contour line constitutes the principal and most accurate method of showing difference in elevation.

A *contour* is an imaginary line which connects points on the surface of the earth having the same elevation. A contour line is plotted on a map to represent a contour on the ground.

The difference between the elevations represented by two adjacent contour lines is designated as the *contour interval*.

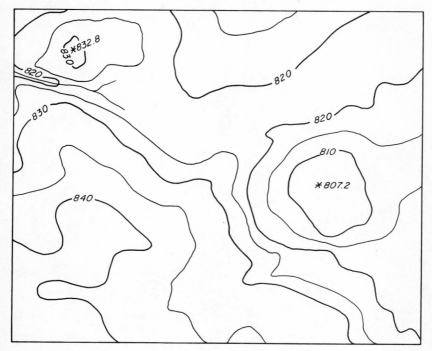

Fig. 2-3. Contour map.

A contour map is shown in Figure 2-3. Figure 2-4 illustrates the use of hachure marks and shading.

Engineers will encounter the topographic map in planning much of their work.

2-4. Route surveys. This term is used to describe a survey which supplies the data necessary to determine alignment, grades, and earthwork quantities in connection with the construction of highways, railroads, canals, airports, and pipelines, and also facilities such as power and communication lines. Here again the product of the survey is a map or series of maps showing the proposed location and other pertinent information. In addition to the maps other data is supplied which, when coordinated, will provide the information necessary for planning, cost analysis, and other basic engineering considerations. A study of this data makes possible the comparison of alternate routes or a determination of the feasibility of a single route.

If the project is considered through the complete cycle of engineering, a route survey may be subdivided into the *reconnaissance* survey, the *preliminary* survey, the *location* survey, and the *construction* survey.

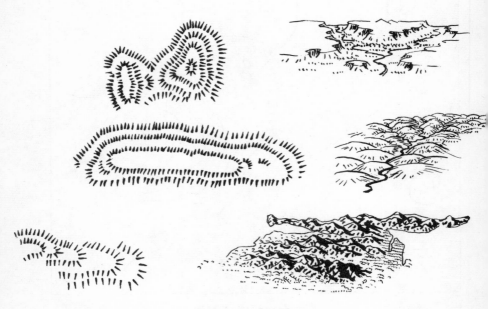

Fig. 2-4. Example of hachure marks and shading to show ground relief.

The reconnaissance survey, made to determine general conditions, is the first step in the route survey inasmuch as the final location of the facility is almost always based upon the examination of several alternate routes. Often the reconnaissance will provide sufficient information for the selection of the more desirable route. At other times it is necessary to gather more data in the preliminary survey before the final selection can be made. After the selection of a route, the final location survey is made. Surveys must continue during and after construction to insure proper construction and provide necessary information for making periodic payments to the contractor. Original plans are often changed as construction progresses. When this occurs, surveys provide the data for *as built* drawings.

The final plans produced from a route survey will include a map of the general area, called a *location* map, and a detailed plan and profile along the center line. Where earth moving is involved the established grades are shown. Information is then given concerning the cross-sections necessary to provide sufficient earthwork information for making cost estimates and for construction.

A more detailed discussion of profiles, grades and cross-sections will be given in later chapters.

2-5. Hydrographic surveys. These surveys are made to acquire data to chart the shore-lines of bodies of water and to determine the shape of the area underlying the water surface. They are

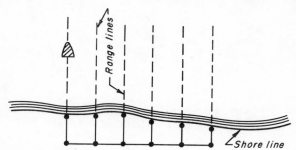

Fig. 2-5. Hydrographic surveying along range lines. Sounding craft is kept in line with established points on shore. Location along the line is determined by triangulation or stadia distance.

also made to determine quantities of flow and other stream characteristics.

Hydrographic surveys are most often made by governmental agencies such as the U. S. Coast and Geodetic Survey, the U. S. Army Corps of Engineers, the U. S. Geological Survey or by the offices of State Engineers. They are of general importance in connection with navigation, and the development of water resources for power, flood control, domestic use, irrigation, and recreation.

Several different types of electronic devices are used in hydrographic surveys for determining location and depths.

Soundings for water depth and the location of objects on the bottom are made by measuring the time required for sound to travel downward and be reflected back to a receiver in the surface craft.

Radio-acoustical methods are used in locating ships off-shore. The basic principle involved is that the vessel detonates a charge of explosives near it and receives reports by radio waves when the sound of the explosion reaches shore stations. With the velocity of sound in water known, the distances to the shore stations can be computed and the vessel is located with respect to them. Radar is also used in a manner similar to the radio-acoustical method.

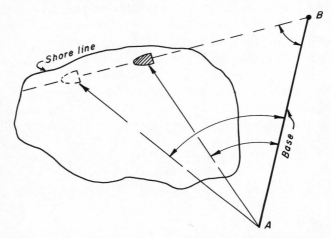

Fig. 2-6. Hydrographic surveying. Position of the boat is determined by turning angles from a shore *base*.

Figures 2-5 and 2-6 give some idea of what is involved in a hydrographic survey for determining water depths.

2-6. Aerial surveys. The applications and uses of aerial surveys have increased steadily since World War I, and with greater acceleration since about 1935.

An aerial survey is made by taking photographs of the ground from an airplane as it moves along a predetermined flight line at an altitude designated in terms of the desired scale of the photographs. The exposures may be continuous for some uses, but are usually individual exposures taken often enough to give a specified amount of picture overlap.

There are two general classes of aerial surveys. One is made by taking photographs from a plane to cover the desired area with no coordinated ground survey. The other has a ground control survey as an integral part of the operation, which establishes by standard surveying procedures the location and elevation of ground points which will appear prominently in the photographs. When proper ground control is provided, topographic maps may be made from aerial photographs by the use of special viewing and plotting equipment. These topographic maps, like maps produced by ground survey methods, can then be used in the location and construction of engineering projects.

Aerial photographs taken without ground control may be made to form a pictorial map by trimming and fitting together photographs so that they represent the terrain features located in the photographed area of the earth's surface. This map is called an *aerial mosaic* and has many uses, including use in planning the growth and development of a city.

It is reasonable to predict that aerial surveys will play an in-

Fig. 2-7. Aerial photographs for pavement condition survey.

creasing part in engineering work as new uses are developed. For example, aerial photographs provide a practicable means of surveying flood damage and estimating cost of repair or replacement, or of making pavement condition surveys in connection with highway maintenance.

Aerial photography is discussed in more detail in Chapter 14.

2-7. Construction surveys. On a construction project, surveying principles and instruments are used to properly locate all of the facilities that are to be built. For example, in constructing a highway it is repeatedly necessary to establish points of control along the center-line and edges of the work so that proper widths and grades will be attained. When constructing a building, a bridge, or some other structure it is necessary to establish the corners or other control points on the structure at the correct location and elevation. The construction of facilities to store, transport, or purify water must be controlled by surveys.

These are only a few examples of the part that construction surveys play in the completion of projects. It can be said truthfully that when construction of any sort is carried on by engineers it will be controlled by surveys.

Construction surveys are discussed further in Chapter 15.

2-8. Mine surveying. Mine surveying is used to establish property limits and other operational locations below ground. Certain variations in techniques facilitate this operation, but the principles do not differ from surveying on the surface. Location and control surveys for the construction of tunnels for purposes other than mining may be placed in the same category as mine surveys.

2-9. Industrial applications. While the term industrial surveying is not commonly used, surveying methods and equipment find a direct use in industry as mentioned earlier in this chapter.

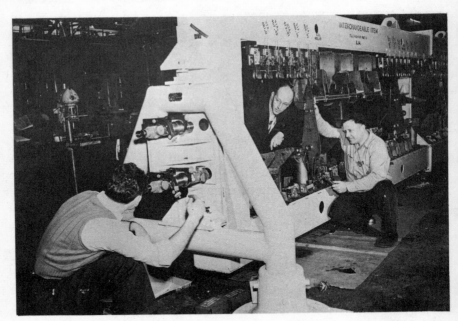

Fig. 2-8. Precision alignment of jig parts for B-47 aileron jig. (Courtesy Boeing Airplane Co.)

Figure 2-8 shows instruments which are similar to those used in surveying being used to locate positions accurately in the construction of airplane parts. In addition there are many indirect applications such as those connected with site location, and plant lay-out and construction.

Further discussion of ways in which knowledge of surveying may find application in industry will be found in Chapter 16.

2-10. Military applications. In general, the uses of surveying in the military parallel those uses found in civilian life, with the specific application of results to some military operation. For example, the maps resulting from topographic surveys or route surveys would be used as strategic information in planning for defense or attack. Aerial surveys play an important part in gathering data.

Because of the need for immediate information in military operations, modifications are often made in both procedure and equipment. The effectiveness of artillery fire is determined directly by the quality of survey information available.

Meteorological subdivisions of the military use the engineer's transit and target balloons for collecting data on the winds aloft.

2-11. Summary. The more common applications of surveying have been given, but there are numerous others, not ordinarily considered engineering applications. For instance, surveying is an essential part of forestry in connection with boundary locations, timber cruising, conservation, and logging. Also, geologists and geophysicists employ surveying in connection with exploration, location, and control in their work.

It should be understood, too, that the various types of surveys will overlap in almost any engineering project. This may be illustrated by considering all of the surveying requirements in connection with a mining development. As a minimum these would consist of:

1. A land survey to establish surface boundaries and permit a legal deed description.
2. Topographic surveys and route surveys to provide information for properly locating buildings, roads, railroads, and other operational facilities.
3. The construction of maps for reference and record.
4. Construction surveys for surface installations.
5. Mine surveys as underground work begins and then progresses.

In addition to these items aerial and/or ground surveys may be made to determine geological features. If milling of ore is to be carried on, industrial applications of surveying may be used in placing machinery. A hydrographic survey may even be necessary if the milling operations call for a large quantity of water.

Chapter 3

~~~~~~

COMPUTATIONS: SOME
FUNDAMENTAL PRINCIPLES

IN SURVEYING as in most engineering work the original or field measurements will rarely be in the form of the physical quantities which must be determined. Computations, however, enable us to convert these measurements to the quantities sought.

Engineers must have the ability to compute easily, quickly, and accurately. This requires a knowledge of the fundamental properties of numbers and the ability to estimate the accuracy of computations based on field measurements. In order to compute rapidly, an engineer must have had much practice and should be able to use any available device to speed and simplify computation.

Most of the mathematics required in the solution of plane surveying problems is simple, but attention must be given to detail and careful checking. Simple addition and subtraction are the cause of more mistakes in surveying computations than all other mathematical operations. This does not, however, preclude the need for a good basic understanding of algebra, particularly in the use of logarithms. Other mathematical tools widely used in surveying are geometry and trigonometry, which form the base for all surveying operations.

Surveying is an excellent introduction to the whole field of engineering mensuration, since the quantities dealt with can usually be seen and mentally estimated.

The same error theory is equally valid for computations based on surveying measurements as for those based on any laboratory experiment which involves measuring. For example, errors made in reading lengths of fluid columns in a manometer to determine pressures are similar to those made in survey taping. The same principles apply to the design of a vernier for micrometer calipers as for a vernier attached to a level rod.

20

3-1. Significant figures. An observed quantity is never absolutely exact. It is necessary to determine what part of an observation is significant in any computation in which the observation is involved. Certainly all correct digits whose value will not change by further refinement in measuring are significant. Also, the digit in which the maximum error is less than half of the unit in the place which the digit occupies is significant. All digits to the left of the rightmost recorded digit are presumed to be significant except zeros to the left of the leftmost digit or unless the recording indicates a different intent.

Here is a list of numbers with the significant figures and maximum errors that are indicated by the recorded form:

Number	Significant figures	Maximum error
100	1	± 50
9000	1	± 500
0.0000065	2	± 0.00000005
10.1	3	± 0.05
100.	3	± 0.5
29°21'	4	$\pm 30''$
100.00	5	± 0.005

Accuracy of computations is most desirable, but the results should not be carried out to indicate a greater number of significant figures than the measurements justify. Carrying them out too far implies an accuracy which does not exist and results in an unreliable solution.

If the sides of a rectangular city lot are measured and recorded as 60.25 feet and 140.50 feet, what is the area of the lot? The width is measured to four significant figures while the length indicates five significant figures. Zeros recorded to the left of the decimal point are presumed to have significance. The recorded values indicate that it was possible to measure correctly to the closest 1/100 of a foot. The results then are: 60.25 ± 0.005 and 140.50 ± 0.005.

Product of *measured* values:

$$(60.25) \times (140.50) = 8,465.1250$$

Product of *minimum* values:

$$(60.245) \times (140.495) = 8,464.121275$$

Product of *maximum* values:

$$(60.255) \times (140.505) = 8,466.128775$$

Obviously the area is known only to the nearest square foot and should be written: 8,465 square feet (four significant figures). In general, the measurement with the fewest significant figures determines the number of significant figures in the result.

It is good practice to carry an extra digit in a computation and to round off to the justified number when the computation is complete. When either of two numbers are equally close to the number to be rounded off, choose the one ending in an even digit. The mean of 99.37 and 99.34 would then be 99.36.

3-2. Algebraic methods. Much of surveying deals with numbers of four or more significant figures; so the related computations must be carried out by equally accurate methods. Included in this category of methods are algebra, arithmetic, geometry, and trigonometry with the related use of logarithmic and trigonometric tables. These mathematical operations can be carried to any degree warranted by the measurements, or permitted by the available tables.

The use of square root occurs so frequently in surveying, particularly in the solution of right triangle problems, that the "long hand" method of extracting it should be studied. Tables of logarithms are not always available in the field, and some square root solutions are found faster and more accurately by direct computation. The following is a sample calculation:

```
5' 29.' 71' 00' 00 |23.015
      4
  40 |1 29
   3 |1 29
    460 |0 71 00
      0 |
      1|  46 01
  46020 |24 99 00
      5 |23 01 25
          1 97 75
```

How many *significant figures* are there in the answer?

3-3. Use of logarithms. For many surveying computations, time will be saved and there will be less chance of mistakes if logarithms are used. The *common* logarithm of a number is the power to which 10 must be raised to produce the number. From the algebraic laws of exponents, to multiply numbers we add logarithms of the numbers and obtain the logarithm of the product, to divide we subtract logarithms, to raise numbers to a power we multiply the logarithm of the number by the power, and to find a root of a number we divide the logarithm of the number by the root sought. Most of these operations are easier than arithmetic methods when several steps or large numbers are involved.

The logarithm of a positive number can be written as the sum of an integer (positive or negative) and a decimal fraction which is always positive. In the logarithm 2.863112, for example, the integer (2) is called the *characteristic* and the decimal fraction (.863112) the *mantissa*. The characteristic of the logarithm of a number greater than 1 is the number of digits to the left of the decimal point, minus 1. The characteristic of the logarithm of a number less than 1 is a negative number whose absolute value is the number of zeros to the right of the decimal point, plus 1. The characteristic of a logarithm depends only upon the position of the decimal point.* The mantissa, on the other hand, is independent of the decimal point position and depends only upon the sequence of digits. Thus, the mantissa for both 0.529 71 and 5,297,100 is 0.724 038.

To insure accuracy of the last figure in a computation by logarithms, the number of places in the mantissas of the logarithms should be one more than the number of significant figures in the final answer. With angles read to the nearest 10 seconds, the logarithmic functions differ in the fifth place. Six place tables are then necessary to maintain computations consistent with data. The tables in the appendix allow us to handle computations involving this accuracy (five significant figures).

The problem shown in Figure 3-1 illustrates a logarithmic computation and the use of tables in the appendix including the auxiliary table for the logarithmic sines of small angles.

3-4. Graphical and mechanical methods. Any procedure which speeds the routine, tedious part of computing and still gives all the significant figures required should be used. *Graphics*, plotting measurements to scale, is a quick method of finding lengths or angles not measured directly in the field. Plane table surveying is based entirely on graphical methods.

Practically all earthwork volumes for highways, railroads, and

---

* The negative characteristic, -1 is commonly replaced by the equivalent form $9 - 10$, and -2 by $8 - 10$ with the -10 omitted. This notation has been followed in the logarithmic tables of trigonometric functions in the appendix.

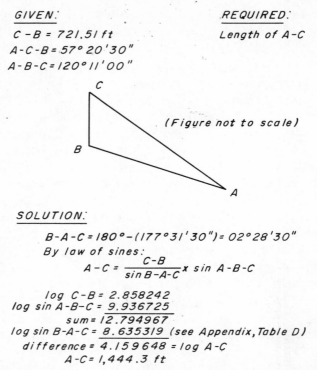

GIVEN: REQUIRED:

C - B = 721.51 ft   Length of A-C

A-C-B = 57° 20'30"

A-B-C = 120° 11'00"

(Figure not to scale)

SOLUTION:

B-A-C = 180° - (177°31'30") = 02°28'30"

By law of sines:

$$A - C = \frac{C-B}{\sin B-A-C} \times \sin A-B-C$$

log C-B = 2.858242
log sin A-B-C = 9.936725
sum = 12.794967
log sin B-A-C = 8.635319 (see Appendix, Table D)
difference = 4.159648 = log A-C
A-C = 1,444.3 ft

Fig. 3-1. Logarithmic computation, using the auxiliary log sin table for small angles.

canals are computed from a combination of graphical and mechanical methods. The cross-section of the cut or fill along the route is plotted to scale and the area found by use of a polar planimeter, which measures the area of any closed figure. A tracer point is run around the outline and then the distance the measuring wheel has gone is read. This instrument may be calibrated to give the area of the enclosed figure directly and is also useful in finding the capacity of reservoirs to be formed behind dams or for evaluating engine indicator diagrams in mechanical engineering studies.

A polar planimeter in use to determine the area of a highway cross-section is shown in Figure 3-2. This instrument is discussed in Article 12-19.

The slide rule is one of the simplest and fastest computing instruments. The processes of multiplication, division, and the finding of powers and roots may be performed to three-figure accuracy with the ordinary 10-inch slide rule. The limited accuracy of the slide rule restricts its use to minor surveying computations or checking

Fig. 3-2. Planimeter tracing highway cross-section for area determination.

longer, more precise methods. There are special trigonometric slide rules frequently used in stadia surveying.

The electric calculator is an invaluable instrument in all engineering offices. Most students, however, do not have access to these machines and must rely on long-hand or logarithmic means to gain more than three-place accuracy. The manufacturers of calculators publish operation manuals which give many short cuts that can be used with their machines. Examples of surveying calculations are often included.[1,*]

3-5. Accuracy and precision. Accuracy is exactness, the correct answer free from errors and mistakes. A measurement is accurate to one less than the number of significant digits it has. Lengths of 102 feet and 971.117 feet are both accurate if all digits indicated cannot be changed by more refinement in measuring. Computations should carry one more significant digit than those which are accurate.

* Numbers refer to selected references, page 313.

For example, a recorded length of 102.3 feet implies that the digits 1, 0, and 2 are accurate. The rightmost digit 3 is significant. All accurate digits are of course significant.

The precision of a measurement is the closeness of the numerical value to the *true value*. Unfortunately, the true value is fundamentally unknown and inaccessible. The precision of a single, isolated measurement is therefore completely unknown. Precision implies a refinement of measurement which necessitates using precision instruments under ideal conditions with the best techniques, and obtaining several repetitions of closely agreeing observations. Precision in surveying is expressed as the ratio of the known error, both linear and angular, to the total distance measured. Thus a specified precision of 1/5,000 would limit the combined errors in a survey of a city lot with a perimeter of 500 feet to 0.1 feet.

3-6. Angle-distance relationships. If the precision of a survey is to be 1/5,000, what is the maximum error we can have in our angular observations? The natural sine or tangent of an angle of 00°01′ is 0.00029. An error of one minute then would vary computations based on the sine or tangent by 29/100,000 or 1/3,450. To achieve our required precision angles must be correct to a fraction of 01′. Assuming a straight-line variation, they should be measured to 3,450/5,000 of 01′ or (7/10)′. The trigonometric functions do not vary directly with the size of the angle so the relation shown is approximate, but close enough for most surveying work.

3-7. Errors and mistakes. Errors are deviations of observations or calculations from their true values, the deviations being beyond the control of the one performing the operation. Errors are inherent in all measurements. They must be studied and their effect reduced to an insignificant amount for the survey being made.

Mistakes are blunders which may be caused by carelessness, inexperience, or indifference of the observer. Mistakes have no place in any engineering work. They should be discovered by routine checks and corrected. Care should be exercised to make these checks by independent methods since everyone is reluctant to find mistakes in his own work. For example, in measuring the distance between two points with a tape, a second or check measurement should be made. This second measurement should be made in the opposite direction and preferably with the head and rear tapemen changing positions to avoid the possibility of repeating the same mistakes.

Mistakes such as transposing figures, 69.24 for 69.42; reading the wrong foot mark on the tape; or omitting a whole tape length are frequently made by surveying students. Practices such as using distinct signals and repeating verbal information before it is recorded help to avoid mistakes. Making mental estimates of quantities to be measured enables the engineer to avoid large discrepancies which yield absurd results.

3-8. Systematic and accidental errors. When making measurements it is important to consider the limitations of the measuring equipment and technique. Failure to do this introduces *systematic* errors. For example, when we measure a distance, it cannot be correct if the tape is inaccurately graduated. Systematic or cumulative errors are added to the work each time an observation is made. A *constant error* is a systematic error which has the same effect upon all observations in a series. For example, in measuring with a tape that is too long, each time the tape is laid down the same error is repeated.

How are these systematic errors to be detected? First, the measuring process and the measuring equipment are studied to see if systematic errors can be traced to these sources. Second, by carefully controlling the conditions of observation and by comparing the results of several observers, it may be possible to detect additional systematic errors. After the observations have been completed, statistical significance tests may be used to determine if systematic errors are still present.[2,3]

The measuring process is affected by another type of error known as the *accidental* or *compensating* error. Accidental errors are random errors because they do not follow any law of action. As soon as a law of action is formulated, these errors become systematic. The effects of accidental errors can be reduced by taking more observations.

3-9. Sources of error. Even if the error factors cannot be made to vanish, an accurate measurement is still possible if enough data is obtained to compute the correction terms. For precision measurement, three sources of error must be considered: (1) instrumental, (2) natural, and (3) personal.

Some of the factors inherent in the design of surveying instruments and other measuring devices which limit the accuracy attainable are: (1) calibration of the scales, (2) readability of the scales, (3) optical accuracy, and (4) mechanical linkages of the instruments. The general considerations for these points follow.

Calibration requires that the instrument give direct readings in the exact units of the quantity being measured. These basic standards are established by natural or legislative law and are maintained by the Bureau of Standards in Washington, D. C., which provides a service for checking the accuracy of calibration of some measuring instruments.

The readability is proportional to the length of the scale and is related to the spacing of graduations, the thickness of index and graduation marks, and parallax effects.

Optics and mechanical features govern the exactness of "pointing" of direction and angle instruments.

The importance of these factors increases with the precision of a measurement. In low-precision instruments the readability is properly made low enough so that the inaccuracies of the instrument are not detectable. With instruments of high precision, on the other hand, the full potentialities are not realized unless all of the sources of inaccuracy are studied and accounted for. For this reason it is possible to obtain poorer data with better instruments.

Since surveying is almost entirely an out-of-doors activity, natural errors present a big problem. The effect of factors such as temperature, curvature of the earth, and ground slopes (systematic errors) can be measured and proper corrections applied. Other natural factors such as wind, refraction of air, and visibility (accidental errors) are generally indeterminate as to their magnitude. High-order surveys must be made when the indeterminate factors will be at a minimum, which may mean doing the work on a still, clear night.

The distinction between *personal errors* and *mistakes* is often confused. The careful, experienced observer may make readings that are in error. Some observers habitually read instruments low while others will read them high. This trait is not too serious since most results are reduced from the differences in readings. Reaction times of observers make little difference in the results as long as they are consistent. However, consistency and simple honesty are essential. Impartiality is important for an engineer or for anyone who deals with obtaining and analyzing data. No amount of mental evasion or wishful thinking can make incorrect measurements correct.

3-10. Error theory. Statistical analysis considers data as a sample of an indefinitely large sequence of repetitions of a measuring process in which, if no systematic errors are present, the mean will give the true value of the quantity being measured. This involves one of the main phases of statistical analysis: that of estimation. The fundamental problem of estimation is to find the best possible value of the mean and the standard deviation of a sample. Standard deviation is a measure of dispersion, showing the extent to which individual values are scattered. It is defined as the root mean square of the differences between the observed values and the mean and is shown in equation form as

$$\sigma = \sqrt{\frac{\Sigma \, v^2}{n}} \qquad (3\text{-}1)$$

where σ is the standard deviation, $\Sigma \, v^2$ the sum of the squares of the residuals (the differences between the observed values and their mean) and, n, the number of observations. When estimating the standard deviation, the question often arises as to what constitutes a small sample and what constitutes a large sample. It seems to be a safe rule to follow that a sample less than 30 is statistically "small" while one greater than 500 is "large." When n is small, as is usually the case with surveying observations, its value in the standard deviation formula is replaced by $(n - 1)$.

The theory of probability gives some important relations. For example, the probability of twice the standard deviation being exceeded is about once in 22 trials; the probability of three times the standard deviation being exceeded is about once in 370 trials. The probability of 0.6745 times the standard deviation being exceeded is once in two trials. This particular value has been named the probable error, and gives us the common least-squares formula,

$$E_s = 0.6745\sigma \qquad (3\text{-}2)$$

where E_s is the probable error of any single observation. The probable error (E_m) of the mean of a series of observations is given by the formula:

$$E_m = \frac{E_s}{\sqrt{n}} \qquad (3\text{-}3)$$

COMPUTATIONS FOR PROBABLE ERROR
IN THE LENGTH OF A LINE

Lengths	Residuals, v	v^2
667.97	0.12	0.0144
667.93	0.08	0.0064
667.88	0.03	0.0009
667.86	0.01	0.0001
667.84	−0.01	0.0001
667.82	−0.03	0.0009
667.76	−0.09	0.0081
667.72	−0.13	0.0169

Mean: 667.85 Sum: 0.0478

$$E_s = 0.6745 \sqrt{\frac{0.0478}{(8-1)}} = \pm 0.06$$

$$E_m = \frac{0.06}{\sqrt{8}} = \pm 0.02$$

These lengths are from student surveys, all of which had an indicated precision of 1/5,000 or better. The precision of the mean is 0.02/667.85 or 1/33,000 while the precision of a single measurement is 0.06/667.85 or 1/11,000. The wide dispersion would reveal by significance tests that systematic errors are present and the results should be used with caution.

These and other statistical methods are used in many phases of engineering; for example, in production engineering, statistical methods are used to control quality of product where the aim is to increase the value of the ratio, quality/cost. Statistical methods are used to a great extent in flood analysis, in the analysis of errors in photogrammetry, and in electronic measurements.

3-11. Weighted observations. Measurements made under different conditions or having different reliability are often combined in determining a most probable value. For example, if an angle is

Angle	Number of repetitions	Weight	Product (angle times weight)
101°18′10″	3	1	101°18′10″
101°17′50″	6	2	202°35′40″
		3	/303°53′50″
			101°17′55″*

* It is doubtful if the mean of such a small number of repetitions should be recorded to a greater accuracy than is shown.

measured by one party using three repetitions and by another party using six repetitions, then the latter observation should be given twice the weight of the first.

Often weights are assigned on the basis of weather conditions prevailing at the time the measurements were made. Thus, a length taped on a calm day might be considered twice as reliable as one taped on a windy day. Obviously, this type of weighting requires good judgment as well as experience in surveying and computing.

If the probable error is known instead of the number of observations, the weight can be computed as follows: For observations made with equal care, (1) weights vary directly with the number of observations and (2) probable errors vary inversely with the square root of the number of observations. The weights then are inversely proportional to the square of the corresponding probable errors.

To illustrate this, assume that the difference in elevation of two points and the probable errors as determined from three independent level circuits is as shown. Find the most probable value of the elevation difference.

Elevation difference	Probable error	Weight
10.71	±0.03	$1/(0.03)^2$
10.67	±0.02	$1/(0.02)^2$
10.65	±0.05	$1/(0.05)^2$

The most probable value for the elevation difference is the weighted mean of the three values given. We need work only with the decimal fraction, as follows:

$$0.71 \times 1/0.0009 \propto 0.71 \times \tfrac{4}{9} = 0.32$$
$$0.67 \times 1/0.0004 \propto 0.67 \times 1 = 0.67$$
$$0.65 \times 1/0.0025 \propto 0.65 \times \tfrac{4}{25} = 0.10$$

$$\tfrac{361}{225} \quad 1.09$$

The weighted mean of the difference then is:

$$10 + \frac{225}{361}(1.09), \quad \text{or} \quad 10.68$$

3-12. Units of measurement. In the United States and other English-speaking countries, the most commonly used linear units are the foot, yard, and inch. The unit of area is the acre, which is 43,560 square feet. In Europe and South America, distances are measured in meters (1 meter = 39.37 inches). The United States Coast and Geodetic Survey also uses the metric unit for its work.

For United States Government land surveys, the Gunter's chain (66 feet long) is the linear unit. This chain is divided into 100 links. Each link then represents 0.66 feet, or 7.92 inches. There are 80 chains to the mile, and, since 1 square mile contains 640 acres, 10 square chains equals 1 acre.

In Texas and the southwestern United States, which were at one time Spanish territories, another unit known as the *vara* has been used. The adopted length of the vara is different in different sections: $33\frac{1}{3}$ inches (Texas), 33 inches (California), 32.99 inches (Mexico).

Volumes are expressed in either cubic feet or cubic yards.

The units of angular measurement are the *degree*, the *minute*, and the *second*. One circumference = 360°; 01° = 60'; 01' = 60''.

In the French system, 1 circumference is divided into 400 grads. The grad is divided into 100 centesimal minutes and the minute is further divided into 100 centesimal seconds. If trigonometric tables based on these units are available, many computations are greatly simplified.

3-13. Field notes. The field notes of a survey should contain all of the information at hand in a sensible arrangement so that another person can quickly see what was done and make any necessary computations. The competency of the surveyor's planning and his knowledge of the work are reflected in the field record more than in any other element of surveying. When a simple question arises as to whether angles were turned to the right or left, or whether a survey followed the center-line of a highway or an offset line, the value of concise, complete notes becomes clear. It is surprising that special and limited notes are usually included, while essentials are sometimes omitted.

Records supply information and should be legible, concise and comprehensive, written in clear, plain letters and figures. Field work should be recorded directly in the permanent book *at the time observations are made*. Use a 4H pencil, well pointed, and follow the Reinhardt style of lettering, shown in Figure 4-10.

Good notekeeping habits, formed in college and constantly maintained, will be of great value in an engineering career. Legible and neat lettering and figuring are excellent working and business assets.

A systematic arrangement of all survey data is essential if the record is to be concise and include all of the information. Accuracy is always aided by methodical apportionment and classification of data. A complete record written in a disorderly and confused manner often causes more mistakes than erroneous information. Forms in general use are shown in this book, but in practice, these must be adapted or new forms devised to meet unusual situations.

TABLE OF	CONTENTS		
Description of Work	Date	Party Chief	Page
1. Differential Levels, B.M.$_{10}$ to B.M.$_{20}$	Oct. 10, 1955	J. Whitaker	2 - 3
2. Profile Levels, ₵ of 10 th Street	Oct. 15, 1955	J. Whitaker	4 - 5
3. Transit - Tape Traverse - J. W. Hill property	Nov. 1, 1955	H. Adams	6 - 7

Fig. 3-3. Field book *Table of Contents.*

Because field books may contain several unrelated surveys, the first pages should be used for a table of contents, which will include the type of survey, the dates of the survey, and the page numbers. The name of the person in charge may also appear. See Figure 3-3.

Following are some important general rules for notekeepers:

1. Record directly in the field book as observations are made.
2. Use a sharp, 4H pencil. Never use ink or a soft pencil which will smudge.
3. Follow a consistent, simple style of lettering. Never write in a field book.
4. Use a liberal number of carefully executed sketches.
5. Make the notes for each day's work on the survey complete with a title of the survey, date, weather conditions, personnel of the crew, and list of equipment used.
6. *Never erase.* If a mistake is made, rule one line through the incorrect value and record the correction above the mistake. This necessitates making the original entries only $\frac{1}{2}$ space in height.
7. If a page has so many mistakes that it is illegible, the entire page should be voided by drawing a diagonal line across the page and lettering "VOID," the date, and the name of the person voiding along the line. Care should be taken not to obliterate voided notes.
8. Number every double page.

9. All significant figures should be recorded. If a length is measured to the nearest 0.01 feet, it should be so recorded; for example, 231.40 feet, not 231.4 feet. There should be no doubt as to the location of the decimal point. Record a zero to the left of the decimal point when the number is less than one, as 0.74.
10. Record angles as 03°09′30″, using at least two digits for each part of the angle.

PROBLEMS

1. What is the area of a rectangular plot which measures 101.1 × 55.5 feet?

2. (a) The probable error introduced by using the plumb-bob in taping is ±0.02 feet per tape length. If one mile is measured using a 100-foot tape and it is necessary to use the plumb-bob for every tape length, what is the total probable error?

(b) If the measurement of this mile is repeated 10 times by the same methods, what is the probable error in the mean of all the measurements?

3. The area of a parcel of land is determined by three independent traverse surveys with the precision of each survey as indicated. What is the weighted mean value of the area?

No.	Area in acres	Precision
1	160.15	1/3,500
2	160.20	1/3,000
3	159.95	1/4,000

4. Each angle of a nonagon is measured with a probable error of ±30 seconds. What is the probable error in the sum of the angles?

5. A line is measured on a windy day as 1,111.1 feet. The same line measured 1,110.2 feet on a calm day. If the latter measurement is given three times the reliability of the first, what is the mean length of the line?

6. If the angles of a survey can be measured with a probable error of ±10 seconds, what is the requirement for distance measurement in order to maintain the same precision?

Part II

MEASUREMENTS

Chapter 4

~~~~~~

DETERMINING DISTANCE

IN PART II the discussion will be confined to general concepts of measurement and to specific procedures and techniques for the measurement of distance, direction, and elevation.

Throughout history the measurement of distance has taken a variety of forms with a marked variation in the accuracies attained. The ancient "rope stretchers" did a more precise job of measuring distance than did the American Indian who knew that a certain hunting ground was two "sleeps" from his village, but in each case the accuracy was sufficient for the use to which the measurements were put.

A similar situation exists in all engineering measurements. In one instance approximate values may serve as well as more precise values. In another instance it may be necessary to employ special techniques and equipment to obtain the required refinement. With few exceptions the cost of making a measurement increases with the required precision of the results. It is important, therefore, to know what methods of measurement are available and their relative accuracies so that for any given job a selection can be made which will be the most economical in keeping with the required precision.

Basically there are only two elements in measuring a distance. (1) Determine and identify the beginning and end points. (2) Find by the most practicable method the distance between the two points.

In plane surveying all distance records in their final form are of the *horizontal*. The distances are either measured on the horizontal or sufficient data is gathered so that the horizontal projection can be computed. Approximate measurements such as pacing do not justify slope corrections.

4-1. Pacing. When an error from two to five per cent is allowable, pacing is a feasible method for obtaining distance, unless the terrain is too rough or obstacles interfere.

To pace a distance it is necessary to know the value for the length of one's pace. This can be determined by walking along a line of known length and dividing that length by the number of steps taken. A line at least 1,500 feet in length is recommended for this purpose. When calibrating the pace and in pacing distances it is important to walk naturally. To attempt to make each step a predetermined length is tiring and will probably give less accurate results.

If the distance to be paced is more than a few hundred feet, it is desirable to have a mechanical counter for recording the number of steps taken. The counter may be hand operated or may be of a type which is strapped to the pacer and will register by impact each time either foot contacts the ground. This latter device is called a *pedometer*.

Some prefer to count strides rather than paces. Still another procedure is to determine to the nearest pace the number of paces per hundred feet and tally only each hundred-foot distance. Unless it happens that you take a whole number of natural steps per hundred feet, this latter method will decrease the accuracy obtained.

4-2. Tachymetry. This term, meaning swift measurement, is sometimes used to designate the procedure of measuring distance by sighting a graduated rod and noting the intercept on it by a pair

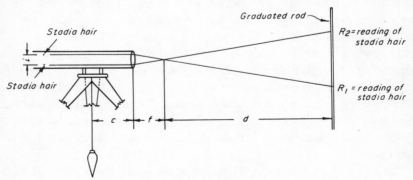

The instrument is constructed so that $\frac{f}{i}=100$. Then, since $R_2-R_1 = $ rod intercept (R), similar triangles indicate that $\frac{f}{i}=\frac{d}{R}$, and by substitution $d=100R$.

Fig. 4-1. The stadia principle.

of cross hairs which are placed within the telescope of the surveying instrument.

The more common method of this type is known as *stadia*. Two of the horizontal cross-hairs in the telescope are called *stadia hairs*. All engineers' transits are equipped with stadia hairs which are placed an equal distance on either side of the central or main horizontal cross-hair. See Figure 6-4(a). The spacing of the stadia hairs is such that at a distance of 100 feet their intercept on a vertical rod will be approximately 1 foot, if the line of sight intersects the rod at right angles. At 200 feet, then, the intercept will be approximately 2 feet, and so on.

The stadia principle is illustrated in Figure 4-1.

James Watt, the Scotsman who invented improvements which resulted in a practical steam engine, devised the stadia method of measuring distance in about 1771 while working as a civil engineer.* At that time it was referred to as a micrometer for measuring distance. The term stadia probably came into use because the rod is held at a known point or station when obtaining a "stadia distance."

Another way of measuring distance, similar to the stadia method, is by the use of *horizontal stadia*. This method is more common in Europe than in the United States. The principal difference is that the stadia rod is in a horizontal position when sighted and the stadia-hairs of the instrument are vertical. An advantage of this arrangement is that the rod intercept is not affected when the line of sight is not horizontal. It will be noted in studying Figure 4-1 that the rod intercept for a given horizontal distance will change as the line of sight varies from a right angle intersection with the rod. A correction can be made for this, but it necessitates extra computations. See Chapter 13.

The *subtense bar* is another means of distance measurement. It also is used more extensively in Europe than in the United States. It consists of a bar made from an alloy having a low coefficient of expansion, and with a target at either end. See Figure 4-2.

The bar is mounted horizontally on a tripod. A transit, or theodolite, is used to measure the angle between the two targets which are at a fixed and known distance apart.

---

* In 1778 a Mr. Green was given recognition by the Royal Society of Arts in Great Britain for discovering the method of measuring which we know as stadia. See *The Life of James Watt* by James Patrick Muirhead, John Murray, Albemarle St., London, 1858.

The horizontal distance from transit or theodolite to subtense bar is equal to one-half the distance between targets multiplied by the cotangent of one-half the angle subtended by the targets.

This method of measuring horizontal distance also makes any correction for the slope of the line of sight between subtense bar and angle measuring instrument unnecessary. In addition the hori-

Fig. 4-2. The subtense bar. A means of obtaining distance by measuring angle subtended at a transit by the targets at either end of the bar. (Courtesy Kern Instruments, Inc.)

zontal distance is yielded directly. It should be apparent, however, that if the line of sight is sloping in the use of horizontal stadia, the distance determined will be on that slope, not on the horizontal.

Because of the small angle subtended in using the subtense bar there is the disadvantage of having the linear measurement appreciably affected by any error in the angle measured between targets.

4-3. Other methods of measuring distance. There are a number of other ways in which approximate distances may be determined.

Where the terrain permits, the *odometer unit* of an automobile speedometer may be used to advantage. If enough work is to be done to justify it, a special odometer, reading to smaller units than the common 0.1 mile, may be used to increase the precision.

Over comparatively smooth surfaces a *measuring wheel* may be a practicable device. This consists of a wheel which is mounted on a rod so that it can be pushed along in front of the operator. A counter records the number of revolutions, or a calibrated recorder gives the distance directly in feet and parts of feet. A procedure similar in principle is to count the revolutions of a vehicle wheel as it moves along the line to be measured.

For reconnaissance work where there are no roads, the number of steps taken by a saddle horse or the time required to travel between points may be used to get approximate distances.

Scaling from *aerial photographs* may yield useable results. The scale can be determined if the height from which the photograph was taken is known. If it is not, the approximate scale can be found by measuring on the photograph some object of known size.

Graphical solutions which relate known and unknown distances geometrically may often be used to advantage. This is basically what is done in plane table work, discussed in Chapter 13.

Triangulation (see Chapter 9) utilizes geometric and trigonometric relationships to obtain distances. This method finds practical use when long distances must be found or when distances over inaccessible terrain are involved.

The most common way of determining distance is probably by the use of a *graduated tape*. This is often referred to as direct measurement, since the tape is actually stretched along the line being measured and the number of tape lengths is recorded.

The refinement to which tape measurement can be made varies with the techniques used and the precautions taken. Some of these will be discussed in detail.

TAPING DISTANCES

Because of long prior usage this procedure in surveying is often referred to as *chaining*. The person ahead along the line being measured is then called the head chainman and his partner the rear chainman. These terms have carried over from the days when the Gunter's chain and the Engineer's chain were in use. Since the chain has been replaced by the tape as a measuring instrument, the term *taping* is used in this book.

4-4. Chains. A discussion of chains is important from the historical viewpoint and because of the relationship of the Gunter's chain to our units of land measurement.

The Gunter's chain, also referred to as the surveyor's chain, consisted of 100 pieces of steel rod linked together by small rings. The total length was 66 feet. The units used for recording distance were *chains* and *links*. For example, a distance of 10 chains 5 links could also be reported as 663.3 feet.

Much of the measurement for the subdivision of public lands in the United States was made with the Gunter's chain. Often field notes and records based upon the use of this instrument must be interpreted by the engineer in determining property boundaries. Tapes which are graduated in chains and links are available and are used in connection with modern land surveying. They are commonly 1, 2, or $2\frac{1}{2}$ chains in length.

The student should become familiar with the following conversion factors for the Gunter's chain:

$$1 \text{ link} = 0.66 \text{ feet or } 7.92 \text{ inches}$$
$$1 \text{ chain} = 100 \text{ links} = 66 \text{ feet} = 4 \text{ rods}$$
$$80 \text{ chains} = 1 \text{ mile}$$
$$10 \text{ square chains} = 1 \text{ acre} = 43{,}560 \text{ square feet}$$

Another chain in use before the advent of tapes was the *Engineer's chain*. It was similar to the Gunter's chain, but was 100 feet in length instead of 66 feet. Both chains had 100 links.

Figure 4-3 shows a Gunter's chain. Note that because of the many wearing surfaces, this type of measuring device will continue to increase in length as it is used. Figure 4-3 shows the threaded adjusting screw on the handle for correcting the total length of the chain.

4-5. Metal tapes. For very precise work a tape made of a nickel steel alloy may be used. These are called *Invar* tapes (from invariable) and have the advantage of being much less affected by temperature changes than is a steel tape. The thermal coefficient of expansion for Invar tapes is only about one tenth of that for steel tapes. However, in addition to the higher cost of Invar tapes, they have the disadvantage of requiring very careful handling.

The most commonly used metal tape is of steel, about $\frac{5}{16}$ths inch wide, 0.025 inch thick, and 100 feet long. Other lengths are available such as 25, 50, 200, 300, and 500 feet, but the 100-foot length is most popular. The cross-section of a steel tape varies,

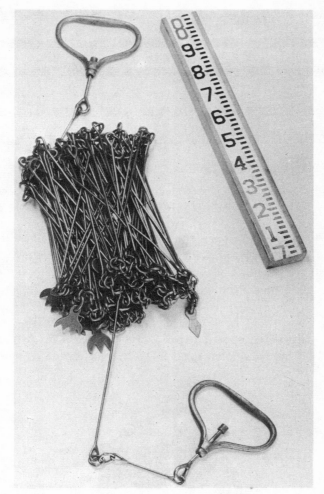

Fig. 4-3. The Gunter's chain. Ten link intervals are marked by the
metal tabs.

depending upon its total length and the type of service it is designed
to withstand.

Figure 4-4 shows some of the common ways in which steel tapes
are graduated.

Notice that the tapes shown in Figure 4-4 are graduated to
tenths of a foot. Also notice that sometimes the extra graduations
are between the zero and 1-foot marks (*cut tapes*) and at other times
an extra foot beyond the zero of the tape is subdivided into tenths
(*add tapes*). These variations make it necessary to be careful when

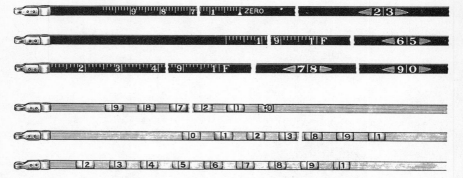

Fig. 4-4. Common styles of graduating tapes that are used in surveying.

using a tape, making sure that the correct point is held for zero.

Units of feet and inches are not normally used in surveying work; hence the graduations of feet and decimals of feet.

Sometimes measurements for precise work are made using metric tapes.

4-6. Handling metal tapes. Steel tapes of 50 feet or less are attached to small reels encased in leather or metal to make a com-

Fig. 4-5. A 100-foot steel tape wound on a hand reel.

Fig. 4-6. Putting up a 100-foot steel tape.

pact carrying unit. Those over 100 feet in length are normally on winding reels for transporting.

The commonly used 100-foot tape may be purchased with or without a reel. Figure 4-5 shows one of these on its reel. It can be easily detached from the reel for use if desired.

This tape is more commonly handled without a reel. To do this it is first put in 5-foot loops with the graduation kept uppermost as the tape is pulled in so that the thin ribbon takes the shape of a figure eight. See Figure 4-6.

The tape is tied securely when done up to this stage and then formed into a circle as shown in the sequence illustrated by Figure 4-7. This is called *throwing the tape.*

Fig. 4-7. Steps in throwing 100-foot steel tape.

Figure 4-8 shows the resulting circular shape which is easily carried in a knapsack or in the hand.

To ready the tape for use the procedure just outlined is reversed. Care must be exercised in taking the tape down so that it does not become tangled.

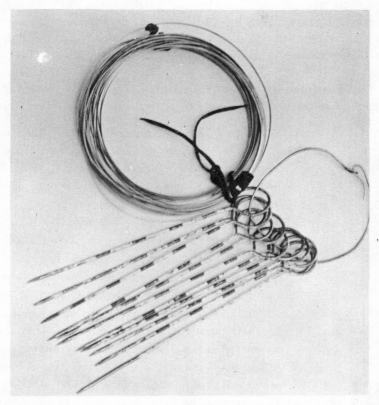

Fig. 4-8. Steel tape *thrown* for carrying when reel is not used. Taping pins are also shown.

The Invar tape must be done up on a large diameter reel to avoid short radius bends and in general requires special handling to maintain its precision.

4-7. Metallic tapes. The metallic tape is a fabric tape, with several very fine copper wires woven into it longitudinally to reduce stretching.

These tapes are more convenient to handle than metal tapes and are satisfactory for measurements where the required precision does not exceed 0.1 foot per 100 feet. They are available in lengths of 25, 50, 100, and 150 feet.

4-8. Nonmetallic woven tapes. These tapes are woven from synthetic materials which have a high dimensional stability. They are coated with a plastic material to help resist abrasion and the effect of moisture. This kind of tape can be used for any work for which a metallic tape is suitable. In addition they are the only safe tape to use for work around electrical installations.

4-9. Equipment other than tapes. In addition to a tape the equipment necessary for measuring distances includes the following:

1. Steel pins for marking tape lengths when the measurement is being made between points which are more than a tape length apart. These pins (see Figure 4-8) are called *taping pins, chaining pins,* or *surveyors' arrows.* A set consists of eleven pins.

2. One or two *ranging poles* or *line rods* (see Figure 4-9). These are used in establishing line. They are of wood or steel and either round or octagonal in cross-section. A common length is 8 feet. They are normally painted with alternate red and white sections, each one foot in length, thus they can also be conveniently used for short, approximate measurements. They are also designated as *range poles* rather than ranging poles.

3. A field notebook in which to record data. A hard-lead pencil (4H) for recording data.

4. Two plumb-bobs for taping across obstacles and for use on sloping ground (see Article 4-11).

5. Other accessories such as a stake bag, tacks, and wooden stakes for marking semi-permanent points, and an ax for clearing brush and driving stakes.

Fig. 4-9.
Range poles
or line rods.

4-10. Taping over flat or gently rolling ground. As has been indicated, the procedure used in taping will vary with the required precision. Ordinary precision is commonly considered to be about 1/5,000, that is, the variation between the measured distance and the true distance shall not exceed 1 foot in 5,000 feet.

The following outline assumes that ordinary precision is required, that a line more than 1,000 feet in length is being measured, and that a 100-foot steel tape is being used. The order of procedure is:

1. Place a range pole behind the distant point so that it is on the line with respect to the starting point.
2. Stretch the tape out along the line with the zero end ahead. The head tapeman is placed on line by the rear tapeman sighting to the range pole. Lining by eye, if carefully done, will yield the precision specified. (Compute the error per 100-foot tape if the head tapeman is off line 0.3 foot.)
3. The head tapeman hands one pin to the rear tapeman even though the starting point is usually marked in some other way. Both men should check to see that ten pins remain on the ring.
4. The head tapeman, carrying the ten pins, picks up the tape and is placed on line by the rear tapeman. The tape is pulled taut and whipped gently to make sure its entire length lies along the line. The tapemen must be alert at all times to avoid kinking the tape.
5. The rear tapeman holds the 100-foot mark about 0.1 foot behind the starting point. The head tapeman, working from the side of the line and with a pin poised on line opposite the zero mark on the tape, begins to apply a slow, steady pull. The rear tapeman resists, but at the same time allows the 100-foot mark to move slowly ahead. With a little practice he can make his resistance such that the required pull on the tape (10 pounds, estimated) is reached just as the 100-foot mark on the tape reaches the starting point. At that instant he calls out "stick" and the head tapeman pushes the pin into the ground opposite the zero. The pin is usually inclined from the vertical about 20 or 30 degrees. As he does this he calls "stuck." If the surface is so hard that a pin cannot be stuck into it, a Y-shaped mark (crow-foot) is scratched with the pin, then the pin is laid down so that it points to the crow-foot.
6. After checking once, the rear tapeman releases his end of the tape and the two move forward along the line, the head tapeman dragging the tape. The rear tapeman watches his end of the tape and when it has nearly reached the pin just placed he calls out "tape." He then picks up his end of the tape, lines the head tapeman in, and the procedure outlined in Step 5 is repeated. Note that the rear tapeman now has one pin in his hand. This serves as a tally of the one tape length measured. One pin is marking the end of the first tape length, and the head tapeman has nine pins.
7. After the second pin has been established by the head tapeman, the rear tapeman picks up the pin which marked the end of the first tape length and the two men move ahead as before. Now the two pins held by the rear tapeman tally the two tape lengths measured.

8. The procedure as outlined is repeated until ten tape lengths (1,000 feet) have been measured. At this point in the operation the head tapeman will be out of pins, the rear tapeman will have ten, and one will be marking the end of the tenth tape length.

9. Both men should count the pins to be sure none have been lost. A tally is made in the fieldbook, showing that a cycle of ten tape lengths has been completed. The entire process from this point until the end of the line is reached is a repetition of the steps already outlined.

10. Unless the line has a length equal to some number of full tape lengths, the last measurement will be a partial tape length from the last pin set to the end point of the line. To make this measurement the rear tapeman selects a foot mark that, when held opposite the pin, the end point of the line will fall within the graduated foot at the end of the tape. Since the zero end of the tape is ahead, the mark held by the rear tapeman will be correct to the closest foot. The distance to decimals of a foot is obtained by correctly reading and applying the value shown by the graduations at the zero end of the tape. As soon as this final length has been determined the value for the total length is obtained by adding it to the distance indicated by the "pin count." This value is immediately recorded in the fieldbook. It is necessary that the count of pins held by the rear tapeman be made before the pin marking the end of the last full tape length is pulled.

						2/5/56 3
TAPING FOR SMOKY HILL POWER LINE						Cool – Clear
						Allen Hd.Ch.
						Worth R. Ch.
Sta.	Tally Per 10 Pins	Final Increment	Total Dist.	Mean		
A – B	++++ 1	876.3	6876.3			Pt. A –S.E. cor. of power house
				6875.8		
B – A	++++ 1	875.2	6875.2			Pt. B – Angle point near junction of
						state highways 21 and 16.
B – C	++++	90.8	5090.8			
				5090.4		Pt. C–S.E. corner of site for Randall
C – B	++++	90.1	5090.1			sub station.
C – D	~	761.5				Pt.D –Junction of center-lines
				761.4		U.S. Highways 6 and 77
D – C	~	761.3				

Fig. 4-10. Field notes for taping distance.

11. It is desirable for the tapemen to exchange positions and measure the line in the opposite direction as a check.

Figure 4-10 shows one form in which notes on taping may be taken. The student should refer to the common rules listed in Article 3-13 while learning to take notes.

4-11. Taping on sloping ground to obtain horizontal distance directly. In the discussion in Article 4-10 it was assumed that "gently rolling" indicated that no slope along the line would

Each horizontal line represents one tape length. Vertical scale exaggerated.

Fig. 4-11. Use of the plumb-bob in taping.

exceed two per cent (2-foot rise or fall per 100 feet). When this is true the difference between the horizontal distance and the distance measured with the tape lying on the ground is negligible for ordinary precision. When the slope is more than two per cent the tape is held as nearly horizontally as it is possible to judge by eye. In this way the horizontal distance is obtained directly. From this position the tape graduations are transferred to the ground by means of a plumb-bob. (See Figure 4-11.)

It will be noted that the tape will sag when unsupported, thus making the indicated or recorded distance greater than the true distance. This effect is reduced by pulling somewhat harder on the tape when measuring by this method than when the tape is supported throughout its length.

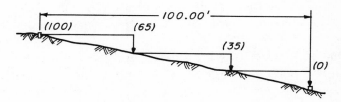

Fig. 4-12. Breaking tape.

The slope may be so steep that the full tape length cannot be conveniently held so that the two ends will be at the same level. When this is the situation, one end of the tape is held on the ground and partial tape lengths are measured in a series of steps until a full tape length has been traversed. See Figure 4-12. This procedure is called *breaking tape.*

A chance for mistakes in computing from partial tape lengths will be avoided if, when breaking tape, the tape is first stretched its full length along the line. Then the head tapeman selects a foot-mark where the tape can be held horizontally at not over chest height. The rear tapeman then advances and holds the same foot mark at the point just established. This is repeated as many times as is necessary to reach the end of the tape. A tape length is then recorded. Care must be taken that the pins used in marking intermediate points along the tape are not counted in the tally of pins.

4-12. Determining horizontal distance from slope measurement. Sometimes it is more convenient or more efficient to measure with the tape stretched along a sloping surface rather than

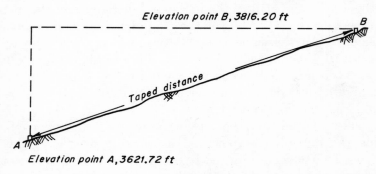

Fig. 4-13. Slope taping between points of known elevation.

to obtain the horizontal distance directly by plumbing. In such a case it is necessary to measure the rate of slope in order to compute the horizontal distance.

One way to do this is to determine the difference in elevation of the end points of the line. It will be seen from Figure 4-13 that the horizontal distance is then available by use of the Pythagorean theorem.

An approximate solution for the horizontal distance d, when the slope distance s and the difference in elevation h are known is:

$$d = s - \frac{h^2}{2s} \quad \text{(approx.)} \tag{4-1}$$

The basis for this expression is as follows. By the Pythagorean theorem, $s^2 - d^2 = h^2$ or

$$(s - d)(s + d) = h^2.$$

For small values of h the distances d and s are approximately equal, so

$$(s - d)\,2s = h^2 \quad \text{(approx.)}$$

From this, Equation (4-1) may be written.

Given the values of h and s as 20.00 feet and 100.00 feet, respectively, the value of d computed by the Pythagorean theorem is 97.98 feet. Computed by the approximate method it is 98.00 feet.

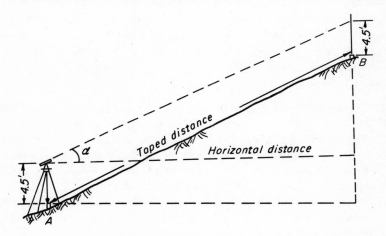

Fig. 4-14. Slope taping with the angle of slope measured with a transit.

Another more commonly used field procedure is to measure the angle between the slope line and the horizontal (the vertical angle) by means of a transit as shown in Figure 4-14. With the slope distance known the horizontal distance may then be found by the cosine relationship. The computation is simplified by using the versine function of the vertical angle.

Table H, in the appendix, lists common trigonometric relationships.

Notice that the sight in Figure 4-14 is taken to a point on the rod or range pole as far above point B as the horizontal axis of the transit telescope is above point A.

Figure 4-15 shows the procedure for measuring when the slope distance is not over one tape length.

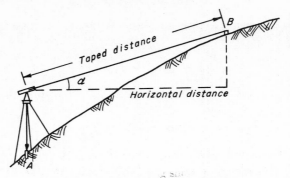

Fig. 4-15. Slope taping short distance.

4-13. Hints for tapemen. It is not possible to become an expert tapeman by reading rules and instructions alone. Practice, general experience, and close attention to details are also necessary factors. However, intelligent use of the experience of others will aid in quickly becoming proficient in the use of the tape.

Remember these tips:

1. The pull applied by the head tapeman must be gradual and steady. If for any reason "see-sawing" begins, stop and begin again.

2. Tapemen should always assume the position most conducive to maintaining balance as tension is put on the tape. Pulling with the body rather than with the arms will lessen the chances of being pulled off balance and result in a steadier pull on the tape.

3. It is desirable to check all points as they are established. Points established by the use of a plumb-bob should *never* be accepted without a check.

4. When using the plumb-bob it is easier to measure downhill. This allows the rear tapeman to work with the tape held on an established point on the ground rather than having to get the plumb-bob over a point while resisting the pull by the head tapeman. When using the plumb-bob it is particularly important to pull the tape by bracing yourself and leaning the whole body "into the pull." See Figure 4-16. For accuracies better than 0.05 foot per 100 feet do not *plumb* more than chest high.

5. Learn to work from the side of the line rather than on line. There will be times when remaining on line will obstruct the view of a transitman.

6. Continually make estimates and compare with what you are recording for reasonableness. For example, an alert tapeman would "pick up" the mistake of reading 89 as 68 by noting that the distance measured was only about 10 feet short of a tape length.

Fig. 4-16. Using the plumb-bob in taping.

7. After the partial tape length at the end of a line has been measured, the head tapeman should hold zero on the end point and the rear tapeman check the distance to the last pin by reading the foot mark and estimating tenths.

8. When numbers are called out for checking purposes or to the note-keeper, the one calling them should call slowly and distinctly. The one receiving the call should recognize it by repeating back, but with different words, for example: called, "twenty-seven point oh five"; repeated, "two seven decimal zero five."

9. When reading the foot mark for a partial tape length, look at the foot mark on either side of it as a check.

10. When placing a range pole behind a point for lining by eye, place it back far enough so that the point is not disturbed (at least 0.5 foot away from the point).

4-14. Common mistakes in taping

1. Losing or miscounting pins.
2. Not using correct zero or 100 foot points on tape.
3. Transposing figures in calling or recording.
4. Incorrectly reading tape in determining partial tape length at end of line.
5. Misunderstanding called numbers.
6. Reading the tape wrong, that is, 6 for 9 or vice versa, or reading one foot too much or too little.
7. Careless use of the plumb-bob.

4-15. Sources of error in taping

1. Tape not straight because of obstruction on line.
2. Variations in temperature.
3. Tape of incorrect length because of kinks, splices, or any other reason.
4. Too much or too little tension.
5. Wind effect on tape and on plumb-bob.
6. Incorrect alignment in either vertical or horizontal plane.

4-16. Care of taping equipment. Any equipment used in engineering measurements must be treated with care to preserve its usefulness. Taping equipment is no exception. The following rules should be observed:

1. Do not allow automobiles or other vehicles to run over a tape.
2. Wipe off wet or muddy metal tapes with a dry cloth and then with a slightly oily one.
3. Do not blunt the metal point of a range pole or plumb-bob.
4. Keep plumb-bob string free of knots.

4-17. Marking and referencing points. Certain control points must be established in surveying work so that they will be permanent. A line to be used over a long period of time might, for example, have each of its end points marked with a bronze disc set in concrete. Metal rods driven into the ground with a center-punch mark to designate the exact point may be used. For less permanent markers, wooden stakes, called *hubs*, are driven into the ground until flush or nearly so. A transit tack, which is a galvanized tack with a depression in the center of the head, is driven into the top of the stake to identify the exact point.

All control points should be *tied in* or referenced. These *ties* are recorded in the fieldbook as they are made. This may be done either by sketch, by word description, or by a combination of both. Ties are made for two purposes: (1) to make it possible to locate the point if it becomes covered or otherwise hidden, and (2) to make it possible to re-establish the point accurately if it is removed. The former need be accurate only enough to locate the point within a few tenths of a foot. For example, "Point A—Iron pin 18.4 ft S.E. of N.E. corner of Student Union Building and 16.1 ft W. of center of square manhole cover." In the second case, ties must be made

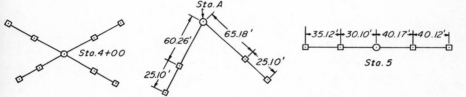

Fig. 4-17. Accurate methods for tying points.

so that from them a tack or other point can be replaced in its original position after the entire marker has been removed. Figure 4-17 shows several ways of making ties for re-establishing a point.

4-18. Precision in taping. The procedure for securing a precision of about 1/5,000 has been discussed. Lack of attention to details as outlined, either through carelessness or because of a need to obtain faster and less accurate values will result in precisions below this. Under extreme weather conditions it may be necessary to apply an approximate temperature correction to obtain a precision of 1/5,000 even with reasonable care in measuring.

To consistently obtain precisions of 1/20,000 to 1/30,000, (1) line is maintained by transit, (2) tension is applied by means of a spring balance, (3) corrections are made for temperature and sag, and (4) care is taken in setting points. To obtain temperature values, the thermometer should be fastened to the tape. Even then there may be a significant difference between the observed temperature and the true temperature of the tape. If a steel tape is used, it may be necessary to make measurements on a cloudy day or at night to increase the precision.

For precisions of 1/100,000 or over an Invar tape should be used. If a steel tape is used, the work will have to be done at night or on a cloudy day during hours when the temperature change is slight.

Special procedures for marking the end of each tape length as well as use of corrections and precautions already mentioned are necessary too. In baseline measurement (see Chapter 9) precisions of 1/1,000,000 are often required.

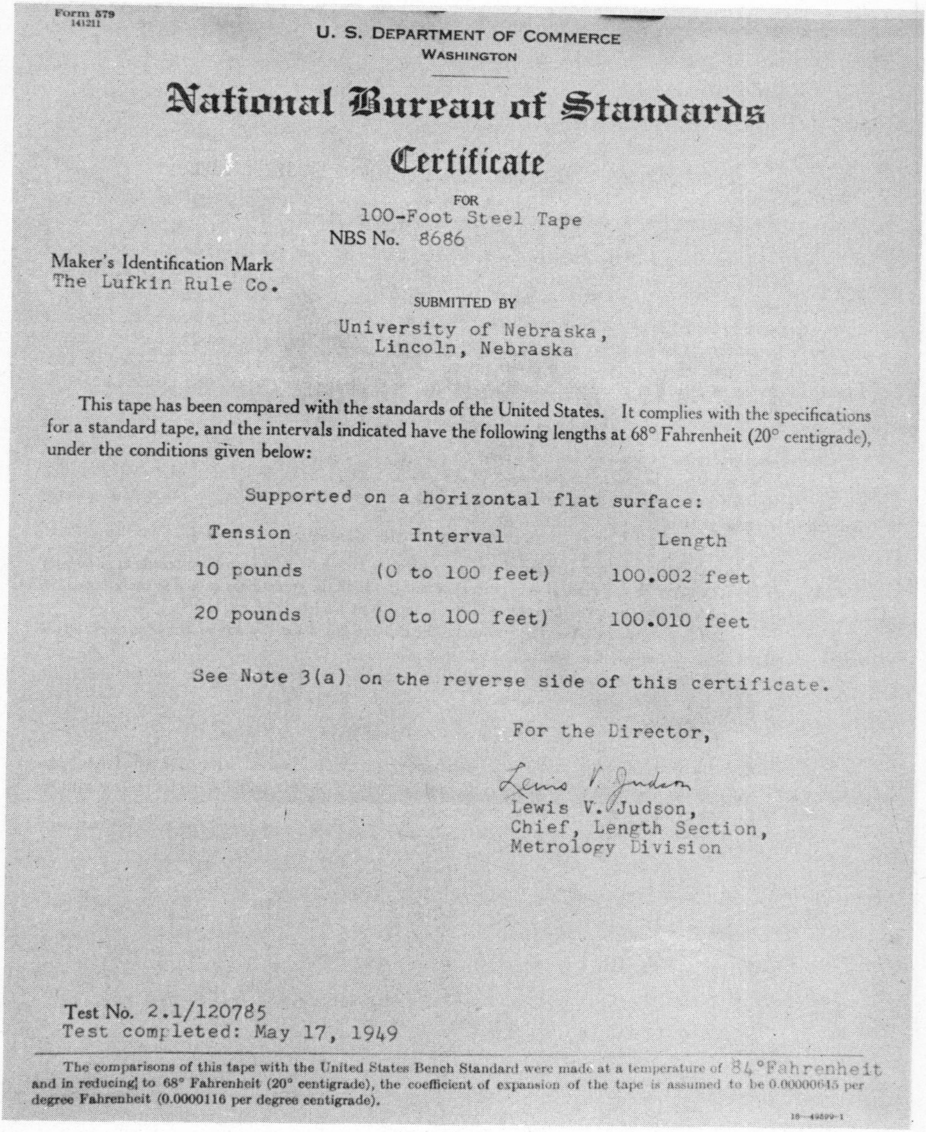

Form 579
141211

U. S. DEPARTMENT OF COMMERCE
WASHINGTON

National Bureau of Standards

Certificate

FOR
100-Foot Steel Tape
NBS No. 8686

Maker's Identification Mark
The Lufkin Rule Co.

SUBMITTED BY
University of Nebraska,
Lincoln, Nebraska

This tape has been compared with the standards of the United States. It complies with the specifications for a standard tape, and the intervals indicated have the following lengths at 68° Fahrenheit (20° centigrade), under the conditions given below:

Supported on a horizontal flat surface:

Tension	Interval	Length
10 pounds	(0 to 100 feet)	100.002 feet
20 pounds	(0 to 100 feet)	100.010 feet

See Note 3(a) on the reverse side of this certificate.

For the Director,

Lewis V. Judson
Lewis V. Judson,
Chief, Length Section,
Metrology Division

Test No. 2.1/120785
Test completed: May 17, 1949

The comparisons of this tape with the United States Bench Standard were made at a temperature of 84°Fahrenheit and in reducing to 68° Fahrenheit (20° centigrade), the coefficient of expansion of the tape is assumed to be 0.00000645 per degree Fahrenheit (0.0000116 per degree centigrade).

16—49699-1

Fig. 4-18. Certificate of tape standardization.

4-19. Standardizing tapes. A tape should be compared with a standard length at the beginning of any job and at intervals thereafter. This can be done by mailing the tape to the National Bureau of Standards, Washington, D. C. There, for a nominal fee, it will be compared with a precisely determined length. If the tape conforms to their specifications, a certificate will be issued showing the actual length of the tape under specified conditions of temperature, tension and support. See Figure 4-18. If the tape does not conform to their specifications, a report will be issued instead of a certificate.

For precise work each tape used should be submitted to the Bureau of Standards. On less precise work it is sufficient to compare all tapes to one which has been standardized and is kept out of service except for comparison purposes.

4-20. Corrections in taping. Taping operations group themselves into two categories: (1) taping to determine an unknown distance and (2) taping for the purpose of laying out a specified or required distance.

Depending upon the accuracy required, there are certain corrections made to the original measurements regardless of which of these two objectives is involved. Standard practice is not to correct each tape length as it is measured, but to record the initial measurement in terms of the nominal length of the tape being used. This means that the original result must be changed on the basis of "over recording" or "under recording" when the tape is assumed to have its standard or nominal length.

There are five items which may make correction necessary. These are:

1. Tape not nominal length under standard conditions.
2. Tape not nominal length because of temperature at time of measurement.
3. Distance between end points of unsupported tape less than nominal length because of sag.
4. Change in length because pull applied (tension) is more or less than that applied when tape was standardized.
5. Tape not horizontal at time of measurement.

Items 3 and 5 will always result in the actual horizontal distance being less than the recorded distance. In the case of the others the recorded distance may be more or less than the actual, depending upon conditions.

When making the corrections it must first be determined whether the distance between the end points of the tape was more or less than the recorded nominal length, and how much. The necessary correction is then added to or subtracted from the recorded value. Care must be used in reasoning what to do or the correction may be made in the wrong way.

4-21. Temperature corrections.

We know that materials expand and contract with temperature changes. The amount of change in length per unit of length per degree change in temperature is called the *coefficient of linear expansion*. For steel tapes this coefficient is 0.0000065 per degree Fahrenheit. The temperature at which a tape is *standard*, that is, when its actual length and designated length are identical insofar as temperature effects are concerned, is usually taken as 68 degrees F.

The significance of temperature corrections in taping is apparent if we consider that a temperature change of 30°F. will result in a change in the length of a 100-foot steel tape of $0.0000065 \times 100 \times 30$, or 0.0195 foot. A change of only 0.5°F. will account for a difference of 1/300,000. This explains why it is necessary to measure when the temperature is constant or changing very little if a high order of precision is required.

The surveyor should cultivate the habit of reasoning whether a correction should be added or subtracted for each situation as it occurs. For example, suppose a line is measured with a 100-foot steel tape when the temperature is 98°F. and recorded as 2,623.65 feet. If the tape is standard at 68°F., it will be 0.0195 feet *too long* at 98°F. The true length of the line is not less than the recorded distance as might first be guessed. The reasoning here is as follows: (1) The recorded measurements are always in terms of the nominal length of the tape. (2) This means that the 2,623.25 feet represents 26.2365 tape lengths each designated as 100.00 feet. (3) Actually each tape length represented 100.0195 feet. (4) The true length, therefore, is 26.2365×100.0195, or 2,624.16 feet.

That is, the value based on nominal tape length was less than the true value (under recorded).

Now, in a situation in which two points are to be set 2,623.65 feet apart under the conditions just outlined, what field measurement must be made?

1. Each tape length actually represents 100.0195 feet.
2. In 26.2365 tape lengths we would over record 26.2365 × 0.0195, or 0.512 feet.
3. The field measurement to be made to set the two points 2623.65 feet apart is (2623.65 − 0.51), or 2623.14 feet.

4-22. Corrections for tension. The standard tension for a 100-foot steel tape is 10 pounds. Obviously the tape will be more or less than 100 feet in length as the pull on it varies above or below that value. The amount of change can be found by the formula:

$$C = L(t_d)/AE, \tag{4-2}$$

where C = change per tape length, in feet; L = length of tape, in feet; t_d = difference between standard pull and actual pull; A = cross-sectional area of tape, in square inches; E = modulus of elasticity in psi (pounds per square inch). E for steel = 30,000,000 psi.

4-23. Correction for sag. As has just been stated, a tape is of standard length when it is fully supported and under standard pull. If the pull is maintained, but the support is removed so that the tape is only supported at its ends, it will sag because of its own weight. The shape of the curve that the tape will take is called a catenary. It is easily seen that the horizontal distance between any two points on the tape is now less than when it was fully supported. The difference between the tape reading and the horizontal distance between supports can be found by the formula:

$$C = \frac{w^2 L^3}{24 t^2}, \quad \text{(approx.)} \tag{4-3}$$

where C = difference between horizontal distance and tape reading; w = weight of tape, in pounds per foot; L = tape reading, in feet; t = tension on tape, in pounds.

PROBLEMS

1. What field measurement should be made to lay out a small building foundation shown on the plans to be 18 ft 0 in. × 42 ft 0 in.? Give measurements for sides and diagonal. The tape to be used is a 50-foot tape, graduated to hundredths of a foot and known to be 0.15 foot short. Assume the shortage is distributed uniformly throughout the length of the tape.

2. In taping a line with a 100-foot tape the head tapeman is off line by 1 foot three different times, but not consecutively. What error will result?

3. A slope measurement of 628.32 feet is made between Points A and B. The elevation of B is 1,325.20 feet. The elevation of A is 1,300.01 feet. Find the horizontal distance $A-B$.

4. A line is measured with a 100-foot steel tape when the temperature is 32°F. The recorded distance is 1736.17. Find the true length of the line if the tape is standard at 68°F.

5. The horizontal distance $B-C$ is 123.15. What is the distance $B-C$ along a 5 per cent slope?

6. Compute by both exact and approximate methods the error induced by holding one end of a 100-foot tape 2 feet too low when measuring horizontal distance on sloping ground.

7. A horizontal line is to be established 1320.00 feet long. It must be measured along a 20 per cent slope when the temperature is 110°F. The tape used is steel and is 100.00 feet long at 68°F. What length line must be laid off in the field under these conditions?

8. A line measured along a 5 per cent slope is recorded as 1,111.11 feet. What is the horizontal length of the line?

9. A tape is known to be 100.00 feet long at 90°F. The tape was used to measure a line which was found to be 1,050.00 feet long when the temperature was 30°F. What is the true length of the line?

10. It is required to establish a distance of 601.00 feet with a tape which is 50.02 feet long. What should the recorded distance be?

11. A high school coach wishes to lay out for his track team a 440-yard straightaway course. He borrows a 100-foot metallic tape known to be 100.20 feet long. Using this tape, what measurements should be made so that the track will have the correct length?

12. A building along the line $A-B$ makes direct measurement impossible. A point C is established at an offset distance of 20 feet from the line $A-B$ and roughly equidistant from A and B. The distances $A-C$ and $C-B$ are then measured: $A-C = 116.00$ feet and $B-C = 120.50$ feet. By both the exact and approximate methods compute the length of the line $A-B$.

13. What measurement must be made to lay out a 220-yard straightaway course with a 100-foot metallic tape that is 98.90 feet long?

14. Are the following statements true or false? Qualify the answer where necessary.

    a. In taping, the head chainman carries the one-hundred foot end of the tape.

    b. The method of "breaking tape" is used for measuring slope distance directly.

c. The formula for approximate correction for slope can be used where the slope is less than 20 per cent.

15. A line was measured with a 100-foot steel tape as 1,837.05 feet when the temperature was 23°F. This line was remeasured as 1,835.87 when the temperature was 103°F. What was the discrepancy between the two measurements? What is the indicated precision of the two measurements?

16. A rectangular building 130.00 × 290.00 feet is to be laid out with a tape that is 101.11 feet long. What measurements should be made for each side and the diagonal?

17. A 100-foot steel tape weighs 2.2 pounds. It is supported at its end points under a pull of 12 pounds. What is the distance between the zero and 100-foot points?

18. A 100-foot steel tape has a cross-sectional area of 0.006 square inch. It is of standard length under a 10-pound pull. How long is the tape when a pull of 25 pounds is applied?

19. Using data from Problems 17 and 18, compute the pull necessary to compensate for the sag.

Chapter 5

~~~~~~

DETERMINING DIRECTION

WE HAVE learned that surveying is concerned with the relative location of points on or near the surface of the earth. This necessitates a known line or point from which to begin. If the location of two points is known, a third location may be determined by distances from those two points. Sometimes relative position must be expressed in terms other than distance alone. In such instances *direction* is used.

A point can be located if we know its distance from one given point and its direction from another. It can also be located if either its direction and distance from a known point or its direction from each of two known points is determined.

The location of points on the horizontal plane, that is, as they would appear on a map, thus requires the determination of horizontal distance (Chapter 4), the determination of direction by means of horizontal angles, or a combination of angle and distance.

Locating points in the vertical plane requires the measurement of vertical angles (Chapter 6), or the determination of differences in elevations (Chapter 7).

5-1. Reference lines. The direction of any line is expressed by the horizontal angle it makes with a reference line. One possibility is to use as a reference one line in a series of intersecting lines. For example, if the location of line *A–B* is known and angle *A–B–C* is determined, the direction of line *B–C* with respect to reference line *A–B* is known. Line *C–D* may then be referenced to line *B–C* by angle *B–C–D*, and so on. Another way of expressing direction is by using a fixed line of reference which is not one of the lines of a traverse (Article 5-10). Such a line is called a *meridian*.

5-2. Meridians. A meridian is an imaginary line which lies in a vertical plane passing through *the observer's position* and through

64

a *point of reference*. If the reference point is arbitrarily chosen, the meridian is an *assumed meridian*. If the reference point is the magnetic pole, the meridian is a *magnetic meridian*. If the reference point is the true (geographic) pole, the meridian is a *true meridian*.

The true meridian is used as a reference in any extensive survey and for surveys dealing with land boundaries. This is because a true meridian does not change with time and because the relationship of true meridians established at different points is always known regardless of the distance between the points.

5-3. Determining true meridian. Observation of any celestial body, the astronomical position of which is known, will make possible the establishment of a true meridian passing through the

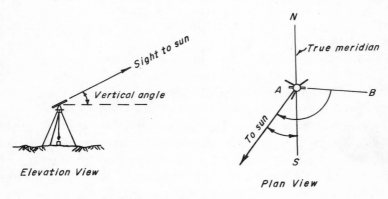

Fig. 5-1. Solar observation for determining true meridian.

point occupied at the time of the observation. The sun and the North Star are the bodies most often used in surveying work.

To obtain the most accurate results when the observation is made on the sun the time should be mid-morning or mid-afternoon. The procedure is to measure the vertical angle between the sun and a horizontal plane through a transit, and the horizontal angle between a line *A–B* and the sun. See Figure 5-1. The time of observation is noted. With the latitude of the instrument position, point *A*, known, the angle between the true meridian, *N–S*, and the sun can be computed for any given time. Since the horizontal angle *B–A*–sun has been measured, the angle *B–A–N* can be computed.[4]

The North Star, also known as the Pole Star, or Polaris, appears to move in a daily orbit about the celestial pole. This pole is an imaginary point where the axis of the earth extended would pierce an imaginary hollow sphere, called the *celestial sphere*. In surveying practice it is assumed that all of the heavenly bodies lie in the surface of this sphere and that the earth is at its center. From this we see that any line passing through a point on the earth and through the celestial pole will be contained in a plane which passes through

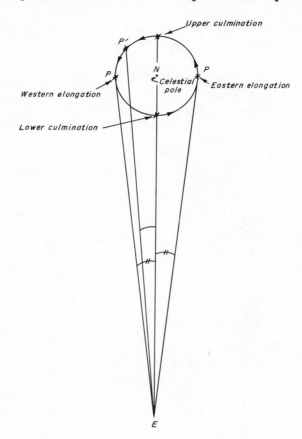

Fig. 5-2. Daily orbit of Polaris about the celestial pole.

the geographic pole of the earth. Refer to Figure 5-2 and it becomes obvious that if we sight from any point, E, on the surface of the earth to the star Polaris, the true meridian through the point of observation can be located by laying off angle $P\text{–}E\text{–}N$. The value of this angle is available in published tables, if the latitude of the point E is known.[5]

It is more accurate and computations are simplified if for determining true meridian the star is observed when it is at either eastern or western elongation. See Figure 5-2. The observation may be made, however, at any position of Polaris and, if the time of the observation and the longitude of the place are known, the angle *P–E–N* between the star at that time and the pole can be computed.

The discussion of the determination for true meridian is given here to indicate to the reader in a general way how a true meridian can be established at any location and whenever necessary. It is felt that the details of computation involve terms and procedures beyond the scope of this book. The references given contain additional information for any who wish to pursue the subject further.

Fig. 5-3. Pocket compass, sometimes called *forestry compass*. (Courtesy Keuffel & Esser Co.)

5-4. The magnetic compass. The needle of a magnetic compass will lie in a vertical plane passing through the compass and the magnetic pole provided the needle is freely "floating" on its pivot. The needle will then define the magnetic meridian unless it is attracted from its normal position by forces other than the magnetic attraction of the pole.

There are three types of magnetic compasses used in surveying:

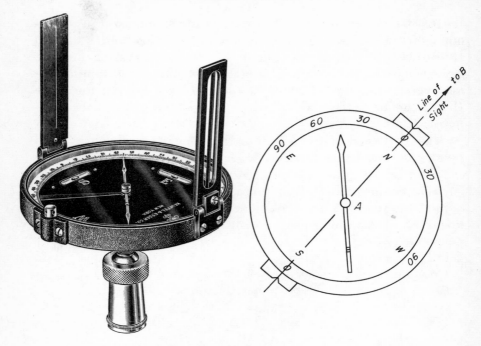

Fig. 5-4. Modern surveyor's compass. Plan view of compass over point A and indicating a bearing to B of N 45° E. (Courtesy Keuffel & Esser Co.)

Fig. 5-5. Surveyor's compass of vintage earlier than shown in Fig. 5-4.

the pocket compass, Figure 5-3; the surveyor's compass, Figures 5-4 and 5-5; and the compass which is an integral part of most engineer's transits, Figure 6-2.

When a compass is in use the needle is lowered so that a jeweled bearing at the center of the needle rests upon a sharp pivot point, thus giving a "freely floating" needle. It is very important that the needle be raised off the pivot and secured whenever it is not in use so that it does not become "sluggish" because of a dulled pivot point or a damaged bearing.

5-5. Basic definitions. In addition to having the property of pointing toward the magnetic pole, the north end of the needle is attracted downward from the horizontal plane (in the northern hemisphere). This is called *dip*. To hold the needle in the horizontal plane so that it will move freely on its pivot, a fine brass wire is wound around the south end of the needle as a counterweight.

If a magnetic attraction is nearby when a bearing is being observed, the needle will be pulled out of its normal position. This may be caused by magnetic metals or direct electric currents. This effect is called *local attraction*.

Only at a relatively few locations on the surface of the earth will the magnetic meridian and the true meridian coincide. The angle between the two meridians is called *declination* or the *angle of magnetic declination*. The needle is said to have an east or west declination depending upon whether it points east or west of true north.

The angle of declination at any given location is not constant. The most significant variation is the *secular variation* which is thought to be an essentially continuous, but erratic, change in one direction for about 150 years and then back in the other direction to complete the cycle. The rate of change is different for different years and different locations. The dotted lines in Figure 5-6 show the annual rates of change in secular variation for 1955.

Other variations in declination are: *annual variations* other than secular variations, variations over a 24-hour period called *daily variations*, and irregular variations caused by magnetic disturbances. The annual and daily variations are too small to be of general significance. The irregular variations cannot be predicted as to amount or occurrence.

A map which shows lines connecting all points which have the same magnetic declination at a given time is called an *isogonic*

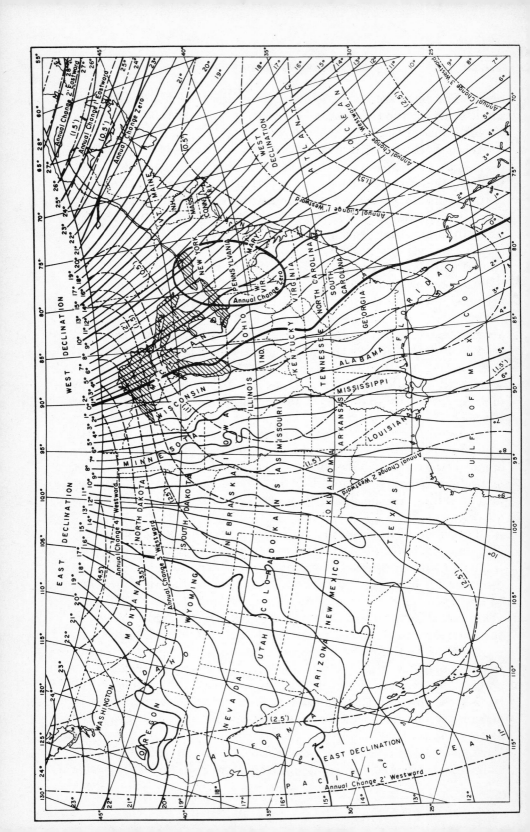

chart. The lines are called *isogonic lines.* Figure 5-6 shows an isogonic chart for the United States.

The line on the map which connects points where there is zero magnetic declination is called the *agonic line.*

5-6. Bearings. One method of defining the direction of a line is by means of its bearing. The *bearing angle* of a line is the smallest angle which that line makes with the reference meridian. It can never be more than 90 degrees.

The *bearing* of a line is the *bearing angle* with the notation of the directional quadrant in which the line lies, thus: N 38°20′ W.

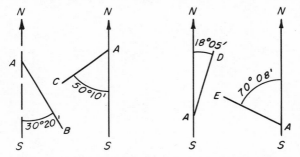

Fig. 5-7. Bearing angles in each of the four quadrants.

In Figure 5-7, the bearing angle of line *A–B* is 30°20′, but the bearing of *A–B* is S 30°20′ E. Obviously, if only the bearing angle of *A–B* were given, the line could lie in any one of the four quadrants. Therefore, to locate a line it is *absolutely necessary* to know the directional quadrant in which it lies as well as the angle it makes with the reference meridian. Referring again to Figure 5-7, determine that the bearings of the other lines shown are:

A–C: S 50°10′ W;   *A–D:* N 18°05′ E;   *A–E:* N 70°08′ W

Bearings may be *true bearings, magnetic bearings,* or *assumed bearings* depending upon the reference meridian used. When bearings are used it is important to clearly indicate the type of reference meridian.

5-7. Azimuths. Azimuth is another term used to indicate the direction of lines. The *azimuth* of any line is the clockwise angle designated as being measured between either the north end or the south end of the reference meridian and the line in question.

It will be noted that this definition differs from that for bearing angle in that azimuth angles are measured clockwise from a definite reference point. A bearing angle cannot be over 90 degrees, but an azimuth may have any value from 0 to 360 degrees. The azimuth angle could, of course, be measured either to the right or to the left, hence the necessity to avoid confusion by designating clockwise measurement.

Azimuths are sometimes preferred to bearings for expressing direction, and in some types of work they are more convenient. However, both methods have their place and both should be understood. Actually, bearings may be expressed as azimuths, and vice versa.

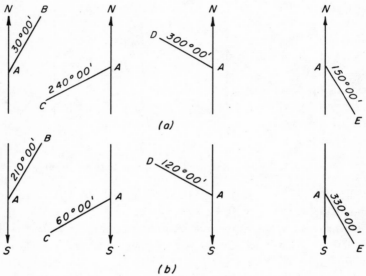

Fig. 5-8. Azimuth angles. (a) North reference. (b) South reference.

To visualize a *sketch* definition of the azimuth of a line, draw a line representing the reference meridian. Place point *A* on this line. Now suppose the azimuth of line *A–B* is given as 102°00′. Where is point *B* located? This question cannot be answered with the information at hand because there are two possible locations for the line *A–B*. It must be determined whether the angle of 102°00′ is clockwise from the north end or from the south end of the reference meridian.

In practice, north point reference and south point reference are both used. Usually a given organization or individual will consistently use one or the other, but since both are used the reference should be noted whenever azimuths are recorded. Unless otherwise noted, north point reference will be assumed for problems in this book.

Figure 5-8(a) shows a series of lines with azimuths measured from a north point reference. The azimuth with south point reference would be the azimuth shown in Figure 5-8(a) plus or minus 180°. These conditions are shown in Figure 5-8(b).

5-8. Observing a magnetic bearing. A magnetic compass consists of: (1) The compass box with a circle graduated from 0 to 90 degrees in each of four quadrants and marked N, S, W and E at quadrant intersections. (2) Fixed sights at the N and S locations on the compass box (the telescope in the case of the compass on a transit). (3) The compass needle with a mechanism for raising it off the pivot when not in use.

The E and W on a compass box are reversed in terms of their true position. See Figures 5-3 and 5-4. This in no way changes our common concept of directions, but merely makes possible the direct reading of a magnetic bearing as the observer looks down on the compass face.

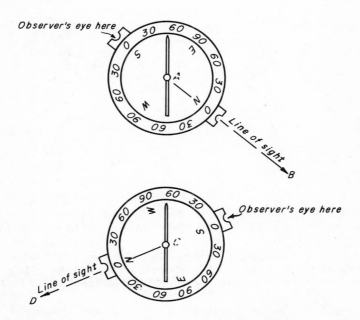

Fig. 5-9. Observed bearing of *A–B* is S 50° E. What is the observed bearing of *C–D*?

To observe a magnetic bearing, *place* N *on the compass box so that it is ahead as you sight along the line being observed. Release the needle and when it has come to rest read the angle and quadrant indicated by the north end of the needle.* Notice that by this rule the bearing of *A–B* in Figure 5-9 is S 50° E. Line *A–B* plotted on a map would of course be running southeasterly.

The reader should verify the fact that, if the procedure outlined is followed, the magnetic bearing of any line can be read directly off the compass by visualizing the graduated circle and sights in Figure 5-9 being rotated into other positions. It must be remembered that the needle will continue to point toward magnetic north as the compass box and sights are rotated.

5-9. Purpose of magnetic bearings. At present the compass is limited to use for reconnaissance surveys, rough mapping, timber cruising, or other jobs where speed is more important than precision.

The compass on a transit can be used to good advantage for roughly checking angles as they are measured in the field by the transit. Observed bearings are often a real advantage in indicating,

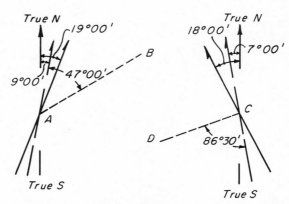

Line A-B has a magnetic bearing of N47°00'E when magnetic declination is 9°00'E. Find magnetic bearing of A-B when declination is 19°00'E. Answer: N37°00'E.

Line C-D had a magnetic bearing of S86°30'W in 1900 when the magnetic declination was 7°00'W. Find the magnetic bearing of C-D at the present time if the declination now is 18°00'W. Answer: N82°30'W.

Fig. 5-10. Relationship between true north, magnetic north, and any given line.

through office computations, the locations where field checks need to be made. Because of their value as a check, engineers often make a practice of observing magnetic bearings on all lines while the transit is set up for measuring angles. The extra time required to do this is not significant and there is a good chance that considerable time might be saved in later checking by virtue of having the observed bearings available.

Most of our original land surveys were made in terms of magnetic bearings. To check these, magnetic bearings must again be used in rerunning the lines. The magnetic declination at the time of the original survey and at the time of the resurvey must also be known, and the observed bearings corrected accordingly. See Figure 5-10.

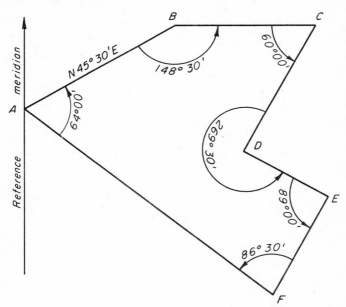

Fig. 5-11. Closed traverse with interior angles shown. Bearing or azimuth of all sides can be computed from data given.

5-10. Relationship between bearings or azimuths and angles. If the bearing or azimuth for each one of any number of consecutively intersecting lines is known, the angles between the lines can be computed. Conversely, if the bearing or azimuth of a line and the angle it makes with any intersecting line are known, the bearing or azimuth of the intersecting line can be computed.

If a series of lines are laid out to form a closed figure, they are referred to as a *closed traverse*. The angle between one of the lines and a reference meridian may be established, thus establishing the bearing of that line. Then by measuring the interior angles of the polygon the bearing of each line is available. See Figure 5-11.

The angles as shown in Figure 5-11 would be designated as interior angles (measured to the left).

If the series of lines does not form a closed figure, they are referred to as an *open traverse*. Here the angular relationships may

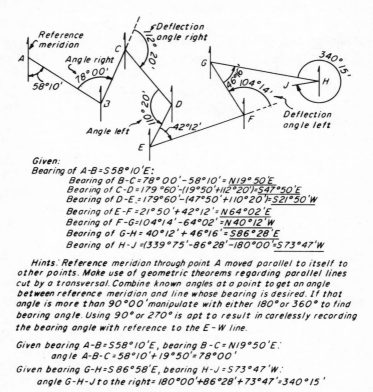

Given:
Bearing of A-B=S58°10'E:
    Bearing of B-C=78°00'-58°10'=N19°50'E
    Bearing of C-D=179°60'-(19°50'+112°20')=S47°50'E
    Bearing of D-E=179°60'-(47°50'+110°20')=S21°50'W
    Bearing of E-F=21°50'+42°12'=N64°02'E
    Bearing of F-G=104°14'-64°02'=N40°12'W
    Bearing of G-H=40°12'+46°16'=S86°28'E
    Bearing of H-J=(339°75'-86°28'-180°00'=S73°47'W

Hints: Reference meridian through point A moved parallel to itself to other points. Make use of geometric theorems regarding parallel lines cut by a transversal. Combine known angles at a point to get an angle between reference meridian and line whose bearing is desired. If that angle is more than 90°00'manipulate with either 180° or 360° to find bearing angle. Using 90° or 270° is apt to result in carelessly recording the bearing angle with reference to the E-W line.

Given bearing A-B=S58°10'E, bearing B-C=N19°50'E:
    angle A-B-C=58°10'+19°50'=78°00'
Given bearing G-H=S86°58'E, bearing H-J=S73°47'W:
    angle G-H-J to the right=180°00'+86°28'+73°47'=340°15'

Fig. 5-12. Open traverse angles.

be designated by the measurement of *deflection angles, angles right* or *angles left* as indicated in Figure 5-12.

Notice that in all cases if the bearings or azimuths are known, any of the angles may be computed. Also, if the angle between one side and a reference meridian is known and the angular relationship between sides is known, the bearings or azimuths of all lines can be computed.

It should also be noted that once the angle between the refer-

ence meridian and a line has been established the reference meridian
may be assumed to have any direction without altering the relationships. That is, Figures 5-11 or 5-12 may be pivoted about points *A*
so that the reference meridian points in any direction and, as long
as no angle is changed, no relationships within the figure change.

5-11. Angle measurement by compass or transit. The
transit will be discussed in detail in Chapter 6, but it is introduced
here to aid in explaining why the compass is no longer used except
for approximate work or for checking purposes.

One of the essential elements of the engineer's transit is a horizontal circular plate graduated in degrees and parts of degrees.
By means of a device called a *vernier*, which accurately subdivides
the smallest divisions on the graduated circle, it is possible to
measure angles to one minute of arc or less. Since bearings can be
computed from angles, it is apparent that use of the transit for
measuring angles makes possible the computation of bearings which
are correct to at least one minute of arc. The compass, on the other
hand, can normally be read direct to thirty minutes with the possibility of estimating to approximately 15 minutes. Combine with
this the facts that sighting is done without benefit of magnification
and that local attraction may deflect the needle, and it becomes
evident that only limited precision is attained with the compass.

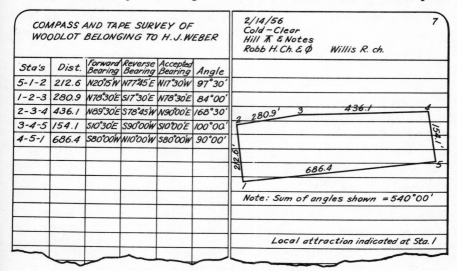

Fig. 5-13. Field notes for compass and tape survey.

5-12. Compass and tape surveys. A precision of 1/1,000 may
be attained with taped distances and directions determined from

observed magnetic bearings. For work requiring less precision, distances may be obtained by less precise methods.

Both forward and reverse bearings should be taken on all lines to aid in detecting local attraction. A *forward bearing* is taken by looking along the line in the direction of the next point to which the surveyor is moving. The *reverse bearing,* or *back bearing,* of a line is the bearing taken by the surveyor as he looks back in the direction from which he came.

Figure 5-13 shows a form of notes for a compass and tape survey.

5-13. Common errors and mistakes in compass work. Some of the sources of error and mistakes related to the use of a compass may be listed as follows:

SOURCES OF ERROR

1. Sluggish needle due to damaged pivot or need for remagnetization.
2. Local attraction.
3. Bent needle or bent pivot.
4. Glass cover of compass box becoming electrically charged and causing needle to stick.

MISTAKES

1. Not releasing needle and seeing that it is oscillating freely.
2. Reading wrong end of needle.
3. Reading wrong way on graduated circle, as 31 degrees for 29 degrees.
4. Parallax in reading, that is, looking down at the needle from an angle instead of from directly above it.

5-14. Other methods of determining angles. In addition to the compass and transit other instruments used for the field measurement of angles and/or direction include: the *tape,* the *plane table,* and the *sextant.*

If the three sides of any triangle are taped, sufficient data are available for determining the value of each of its angles. See Table I in the appendix.

A value for the angle between any two intersecting lines can be determined by *taping the angle.* The computation is simplified if *equal* distances are measured from the vertex along each leg of the angle. The distance between the two points thus established is then measured. The distances along the legs may have any convenient value. One hundred feet is the most logical selection unless an obstruction interferes.

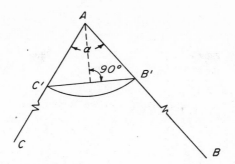

Measure $A-C' = A-B'$, then measure $B'-C'$.

$$\sin \frac{a}{2} = \frac{C'-B'}{2} \div A-B' \text{ or } A-C'$$

Suppose $A-C' = A-B' = 100.0'$ and $C'-B' = 110.0'$.

$$a = (\text{arc } \sin 0.550)2.$$

Points C' and B' are normally placed on line by eye. It is important that this be done carefully since any error in alignment will be reflected directly into length $B'-C'$.

Fig. 5-14. Determination of angular value by linear measurement.

The principle of taping angles is shown in Figure 5-14.

Angles may be scaled or determined mathematically from lines plotted on a plane table map. These lines are located directly on the map in the field and represent accurately the relative locations on the ground. The principle of the plane table is discussed in Chapter 13.

The sextant is an angle measuring instrument, held in the hand of the user, which functions by the physical principle that a light ray striking a plane mirror causes the angles of incidence and reflection to be equal. By sighting through the small telescope and adjusting the movable arm until the correct reflections of the objects being sighted appear in the mirrors, the angle between these objects is measured. A sextant is shown in Figure 5-15.

Because it is not necessary for the observer to remain stationary during observation, this instrument is widely used in navigation. It is also used in hydrographic surveying when angles must be measured from a boat. The instrument can be used, of course, when the observer is on the ground. Any angle measured with the sextant is in the same plane as the points concerned. If the elevation differences are not too great, observed angles may be considered as horizontal without excessive error. The maximum size of angle measurable is 120 degrees.

Fig. 5-15. Sextant in use to measure vertical angle.

PROBLEMS

1. Given the following bearings, find the smallest angle between *A–B* and the other lines: *A–B*, S 20°10′ W; *A–C*, N 21°15′ E; *A–D*, N 02°05′ W; *A–E*, S 89°00′ E.

2. Compute two sets of azimuths for the lines in Problem 1. Use the same reference meridian as in Problem 1, but use S point reference for one set and N point reference for the other.

3. Given the bearing of line 1–2 as N 80°10′ E and the bearing angle of 2–3 as 60°10′, plot all four of the possible locations of 2–3.

4. Complete the following tabulation and check values. Draw a sketch to show the shape of the traverse.

Station	Interior angle	Deflection angle	Line	Bearing	Azimuth
A			A–B	N 70°00′ E	
B			B–C	N 51°40′ E	
C			C–D	S 20°50′ E	
D			D–E	S 68°30′ W	
E			E–A	N 24°50′ W	

5. Given the traverse with the respective bearings, compute the azimuths, deflection angles, angles to the right, and interior angles. Make a sketch of this traverse. Note that your sketch will show shape only, since distances are not given. Do the angles satisfy the geometric requirements for a pentagon?

Line	Azimuth	Deflection angles	Angles to the right	Bearings	Angle	Interior angles
A–B				N 22°00′ W	A	
B–C				S 86°10′ W	B	
C–D				N 65°30′ E	C	
D–E				S 19°00′ W	D	
E–A				S 01°00′ W	E	

6. In 1850 a line has a magnetic bearing of N 88°30′ E. At that time the magnetic declination was 02°30′ E. In 1955 the declination had changed to 01°30′ W. Find the magnetic bearing of the line in 1955.

7. Interchange the declinations in Problem 6 and determine the magnetic bearing of the line in 1955.

8. Given the following facts, explain what condition exists. True bearing of A–B, S 40°30′ W; magnetic declination, 03°30′ E; observed magnetic bearing of A–B, S 41°30′ W. Assume no mistake has been made in the readings.

9. Find the true bearing of the line in Problem 6 in the year 1850. Find the true bearing of the line in Problem 6 in the year 1955.

10. The bearing of line A–B is S 83°15′ E, angle A–B–C is 125°25′ and point C is southerly from point B. Compute the bearing of B–C. Compute the azimuth of B–C (N point reference).

11. A line has a magnetic bearing of S 80°30′ W when the declination is 04°30′ W. Find its magnetic bearing when the declination is 01°30′ E.

12. From point A a distance of 100.00 feet is measured toward point B, and a marker is placed. A distance of 100.00 feet is measured from point A toward point C and a marker is placed. The distance between markers is found to be 81.20 feet. Find angle B–A–C.

13. The following observed data were recorded for a compass survey.

Station	Distance	Forward bearing	Reverse bearing
5–1–2	280.9 ft	N 78°30′ E	S 16°30′ E
1–2–3	436.2	S 89°30′ E	S 76°30′ W
2–3–4	154.1	S 07°00′ E	N 86°30′ W
3–4–5	686.4	S 81°30′ W	N 10°00′ W
4–5–1	212.7	N 14°30′ W	N 83°30′ E

(a) Note the stations where there is local attraction. (b) Compute the interior angles. (c) Readjust bearings to satisfy geometric conditions. (d) Plot the traverse.

14. A reference meridian passes through one of the angle points on a regular hexagon. The angle measured to the right from the reference meridian to one side of the figure is 56°10′. Find the bearings of all sides of the figure.

Chapter 6

THE ENGINEER'S TRANSIT

CREDIT for the invention of the first transit instrument has been given to Roemer, a Danish astronomer, at Copenhagen in 1690. His instrument was used to observe the passage (transit) of stars across any portion of the celestial meridian. This meant that the telescope had to be mounted on a horizontal axis in such a way that it could be rotated in the vertical plane.

About a century later a similar instrument was used in surveying work. This early transit consisted of a telescope mounted on a horizontal axis with this axis supported at either end by vertical uprights. This assembly was attached to a "pointer" which moved around a graduated circle. The circle could be made horizontal by means of leveling screws. With such an arrangement it was possible to measure the horizontal angle through which the telescope moved as pointings were made, first at one object and then at another.

Later, additions to this basic instrument made possible the measurement of several things in addition to horizontal angles. The instrument with these additions became known as the *engineer's transit*. The first instrument of this type was made about 1830.

The engineer's transit is sometimes referred to as the "universal instrument," because of its variety of uses. These include the measurement of horizontal and vertical angles, approximate distances (by stadia), differences in elevation by direct leveling, and direction by the magnetic needle. The transit is also used for establishing and extending straight lines.

6-1. General description. Figure 6-1 shows a transit complete except for the plumb-bob which is suspended from the center of its vertical axis. A cut-away view is shown in Figure 6-2. In this view the linkage from which the plumb-bob is suspended can be seen.

83

Figure 6-3 shows an "exploded" view of a transit. The main parts of the instrument are shown here as well as their relation in assembly. At the top of the figure is the alidade assembly which includes the telescope and the upper plate, next is the circle assembly (lower plate), and at the bottom is the leveling head assembly.

Fig. 6-1. An engineer's transit.
(Courtesy W. & L. E. Gurley)

The measurement and layout of horizontal angles is the most common use for the transit. The two horizontal plates, each attached to its own tapered vertical shaft or spindle, are used for this purpose (Figure 6-3). The plates can either be rotated independently or clamped together and rotated as a unit.

The thin plate (shifting center) at the base of the leveling head allows some movement of the transit proper in relation to the foot-

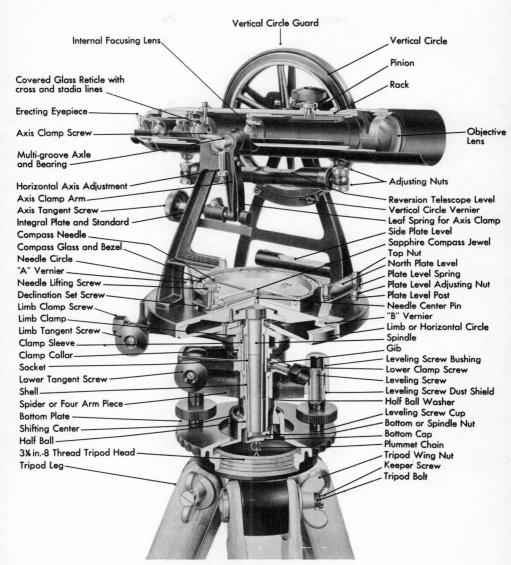

Vertical Circle Guard

Internal Focusing Lens

Vertical Circle

Pinion

Rack

Covered Glass Reticle with cross and stadia lines

Erecting Eyepiece

Axis Clamp Screw

Objective Lens

Multi-groove Axle and Bearing

Horizontal Axis Adjustment
Axis Clamp Arm
Axis Tangent Screw
Integral Plate and Standard
Compass Needle
Compass Glass and Bezel
Needle Circle
"A" Vernier
Needle Lifting Screw
Declination Set Screw
Limb Clamp Screw
Limb Clamp
Limb Tangent Screw
Clamp Sleeve
Clamp Collar
Socket
Lower Tangent Screw
Shell
Spider or Four Arm Piece
Bottom Plate
Shifting Center
Half Ball
3⅛ in.-8 Thread Tripod Head
Tripod Leg

Adjusting Nuts

Reversion Telescope Level
Vertical Circle Vernier
Leaf Spring for Axis Clamp
Side Plate Level
Sapphire Compass Jewel
Top Nut
North Plate Level
Plate Level Spring
Plate Level Adjusting Nut
Plate Level Post
Needle Center Pin
"B" Vernier
Limb or Horizontal Circle
Spindle
Gib
Leveling Screw Bushing
Lower Clamp Screw
Leveling Screw
Leveling Screw Dust Shield
Half Ball Washer
Leveling Screw Cup
Bottom or Spindle Nut
Bottom Cap
Plummet Chain
Tripod Wing Nut
Keeper Screw
Tripod Bolt

Fig. 6-2. Cut-away showing the parts of a transit. (Courtesy W. & L. E. Gurley)

plate when all of the leveling screws are loose. This facilitates positioning the plumb-bob directly over any point as the instrument is being set up.

Again referring to Figure 6-3, notice that the lower plate contains a graduated circle. Notice, too, that there is a lower clamp

Fig. 6-3. "Exploded" view of transit.
(Courtesy W. & L. E. Gurley)

on the leveling head which, when tightened, fixes the lower plate to the leveling head. Thus, the rotation of the lower plate is controlled by the lower clamp. The lower tangent screw makes possible slow movement for accurate settings after the lower clamp has been tightened.

The upper plate is attached to the uprights (standards) supporting the telescope, and to it are fastened the *verniers* ("pointers"). There are two of these, 180 degrees apart, consisting of segments of a circle so graduated that the smallest divisions on the graduated circle of the lower plate are accurately subdivided. The segments are each approximately 2 inches long and are called the *A vernier* and the *B vernier*. They fit close to the graduated circle as they rotate around it. See Figure 6-8.

Further study of Figure 6-3 will show that the upper plate fits down over the lower plate and the upper plate spindle (inner spindle) fits down inside the hollow spindle of the lower plate. The upper clamp, when tightened, exerts pressure on the inner spindle thus locking the upper and lower plates together. The upper tangent screw provides for slow motion of the upper plate past the lower, *after* the upper clamp is tight.

To summarize, the relative action of the upper and lower clamps is as follows: with both clamps tight the entire instrument is immobile in relation to the leveling head and tripod. With the upper clamp tight and the lower clamp loose, the two plates cannot move in relation to each other, but the telescope can sweep through 360 degrees in the horizontal plane. With the lower clamp tight and the upper one loose the same 360-degree sweep is allowed, but this time the "pointers" (verniers) on the upper plate will pass by graduations on the lower plate. This simplifies the measurement of horizontal angles between any given pointings of the telescope.

6-2. Rotation in a vertical plane. The vertical graduated circle with its vernier makes possible the measurement of vertical angles as the telescope is moved to different pointings in the vertical plane. A telescope clamp and tangent screw control this motion.

The bubble tube attached to the telescope is used to show when the longitudinal axis of the telescope is horizontal. The telescope can be clamped in this position and the transit used as a leveling instrument.

Since the telescope can be moved in the vertical plane (rotated about its horizontal axis) the transit can be used to prolong a straight line. This is done by setting the instrument over one point on the line and sighting the vertical cross-hair on another point on line to orient the telescope. With both horizontal circle clamps tight, the telescope is reversed by turning it through approximately 180° in the vertical plane to make the line of sight lie along the original line produced. The operation of reversing the telescope is called *plunging, inverting,* or *telescoping.*

6-3. The telescope. The optics of the telescope on an engineer's transit are shown in Figures 6-2 and 6-5. In addition to the objective

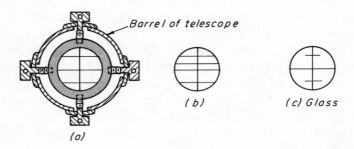

Fig. 6-4. Reticule patterns. (a) Section through telescope showing method of positioning cross-hair ring.

and eyepiece lenses there is a cross-hair ring set in front of the eyepiece. The cross-hair ring consists of an annular frame on which the horizontal and vertical cross-hairs are set. On the same frame are the two stadia hairs, one on either side of the horizontal cross-hair. The cross-hairs and stadia hairs are made of spider web, very fine wire, or, in some instruments, fine lines etched on glass. The four screws which hold the cross-hair ring in place fit through holes in the telescope tube which are enlarged, permitting the entire ring to be rotated slightly for adjustment after all of the screws have been loosened. See Article 8-9. Because the cross-hairs and stadia hairs form a network of lines, the assembly is sometimes called the *reticle* or *reticule.* Figure 6-4 shows some of the types used.

In some telescopes the objective lens is mounted on a sleeve which moves back and forth in the telescope barrel as an object is brought into focus. This is called *external focusing. Internal focusing,* used in improved instruments, is accomplished by the addition of a lens which moves back and forth between the objective and the cross-hairs as the focusing screw is turned. See Figure 6-5. In either case the image of the object being sighted is brought into focus in the plane of the cross-hairs. This means that both the image and the cross-hairs are magnified by the eyepiece. The cross-hairs must be in the focal plane of the eyepiece or apparent displacement of the cross-hairs will result as the viewer sights through the telescope. This effect is called *parallax of focusing*. When existing, it will cause errors in sighting.

To test for parallax, first focus the eyepiece on the cross-hairs, that is, bring the cross-hairs into sharp focus by adjusting the eye-

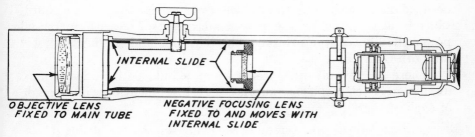

INTERNAL SLIDE

OBJECTIVE LENS
FIXED TO MAIN TUBE

NEGATIVE FOCUSING LENS
FIXED TO AND MOVES WITH
INTERNAL SLIDE

Fig. 6-5. Schematic view of internal focusing telescope. (Courtesy W. & L. E. Gurley)

piece. This may be aided by pointing the telescope at the sky or at a white background. Next, point the telescope so that the cross-hairs fall on some well-defined line or object which has been brought into sharp focus with the objective focusing screw. Now, while looking through the telescope, move the eye quickly back and forth by moving the head slightly. If this movement causes the cross-hair to appear to "jump" away from the point being sighted, parallax exists. To correct this, adjust the eyepiece and objective simultaneously until there is no apparent motion as the eye is moved, but retain as much as possible the sharpness of both cross-hairs and image.

Once the instrument is properly focused, the eyepiece adjustment *should not be disturbed,* unless the eyes become tired and their focus changes. After parallax has been removed, only the main focusing screw for the objective lens is moved to bring in a clear image as the distance from object to instrument varies.

An eyepiece is designated as *erecting* or *inverting* depending upon whether the image appears erect or inverted. The latter has only two lenses while the erecting eyepiece requires four. The erecting eyepiece is more popular among American engineers. Most instruments made in Europe have inverting eyepieces.

Erecting eyepieces, although convenient, do not give quite as bright an image as do the inverting because they have more lenses and, therefore, allow less light to pass through.

Some telescopes have eyepiece lenses which are interchangeable so that different powers of magnification can be readily obtained with the same instrument. In general, the magnification varies from 20 to 50 diameters. The higher powers are sometimes a disadvantage because distortation due to heat waves or other atmospheric conditions is aggravated as the power increases; also, with increased power the light passing through the telescope and the field of view are both reduced.

There are several other items which should be included in any discussion of telescope characteristics. A brief mention will be made of each of these.

1. *Length of telescope:* On American-made transits the standard telescope lengths are 8, 10, and 11 inches. In general the longer the telescope the larger the graduated circle and, with the conventional vernier, the more precise the instrument. Improvements in optical techniques and design are bringing about a trend toward a shorter telescope on smaller, lighter instruments, particularly those of European design.

2. *Minimum focus:* Transit telescopes cannot be focused on objects which are too close to the instrument (about 5 feet). This distance is being reduced as instrument optics are improved.

3. *Achromatic lenses:* The achromatic (color corrected) objective lens eliminates the annoyance of a rim of colored light around the lens. This is done by combining a convex and a concave lens. The colored light which results from the refraction of white light near the edge of the convex lens is transformed back to white light by refraction through the concave lens.

4. *Coated lenses:* The amount of light reflected from the surface of a lens is reduced by coating the lens with a very thin film. The light which would otherwise be reflected passes through a coated lens and thus increases brightness and image contrast.

5. *Resolving power:* An important characteristic of the optics of a transit is resolving power. A telescope with high resolving power will cause small objects which are close together to appear as distinct objects when viewed from a distance. A telescope with low resolving power would cause them to appear blurred.

The resolving power of a telescope is a function of the angle which the lenses are able to distinguish. This angle is called the angle of resolution. For example, an angle of 3 seconds will subtend approximately $\frac{1}{16}$ inch at a distance of 300 feet. If a transit has an optical system with an angle of resolution of 3 seconds, objects closer together than $\frac{1}{16}$ inch will not appear as distinct from each other when viewed through the telescope from a distance of more than 300 feet. The smaller the angle of resolution the higher the resolving power of the telescope.

A lens system with high resolving power will also have better definition, that is, the image will appear clearer and sharper than if the resolving power is low.

6-4. The vernier. A vernier is a mechanical device for accurately subdividing the smallest division on a scale. It was invented in 1620 and is named for its inventor, Pierre Vernier. This device can be adapted to any linear scale.

The length of a vernier is determined by the value of the smallest divisions on the scale with which it is to operate, and the value desired for the reading which the vernier will give.

The reading a vernier will give is called the *least count* of the vernier. It is equal to the value of the smallest scale division divided by the total number of vernier divisions.

To illustrate this, assume that a vernier is desired which will read to $\frac{1}{64}$ inch with a scale having $\frac{1}{4}$-inch graduations. Let the required number of vernier spaces be n. Then the least count ($\frac{1}{64}$) is equal to $\frac{1}{4}$ divided by n, or 16 spaces are required on the vernier.

The next question is how long the vernier is to be made. This is answered by the basic principle of construction for any vernier which states: The length of the vernier is such that it covers a number of full scale spaces equal to one less than the number of spaces which the vernier has.* Thus in the example the vernier must be 15 main scale spaces, or $3\frac{3}{4}$ inches in length.

To read a scale and vernier, first determine the value of the scale reading up to the last scale division passed by the vernier zero (index). Add to this the reading of the vernier.

A vernier reading is obtained by locating the vernier line which coincides with a scale line. The number of that vernier line is then multiplied by the least count of the vernier to get the reading.

---

* A vernier may be constructed by making its total length equal to n plus one spaces on the main scale. These are called retrograde verniers.

For example, if the third line of the vernier coincides with a scale line, the vernier reading is three times the least count; if the fourth line of the vernier coincides, the reading is four times the least count, and so on.

Figure 6-6 shows a scale and vernier with the least count shown as a dimension. It can be seen from this that if the zeros are moved apart until line 1 of the vernier coincides with a line on the scale, the vernier zero (index) indicates a scale reading of $0 + (1 \times \textit{least count})$ or $\frac{1}{32}$ inch. If line number 2 on the vernier coincides with a scale line the reading will be $2 \times \frac{1}{32}$ or $\frac{1}{16}$ inch, and so on until the index reaches the first line on the scale. The procedure repeats, except now the scale reading will be $\frac{1}{4}$ inch plus the vernier reading until the second scale division has been passed.

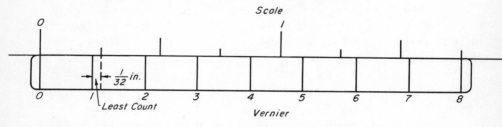

Scale reads to $\frac{1}{4}$ inch. Least count $= \frac{1}{8}$ of $\frac{1}{4} = \frac{1}{32}$ inch.

Fig. 6-6. Vernier with least count shown as a dimension.

If the numbers on the scale in Figure 6-7 are designated as feet, the least reading obtainable directly on the scale is $\frac{1}{10}$ foot. Nine of these spaces are chosen as the length for the vernier. By the principle of construction for any vernier, there must then be ten equal vernier spaces. From this it follows that each vernier space is $\frac{9}{10}$ of a scale space. The distance between the line marked v and the line marked s is therefore $\frac{1}{10}$ of a scale space, or $\frac{1}{10}$ of $\frac{1}{10}$ foot. This distance of $\frac{1}{100}$ of a foot is the *least count* of this particular vernier.

In Figure 6-7(a) the index or zero of the vernier coincides with a scale division, so the vernier is not used in obtaining the reading of 7.00. In Figure 6-7(b) the zero does not coincide with any line on the scale, but since line 1 of the vernier does coincide, the reading is 7.01 feet. The student should verify the reading of 7.08 feet in Figure 6-7(c).

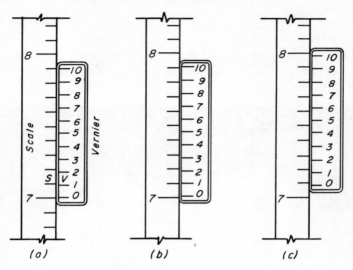

Fig. 6-7. Vernier and scale.

A summary of the procedure to be followed in using any vernier is as follows:

1. Determine the least count by dividing the value of the smallest scale division by the number of divisions on the vernier.
2. Determine the scale reading as indicated by the last scale mark passed by the index (zero) of the vernier.
3. Determine the vernier reading by multiplying the least count of the vernier by the number of the vernier line which is coinciding with a line on the scale.
4. Add the vernier reading to the scale reading to obtain the total reading.

These steps *should* **not** *be memorized* to be applied as a routine. They are given as an aid to visualizing what is actually involved and how a vernier does subdivide the smallest division of a scale. When this is really understood no sequence of steps need be learned.

6-5. Transit verniers. As has been stated, transits have two verniers, (*A* and *B*), on opposite sides of the upper plate. Most transits have two sets of numbers on the graduated circle of the lower plate. Each set goes from 0 to 360 degrees in increments of 10, but the outer row reads to the right and the inner row reads to the left. There are actually four verniers on an instrument so

graduated. The right half of the *A* vernier is used for readings
when the vernier has moved to the right over the scale and the left
half of the *A* vernier is used when the vernier has moved to the left
over the scale. The *B* vernier is used in a similar way. See Figure 6-8.

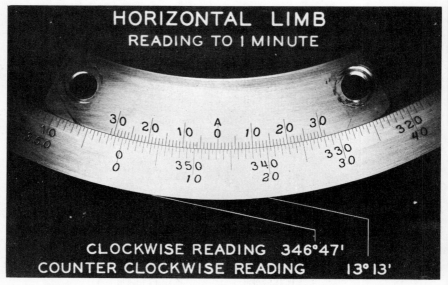

Fig. 6-8. A section of transit scale and the vernier. (Courtesy W. & L. E. Gurley)

For ordinary work the *A* vernier is usually the only one used.
In more precise work both the *A* and *B* verniers are read and the
mean of the two readings used. This practice helps to compensate
for any eccentricity or imperfection in subdivision which might
exist in the circular scale. When only one vernier is read it is important that the one read is the same one that was set at zero.

Common least counts found on modern transits are either 01′
or 30″. Transits are available which have vernier-scale combinations
that will yield readings of 10″ or 20″. These are sometimes called
city transits.

USING THE TRANSIT

6-6. Setting up. After the transit has been removed from its
carrying case and is screwed onto the tripod head, the following
checks should be made:

1. Has the tripod cap been placed in the transit case so it will not be misplaced or lost?
2. Has the telescope dust cap been removed, put in the transit case, and replaced by the sunshade?
3. Are the threads in the base of the transit firmly seated in those of the tripod? The threads should be brought up snug, never forced.
4. Are the leveling screws adjusted so that approximately the same number of threads are showing on each? Is each screw seated snugly against the foot-plate?
5. Is the shifting head of the transit centered so that the same amount of movement is available in any direction upon loosening all four leveling screws.
6. Are the wing nuts on the tripod legs just tight enough so that when raised the tripod legs will not fall because of their own weight?

The instrument is now ready to be set up so that the plumb-bob will be directly over the transit tack or other point marking the station. To do this skillfully and rapidly requires practice. However, a system, followed from the beginning, will lead to proficiency. Assume a setup is to be made over a tack in a hub. The following routine is suggested:

1. Without reference to the point, spread the tripod legs so that they are about $2\frac{1}{2}$ to 3 feet apart and the tripod head remains horizontal as judged by eye. The tripod will be unstable if the legs are spread either too much or not enough.
2. Attach the plumb-bob to the transit. A slipping device or a slipknot which will untie easily should be used on the plumb-bob string, to keep the string from knotting.
3. Pick up the tripod and set it over the point. If on sloping ground, two legs should be placed down the slope. Keep the tripod head approximately horizontal.
4. Adjust the plumb-bob so that it clears the stake by about 2 inches. If it is not within approximately $\frac{1}{2}$ inch of being over the tack, again lift the whole instrument and set it so the plumb-bob is nearer the tack.
5. Push each tripod leg firmly into the ground, adjusting each one as necessary so that when the legs are stable the plumb-bob will be near enough over the tack that the remaining adjustment can be made with the movable head of the instrument.
6. Adjust the plumb-bob so that it barely clears the stake. Loosen the leveling screws, shift the transit on its movable head until the plumb-bob is exactly over the tack and tighten the leveling screws.

6-7. Leveling the instrument. Turn the plates until the plate bubbles are approximately parallel to a line through two opposite leveling screws. Begin leveling by turning two opposite leveling screws uniformly so one is loosened as much as the other is tightened. When the bubble controlled by these screws is nearly in the center of its tube, shift to the other set of leveling screws and with them bring the other bubble near center. Alternate until both plate bubbles are centered. Be sure to keep all four leveling screws snug against the footplate at all times.

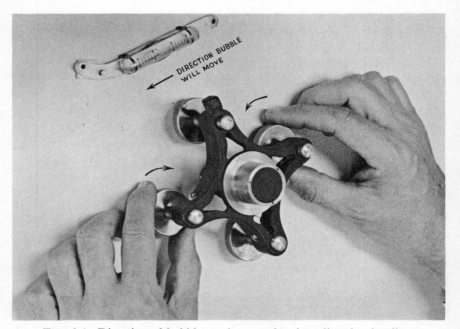

Fig. 6-9. Direction of bubble motion as related to direction leveling screws are turned.

A convenient rule for determining in which direction to turn the leveling screws is to note that the bubble will always move in the direction of the left thumb as the surveyor grasps and turns the screws. Thus in Figure 6-9 the bubble controlled by the set of screws being turned would move to the left in its tube.

The plate bubbles, once adjusted, will remain centered as the instrument is rotated through 360° about its vertical axis unless they are out of adjustment. See Article 8-8. If out of adjustment, they should be adjusted. If the bubble leaves the center only slightly (less than one division) as the transit is rotated it should not be recentered for ordinary work. Accuracy is decreased and time is wasted by continually manipulating the leveling screws on a transit once it has been leveled.

6-8. Measuring a horizontal angle. Assume the transit is set up over the point and leveled, and that all clamps are loose.

By reaching the fingers beneath the lower plate and turning it, bring the vernier index and the zero of the circle approximately opposite each other. Tighten the *upper* clamp and accurately set zero with the *upper* tangent screw. Use a small hand lens for magnification and judge the exact setting by the lines on either side of the zero as well as the zero lines themselves.

Orient the instrument by pointing the telescope toward the object to be sighted, focus carefully, bring the vertical cross-hair approximately on the object, tighten the *lower* clamp and bring the cross-hair to exact setting with the *lower tangent screw.* When using a tangent screw always *make sure that the last turning motion is one which will compress the spring against which the screw works.*

The line of sight is now on one leg of the angle to be measured, and the instrument is set at zero. Loosen the *upper* clamp, rotate the telescope in the horizontal plane to the second point, focus, get the vertical cross-hair approximately on the point and tighten the *upper clamp.* Bring the cross-hair exactly on the second point by means of the *upper tangent screw.* The angle is now recorded on the lower plate. Read it with the aid of the magnifying glass and enter it immediately in the fieldbook. Be sure to read both scale and vernier *in the direction that the vernier index passd over the scale.*

A valuable check against mistakes is provided by doubling each angle. This is done by loosening the lower clamp after the single angle has been measured and orienting on the first point as before. The only difference now is that the vernier is set at the value of the angle instead of at zero. Obviously if the same procedure is followed as for the single angle, the reading should be twice the first reading. The difference between the double angle and two times the value obtained for the single should agree within the least count of the vernier. Much of the value of the check is lost unless the instrumentman deliberately tries to forget the recorded value of the single angle and then makes the comparison *after* the double angle has been read and recorded. If the values do not check sufficiently close, the entire procedure should be repeated while the transit is still set up at that point.

6-9. Measuring an angle by repetition. Measurement of an angle by repetition is identical to the procedure described for doubling except that there are from six to twelve repetitions instead of only one. It is used when it is desired to gain accuracy beyond the least count of the instrument at hand. For example, suppose that the value of an angle is actually 20°20'10''. With a one minute transit the single angle would be read 20°20' and the

Sta.	Dist.	Single Angle	Double Angle	Mean Angle	O.M.B.	
F-A-B	176.51	100°47'	201°34'	100°47'	N64°00'E	
A-B-C	226.73	151°03'	302°05'	151°02'30"	S87°30'E	
B-C-D	224.94	107°27'	214°55'	107°27'30"	S20°30'E	
C-D-E	381.46	180°42'	361°23	180°41'30"	S23°00'E	
D-E-F	395.90	89°45'	178°23'	89°44'30"	S75°00'W	
E-F-A	673.71	90°18'	180°35'	90°17'30"	N16°30'W	
			Sum =	720°00'30		

BOUNDARY SURVEY - ALBERT RIGGS PROPERTY

4/4/56 Cool and Windy 3
Marks ⊼
Hort R.Ch.
Mills H.Ch. Transit No. 16

Note: Distances in feet. All angles measured as interior left.

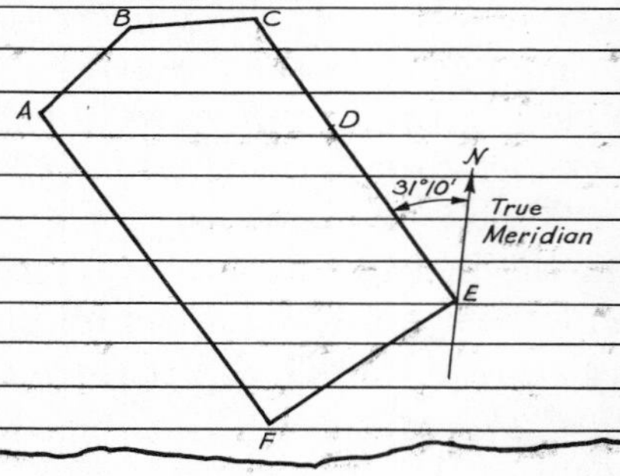

31°10' True Meridian

Fig. 6-10. Field notes for a transit-tape survey.

double angle, although actually being 40°40'20'', could only be read 40°40'. However, after six repetitions the reading would be 122°01'. This value divided by 6 equals 20°20'10''.

When the required precision justifies measuring an angle by repetition, it is desirable to make half of the repetitions with the telescope normal and half with the telescope inverted. This compensates for some errors in the instrument. The repetitions may be made so that the final reading will be near zero, or turning may be continued in the same direction so that the final angle will be near the value of the single angle times the total number of repetitions.

Figure 6-10 shows a suggested form of notes for a transit and tape survey.

HORIZONTAL ANGLES FOR ACMEY PLANT LAYOUT						Observer – T. Jones 4/18/56 Recorder – K. Kane Cool and clear Inst. № 5	
Object	Tel.	Rep.	Ver. A	Ver. B	Mean	Hor. Ang.	
		π at	Δ Kern				
Δ Hill	D	O	0°00'	59'	-0°00'30"		
Δ Davis		1	30°15'				
		3	90°47'	46'	90°46'30"		
		6	181°35'	35'	181°35'00"	30°15'55"	
Δ Hill	R	6	0°01'	00'	0°00'30"	30°15'45"	Mean Hor. Ang. 30°15'50"

Fig. 6-11. Field notes for angles measured by repetition.

A suggested method of recording angles measured by repetition is shown in Figure 6-11.

6-10. Repetition to lay off an angle. It may be necessary at times to lay out an angle more accurately than can be done with a single reading of the transit at hand. This may be accomplished as follows: Suppose the desired angle is 36°22'00", and that you have a 01' transit. With the transit at the vertex of the angle, lay off 36°22' with the two points on the legs of the angle set about 300 feet from the vertex. Measure this angle by repetition. Suppose the results show it to be 36°22'10". Reduce the angle by setting one of the points over by 0.015 feet. The basis for this is that the natural tangent of 01" is 0.000005. The angle as now laid out should be checked again by repetition.

6-11. Types of horizontal angles. Horizontal angles may be classified according to the method of orienting the line of sight and whether the measurement is clockwise or counterclockwise. By this classification all horizontal angles measured with a transit will fall into one of the following categories:

1. An angle to the *right* or *left*.
2. A *deflection angle* to the *right* or *left*.

In Figure 6-12 the designation for each of the four angles shown are: 20°05' right, 40°20' left, 30°07' deflection right, and 115°12' deflection left.

Now suppose we are in the field measuring each of these angles with a transit. The procedure would be as follows:

For the *first*, set up over point *B* with the index at zero and the lower clamp loose. Orient by placing vertical cross-hair exactly on point *A* with lower clamp and lower tangent screw, loosen upper clamp and turn to the *right* until the cross-hairs are on point *C*.

For the *second*, set up at *C*, orient as before by sighting point *B*. Loosen upper clamp and turn to the *left* until point *D* is sighted. When the final adjustment of placing the cross-hair on the point has been made the angle 40°20′ will be recorded on the plates.

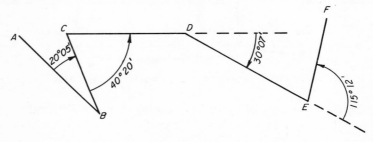

Fig. 6-12. Measurement of horizontal angles.

For the *third*, set up at *D* and sight *C*, but this time plunge the telescope before beginning to measure. The telescope will now be pointing along the line *C–D* produced. Loosen the upper clamp and swing the telescope to the *right* to sight point *E*.

For the *fourth*, the procedure is identical to that for measuring the other deflection angle except that the telescope is swung to the *left* to sight point *F*.

A sight taken to orient the line of sight is called a *backsight*. Sights to other points are called *foresights*.

It should now be apparent that an angle is called *right* or *left* depending upon whether the instrumentman turns the telescope to his right or left as he stands behind the eyepiece end of the telescope ready to loosen the upper clamp and measure the angle. It is essential that the way in which each angle was measured be recorded as the field measurement is made. If all angles measured on a given job are of the same type, a note to that effect is made. If they are not, each angle must be marked in the notes.

6-12. Traverses. From the discussion in Chapter 4 it will be remembered that in surveying, the term *traverse* is used to designate a series of connected lines. If the lines bound a figure or area, we speak of it as a *closed traverse*. When the last line of the traverse in the field does not return to the beginning point the designation *open traverse* is used.

In Figure 6-13 several traverses are shown. Notice the variety

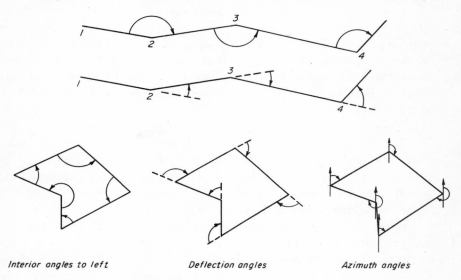

    Interior angles to left   *Deflection angles*   *Azimuth angles*

Fig. 6-13. Open and closed traverses.

of ways in which angular relationship may be shown. Visualize the measurement of each of these angles with a transit in the field.

6-13. Establishing and prolonging a straight line. The three general situations involved in running straight lines between two or more points are (1) when the two points can be seen from each other, (2) when the end points are not intervisible, but can both be seen from some common point between them, and (3) when the end points of the line are neither intervisible or visible from any point on line between them.

Suppose points on line are to be set between two points, *A* and *B*, in the first situation. The transit is set up over either point, a backsight is taken on the other, and as many points as desired are set by placing them so they appear to be bisected by the vertical crosshair. Sometimes it is necessary to extend (prolong) a line. To understand this procedure, again visualize a line identified by end points *A* and *B*. The line is to be extended beyond point *B*, but with the transit at point *A* the instrumentman cannot see beyond

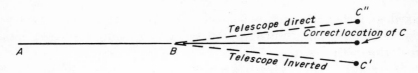

Fig. 6-14. Double centering.

point B. To prolong the line set up at point B, take a backsight on point A, plunge the telescope and put in point C. Point C will lie on the extension of line A–B if the instrument is in adjustment. That is, if the line of sight is perpendicular to the horizontal axis about which the telescope rotates. See Article 8-10. If this condition does not exist, point C can be established as follows:

With instrument at B take a backsight on A, plunge the telescope and put in point C'. See Figure 6-14. With the telescope still inverted (bubble tube on top of telescope) again sight point A, plunge and set point C''. Point C lies halfway between C' and C''. This procedure is called *double centering*.

When the two points between which a straight line is to be established are not intervisible, but both can be seen from a point between them, the point on line is located by trial. This is done by setting up as near on line as can be judged, orienting on one

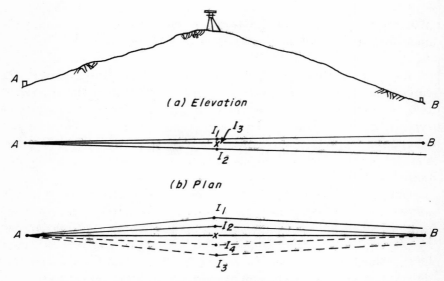

Fig. 6-15. Wiggling in on line.

point and then plunging the telescope to see how near the line of sight comes to the other point. See Figure 6-15(b). Other trials are made as necessary until the intermediate setup is on line. This presumes that the instrument is in adjustment. If it is not, the condition shown in Figure 6-15(c) will exist and the necessary correction must be made. This can be done by coming in from the opposite side as shown by the dotted lines. The point on line then lies midway between I_2 and I_4. The trial procedure just described is known as *wiggling in on line* or *working in on line*.

When two points are neither intervisible nor visible from a common point between them the direction of a straight line which will connect them must be computed. This is done by first running a random line. Complete details for doing this are given in Articles 11-5 and 12-11.

6-14. Sights and signals. The cross-hairs must be set on an object of known relative position when measuring angles or establishing line with the transit. The basic rule to be followed by the person giving the sight (the rodman) is to use as a sight an object which will appear to be about three times the width of the vertical cross-hair. For the instrumentman the rule to be followed is, sight as low on the object used to give sight as possible. That is, sight as near the point itself as possible. When necessary, sights are taken on a range pole (Figure 4-9). Other objects used when sighting conditions permit are: pencil, taping pin, edge of card, plumb-bob string, or nail.

The rodman should stand erect behind the range pole and balance it between his fingers to help insure its being plumb. When using any object to give sight he should consider the background for the sight. A white card or similar object may have to be placed behind the sight so that it will be clearly visible to the transitman. A good rodman learns to anticipate the instrumentman's wishes and is continually alert for any signals that might be given.

In many instances it is necessary or practical to use signals rather than call directions. When giving signals the instrumentman must remember that the rodman does not have the benefit of a telescope. All of his signals, then, must be distinct and with enough motion to be understood. Often it may be necessary to hold a handkerchief or bright-colored object when signaling if the background is poor or the rodman is some distance away. Following are some of the commonly used signals.

Move right or left: Motion with the hand horizontally out from the body. A fast motion to indicate very little movement necessary, a slow motion for greater distance.

All right: Extend both arms horizontally and wave them up and down a few times.

Give sight: The instrumentman raises his hand vertically above his head and brings it down in a vertical plane in front of him.

Plumb sight: Extend the arm vertically above the head and motion in the direction the sight should be plumbed.

Take sight: Same as for *give sight* and then immediately holding the object to be sighted on the point.

Give line: The rodman holds the range pole horizontally above his head and then brings it down to be motioned onto the line.

Move instrument: On parties where the instrumentman is not party chief the signal from the party chief to move the instrument is made by extending both hands downward and outward and then raising them simultaneously.

Special signals should be arranged beforehand whenever it is thought that they may be needed. For very great distances, such as in triangulation, light reflected from mirrors is sometimes used for sights. Lights are also used as sights for night work.

6-15. Vertical angles. Vertical angles as used in surveying are angles measured in the vertical plane with zero or reference being the horizontal. That is, a vertical angle is not measured from a low point to a high point, but from the horizontal to the high point, $a(+)$ vertical angle, and from the horizontal to the low point, $a(-)$ vertical angle. Obviously it is just as important to record whether a vertical angle is $(+)$ or $(-)$ as it is to record whether a horizontal angle is Rt. or Lt. This is done in the fieldbook at the time of measurement.

A vertical angle is measured by carefully leveling the horizontal plate and sighting the horizontal cross-hair on the point to which the vertical angle is to be measured. The value of the angle is read from the vertical circle and its vernier. This will be the vertical angle if the instrument is properly adjusted. Instrument conditions which affect the accuracy of a vertical angle are: (1) line of sight not parallel to axis of telescope bubble, (2) horizontal plates not truly horizontal when plate bubbles are centered, and (3) vertical circle not reading zero when telescope bubble is centered. To correct the last of these, center the telescope bubble carefully and read the vertical circle. The amount that this reading differs from zero is called the *index correction*. The index correction is then applied to the vertical angle as read. Care must be exercised in applying it so that it is not added when it should be subtracted or vice versa. Procedures for adjusting the plate bubbles and for making other adjustments on the transit are given in Chapter 8.

6-16. Mistakes and sources of error in using the transit.

1. Plumb-bob not over the point when sights are taken.
2. Slight errors in graduating circles or circles not concentric.
3. Uneven settling of the tripod, especially on wet or frozen ground.
4. Parallax in focusing.
5. Atmospheric conditions such as haze and heat waves.
6. Wind and temperature variations.
7. Instrument not in proper adjustment and precautions such as double centering not taken.
8. Errors in pointing.
9. Reading the wrong way on either the circle or vernier or both.
10. *Zeroing* the *A* vernier and reading the angle on the *B* vernier or vice versa.
11. Using the wrong tangent screw.
12. Not using total scale reading when adding vernier reading to it; for instance, 36°12′ instead of 36°42′.
13. Failure to mark all vertical angles with (+) or (−) sign at the time they are measured and recorded.
14. Not indicating type of horizontal angle in notes; for instance, left, right, deflection left, deflection right.
15. Applying index correction in the wrong direction on vertical angles.
16. Setting cross-hair on something which looks like the sight, but is not.

6-17. Care and adjustment.

There are certain routine checks and adjustments which can be made on the transit in the field, but any major adjustment or repair should be referred to a reliable instrument maker or repairman. Even the field adjustments discussed in Chapter 8 should be attempted only by an experienced person or under careful supervision.

Any of the equipment used in surveying should be handled with care to prevent damage and preserve accuracy. Some of the precautions to be taken in handling the transit are:

1. When the transit is to be transported for any distance or in a vehicle, remove it from the tripod and place it in its case, making sure all clamps are tight.

2. When using the clamps, tighten them only until they are snug. Never tighten down hard or force them.
3. When leveling keep the leveling screws bearing snugly against the foot plate, but not so tight that they bind or become hard to turn.
4. If the instrument becomes wet or damp, dry it off gently with absorbent cloth. Do not wipe the objective lense as it is easily scratched. To clean the lens use a brush made of camel's hair. If necessary, rub gently with a clean piece of soft linen moistened in alcohol or with a piece of lens paper.
5. Protect the instrument at all times from any shock or sudden jolt.
6. On the job carry the transit cradled in your arm with the tripod legs sticking out to the side or behind unless you are walking completely in the open. When there is no danger of striking the instrument against a tree, building, or other obstruction it may be carried over your shoulder.

6-18. The theodolite. The origin of this term for a surveying instrument is not known for certain. There is also some variation in the use of the term, as to exactly what it designates. Some instruments called theodolites are essentially the same as a transit except that they are larger and read to a smaller angular value, 10″ or less.

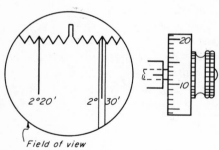

Field of view

Fig. 6-16. Micrometer microscope for reading angular values from a theodolite.

These are sometimes called *repeating theodolites*. Another distinction sometimes used is that a theodolite is not only more accurate than a transit, but has only one *horizontal motion* and clamp. These are sometimes referred to as *direction instruments*.

The vernier as described in connection with the transit has been found to be impractical for the more precise angular readings. One means of reading angles measured with a theodolite is by use of a micrometer microscope. Small microscopes are attached to the side of the instrument and directed downward to the graduated circle. A pair of parallel hairs so set that a line on the scale nearly fills the space between them is moved across the microscope field by a micrometer screw. The relationship between the pitch of the screw and the focal length of the objective of the microscope is such that some whole number of turns of the micrometer head equals

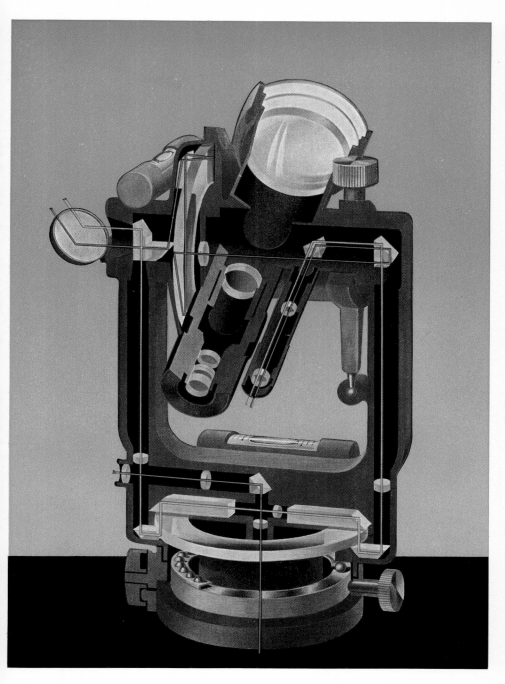

Fig. 6-17. Cut-away view of an optical reading theodolite
(coincidence micrometer). Courtesy Kern Instruments, Inc.

a space on the graduated circle. The micrometer head is subdivided so the angle can be read to seconds. Figure 6-16 shows the scale as seen through the reading microscope. At the side is shown the micrometer head which is attached to the screw which moves the notched frame and the parallel hairs.

Figure 6-17 shows another kind of reading device called the coincidence micrometer. In this type of instrument the diametrically

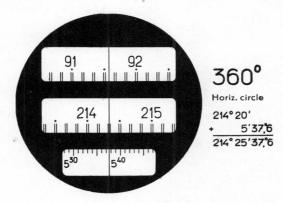

Fig. 6-18. Example of circle readings.
(Courtesy Kern Instruments, Inc.)

opposite parts of the graduated circle are viewed simultaneously through the reading microscope alongside the telescope, and the mean is automatically obtained. This is done by the *train* of prisms shown in the cut-away. Either the horizontal or vertical circle can be brought into view, depending upon how the prisms are adjusted by the operator.

Figure 6-18 shows how the graduated circle appears through the reading microscope. The top scale is the vertical circle reading and the middle one is the horizontal circle reading. The small scale at the bottom is the scale of the micrometer head which is turned to produce the "coincidence setting." That is, to bring the diametrically opposite scale points into perfect coincidence.

Figure 6-19 shows the instrument to which Figures 6-17 and 6-18 refer.

Some of these instruments are equipped with a device called a vertical collimator. This consists of a horizontal microscope through which, by means of a prism, the observer is able to view the point directly beneath the instrument. A small circle which lies in the vertical plane through the center of the instrument is also visible.

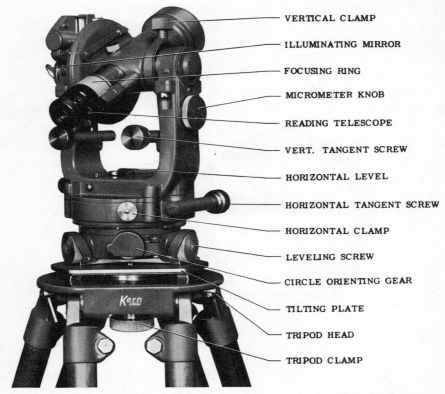

VERTICAL CLAMP

ILLUMINATING MIRROR

FOCUSING RING

MICROMETER KNOB

READING TELESCOPE

VERT. TANGENT SCREW

HORIZONTAL LEVEL

HORIZONTAL TANGENT SCREW

HORIZONTAL CLAMP

LEVELING SCREW

CIRCLE ORIENTING GEAR

TILTING PLATE

TRIPOD HEAD

TRIPOD CLAMP

Fig. 6-19. A modern theodolite. (Courtesy Kern Instruments, Inc.)

When the point over which the instrument is being set coincides with the small circle the instrument is centered over the point. The vertical collimator is used in place of the plumb-bob for making the final setting over the point. The vertical collimator can be seen near the base of the instrument in Figure 6-17.

A transit similar to the one shown in Figure 6-2 except that it has no compass and has a special slow-motion shifting head is available with an *optical plummet* which is similar to the vertical collimator just described.

PROBLEMS

1. Construct a scale with vernier reading to $\frac{1}{8}$ inch. The main scale is to be graduated to quarter inches.

2. A distance $A-B$ is measured along a uniform slope and found to be 3,376.24 feet. The vertical angle measured at $A = +10°11'$. Find the horizontal distance $A-B$.

3. What is the rate of grade of line A–B?

4. A transit scale has a total of 1,440 divisions. The vernier has 45 divisions. An angle has been measured and the 937th division of the scale has been passed by the zero of the vernier and the 33rd line of the vernier coincides with a line of the scale. What is the value of the angle?

5. Given the following angles: A–B–C: 38°00′ right; B–C–D: 110°30′ left; C–D–E: 88°30′ deflection left; D–E–F: 150°00′ deflection right; E–F–G: 115°30′. Plot this traverse assuming all lines to be 300 feet in length and line A–B to have an azimuth of 28°00′ (S point reference). Show all possible positions of line F–G.

6. A rod that has graduations indicating every $\frac{1}{5}$ inch is to be equipped with a vernier that will give direct readings to $\frac{1}{100}$ inch. How many divisions will this vernier have? What will the total length of the vernier be?

7. A rod is divided into feet and inches. A vernier designed to indicate readings to $\frac{1}{16}$ inch will have ...... divisions each equal to ...... of a foot in length.

8. Draw a vernier to full scale which will give readings to the nearest 0.002 of a foot when used with a Philadelphia level rod. See Article 7-9.

9. A scale is divided into inches and quarters. Describe and show by a sketch drawn to scale a vernier which will permit readings to $\frac{1}{16}$ of an inch.

10. A level rod is divided into feet and inches and is equipped with a vernier of 8 divisions. What reading is indicated by 42 main scale divisions and 3 vernier divisions?

11. A rod is divided into tenths of a foot. It is desired to read to fiftieths. Describe and show by a sketch a vernier constructed to accomplish this. Do the same for a scale having divisions of 0.20 inch, reading to be $\frac{1}{30}$ of an inch.

12. A circle is divided into fifths of a degree. How many spaces must a vernier have to permit reading to 30 seconds?

13. A circle is divided into 2-degree divisions. How many divisions must a vernier for this circle have to give a reading of 15′? How many main scale divisions would these vernier divisions equal?

14. A transit plumb-bob is 0.02 foot to the side of point A when point B is sighted. What is the angular error between the line of sight and line A–B when: A–B = 100 feet? A–B = 500 feet? A–B = 1,000 feet?

15. What angular error is made in a sight 700 feet away if only the top of the range pole is sighted and it is 0.1 foot out of plumb?

16. It is desired to "wiggle" onto line A–B at a point 400 feet from A.

Distance *A–B* is 1,850 feet. Point *A* is sighted and the telescope plunged. The line of sight is 4 feet to the right of point *B*. Where should the next setup be made? Draw sketch.

17. A vertical angle measured by a transit is read as $-(26°27')$. When the telescope bubble is centered the vertical circle reads $+00°03'$. What is the corrected value of the angle? What is the corrected angle if the index correction is $-(00°02')$?

18. A linear precision of 1/20,000 is required. What precision is required in horizontal angle measurements to maintain consistency with this? That is, angles must be measured to . . . . . . seconds.

Chapter 7

~~~~~~

MEASURING ELEVATIONS

THE RELATIVE positions of points in terms of the vertical distance
which one point is above or below another is designated by their
elevations. The elevation of a point is its vertical distance from a
datum or reference surface considered to have zero elevation. Sea
level is the standard datum, but sometimes the reference is taken
as an arbitrarily assumed surface.

In effect, the sea level reference is the surface of a body of still
water covering the earth. Obviously any point on the surface of
the earth which is not submerged would have to be above this
imaginary surface unless it is protected by a natural or an artificial
barrier. Death Valley in California, approximately 280 feet below
the level of the Pacific Ocean, and the Dead Sea in Palestine, nearly
1,300 feet below the level of the Mediterranean Sea, are examples
of the natural barrier. The dikes of the Low Countries of Europe
are an example of the artificial barrier.

The value for mean sea level has been obtained by averaging
the elevations of high and low tide at many points for long periods
of time. Continuing observations are made to detect changes.

Any assumed surface may be used as a datum when relative
elevations over a limited area are to be established. This is done
by assigning an elevation to some permanent control point and determining all other elevations in the area with regard to this value.
The assigned elevation can be of any magnitude. However, for
convenience, a large enough value should be used so that no point
in the system will have a negative elevation.

An assumed value of one hundred feet is common in flat or gently
rolling terrain. If the area is mountainous, perhaps one thousand
feet will be the assigned elevation. In any case, to avoid confusion,
the assumed value should be quite different from the sea level elevation of the point. In addition a specific note should be made as
to whether the elevations are in terms of an arbitrarily assumed
reference surface.

7-1. Horizontal vs. level. From the preceding discussion, it is apparent that a level surface is a curved surface. Then a *level line*, which is any line contained in a level surface, is necessarily a *curved line*.

This means that the common usage of the word *level* is technically incorrect. What we should say is that a line or surface, as commonly defined by the use of a spirit level, is horizontal.

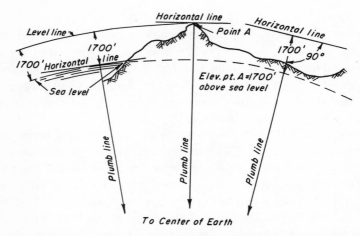

Fig. 7-1. Relationship between horizontal line, level line, and plumb line.

A level line may be defined as a *curved line*, all parts of which are equidistant from the center of the earth. A *horizontal line* is a straight line tangent to a level line. It is perpendicular to the action of gravity through the point of tangency. See Figure 7-1.

Because of the comparatively large radius of the earth, a level line and a horizontal line are, for most practical purposes, the same for short distances. Theoretically, however, they coincide only at the point of tangency.

7-2. Curvature and refraction. The rate at which a level line departs from the horizontal is approximately 0.66 foot in 1 mile and varies as the square of the horizontal distance from the point of tangency. That is, if we could sight along a horizontal line for one mile, the level line passing through our eye would be about 0.66 foot below the line of sight at the 1-mile point. However, because of atmospheric refraction the line of sight does not follow the horizontal, but is bent downward at the rate of approximately 0.09 foot per mile. The net result is that the level line falls away from the line of sight at the rate of approximately 0.57 foot per mile, varying as the *square* of the horizontal distance. A commonly used formula is:

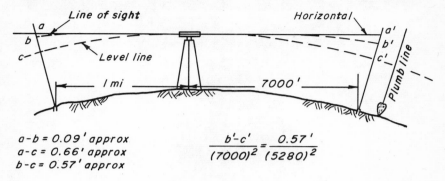

$$\frac{b'-c'}{(7000)^2} = \frac{0.57'}{(5280)^2}$$

a−b = 0.09' approx
a−c = 0.66' approx
b−c = 0.57' approx

Fig. 7-2. Curvature and refraction.

$C = 0.574D^2$, where C is the correction in feet and D is the distance in miles. In Figure 7-2, note that the offset from the line of sight is measured along a radius (the line of action of gravity) rather than along a line normal to the horizontal.

7-3. Methods of leveling. The three methods of leveling (determining differences in elevation) used in surveying are: (1) *barometric leveling*, which involves determining the difference in elevation between points by measuring the variation in air pressure at each point; (2) *trigonometric leveling*, which is the method of measuring the vertical angle between points which are a known distance apart and determining by trigonometry the vertical distance between them; and (3) *direct leveling*, which consists of establishing the horizontal with a spirit level and measuring vertical distances by taking readings on a graduated rod, also called *spirit leveling*.

7-4. The engineer's level. This is the most widely used direct leveling instrument. It consists of a telescope with a bubble tube attached. The assembly is mounted on a foot-plate which has leveling screws attached to permit leveling (bringing bubble to center of bubble tube). The entire telescope-bubble tube assembly can be rotated through 360 degrees in the horizontal.

These levels are divided into two classes according to the method of support: the *wye level* shown in Figure 7-3 and the *dumpy level* shown in Figure 7-4.

The wye level is so named because the telescope tube is supported by two Y-shaped uprights fixed to a horizontal bar and at-

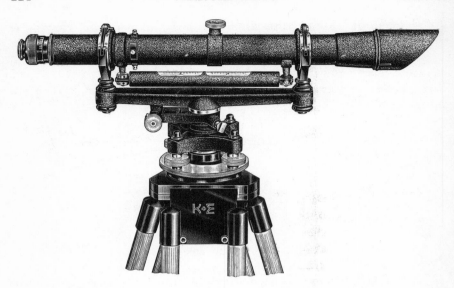

Fig. 7-3. The *wye* level. (Courtesy Keuffel & Esser Co.)

tached in turn to the vertical spindle about which the instrument rotates. The telescope can be lifted clear of the Y-supports by releasing the two clamping collars which fit across the tops of the Y's.

In the dumpy level the vertical spindle, horizontal bar, telescope supports, and telescope tube form a single unit.

Either of these levels will give good results when properly used. The dumpy may be more sturdy than the wye and stay in adjust-

Fig. 7-4. The dumpy level. (Courtesy Keuffel & Esser Co.)

ment longer, but the wye is considered by some to be easier to adjust than the dumpy.

Notice in Figures 7-3 and 7-4 that the arrangement of leveling screws and leveling head is similar to that of the transit. However, since the level need not be set up over any particular point, there is no movable head nor plumb-bob as in the transit.

7-5. The precise level. This instrument is used for obtaining the most precise results in direct leveling. It is basically the same as the engineer's level, but has the following refinements: (1) a

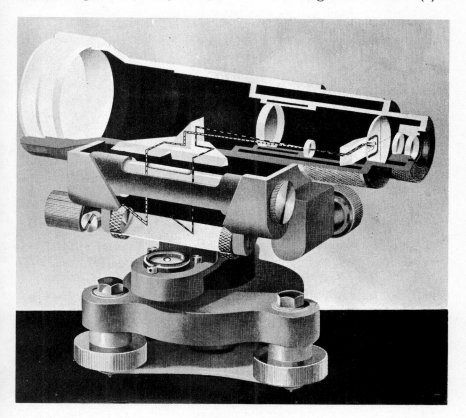

Fig. 7-5. A modern, precise level. (Courtesy Kern Instruments, Inc.)

micrometer screw which tilts the telescope-bubble tube assembly for more exact centering of the bubble, (2) a prism arrangement so that the bubble can be observed at the instant the rod reading is taken, and (3) a heavier, more stable tripod than used for the engineer's level. Figure 7-5 shows a cutaway of one type of precise level.

Some precise levels have three horizontal cross-hairs, two equally spaced on either side of the central one. A reading is taken for each one at each pointing. If the rod is graduated in yards and hundredths of yards, the three readings are added to give a reading in feet. If the rod is graduated in the metric system, three readings are taken and the mean of the upper and lower readings checked with the reading of the central cross-hair.

To insure more exact centering of the bubble, precise levels have an arrangement of prisms which make the bubble appear "split" as shown in Figure 7-6. When it is not centered it appears as shown, but, when centered, the two halves move into coincidence.

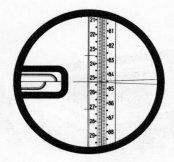

Fig. 7-6. The split bubble as it appears through the telescope. The precise level rod is graduated in the metric system. (Courtesy Kern Instruments, Inc.)

7-6. The self-leveling level. A time saving development in surveying instruments is a level which has no tubular spirit level. It does have a small circular spirit level, sometimes called a *bull's-eye* level, and three leveling screws. These are used to approximately center the bubble of the circular level. The line of sight then becomes automatically horizontal and remains horizontal as long as the circular bubble remains approximately centered.

The self-leveling level utilizes the action of gravity in its operation. A prismatic device called the *compensator* is suspended on fine, nonmagnetic wires. When the instrument becomes approximately level the action of gravity on the compensator causes the optical system to swing into the position which defines a horizontal line of sight. Any settlement or other movement which would disturb the bubble and line of sight in the conventional level cannot affect it here; the pendulum action automatically shifts to maintain the correct position of the line of sight whenever any slight disturbance occurs.

A self-leveling level is shown in Figure 7-7.

7-7. Hand level. This instrument is used for short sights or when high accuracy is not required. It consists of a tube about 6 inches long through which the observer sights. On top of this tube is a small bubble reflecting through a prism so that it appears to move vertically as seen by the observer, sighting through the tube at a level rod. See Figure 7-8.

Fig. 7-7. The self-leveling level. The only spirit level is the circular one shown under the viewing prism on the right. (Courtesy Keuffel & Esser Co.)

There is no magnification by the hand level. The observer sees the rod through one part of the sighting tube and the bubble image is seen in the other part. When the bubble appears to be on the cross line (Figure 7-8) it is in the center of the tube. The rod reading is taken at this time.

Fig. 7-8. One type of hand level. (Courtesy Keuffel & Esser Co.)

Another similar instrument is the *Abney hand level*, or the *clinometer.* Here, the bubble tube is movable with respect to the sighting tube. Attached to the bubble tube is a pointer which moves along an arc graduated in degrees and in per cent of slope. When the pointer is set at zero the clinometer is used as an ordinary hand level. In addition, the vertical angle or per cent slope can be measured if a sight is taken to the desired location and the bubble tube rotated until the bubble comes to the center of the tube. Figure 7-9 shows the clinometer.

Fig. 7-9. Clinometer. (Courtesy Keuffel & Esser Co.)

7-8. The transit as a level. To use the transit for leveling, the plate bubbles are centered after setting up, just as in transit work. The setup is easier, however, because it is not made over any particular point. Next, the telescope is rotated in the vertical plane until the telescope bubble is nearly centered. The telescope clamp is tightened and the bubble exactly centered by use of the telescope tangent screw. The transit is now ready to use as a level.

The transit gives less precise results than the wye or dumpy level, having a less sensitive bubble and, in general, a less powerful telescope.

7-9. Leveling rods. The distance between the line of sight through a leveling instrument and the point whose elevation is either known or required, is measured on a graduated rod, called a *leveling rod.*

There are many types of leveling rods. Some are in one piece; others either hinging or telescoping for ease in transporting.

Most rods are graduated in feet, tenths and hundredths of feet. However, they are also available with graduations in feet, inches, and fractions of inches for use in the building trades.

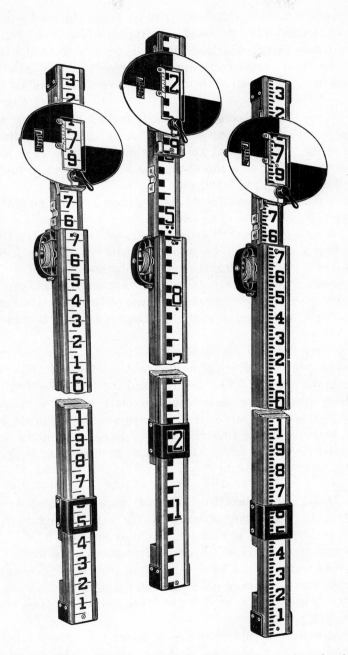

Fig. 7-10. Philadelphia rod with different types of graduations. The one at the right is the most common. The center one is graduated in the metric system. (Courtesy Keuffel & Esser Co.)

Some rods are direct-reading, that is, they are read from the instrument. Others may be used as direct-reading rods, but also have a movable target which is set by directions from the instrumentman until the cross-hairs appear to bisect it. The reading is then made by the rodman with the aid of a vernier attached to the target.

Figure 7-10 shows a commonly used leveling rod known as the *Philadelphia rod.* It is about seven feet in length when fully telescoped and can be extended to approximately twice that length. It can be used either as a direct-reading or target rod in both the telescoped and "long rod" positions.

When long rod is used for direct readings it is important that the rod be *fully* extended. For long rod, target readings, the rod is first fully telescoped, then the target vernier is set at exactly the same reading as that given by another vernier on the back of the rod. The target is then brought into apparent coincidence with the cross-hairs by extending the rod as necessary. The reading is made by means of the vernier on the back of the rod. Graduations on the back increase consecutively from top to bottom to make this possible.

A direct-reading rod graduated to hundredths of a foot can be read to that precision and estimated to the closest 0.005 foot at distances up to 300 feet. The vernier used for target readings on a rod similarly graduated gives readings to 0.001 foot. It is important to note, however, that target readings are only as accurate as the accuracy attained in setting the target. Recorded values to the nearest 0.001 foot may imply an accuracy greater than is actually obtained.

7-10. Differential leveling. The determination of differences in elevation between two or more points without regard to the alignment of the points is called differential leveling.

The spirit level (Article 7-3) is used to establish a line of sight which is horizontal except for the effect of atmospheric refraction. A rod graduated in units of linear measure is used to determine the distance between the line of sight and the point on which the rod is held.

The procedure for running a line of differential levels follows:

1. Select a reference point. This is called a *bench mark* (B.M.). A bench mark is a *permanent* point of known or assumed elevation. A permanent monument referred to mean sea level is shown in Figure 7-15.

The bench mark is the top of the brass disk set in a concrete post.

2. With the bubble of the leveling instrument exactly centered take a reading on the rod held on the bench mark. This is called a *backsight* (B.S.). A backsight is a reading on a rod held on a point of known or assumed elevation.

3. Compute the elevation of the line of sight by *adding* the backsight reading to the bench mark elevation. This is called the *height of instrument* (H.I.). The height of instrument is the elevation of the line of sight above the datum (surface of zero elevation).

4. With care not to disturb the instrument, thus changing the H.I., sight the rod held on a solid point which is as far from the instrument as the bench mark is and in the general direction in which you wish to advance. This is called a *foresight* (F.S.). A foresight is a reading on a rod held on a point of unknown elevation. The point in this case is called a *turning point* (T.P.). A turning point is a stable point, first of unknown elevation and then of known elevation used to carry forward a line of levels. It must not change elevation while in use.

Turning points are *never taken on the ground.*

The elevation of the turning point is computed by subtracting the F.S. from the H.I.

5. Move the instrument to any new location from which a sight can be taken to the T.P. just established, and which is advantageously located for sighting another T.P. This step is a most important factor in determining the overall speed of running a line of levels.

6. From this new setup take a backsight to the T.P. just established. The new H.I. can now be computed in the same way as when a backsight was taken to the bench mark. With the H.I. known, the elevation of the second T.P. is now determined by taking a foresight to it.

Continuation of the line of levels for any distance desired is accomplished by successive repetitions of the steps outlined.

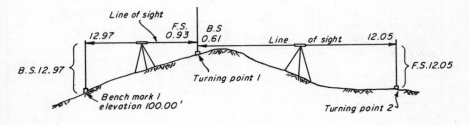

Figures on "line of sight" indicate rod readings when bubble is exactly centered in tube.

Fig. 7-11. Differential leveling.

Sta.	B.S.	H.I.	F.S.	Elev.		
		DIFFERENTIAL LEVELING FOR CONTROL ON POWER PLANT SITE			1/16/56 Cloudy-Cold Janson 人 Reed ∅ Level № 4	3
B.M.₁	———		———	100.00	Top of iron pipe set in concrete.	
	12.97	112.97			On property line 200'E. of S.W.	
T.P.₁			0.93	112.04	corner of site boundary	
	0.61	112.65				
T.P.₂			12.05	100.60		
	3.17	103.77				
T.P.₃			5.71	98.06		
	4.13	102.19				
B.M.₂			5.08	97.11	Top of iron pipe set in concrete.	
	∑ 20.88		∑ 23.77	100.00	100' S.E. of N.W. corner main footing.	
			20.88	97.11		
		Check	2.89	= 2.89		

Fig. 7-12. Field notes for differential leveling.

Figure 7-11 illustrates graphically the principle of differential leveling. It is important to understand that, while the figure might imply that the points are all on a straight line, they may in fact have any conceivable pattern in plan. This means that a backsight does not necessarily indicate a sight backward, and a foresight a sight ahead. Actually both might be in the same direction.

Figure 7-12 shows a form of differential leveling notes. Readings for the first two setups are from Figure 7-11.

Sta.	B.S.	H.I.	F.S.	Elev.		
		DIFFERENTIAL LEVELING FOR CONTROL ON POWER PLANT SITE			1/16/56 Cloudy-Cold Janson 人 Reed ∅ Level № 4	3
B.M.₁	———			100.00	B.M.₁ — Top of iron pipe set in	
T.P.₁	12.97	112.97	0.93	112.04	concrete.	
T.P.₂	0.61	112.65	12.05	100.60	On property line 200'E. of S.W.	
T.P.₃	3.17	103.77	5.71	98.06	corner of site boundary.	
B.M.₂	4.13	102.19	5.08	97.11	B.M.₂ — Top of iron pipe set in	
	20.88		23.77	100.00	concrete. 100' S.E. of N.W. corner	
			20.88	97.11	main footing.	
		Check	2.89	= 2.89		

Fig. 7-13. Differential leveling notes.

Figure 7-13 shows another form of notes for the same work.

Notice that in leveling notes the *station* is where the rod is held, not the instrument location.

A check on the addition and subtraction in each step can be made by adding all backsights and adding all foresights. The difference in these two sums must equal the difference in elevation between the first and last stations.

7-11. Using the level. In general the care, handling, and setting up of the level is similar to that outlined for the transit. Some of the items to keep in mind will be discussed.

Since the level need not be set over a point the setting up is somewhat simplified. The first step, that of determining where to locate the instrument, is controlled by these considerations: (1) the instrument must not be too low or too high to permit a rod reading on the point of known elevation, (2) the length of backsight should not appreciably exceed 300 feet, (3) the length of foresight and backsight from any given setup should be approximately equal, (4) the foresight should be so located that it will advance the line of levels, and (5) in general if the slope is downward in the direction of progress, backsight readings should be small and foresight readings large. For working up the slope the opposite is true.

When the position for the setup has been determined, the legs of the tripod are spread apart and adjusted so that the tripod head is as nearly horizontal as can be judged by eye and the instrument is at a convenient height for use. Two of the tripod legs are then pushed firmly into the ground. Before the third leg is set, it should be positioned to keep the tripod head horizontal; then it too is pushed into the ground. All tripod legs should be checked to see that they are firmly set.

Check the instrument for parallax as described in Article 6-3. (Usually necessary only on the first setup.)

Next the telescope is turned until it is over two diagonally opposite leveling screws. Then it is leveled by bringing the bubble within one or two divisions of the center of the tube. The telescope is then turned until it is over the other set of leveling screws and the bubble brought near the center of the tube as before. The first position is turned back to again and the bubble is centered more carefully this time. This leveling process is repeated, with the bubble brought nearer the center each time, until it remains centered in both positions.

The adjustment of the bubble tube is checked after the instrument has been carefully leveled in the two positions at 90 degrees to each other. This check is made by turning the telescope 180 degrees, until it is over the same two leveling screws, but pointing in the opposite direction. The position of the bubble is noted. If it does not remain centered, the bubble tube is out of adjustment and should be adjusted as described in Article 8-2.

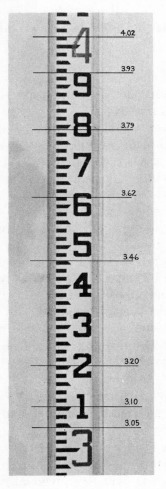

Because the bubble is very sensitive and easily disturbed, avoid walking around the instrument or touching the tripod legs. Note that wind may also cause the bubble to leave the center of the tube.

If the bubble is not centered when the rod is sighted, it is brought to exact center by the two diagonally opposite leveling screws most nearly under the telescope. The rod reading is then taken and the bubble checked again *after* the reading. If this check does not find the bubble centered, it is centered again and the reading is repeated. For accurate results the bubble must be in the center of the tube *at the instant the rod reading is taken*.

Fig. 7-14. Various readings on a Philadelphia rod. Lines represent the horizontal cross-hair of instrument.

7-12. Rod readings. For direct readings the instrumentman notes the value of the graduation where the horizontal cross-hair of the level appears to intersect the rod when the level bubble is centered. See Figure 7-14.

The instrumentman should check each reading by counting from control points on the rod. For example, if the reading is 3.67 feet (Figure 7-14), he should first mentally note that the crosshair lies between the red 3 and the red 4 designating the foot marks, and above 3.6; then, that it lies above the 3.65 foot mark, and finally count 3.65, 3.66, 3.67.

Unless the foot mark is consciously included in a *count*, it is easy to misread a value like 3.91 as 4.91, particularly if the rod is close enough to the instrument so that the red 4 shows, but the red 3 does not.

If no foot mark shows, the rodman should lift the rod slowly upon the instruction from the instrumentman, "raise for red." The instrumentman reads the first red foot mark which comes into view.

When taking target readings, much time will be saved if an approximate reading is made from the instrument and called or signaled to the rodman. The rodman will set the target at the specified value, which will place it close to where it should be. The instrumentman then motions to move the target up or down until it is bisected by the horizontal cross-hair. When this happens, he signals, "all right," and the rodman clamps the target, lets the instrumentman make a final check, and then reads the value indicated by the vernier.

It is obvious that no target setting will be correct unless the rod is plumb at the time of the reading.

The instrumentman can tell that the rod is out of plumb in one plane by comparing it to the vertical cross-hair of the instrument. The vertical cross-hair should be near the rod, but need not coincide with it. If it does not appear plumb, he signals the rodman by raising his arm vertically and moving it in the proper direction.

The rodman ascertains that the rod is plumb by standing directly behind the rod and balancing it between his finger tips. Comparing the rod to building walls, trees, or other vertical objects is an aid to plumbing. When there is a strong wind, particularly if long rod is being used, it may be necessary to wave the rod.

7-13. Waving the rod. The rod is waved to determine whether it is plumb. The waving is accomplished by rocking the rod back and forth through an arc toward and away from the instrument. The minimum reading is then recorded as the correct one.

For precise work a *rod level* is used, one type of which consists of a small circular spirit level fastened either to the rod or to a small bracket held against the side of the rod. When the bubble is in the center of the circle the rod is plumb. Other types have conventional bubble tubes.

7-14. The tape rod or "automatic" rod. This rod eliminates the need for addition and subtraction in the notes. It is not widely used, but has the advantage over the conventional rod when many elevations are to be determined from one H.I.

The rod consists of a frame with rollers at both ends over which an endless, graduated, metal tape moves. The tape is graduated with numbers increasing downward; it may be clamped in any position.

To illustrate the use of this rod, suppose the B.M. elev. is 962.42. The rod is set on the B.M. and the tape moved until the reading by the levelman is 2.42. There it is clamped. The rod is then moved to a point of unknown elevation and read. Suppose the reading is 4.62. The elevation of that point is 964.62.

7-15. Bench mark levels. When a large amount of leveling is to be done in an area, bench marks are set at various points to aid in establishing other elevations as needed. It is important that this work be accurately done so that elevations referred to one bench mark will check with those referred to any other bench mark in the circuit.

To help insure accuracy the rod should be checked periodically with a steel tape. If the comparison shows appreciable error, new graduations should be placed on the rod, or it should be discarded.

The line of sight cannot be assumed to stay in adjustment, that is, parallel to the axis of the bubble tube. The distance to the backsight and foresight points from any given setup should be made equal. If this is done, errors in the line of sight and in the effect of curvature will be cancelled, one rod reading being added and the other subtracted in computing the H.I. and elevation from each instrument setup.

Bench marks in the system or circuit should have their elevations determined by more than one line of levels. Variations in elevation values for the same point are balanced out by an adjustment based upon the error theory of probability (Articles 3-10 and 3-11). An explanation of the more exact method of least squares can be found in texts on advanced surveying.[6]

In ordinary surveying work the adjustment may be made by proportioning the discrepancies according to the lengths of the routes.

Suppose the difference in elevation in feet between two bench marks is found to be 10.32, 10.35, and 10.37 by three different routes. If the routes are all of the same length and all field conditions are the same, the value to be used would be the mean of the three results. Assume, however, that the three routes are 0.60, 0.90, and 1.35 miles in length. For adjustment, the results are assigned weights inversely proportional to route lengths. The elevation to be used would then be the sum of the weighted differences in elevation divided by the sum of the weights, thus:

Line	*Weight*		
1	$5.4 \div 0.60 =$	9	$9 \times 10.32 =$ 92.88
2	$5.4 \div 0.90 =$	6	$6 \times 10.35 =$ 62.10
3	$5.4 \div 1.35 =$	4	$4 \times 10.37 =$ 41.48
		19	196.46

weighted mean difference = 196.46 ÷ 19 = 10.34 feet

If intermediate bench marks are to be set in any circuit, the error in the levels is proportioned directly as the distance. For example, if a bench mark were set at one-third the distance along the 1.35-mile route, the correction would be 0.01 which is one-third of 10.37–10.34.

One or more bench marks set previously will often be available as a reference or control for a new circuit of bench marks.

The U. S. Coast and Geodetic Survey has established a network of precise levels referenced to sea level which covers the entire United States. Bench mark elevations have been adjusted on all published portions of the network. See Figure 9-2. The location and elevation of bench marks along these lines can be obtained by writing the U. S. Coast and Geodetic Survey, Washington, D. C. Figure 7-15 shows one of the bench marks.

The following is a description of a bench mark in the second-order leveling net of the U. S. Coast and Geodetic Survey as published by them in a list of bench mark descriptions.

D 167: 2.6 miles east along the Chicago, Burlington & Quincy Railroad from the station at *Republican City*, Harlan County, at milepost 233, in the northwest corner of section 11, T 1 N, R 17 W, at the crossing of a north-and-south road between sections 10 and 11, 40 feet east of the center line of the road, and 30 feet north of the north rail of the track. A standard disk, stamped "D 167 1934" and set in the top of a concrete post. (588.300 meters or 1,930.114 feet.)

Fig. 7-15. Coast and Geodetic Survey bench mark tablet set in concrete post.

The U. S. Geological Survey, Washington, D. C. also can furnish level data covering a large area of the United States.

Many circuits of bench mark levels have been run by railroads and other companies, as well as by city, county, and state engineering offices. These data are normally available upon request.

7-16. Double rodded lines. *Double rodding* is used when it is not practical to rerun a line of levels, and yet a check is desired.

This process differs from conventional differential leveling in that two turning points are established at each setup instead of one. The rodman selects T.P.'s near each other, but with different elevations. The result is an independent check on the value of each H.I. Compared to a complete circuit (forward and back) the number of setups between any two bench marks is cut in half. Figure 7-16 shows a set of notes taken on a double rodded line.

7-17. Reciprocal leveling. It may be necessary to determine the difference in elevation between two points that, though visible from each other, are separated by a ravine or river, making it impossible to balance lengths of backsight and foresight.

Sta.	B.S	H.I.	F.S.	Elev.	Mean	
DOUBLE RODDED LEVELS – B.M.₁ TO B.M.₃, HOMES SUBDIVISION						4/12/56 Warm – Cloudy Janson ⊼ Reed ∅ 5
B.M.₁	———		———	852.76		U.S.C.G.S. B.M. East city limits of
	3.74	856.50				Minford, Conn.
	3.74	856.50				
T.P.₁	5.17	854.53	6.14	849.36		
T.P.₁L	6.31	854.54	7.27	848.23		
T.P.₂	3.15	853.44	4.25	850.29		
T.P.₂L	4.06	853.44	5.16	849.38		
T.P.₃	6.18	856.50	3.12	850.32		
T.P.₃L	7.20	856.49	4.15	849.29		
B.M.₂	3.11	854.10	5.51	850.99	850.98	Concrete monument at s.w. corner of
B.M.₂	3.11	854.10	5.51	850.98		park area.
T.P.₄	2.65	849.12	7.63	846.47		
T.P.₄L	3.54	849.10	8.54	845.56		
B.M.₃			5.15	844.97	844.96	Concrete monument at N.E. corner
B.M.₃			5.15	844.95		of park area.
						Check : Σ "B.S. = 51.96, Σ F.S. = 67.58
						(67.58 – 51.96) ÷ 2 = 7.81
						852.76 – 844.96 = 7.81

Fig. 7-16. Field notes for double rodded levels.

The instrument is set up near one point (*A*) and a rod reading is taken on it and on the other point (*B*). See Figure 7-17. From these readings the apparent difference in elevation of points *A* and *B* can then be computed.

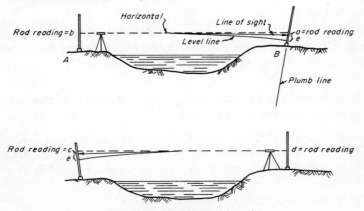

Fig. 7-17. Reciprocal leveling.

The instrument is next moved to a location near point B and readings are again taken on both points as shown. The apparent difference in elevation is again computed. The true difference in elevation between A and B is equal to the mean of the two apparent differences, provided the effects of atmospheric refraction (a significant factor over bodies of water) remained constant during the reading times. The following shows that this gives the true difference:

Suppose e in Figure 7-17 represents the error caused by curvature and non-adjustment of the instrument. In each case the error in the reading on the near point caused by these factors is negligible because the length of sight is only a few feet. The value e is the same in each of the long sights because the lengths of these sights are essentially the same.

In the first case the difference in elevation is $D = (a - e) - b$. In the second case, $D = d - (c - e)$. Adding, $2D = (a - b) + (d - c)$. Therefore, $D = \frac{1}{2}(a - b + d - c)$. This is the mean of the two apparent elevation differences.

If the two points have approximately the same elevation, it is easier to carry the signs in the calculation if the readings taken on the point of known or assumed elevation, point A, are thought of as backsights and those on the point of unknown elevation, point B, are thought of as foresights. The difference in elevation will always be equal to the sum of backsights minus sum of foresights divided by the number of instrument setups. Normally, several pairs of readings would be taken.

Point A is higher than point B if the value of the difference in elevation D is negative. Point B is higher than point A if the value of D is positive.

The use of two instruments making simultaneous observations will facilitate the work and eliminate the error caused by variations in atmospheric refraction.

7-18. Errors and mistakes. Some of the more common sources of errors and mistakes in leveling are:

1. Not selecting definite, stable turning points, and not holding the rod on exactly the same point for both foresight and backsight.
2. Not having bubble *exactly* centered at instant of reading or setting target.
3. Not properly focusing telescope (parallax).

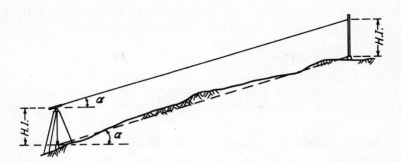

Fig. 7-18. Trigonometric leveling for short distance.

4. Assuming instrument is in adjustment and therefore not balancing lengths of foresights and backsights.
5. Allowing mud, snow, or ice to accumulate on the base of the rod.
6. Effect of wind on both instrument and rod.
7. Effect of heat waves (shorten sights and keep line of sight as far above ground as possible).
8. Not holding rod plumb.
9. Not fully extending rod for direct readings on long rod.

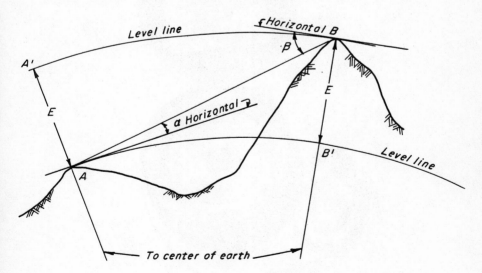

Because radius of earth is large, A-center of earth is assumed parallel to B-center of earth. Then horizontal distance between points = A-B = A'-B' = h.

$$E = h\,(\tan\alpha + \tan\beta) \div 2$$

Fig. 7-19. Trigonometric leveling.

10. Not setting target vernier at exactly the same reading as the vernier on the back of the rod with the rod fully collapsed in preparation for target readings, long rod.
11. Making arithmetical mistakes.
12. Recording backsight or foresight in wrong column.
13. Confusing numbers or graduations when reading the rod.
14. Subtracting backsight or adding foresight when completing notes.

7-19. Trigonometric leveling. This is sometimes called *indirect leveling*. It involves observing vertical angles and computing vertical distances by trigonometry from this angle and the measured horizontal distance or slope distance between the points whose elevation difference is desired. Figure 7-18 shows one method of accomplishing this.

Fig. 7-20. Aneroid barometer for barometric leveling. (Courtesy Wallace & Tiernan, Inc.)

Where the distance is great enough to make the effect of curvature significant, a procedure somewhat like reciprocal leveling may be used. Figure 7-19 illustrates this.

7-20. Barometric leveling. The *aneroid barometer* is a practical instrument for observing elevation differences with accuracy of from 10 to 20 feet. By careful procedures, accuracies of from 3 to 10 feet may be attained.

The barometer consists of an instrument containing a system of levers which magnify, and record by a moving hand, the variations in atmospheric pressure on a "cell" of flexible metal.

The face of the instrument, Figure 7-20, is graduated to read in feet of elevation and in inches of mercury.

Fig. 7-21. The Alticorder (recording altimeter). (Courtesy Wallace & Tiernan, Inc.)

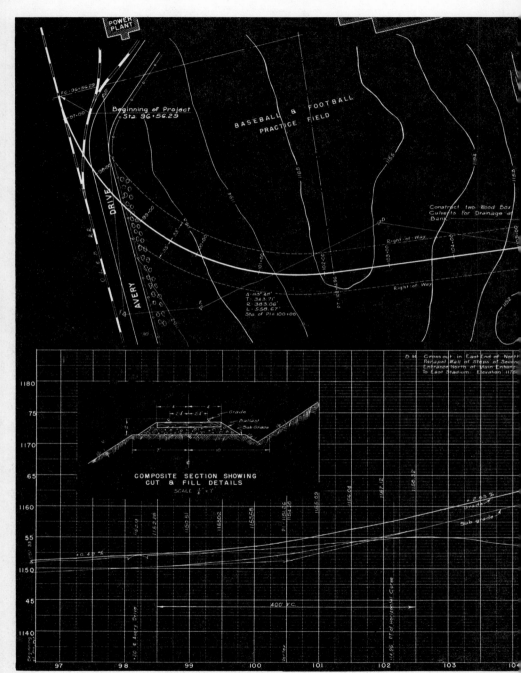

Fig. 7-22. Plan-profile sheet for proposed railway spur.

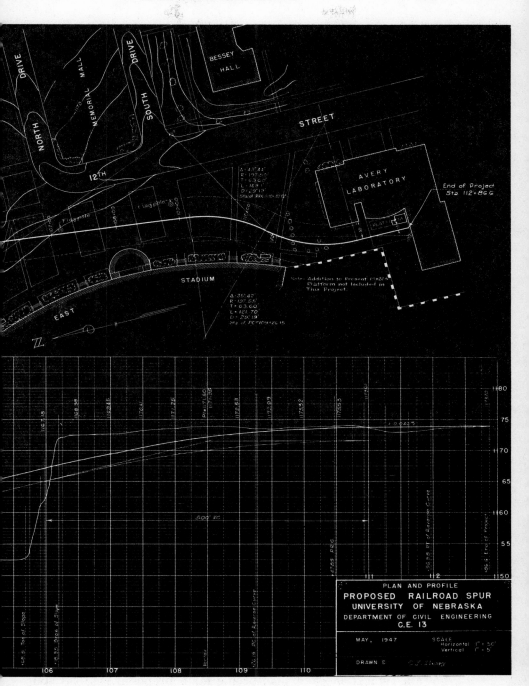

PLAN AND PROFILE
PROPOSED RAILROAD SPUR
UNIVERSITY OF NEBRASKA
DEPARTMENT OF CIVIL ENGINEERING
C.E. 13

MAY, 1947

SCALE
Horizontal 1" = 50'
Vertical 1" = 5'

DRAWN E

The aneroid barometer is usually *compensated* so that temperature changes within the instrument itself will not be reflected in the accuracy of the readings. Because the weight of air, and hence the atmospheric pressure at any point, changes with temperature, it is necessary to correct for any significant temperature change in the interval between observations.

This is a rapid and sufficiently accurate means of determining elevations for reconnaissance or other work requiring approximate values.

This method is not desirable when pressures in the area are changing rapidly unless results of the moving barometer are correlated with a continuous record made by an instrument located at a station of known elevation. Figure 7-21 illustrates an instrument used for obtaining such a record.

7-21. Profile leveling. This method differs from differential leveling in purpose, but not in principle.

Profile leveling may be defined as the determination of differences in elevation between points at designated intervals along an established line. The purpose is to provide data from which a vertical section of the ground surface along a surveyed line can be plotted. This line is called a profile and is plotted on a linear scale which shows the true length of the surveyed line. It does not, therefore, show a true side view if the line is curved or contains angle points. For example, the plotted profile of a circular path has the same length as a straight path whose length is equal to the circumference of the circle.

The profile is plotted as a graph with the elevation of the various points represented by the ordinate and the horizontal distances between the stations shown on the abscissa. The plotted points are connected by a freehand line. A common scale relationship is 1 inch = 100 feet horizontally, and 1 inch = 10 feet vertically. The vertical scale is exaggerated so that relatively small elevation differences will be apparent. Readings are taken and points plotted for each station regardless of slope changes and at as many intermediate points ("plus stations") as necessary to show changes in slope along the line.

The plan view of the profiled line is usually shown on the top portion of the sheet and the profile on the lower portion. Figure 7-22 shows a typical sheet of plan-profile for a proposed railroad spur.

7-22. Field procedure in profile leveling. Since profile leveling consists of determining elevations along a particular line, the
line must first be established. This is usually done at some time
before the profile levels are run, but a line is sometimes profiled as
it is established.

The initial point or beginning of the line is designated as station
(Sta.) 0 + 00. A transit and tape survey is made, beginning at
Sta. 0 + 00 and defining the path of the line by stakes set at each
station (100 foot interval). Profile levels are then run to determine
the elevation at each station and at intermediate points necessary
to adequately show the shape of the ground surface along the surveyed line. These intermediate points are called *plus stations.* For
example, a point 120 feet from the beginning would be Sta. 1 + 20.
A point on the line 60 feet ahead of Sta. 20 + 00 would be Sta.
20 + 60.

The procedure in profile leveling is as follows:

1. Select a bench mark from which to start. It should be located rea-
   sonably close to Sta. 0 + 00.
2. The instrument is set up near the line to be profiled, but preferably
   off the line. Assuming the bench mark to be near Sta. 0 + 00 and
   also that no obstacles or terrain features interfere, the first setup
   should be approximately opposite Sta. 3 + 00. If the bench mark
   is not near station 0 + 00, one or more setups of differential levels
   will be necessary to reach the first setup for profiling.
3. Assume the instrument is properly set up. Take a backsight on the
   bench mark and determine the H.I. Next, take foresights on the
   rod held on the ground at stations 0 + 00 to 6 + 00 inclusive. If
   any plus stations are required, measurements are made from the
   nearest station to the "plus" location, where the rod reading is then
   taken.

   Rod readings at the stations (taken on the ground) are read only
   to the closest 0.1 foot. Those on bench marks and turning points
   are usually read to the closest 0.01 foot.
4. The rodman selects a T.P. near Sta. 6 + 00 and gives a foresight
   there. Note that the length of backsight and of the foresight to the
   T.P. will each be approximately 300 feet.

   Foresights to points on the line cannot be kept equal in length
   to the backsights unless a new setup is made for each station. However, this is not done because the precision required for elevations
   on profile does not warrant it.

   Notice, too, that the position for the first setup was suggested
   to give maximum advantage of that setup. However, the instrument

can have any convenient location, as long as the sights affecting the
T.P. are approximately balanced.

5. After the first T.P. has been established, the instrument is moved
ahead, a new H.I. is determined, and the procedure for obtaining
foresights on points on profile is repeated. Rod readings from which
profile elevations can be obtained are taken for the entire length of
the line.

Profile leveling consists of a line of differential levels which must
be within range of the line being profiled. It also requires several

Sta.	B. S.	H. I.	F. S.	Elev.		
						PROFILE LEVELS ON ℄ OF MAIN CANAL—SUMNER FLATS IRRIGATION PROJECT. / 7/16/56 Clear and Hot Janson ⊼ Reed ∅ 8
B.M.₁				4678.21		U.S.G.S. Bench Mark at S.E. corner of
	3.72	81.93				intersection of State Highways 10 and 41
0+00			4.7	77.2		
+56			3.2	78.7		
1+00			5.1	76.8		
2+00			4.2	77.7		
3+00			7.2	74.7		
4+00			6.3	75.6		
T. P.₁	4.68	79.04	7.57	74.36		
5+00			8.4	70.6		
6+00			8.8	70.2		
7+00			7.3	71.7		
8+00			6.3	72.7		
9+00			4.5	74.5		
10+00			5.6	73.4		
B.M.₂	5.77	82.08	2.73	76.31		Concrete monument 100 ft. N. of sta.
11+00			6.1	75.0		9+40.
12+00			7.2	74.9		
13+00			3.6	78.5		
14+00			3.3	78.8		
T.B.M.			3.77	4678.31		Spike in Tel. pole, 120 ft. E. of sta. 14+00

Fig. 7-23. Field notes for profile leveling.

intermediate foresights from each setup in order to compute elevations which will show the shape of the ground along a predetermined line.

Figure 7-23 shows a form of notes for profile leveling. The computations for heights of instrument and the turning point and bench mark elevations should be completed in the field as the survey progresses. Profile elevations may be computed in the office if the instrumentman is keeping notes.

A variation in the form of notes shown is the use of two columns for elevations. One is headed *Profile Elev.* and the other is headed *T.P. and B.M. Elev.*

PROBLEMS

1. Neglecting the effect of tide and waves, determine how far out to sea a ship will be when a light on its mast 60 feet above the water disappears from the sight of a man on shore whose eye level is 5 feet above the water.

2. Rule a sheet of paper to represent an open fieldbook. Assume the B.M. from which you start has an elevation of 100.00 feet. Show the *complete* form of notes for differential leveling with rod readings assumed for four setups. End the notes with a T.B.M. (Temporary bench mark). Show note check.

3. The center line for a 600-foot diameter park drive has been staked. A level set in the center of the circle has an H.I. of 115.68 feet. Beginning at Sta. 0 + 00, rod readings are taken at each full station as follows: 3.7, 4.6, 5.9, 6.1, 6.2, 8.1, 3.4, 2.1, 0.1, 1.8, 3.6, 7.2, 6.2, 5.9, 5.5, 5.0, 4.7, 4.0, 3.9. Plot the profile and plan for the stations shown.

4. The line of sight on a level is out of adjustment, making it 0.22 foot high in 200 feet. From a given setup the length of backsight to a point of 118.93 foot elevation is 20 feet. The rod reading is 5.71. Find the elevation of a point 300 feet from the level if the rod reading on it is 6.95.

5. Given the following rod readings taken by reciprocal leveling between A and B (2,000 feet apart and separated by a river):

Inst. near A:

rod at A = 4.37,   rod at B = 6.73

Inst. near A:

rod at A = 5.00,   rod at B = 7.37

Inst. near B:

rod at A = 6.46,   rod at B = 4.81

Inst. near B:

rod at A = 6.69,   rod at B = 5.03

(a) If the elevation of point A is 777.77, what is the elevation of point B?

(b) What is the direction and magnitude of the error in the line of sight of the instrument or instruments used?

6. Given the following rod readings taken by reciprocal leveling between A and B (2,000 feet apart and separated by a deep ravine):

$A1 = 4.01$ $B1 = 5.41$
$A2 = 3.44$ $B2 = 4.03$
$A3 = 4.24$ $B3 = 5.63$
$A4 = 4.04$ $B4 = 4.67$

(a) What is the elevation of point B if $A = 100.00$ feet?

(b) What would constitute ideal field conditions for making these observations?

(c) What is the error of the line of sight per 100 feet, and what direction is the line of sight (up or down)?

7. Copy the following questions and mark each one true or false.

(a) The engineer's transit may be used for leveling.

(b) The engineer's level must be set over an exact point by means of the plumb-bob.

(c) The dumpy level has a telescope which may be removed from its supports.

(d) The Philadelphia rod is scaled into feet, inches, and tenths of inches.

(e) Backsights are added to elevations to obtain the H.I.

(f) A backsight is a rod reading taken on a point of unknown elevation.

(g) There are two general classes of engineer's levels: the wye level and the dumpy level.

(h) The Philadelphia rod can be used either as a self-reading or as a target rod.

(i) A turning point is the point at which the instrument is located.

8. Define by use of a sketch the following leveling terms: horizontal line, level line, line-of-sight, datum, curvature, and refraction.

9. By reference to Article 8-3 compute the rod reading for horizontal line of sight if you are given the following information in making the "11/10 Peg" adjustment of the dumpy level, distance $AB = 300$ feet:

Inst. between A and B   *Inst. 30 feet beyond B*
Rod on A: 4.000   Rod on B: 3.000
Rod on B: 3.000   Rod on A: 3.907

10. Complete the following level notes and show check. Write a complete description for B.M.'s. Assume any information necessary in making these descriptions.

Station	B.S.	H.I.	F.S.	Elevation
B.M. 9				1,171.09
	7.21			
T.P. 1			0.93	
	8.63			
T.P. 2			1.03	
	6.95			
T.P. 3			0.44	
	9.32			
B.M. 10			0.13	

Chapter 8

ADJUSTMENT OF INSTRUMENTS

THE BASIC principles for the adjustment of surveying instruments are similar to those for other pieces of precision measuring equipment. Every engineer should have some concept of these principles.

Unfortunately an engineer's transit or level cannot be manufactured with a lock to keep the adjustment always perfect. This means that there must be periodic checks and necessary adjustments on these instruments in the field if the best results are to be obtained. Efficient use of precision instruments is obtained by (1) frequent checks to ascertain that the instrument is not out of adjustment and (2) adjustment by the user when necessary.

Because the instruments are designed so that field adjustments can be made, it should not be necessary to return them to the manufacturer. Of course, an instrument may occasionally be sent to an expert or to the factory for repairs on such things as bent or excessively worn spindles and bent transit standards, or for adjusting transit verniers to be exactly 180 degrees apart, or for centering the graduated circle with respect to the vertical axis so that there is no eccentricity. However, to send an instrument away for routine adjustment is both uneconomical and unnecessary; someone should be available who understands field adjustments.

As indicated in earlier chapters, certain precautions may be taken to cancel the effects of maladjustment, but a good surveyor will not continue to use an instrument in need of adjustment.

Some engineers advocate using an instrument as though it were out of adjustment at all times, doing such routine things as double centering when prolonging a line or reading both verniers and taking the mean of the two readings. But even if this practice is followed, periodic adjustments will save time.

Adjustment involves a succession of manipulations, some affecting the others; no certain order or procedure will entirely prevent

141

this. The order discussed here will serve to minimize the effect of any one adjustment on those already made. No single adjustment should be made without checking the entire group.

When the entire series of adjustments has been made, it must be checked through again. The second cycle may find everything in order; if not, the complete series must be repeated until all checks are satisfied.

ADJUSTMENT OF THE DUMPY LEVEL

8-1. Cross-hairs. In surveying instruments, the vertical and horizontal cross-hairs are mounted on the same ring, remaining at right angles to each other. Because of this, it is only necessary to check the horizontal or the vertical hair. The horizontal cross-hair is commonly checked in a level and the vertical one in a transit.

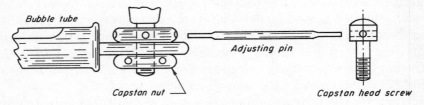

Fig. 8-1. Capstan head screw, capstan nut and adjusting pin.

To test for need of this adjustment, level carefully and sight the end of the horizontal cross-hair on some well defined, stationary point. Move the telescope in the horizontal plane and see if the point appears to follow the hair throughout its length. If it does not, the adjustment is made by loosening all four capstan head screws which hold the cross-hair ring and rotating the ring as necessary by gently tapping one of the screws with a pencil.

A capstan head screw or a capstan nut has small holes around the circumference of the screw head or the nut. A small metal pin called an *adjusting pin* is inserted into one of the holes and the screw or nut is turned by using the pin as a lever. See Figure 8-1.

In manipulating any adjusting screw or nut it is necessary to proceed gently. The screw or nut should not be forced. They should be turned slowly and only a small amount at a time. As an adjustment is finished the screw or nut should be brought up snugly, but not with any appreciable pressure.

8-2. Bubble tube. The purpose of this adjustment is to make a tangent to the arc of the bubble tube at its center (axis of the bubble tube) perpendicular to the vertical axis about which the instrument rotates.

To test, level carefully and see if the bubble remains centered as the telescope is rotated in the horizontal plane. If it does not, level over one set of screws, turn the telescope through 180 degrees so it is over the same set of screws and bring the bubble halfway back to the center by raising or lowering one end of the bubble tube by means of the capstan nut at one end. Now center the bubble by means of the leveling screws.

The student should visualize what is involved here and verify in his own mind that to bring the bubble all the way back to the center of its tube by raising or lowering one end of the tube would result in the bubble being as far out of adjustment as before, but in the opposite direction. See Figure 8-3.

8-3. Line of sight. This adjustment assures a horizontal line of sight when the bubble is centered. In other words, it makes the line of sight and the axis of the bubble tube parallel to each other.

A procedure known as the *peg adjustment,* or the *11/10 peg adjustment,* is used to check the line of sight as well as to provide the necessary data for making the adjustment when it is needed. The procedure is as follows:

1. Set two solid stakes 200 feet apart and with 0.5 to 1.0 feet difference in elevation.
2. Set up the level halfway between them.
3. Take a rod reading on each stake. The difference in these two readings gives the true difference in elevation between the stake tops, because the sights are of equal length.
4. Move the instrument to a point approximately on line and 20 feet from one of the stakes.
5. Take a rod reading on the near stake.
6. Compute what the rod should read on the far stake by use of the known difference in elevation between the stakes.
7. Take a reading on the far stake. The difference between what the rod should read on the far stake and what it does read is the amount the line of sight is up or down in 200 feet. Designate this the *apparent error.*
8. Take 11/10 of the apparent error. This gives the amount the line of sight is above or below the horizontal in 220 feet, the distance

from the instrument to the far stake. Note whether the line of sight
is up or down.

9. Add the error to or subtract it from the actual reading on the far
   stake, depending upon whether the line of sight needs to be raised
   or lowered. The result is the reading on the far point which will
   make the line of sight horizontal.

10. While the bubble remains centered, move the horizontal cross-hair
    parallel to itself until it is on the correct reading. This is done by
    loosening one of the vertical capstan head screws on the cross-hair
    ring and tightening the other.

This test is based upon the principle that if the line of sight of
the instrument is not horizontal, it will deviate up or down in direct
proportion to the horizontal distance from instrument to rod.

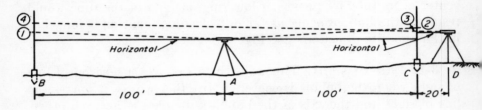

① Instrument at A, rod reading on B = 6.295 ft
② Instrument at A, rod reading on C =   5.164 ft
                                        1.131 ft, true difference in elevation between
                                                 B and C (C is higher than B).
③ Instrument at D, rod reading on C =   5.838 ft
                                         1.131 ft
   Instrument at D, rod reading on B should be 6.969 ft
④ Instrument at D, rod reading on B is ⟶ 7.154 ft (line of sight is up)
   Apparent error (i.e., error in 200 ft) is ⟶ 0.185 ft
   Error in 220 ft = $\frac{11}{10}$ x 0.185 = 0.204
   Instrument at D, target setting on rod at B for horizontal line of sight
   = 7.154 - 0.204 = 6.950 ft.

Fig. 8-2. The 11/10 peg adjustment.

Figure 8-2 shows the relative positions of the stakes or pegs
and the instrument in the 11/10 peg test and gives a numerical
example of the test.

A variation of the 11/10 peg test, sometimes referred to as the
two peg test is performed as follows:

1. Set the instrument midway between two points to obtain their true
   difference in elevation.

2. Move the instrument very close to one point so that the eyepiece
   of the telescope nearly touches a rod held on the point. Bring the

eyepiece in line with the rod and note the rod reading opposite its center. This reading is of course unaffected by error in the line of sight.

3. From the data now at hand, compute what the reading should be on the rod when it is held at the other point.

Still another variation of the peg test is to proceed in the same way as is outlined in the article on reciprocal leveling (Article 7-17).

ADJUSTMENT OF THE WYE LEVEL

8-4. Cross-hairs. This adjustment is identical to the first adjustment explained for the dumpy level, with one exception. Some wye levels have a *stop screw* which allows the whole telescope to rotate when clamped in the Y's. This screw may be adjusted to rotate the telescope and cross-hairs as a unit, thus accomplishing the same result as loosening and rotating the cross-hair ring. On others the cross-hair ring must be rotated just as in the dumpy level.

8-5. Line of sight. This adjustment is to make the line of sight parallel to the horizontal axis through the Y-supports.

To check, loosen the clips which hold the telescope in the Y's, and after leveling carefully sight the intersection of the cross-hairs on a definite point which is 200 to 300 feet away. Rotate the telescope until the bubble tube is on top. See if the point appears to move off the intersection. If it does, bring each cross-hair halfway back toward the point. Adjust each hair separately by means of the capstan head screws on the cross-hair ring.

Here, as in the case of the bubble tube adjustment on the dumpy level, it should be apparent that to move the cross-hairs all the way onto the point would result in the same amount of error in the opposite direction.

8-6. Bubble tube. To bring the axis of the bubble tube into the same vertical plane as the line of sight, loosen the Y-clips, level carefully, and rotate the telescope about its longitudinal axis through about 10 degrees in each direction. The bubble should remain centered. If it does not, move the bubble tube laterally by means of the lateral adjusting screws until it does.

To make the axis of the bubble tube parallel to the horizontal axis through the Y-supports, loosen the Y-clips and level carefully.

With the telescope over one set of leveling screws and the bubble centered, gently lift the telescope and turn it end for end in the Y's. The bubble should return to the center of the bubble tube. If it does not, bring it halfway back to the center by raising or lowering one end of the bubble tube by means of the capstan nuts at one end of the bubble tube.

If the Y's and collars are worn, or for any reason are not true, the adjustments mentioned above will not result in the axis of the bubble tube and the line of sight being parallel.

It is preferable to check the line of sight by the peg adjustment outlined in Article 8-3. After the correct rod reading for a horizontal line of sight has been determined by this method, the horizontal cross-hair is brought onto the correct reading by means of the *leveling screws*. The bubble is then brought to the center of the tube by raising or lowering one end of the bubble tube with the capstan nuts at one end.

8-7. Wye adjustment. This adjustment is not necessary for accuracy if the bubble is centered *at the instant of sighting;* it is convenient and will save time to have a level so adjusted.

The purpose of the adjustment is to make the axis of the bubble tube perpendicular to the vertical axis about which the telescope rotates.

To test, level carefully and with the bubble exactly centered over one pair of leveling screws revolve the telescope 180 degrees in the horizontal plane over the same set of screws. If the bubble does not remain centered, bring it halfway back to the center by raising or lowering one of the Y-supports by means of the adjusting nut at its base. Now center the bubble with the leveling screws and repeat the check until the bubble will remain centered throughout a complete revolution in the horizontal plane.

ADJUSTMENT OF THE TRANSIT

8-8. Plate bubbles. When in perfect adjustment the plate bubbles of a transit, once centered, will remain centered for all positions of the horizontal plate, unless the instrument settles or is otherwise disturbed.

If either or both bubbles do not do this, adjustment is required.

To test for need of adjustment, level carefully. Then, with one plate bubble centered over a pair of leveling screws, rotate the instrument through 180 degrees in the horizontal plane; the bubble should remain centered. If it does not, bring the bubble halfway back by raising or lowering one end of the bubble tube by means of the capstan head screws at the end. Bring the bubble the remain-

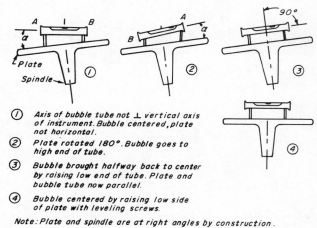

① Axis of bubble tube not ⊥ vertical axis of instrument. Bubble centered, plate not horizontal.

② Plate rotated 180°. Bubble goes to high end of tube.

③ Bubble brought halfway back to center by raising low end of tube. Plate and bubble tube now parallel.

④ Bubble centered by raising low side of plate with leveling screws.

Note: Plate and spindle are at right angles by construction.

Fig. 8-3. Plate bubble adjustment.

ing distance to the center by means of the leveling screws. Test each bubble separately. See Figure 8-3.

8-9. Cross-hairs. This adjustment is made to get the vertical cross-hair truly vertical.

To test, level carefully and sight a plumb-bob string at rest. If the vertical hair does not coincide with the string, loosen all four capstan screws on the cross-hair ring and carefully rotate the ring until hair and string coincide. The screws are then tightened snugly, but without any appreciable force.

8-10. Line of sight. If the line of sight through the telescope is not at right angles to the horizontal axis about which the telescope rotates, the condition shown schematically at the bottom of Figure 8-4 will exist when the instrument is *double centered.*

To test whether the line of sight needs to be adjusted, set up where there is an unobstructed view for two or three hundred feet on either side of the instrument and where there is little change in ground elevation. Level carefully and sight on point *A* on one side of the instrument. Both motions should be clamped for final sighting. Plunge the telescope and set point B on the opposite side of the instrument. Loosen the lower clamp and rotate the telescope to again sight point A. Tighten the lower clamp and get the vertical cross-hair exactly on point A. Bring the telescope to normal posi-

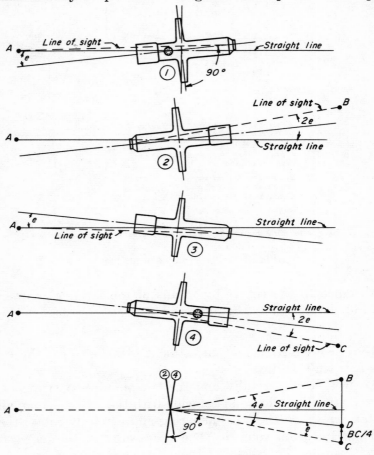

Fig. 8-4. Adjusting line of sight perpendicular to horizontal axis of transit telescope. Error is shown by angle e.

tion and see if the vertical cross-hair is on point B. If it is not, the line of sight is not normal to the horizontal axis of the telescope and adjustment is necessary. See Figure 8-4.

To adjust, set point C beside point B and on the present line indicated by the vertical hair. Locate a point at one-quarter the distance C–B (measured from C toward B). By means of the capstan head screws on the sides of the cross-hair ring move the vertical hair parallel to itself until it is on the point so located, point *D* in Figure 8-4.

8-11. Standards. This adjustment is necessary when the vertical cross-hair does not "sweep" a vertical plane as the telescope is moved from a sight on a high point to a low point on the same side of the instrument. If it will not, the horizontal axis of the telescope is not perpendicular to a plane containing the vertical axis through the instrument. See Figure 8-5.

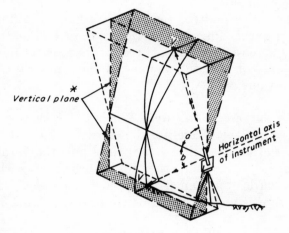

If $a=b$, correction $=\frac{1}{4}$ apparent error

If $b=o$, correction $=\frac{1}{2}$ apparent error

* *The same relationship exists even though plane labeled "Vertical" is not truly vertical. Therefore, instrument need not be leveled so long as it maintains the same position. Unless it is carefully leveled, however, uneven settlement during the test cannot be detected.*

Fig. 8-5. Rotation of telescope about its horizontal axis.

To test for the need of this adjustment, level carefully and, with the telescope normal, sight a high point *A*. With both clamps tight, lower the telescope and set point *B* on the same side of the instrument. The points should be selected so that the vertical angle is as large as practicable. Now rotate the transit approximately 180 degrees in the horizontal plane, plunge the telescope, and again sight point *B*. The vertical cross-hair should be on point *A* when the telescope is raised. If it is not, note the distance it misses point *A* and move it from one-half to one-fourth of that distance back toward point *A* by raising or lowering one end of the horizontal axis of the telescope. This is done by means of the capstan screws on one of the standards. Repeat the check until points A and B are in the same vertical plane. The amount of movement required depends on the relationship of angles a and b, Figure 8-5.

8-12. Telescope bubble tube. This adjustment is significant when the transit is to be used as a level or for measuring vertical angles from a horizontal base. Its purpose is to make the line of sight through the telescope and the axis of the telescope bubble tube parallel to each other.

Determine the correct rod reading for a horizontal line of sight by the 11/10 peg test. Place the horizontal cross-hair on this reading by means of the telescope tangent screw. Then center the telescope bubble by raising or lowering one end of the bubble tube with the capstan nuts at one end.

8-13. Vertical circle vernier. When the telescope bubble is centered the zero of the vernier for the vertical circle should coincide with zero on the vertical circle. If it does not, the vernier can be moved to coincide by loosening the capstan head screws which fasten it to the standards. Care must be taken not to move the vernier again as the screws are tightened down after adjustment.

8-14. Summary. The procedures for adjusting a transit or level are not difficult and can be carried out by following a set of directions. In doing this the student should study each procedure carefully by first visualizing what may become out of adjustment. Next he should reason logically what the evidence of maladjustment in each particular case will be. Finally he should think about what would seem a reasonable procedure to bring the unadjusted component back into adjustment.

If the opportunity arises, it might be best to actually go through the adjustments one by one as the directions are studied. However, the first time, this should only be attempted under the supervision of someone completely familiar with the procedures and techniques of field adjustment.

Tables 1, 2, and 3 are presented, **not** to be memorized as an automatic series of steps, but with the idea of providing some aid to an organized and logical approach in the understanding of the field adjustment of surveying instruments, and to serve as a convenient reference.

Table 1: ADJUSTMENT OF DUMPY LEVEL

NAME	ADJUSTMENT	TEST	HOW TO ADJUST
Cross-hairs:	To make horizontal cross-hair truly horizontal and vertical cross-hair truly vertical.	Vertical hair: sight plumb-bob string at rest. Horizontal hair: sight definite point with one end of horizontal hair; see if point stays on hair as telescope moves from side to side.	Loosen all capstan-headed screws on cross-hair ring, and rotate until test is made.
Bubble Tube:	To make axis of bubble tube ⊥ to vertical axis of instrument.	Level instrument, then see if bubble remains centered as telescope is rotated 180 degrees.	Raise or lower one end of bubble tube. Correct for ½ apparent error.
Line of Sight:	To make line of sight parallel with axis of bubble tube.	11/10 Peg method.	Level instrument and move cross-hair onto correct target setting by use of upper and lower screws on cross-hair ring.

Table 2: ADJUSTMENT OF WYE LEVEL

NAME	ADJUSTMENT	TEST	HOW TO ADJUST
Cross-hairs:	Same as dumpy level.	Same as dumpy level.	Same as dumpy level.
Line of Sight:	To make line of sight parallel to axis of collars in Y's.	Level instrument carefully after loosening telescope in Y's. Sight intersection of cross-hairs on definite point and rotate telescope in Y's. See if point stays on cross-hair intersection.	Adjust horizontal cross-hair by means of upper and lower screws on ring. Use side screws to adjust vertical cross-hair. Adjust for ½ apparent error.
1. *Bubble Tube:*	To bring the axis of bubble tube into same vertical plane as line of sight.	Loosen telescope in Y's. Level carefully and rotate telescope from side to side. The bubble should remain centered.	Move one end of bubble tube to one side or the other with lateral adjustment. Move until bubble remains centered as telescope is rotated slowly in Y's.
2. *Bubble Tube:*	To make the axis of bubble tube parallel with the horizontal axis through the Y supports.	Loosen telescope in Y's. Level carefully. Turn over one set of leveling screws. Gently lift telescope from Y's, turn it end for end and set it back in the Y's. The bubble should again come to the center of the tube.	Bring bubble half way back to center by raising or lowering one end of the bubble by means of capstan nuts at one end. Now center the bubble with the leveling screws.
3. *Bubble Tube:*	To make axis of bubble tube parallel with line of sight.	11/10 Peg method.	Put cross-hair on target by use of leveling screws. Raise or lower one end of bubble tube to bring it to center of tube. Correct for 11/10 apparent error.

NAME	ADJUSTMENT	TEST	HOW TO ADJUST
Wye Adjustment:	To make axis of bubble perpendicular to vertical axis of instrument.	Level instrument then see if bubble remains centered as telescope is rotated 180 degrees in horizontal plane.	Raise or lower Y by adjusting nut on bottom of Y. Correct for ½ apparent error.

Table 3: ADJUSTMENT OF TRANSIT

NAME	ADJUSTMENT	TEST	HOW TO ADJUST
Plate Bubbles:	To make axis of plate bubble perpendicular to vertical axis of instument.	Level carefully over one set of screws, rotate 180 degrees over same set of leveling screws. See if bubble remains centered. Test each bubble separately.	Raise or lower one end of bubble tube. Correct for ½ apparent error (bring bubble only half way back to center of tube).
Crosshair:	To make vertical crosshair truly vertical.	Sight plumb-bob string.	Loosen all capstan screws on cross-hair ring, and rotate to desired position.
Line of Sight:	To make line of sight perpendicular to the horizontal axis of the telescope.	Sight point *A* on one side of instrument. Turn telescope over (plunge telescope) and set point *B* on opposite side. Turn 180 degrees in horizontal plane, again sight point *A*. Plunge telescope and set point *C*. Points *B* and *C* should coincide.	Move vertical cross-hair parallel to itself, using side screws on cross-hair ring. Correct for ¼ apparent error, i.e., bring crosshair ¼ of distance *B–C* measured from *C* toward *B*.
Standards:	To make horizontal axis of telescope perpendicular to the vertical axis of the instrument.	Sight point *A* high, lower telescope and set point *B* low. Rotate 180 degrees in horizontal plane, reverse telescope, and again sight point *B*. Raise telescope and sight point *A*. Crosshair should be on point *A*.	Raise or lower one end of horizontal axis of telescope by means of capstan-headed screws on one of standards. Correct for ⅓ to ½ of apparent error. Repeat until points *B* and *A* are in same vertical plane.
Telescope Bubble:	To make axis of bubble tube parallel with line of sight.	11/10 peg method.	Put cross-hair on target by use of telescope tangent screw. Raise or lower one end of bubble to bring it to center of tube. Correct for 11/10 apparent error.

Part III

APPLICATIONS

Chapter 9

~~~~~~

CONTROL SURVEYS

PARTS One and Two have been concerned with fundamental theory and basic operations and techniques of surveying measurements. Part Three discusses some of the applications of surveying met in engineering practice. The conditions and problems found in practice are unlimited, but can all be reduced to the basic operations of measuring distance, angles, and elevations. If the problem is first broken into its components, an intelligent start can be made on any measuring problem.

Errors are inherent in any measurement. By studying a problem and adopting corrective measures, certain errors can be eliminated. Others can be minimized and some will have to be recognized as factors limiting over-all precision. The effect of errors must be remembered when selecting the procedure for making measurements.

Most engineers will not make nationwide control surveys as outlined in this chapter, but an understanding of the system and of the precision involved will be of use on local surveys. Many surveys are completed as isolated pieces of information, overlooking the fact that when ties are made to precise control points, a survey becomes part of an extensive system. Then the quality of the work can be accurately computed, and data duplicated and extended for engineering work other than that for which it was originally done. The need for expansion or refinement of original surveys is rarely appreciated before the need arises.

9-1. Geographic coordinates. All surveys locate points near the earth's surface. The only method for precisely defining such points on the spheroidal surface of the earth is by use of the geographic coordinates, *latitude* and *longitude*. The axis of rotation of the earth provides the *physical* reference line for this coordinate system. Latitude is defined as the intersection of the earth's surface with planes perpendicular to the earth's axis of rotation. The equator is designated as zero latitude; 90 degrees north or south latitude indicates the poles. Since the earth is not a true sphere (Article 2-1), a degree of latitude near the poles subtends a slightly longer arc than one degree near the equator.

Longitude is represented by *meridian* lines, the intersection of the earth's surface with planes containing its polar axis. These lines converge at the poles, making the length of any arc of longitude dependent upon the latitude of the position. Greenwich, England is the arbitrary reference point for longitude. These arcs are designated from 0 to 180 degrees, both east and west from Greenwich. As exact as this geographic coordinate system may seem, there is evidence that the retreat of the glaciers and a consequent rise in sea level in the past 100 years has shifted the north pole of rotation some 10 feet toward the North Atlantic.*

9-2. Horizontal control. Most of the geodetic surveys are run by organizations of our national government. The Federal Board of Surveys and Maps of the United States has established specifications for these surveys. This board is composed of representatives of each of the various federal surveying and mapping agencies.

When federal control surveys for the United States were first begun, the latitude and longitude of one or more stations of each separate survey were determined by astronomic observations. However, when the isolated surveys were tied into a large network, the measurement of the surveys were of a much higher degree of accuracy than were the determinations of the geographic positions by astronomic observations. It was then decided to establish near the center of the national triangulation network a station that would have its geographic position based on the mean of the many individual geographic positions which had already been established by astronomic observation. The station finally chosen for this purpose is Meades Ranch, it has been assigned the coordinates of 39°13′26.686″ North Latitude and 98°32′30.506″ West Longitude. The mean geographic position of this station is the origin for all stations in the network known as the North American Datum of 1927, used by the United States, Canada and Mexico, whose national surveys are connected at their respective borders.

---

* Walter Munk and Roger Revelle, "Sea Level and the Rotation of the Earth," *American Journal of Science*, November, 1952.

The first-order horizontal control network of the United States is shown in Figure 9-1. The location of the Meades Ranch station is also indicated on this map. The U. S. Coast and Geodetic Survey (U.S.C. & G.S.) whose responsibility it is to run the control surveys of the United States contemplates establishing horizontal control stations (permanent monuments) whose latitude and longitude are accurately determined in each $7\frac{1}{2}$-minute quadrangle of area except in the mountainous areas of the West, where one point in every 15-minute quadrangle is considered adequate. The sides of these quadrangles are arcs of latitude and longitude. The U. S. Geological Survey issues maps of these quadrangles which are known as *quadrangle maps.*

Horizontal control surveys are of two general types, *triangulation surveys* and *traverse surveys.* Triangulation surveys consist of networks of geometric figures with all or almost all of the angles measured directly in the field and with relatively few of the sides measured in the field. Traverses for control surveys consist of closed polygons with most of the sides and angles measured directly in the field. For precise or high-order work all of the angles and sides of a traverse or all of the angles of a triangulation net should be measured directly in the field.

Control surveys using geographic coordinates of latitude and longitude are often called *geodetic* or *precise* surveys. The Federal Board of Surveys and Maps, specification of 1933, requires a precision of 1 in 25,000 for first-order triangulation work. At one time this order of precision was generally limited to the nation-wide networks of federal surveys. Today, however, many large industrial sites are controlled by surveys of this type and most city control systems are of even higher precision.

Equal precision can be obtained by either triangulation or traverse methods. The choice is an economic one. Usually in mountainous or hilly country where stations can be located for long intervisible sights, triangulation will be the choice. In flat, open country, or where stations must be close together, traverse surveys are run. Figure 9-1 is titled the Horizontal Control System of the United States, since it includes both first-order triangulation and traverse lines. Most of the latter appear in the Southeastern and Great Lakes regions of the United States.

9-3. Vertical control. High-order spirit level circuits have been run throughout the United States to determine elevations for accu-

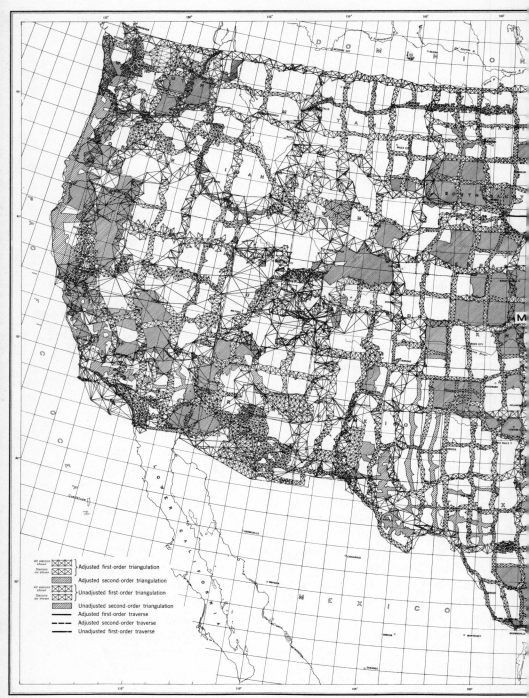

Fig. 9-1. Horizontal Control System of the United States.

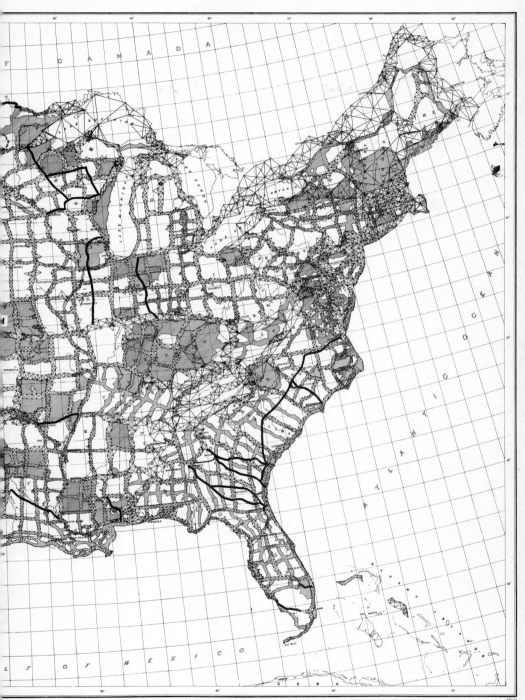

(From U. S. Coast and Geodetic Survey chart)

159

Fig. 9-2. Vertical Control System of the United States.

U. S. DEPT. OF'COMMERCE
COAST AND GEODETIC SURVEY
R. F. A. Studds, Director

LEVEL NET OF THE UNITED STATES

January 1, 1955

———— First - order Leveling
--------- Second - order Leveling
• Additional Second - order Leveling
Within This Area

(From U. S. Coast and Geodetic Survey chart)

rately defining the position of all control points. These precise level lines are shown in Figure 9-2. The pattern of horizontal control (Figure 9-1) and vertical control (Figure 9-2) is very similar, because the elevation of all horizontal control points must be known in order to reduce all points to the same datum, which for the nation-wide system is mean sea level.

Trigonometric leveling (see Article 7-3) is often used to transfer elevations from precise leveling circuits to triangulation stations, these stations generally being located on high, commanding points, while the levels are run, insofar as possible, over level or gently sloping terrain.

9-4. Triangulation procedure. Horizontal control by triangulation requires the determination of the positions and elevation of widely separated points, and the directions and lengths of the lines joining these points. The accurate locations established by these surveys provides information which makes possible the correction of errors in ordinary surveys.

The steps followed in establishing a triangulation control system are:

1. Reconnaissance to establish stations.
2. Measurement of base lines.
3. Measurement of angles.
4. Astronomic checks of position and direction.
5. Office computations.

9-5. Triangulation systems. The different geometric figure arrangements used to form triangulation networks are: (1) chain of triangles, (2) central-point figures, and (3) chain of quadrilaterals. These basic figures are linked together as illustrated in Figure 9-3. The same maximum length of sight L is used in all three cases in the illustration. The chain of quadrilaterals shown has 18 stations while the other two systems each have 17 stations.

The single row of triangles is usually the least costly to run, but its use is limited by its lack of accuracy. The central-point figures are double rows of triangles which cover a wide area at moderate cost. If the three diagonals indicated by dashed lines in the lower hexagon of this system are observed, the checks on the figure are greatly improved. The third system shown is the single row of quadrilaterals. It is the most expensive, but gives the highest accuracy.

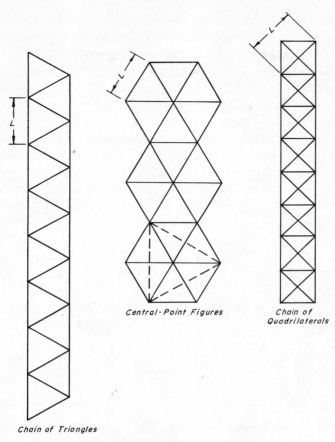

Central-Point Figures   Chain of Quadrilaterals

Chain of Triangles

Fig. 9-3. Triangulation systems.

The system of quadrilaterals requires twice as many stations as either of the other two systems for the same area coverage. The amount of line to be cleared is approximately the same in all three systems for an equal number of stations; however, the distance covered between the extreme points in the chain of triangles is 60 per cent greater than in the other systems. The quadrilateral system affords the most *conditions* for adjustment of the observed angles. The conditions are rigid geometric laws (such as the sum of the interior angles of a triangle equaling 180 degrees). Additional condition equations increase the accuracy of final results.

9-6. Triangulation figures. In order that small errors of measurement shall produce minimum errors in computed values, it is essential that only well-shaped figures be used in triangulation systems. The best shaped triangle is equilateral and the best shaped quadrilateral is a perfect square. However, field conditions rarely make the use of perfect figures practical, and it will often be necessary to select figures which only approximate the ideal. Figures sufficiently near the ideal should be employed in order to maintain the accuracy of the computed lengths of sides in the system from one known or measured line to the next.

After all adjustments are made, the length of the unknown side or sides of each triangle is computed by the sine law: that the sides of a triangle are proportional to the sines of the angles opposite.

In every case the computation of the sides involves only two of the three angles of each triangle. These angles used in the length computation are called the *distance angles*. Referring to Figure 9-4,

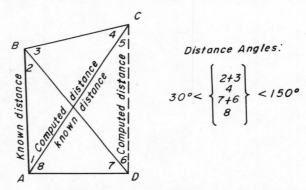

Fig. 9-4. A quadrilateral with angles which make it a strong figure.

in triangle *A–B–C*, the angles *B* and *C*; and in triangle *A–C–D*, angles *A* and *D* are the distance angles. The remaining angle of each triangle can be used to carry forward the direction and is therefore called the *azimuth angle*, or *direction angle*. The distance angles are always opposite the known and required sides of the triangle.

The differences in the logarithmic sines for angles near 90 degrees are very small. For angles near 0 and 180 degrees, these differences are large. Hence, it is desirable to avoid distance angles near 0 and 180 degrees. In general, the distance angles should be kept between the limits of 30 and 150 degrees and preferably near 90 degrees. This is done by careful reconnaissance in selecting station locations. Figures having interior angles within these limits are referred to as *strong figures*.

9-7. Reconnaissance. The reconnaissance party selects the system pattern which best meets the requirements and fits the topography of the area, but is still reasonable in cost. The choice of station locations which will form the strongest and most feasible figures should be made by experienced geodetic engineers. The accuracy and future usefulness of the system, and the amount of field work to be done, depends upon the reconnaissance, which not only selects the station points and base lines, but also prepares descriptions of the points, determines the type and height of signals and towers, and estimates the amount of clearing to be done.

The stations selected should be easily accessible for use in other surveys, yet at a location not likely to be disturbed. When consistent with these considerations, the station should be at a point easily identifiable on aerial photographs. Permanent monuments, such as brass disks set in concrete posts, should be used to mark the stations.

9-8. Base lines. Triangulation systems are *built* from base lines and angle measurements. The base lines should form part of well-conditioned figures in the network. This is more important than locating them in the best place for taping. A material part of the accuracy of the base measurement may be lost by extending that length through a weak base net.

The required precision of first-order base lines has been specified as 1 in 1,000,000. This type of work obviously necessitates using the best techniques and instruments under ideal conditions. Special publications of the U. S. Coast and Geodetic Survey give the detailed procedures for this work.[7]

The first step is to clear the base line so that the ends are intervisible and all obstructions which might impair the accuracy of the measurement are removed. A transit is set at one end and used to position 4 × 4-inch posts accurately on line. These posts are set solidly into the ground and spaced one tape length apart (normally 50 meters). A copper strip is tacked to the top of each on which to mark the distance measurements. Intermediate 2 × 4-inch posts are set just off line so that nails can be driven in their sides to provide the support conditions desired for the tape. The posts at the end of each kilometer are securely braced. Measurements, forward and back, are made and compared for each kilometer section of the base line as it is measured. The discrepancy between two measurements of a kilometer section are limited to 10 millimeters for first-order work.

Measurements of base lines over rocky ground or along paved streets are made using taping bucks. These are short tripods standing about 2 feet high. The tripod head has a curved section, covered with a sheet of copper on which to scribe distance marks. A line of levels must be run on the tops of the bucks as taping progresses to determine the slope of the tape at each measurement. This data is necessary to compute the horizontal length of the base line.

Corrections are applied to the field measurements in the order listed:

1. Standard length of tape.   5. Alignment.
2. Temperature.   6. Slope.
3. Sag.   7. Setups and setbacks.
4. Tension.   8. Sea Level.

High-order base lines are measured with standardized Invar tapes. Any control base line should be measured with a tape checked by the U. S. Bureau of Standards (see Article 4-19). If a tape is used under the conditions of support and tension used during the standardization, these corrections need not be made. Care in alignment of the points along the line will eliminate the need for alignment corrections.

Except for *setups* and *setbacks,* and *sea level corrections,* all of the corrections itemized were discussed in Chapter 4. Setups and

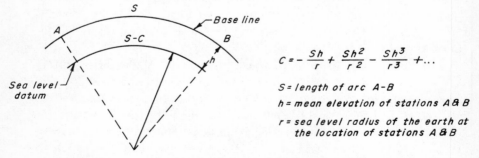

Fig. 9-5. Reduction of base line measurement to sea level distance.

setbacks are used when posts are set along the base line. They are distances of a few centimeters through which the tape is shifted when its end points do not both fall on the copper strip previously set on top of the posts for the distance marks. A setup is added to the length of the base line while a setback is subtracted. The rear tapeman makes both types of measurement with an auxiliary rule from the established mark at his end of the tape.

Since all stations in a triangulation network do not lie in the same plane, it is necessary to correct all base line lengths to a sea-level datum in order to make the geometric checks and complete the computations. The principle of reduction to sea-level lengths is shown in Figure 9-5. The first term of the correction formula shown is usually the only significant one.

9-9. Measurement of angles.

Accurate angles are the strong feature of a triangulation system, just as accurate distances are the strong part of traversing. Skilled observers and suitable instruments are needed to maintain the accuracy specified for high-order triangulation. In measuring angles, instrumental and human errors are reduced or eliminated by:

1. Taking a number of readings to diminish the error in pointing.
2. Taking half of the readings with the telescope direct and half with the telescope inverted.
3. Taking initial readings at different points around the graduated circle of the instrument to reduce graduation and eccentricity errors.

A good observer is one who can consistently secure results expected from the instrument which he is using. The most satisfactory observations are usually those which are made rapidly and methodically, but not carelessly. Speed can be attained by the observer training himself in deftness of movement in manipulating the instrument and in studying how he can perform the manipulation with the fewest movements (time and motion study). Aside from blunders, such as reading a vernier incorrectly, and the allowable inaccuracies of pointing to an object, the following are the principal causes of error in the measurement of horizontal angles: (1) instability of instrument support, (2) instrumental errors, (3) target not centered over the point observed, and (4) lateral refraction. The relative importance of these factors will vary with the field conditions encountered.

A program of observations should be designed to balance out small errors in instrument adjustment. Errors caused by parallax and the plate bubbles not being level cannot be eliminated by compensation or correction of the measurements. These are the direct responsibility of the observer.

The adjustment of the horizontal axis of the telescope (see

Article 8-11) should be tested frequently, especially when sights are being taken at widely varying vertical angles. Precision angle instruments usually are equipped with an auxiliary bubble tube which can be clamped directly to the horizontal axis of the telescope. If the bubble on this attachment, called a *striding level*, remains centered both before and after it is turned 180 degrees on its supports, the horizontal axis of the instrument is truly horizontal.

For the best results the instrument and tripod should be protected from direct sunlight and wind.

The observer should not try to force the observations by sighting upon a different part of the object from that which his judgment says is the proper point, for a poor triangle closure may be caused by an error at any one of the three stations involved. He must cultivate an impersonal attitude toward his results and read the angles without bias. An angle forced to give good triangle closure will often result in large angle and side corrections when the office adjustment is made.

Close agreement of several different measurements of an angle is not a positive check on the triangulation. Angle readings materially different from other values for the same angle indicate errors in pointing or reading. Even the horizon closure, the sum of all the mean angles around a station equaling 360 degrees, is not a check to prove that the angles are correct. First-order specifications require that the average triangle closure shall not exceed one second of error.

The sum of the angles in a plane triangle should equal 180 degrees. When a triangle is projected upon a spherical surface, such as the earth, it becomes a spherical triangle, and the sum of the angles will be more than 180 degrees. The amount this sum is greater than that of a plane triangle is called *spherical excess*. This is about one second of angle for triangle with an area of 75 square miles. The amount of spherical excess varies with the area of the triangle.

9-10. Astronomic checks. Accurate checks of position (latitude and longitude) and direction are made by astronomic observations. These checks are independent of any of the other measurements involved in the triangulation. Their main value is to serve as checks since the precision of the angle and base line measurements is usually higher than the astronomic observations.

9-11. Computations. The complete solution for an extensive triangulation network is a long and somewhat involved computation; the adjustment requires that several geometric and trigonometric relationships be met. Students are referred to books on geodetic surveying[6,8] and to publications of the U.S.C. & G.S.[9] for the details of the more rigorous methods of adjusting triangulation networks.

The programing of triangulation computations on electronic computors has been very successful by the organizations which have made this application. Solutions are turned out in a matter of hours, that would take many man-months under the conventional hand methods.

The first angle adjustment is known as the *point adjustment*. It is simply proportioning the error in angles measured around a station so that the sum of all of the adjusted angles is 360 degrees.

The *figure adjustments* are made next. For a single chain of triangles, this involves only the requirement that the sum of the angles for each triangle equals 180 degrees. For a single quadrilateral, we have the requirement that the sum of the angles shall equal 360°, plus the necessity for each of the eight different triangles within this quadrilateral to have angle sums of 180 degrees. All of these statements of mathematical relationships in the figures are called *condition equations*. From trigonometry, we have the requirement that the sines of the angles within a triangle shall be proportional to the length of the sides opposite each angle.

The angular error is distributed to the most probable locations by mathematical methods so that final adjustment will satisfy all of the condition equations.

9-12. Federal control specifications. The Federal Board of Surveys and Maps issued specifications for horizontal and vertical control in 1933. The rapid development and refinement of surveying instruments and procedures since World War II resulted in recommendations for new standards being proposed in 1955.

The specifications recommended in 1955 for first-order triangulation requires the length checks on base lines to be twice as accurate as the 1933 standards. The discrepancy between measured and computed lengths must not be more than 1 in 50,000. In general the new recommended standards are advanced one step; that is, what was first-order work is now second-order and a higher standard has been set for the top grade measurements.

First-order traverse requirements are changed to 1 in 35,000 by the 1955 recommendations. A new concept is introduced in the accuracy requirement for traverse surveys in limiting the allowable error in terms of a constant times the square root of the length of the traverse in miles. This type of specification has long been in use for levels and is consistent with the theory of probability in the compensation of accidental errors (Article 3-8). Large tolerances in long traverses permitted under the straight proportional specification of 1933 are restricted. The recommended standards are so arranged that the straight proportional tolerance is more restrictive at traverse lengths of less than ten miles, and the exponential tolerance is more restrictive at lengths of more than ten miles. Another limitation was introduced to state the permissible closures between fixed azimuths. This specification is also dual, providing a tolerance that is proportional to the number of stations for traverses with few stations, and making the tolerance proportional to the square root of the number of stations for traverses with a large number of stations.

Another change from the 1933 specifications involves the recommendation for spacing of the horizontal control stations. The recommendation is that first-order arcs are to be spaced at not more than 60 miles rather than 120 miles as set by the 1933 specifications. Second-order stations are to be located so that no point will be more than 10 miles from a control point. These closer spacings should accelerate the use of the national network of horizontal control by state and local governments, and engineers in private practice.

Some of the standard specifications set by the Federal Board of Surveys and Maps in 1933 follow:

Precise levels are classified by the amount of discrepancy between the results obtained in two independent runs of the same circuit. The maximum discrepancy allowed is given by the formula, $e = C\sqrt{K}$, where e is the discrepancy in millimeters, C is a constant and K is the length of the circuit in kilometers. If the work is done in English units, the formula is written, $e = C'\sqrt{M}$, where e is the discrepancy in feet, C' is a constant, and M is the length of the circuit in miles. The requirements are:

	First order	Second order	Third order
C	4	8.4	12
C'	. . .	0.035	0.05

Precise traverse requirements are:

	ORDER OF ACCURACY		
	First	*Second*	*Third*
Number of main stations between astronomic checks...............	10 to 15	15 to 25	20 to 35
Average azimuth discrepancy per main station, in seconds, not to exceed........................	1.0	2.0	5.0
Minimum Precision..............	1:25,000	1:10,000	1:5,000

Precise triangulation must meet these standards:

	ORDER OF ACCURACY		
	First	*Second*	*Third*
Average triangle closure, in seconds, not to exceed...................	1	3	6
Usual number of observations: with a 1-second direction instrument.......................	16	4	2
with a 10-second repeating theodolite, sets of repetitions.........	5 to 6	2 to 3	1 to 2
Probable error in Base Measurement, not to exceed...................	1:1,000,000	1:500,000	1:250,000
Discrepancy between computed and measured length of base or adjusted check line, not to exceed...	1:25,000	1:10,000	1:5,000

The items listed give some idea of the requirements for control work. They are *not* complete specifications.

9-13. Flare triangulation. The extension of our continental control system to nearby islands has been made possible by surveying with parachute flares (dropped from airplanes) used as intersection stations. The flares are observed simultaneously from several known stations and from points whose position is to be determined.

The theodolites used for this work employ photographic registration of horizontal and vertical readings. Thus the operator can concentrate on sighting the target and centering the altitude index level. The film is exposed in a fraction of a second and moves automatically for a new reading.

Four items are recorded on the film strip: (1) the image of the horizontal and vertical circles; (2) the position of the plate level; (3) the time to seconds; and (4) notes made by the observer of such things as the date, location, station observed, and his name.

The area covered can be large; stations can be several hundred miles apart. A plane flies between the stations and drops a brilliant flare, usually one of a million candlepower. A surveyor rides in the plane and, as the flare is released, he alerts the instrumentmen, who are all in communication with him via short-wave radio. The instrumentmen train their instruments on the flare and track it as it slowly drops through the sky.

As the tracked flare descends, the surveyor in the plane sends out a series of signals which activate a solenoid on the radio receiver at each theodolite position. The solenoid operates the shutter of the camera built into the theodolite. Robot-controlled by short-wave signal, all of the instruments thus record their readings at the same fraction of a second. The results of triangulating on the flare, although it is falling to the earth, are the same as if it were solidly mounted on some mountaintop.

The possibilities for bridging mountainous terrain, jungles, deserts, and polar regions by this method are intriguing.

9-14. Trilateration. Another method used for extending control systems over long distances is trilateration: the measurement of the length of each side of a triangle. The application of radar and other electronic devices to length measurement has increased the distance between adjacent stations to 500 miles. High-order precision has been obtained by these methods. Most of these devices depend upon the accurate timing of the interval required for electromagnetic waves to travel between control points.

Shoran (*SHOrt RAnge Navigation*) has proved to be one of the most practical devices in this new area of surveying. Shoran is a transceiver-transponder system by means of which radio wave travel time is accurately measured from a plane to each of two antennas at ground stations. This time measurement is directly translated into distance which is read on dials or automatically recorded. Precisions of 1:15,000 are often exceeded with this type of equipment.

The angles in any triangle derived mathematically from measured lengths may contain errors considerably larger than those found in conventional triangulation. But a single triangle, where the angles have been measured, has to satisfy only the condition that the sum of the angles equal 180 degrees. There is no check on the angles if only the sides are measured. In a single quadrilateral where the distances are measured, only one condition equation occurs as compared with four conditions obtained when all of the angles are observed. Independent azimuth determinations are desirable additions to trilateration to produce an accurate survey.

The advantages of electronic surveying are:

1. Geodetic accuracy can be obtained over distances as great as 500 miles.
2. Errors are functions of time and therefore do not increase with distance.
3. Aerial photography can be controlled by shoran distance, permitting accurate mapping of all areas within the range of shoran ground stations.
4. Navigational devices utilizing the shoran distance readings permit flight line navigation of great accuracy.
5. Shoran photographic techniques permit the establishment of control points of lower accuracy without setting foot on the ground.
6. Vertical control of various degrees of accuracy is possible by shoran-photographic-radio-altimeter methods.*

Shoran was used to tie the islands of the West Indies into a single control system as required by the Air Force Missile Test Center, at Cocoa, Florida.

In shoran geodetic control, the schemes can be situated to span mountain ranges or other areas inaccessible for conventional surveying stations; the plane flies over the difficult terrain and the ground stations are located at convenient sites.

The *geodimeter* is another electronic device which indicates great promise for distance measurements. It is an electronic-optical device with which measurements are made by accurately timing the interval required for a light beam to travel from the geodimeter to a distant plane mirror and return. With the velocity of light known, distances can be readily computed. This instrument was invented by Dr. Erik Bergstand, Swedish geodesist, and is now being manufactured in his country.

Preliminary tests have been made and precisions in excess of 1:300,000 reported over distances of 50 miles.†

Distance measurements can normally be made and checked in two to three hours under conditions similar to those needed for conventional triangulation, and the results computed in another

* Carl I. Aslakson, "The Importance of Shoran Surveying in the Southern Hemisphere," *ASCE Separate No. 353*, November, 1953.

† Carl I. Aslakson, "Some Aspects of Electronic Surveying," *ASCE Separate No. 52*, January, 1951.

two hours. The U. S. Coast and Geodetic Survey has experimented with this instrument for measuring second-order base lines.

9-15. State plane coordinate systems. In order to facilitate the use of geodetic stations as control stations for ordinary plane surveys, the U.S.C. & G.S. has developed a system by which a spherical coordinate of a station may be changed to a plane coordinate.

The plane coordinates for many of the established geodetic stations have been computed and are available at the office of The Superintendent of Documents, Government Printing Office, Washington, D. C. To convert from coordinates on a sphere to coordinates on a plane would of course involve projection of the points from the sphere to the plane, causing distortion in proportion to the size of the plane area. In order to eliminate excessive distortion in distances as projection is computed, the U.S.C. & G.S. has established a number of independent plane-coordinate systems, and also published tables to facilitate the use of these systems. For some small states, a single system may be used for the entire state, but in many states more than one system is necessary to avoid excessive distortion.

State plane coordinates are obtained from spherical coordinates by the use of one of two methods of projection: the *Lambert conformal conic projection* and the *transverse Mercator projection*, both conformal true shape projections.[6]

In each area controlled by a particular state plane-coordinate system, a reference meridian is centrally located, commonly called the *central meridian*. The zero of the plane coordinates is located arbitrarily at a point that is west and south of the area involved, so that all coordinates will be positive. When a state plane-coordinate system is used as a basis for computing and expressing the results of control surveys, the plane coordinates of each new station established during a traverse survey are determined from those of a known station by the usual method of latitude and departures (Art. 12-3).

Some engineers regard the government stations with bewildered awe, not realizing that, as far as their jobs are concerned, the Coast and Geodetic Survey method may be just as simple and no more accurate than their own. Its chief advantage is that it correlates or coordinates all surveys into one uniform system, making each survey permanent and useful for future purposes.

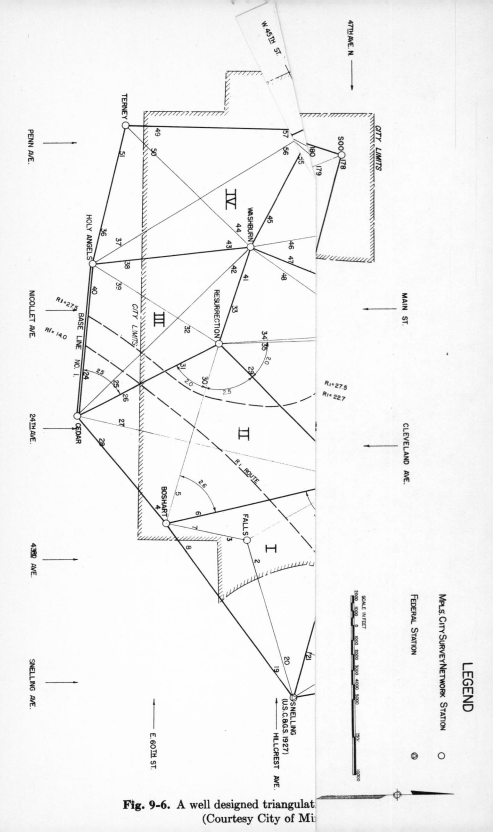

Fig. 9-6. A well designed triangulat
(Courtesy City of Mi

For details of converting from geographic to plane coordinates see books on advanced surveying.[6,8]

9-16. City surveys.[10] A modern city requires extensive high-precision control, construction, and record surveys. Accurate maps and surveys are the prerequisites of intelligent planning for the rapid growth of cities. In many instances, precise surveying and mapping only keep pace with, and sometimes even follow, subdivision construction, rather than preceding it to promote sound development policies.

Precise control surveys should come first in planning any city survey program. Triangulation is used for the major city control systems because of the difficulty of taping long lines in the streets. See Figure 9-6.

The stations are usually located on high buildings in commercial and industrial areas. To complete the horizontal control system, traverses are used to set intermediate points between triangulation stations at street level. Precise spirit levels are run to establish vertical control. Because of the high value of metropolitan property, the required precision of these surveys is often greater than Federal standards for first-order surveys.

Often city surveys have been done in isolated sections for one specific construction at a time. If locating engineers were required to (1) base their surveys upon the U. S. Government stations, (2) secure reasonable accuracy in their extension therefrom, and (3) place at suitable intervals permanent monuments with state plane coordinates, azimuths, and elevations determined, cities and the general public would gain valuable survey information at little additional cost.

No new principles are involved in city surveying, but a few problems should be considered. For instance, in locating high triangulation stations from nearby base lines, the station may not be visible from both ends of the base line or, if it is, a poor triangulation figure may be formed. The problem is solved by locating high stations near each end of the base line and using only a portion of the base line to triangulate to these high stations. From this data, the distance between the two high stations can be determined.

The reverse of this situation, the location of traverse monuments on the ground from high triangulation stations, is a common occurrence. The procedure is to locate two nearby points by turning angles from the triangulation station. These ground points must be intervisible and easy to tape between. The high triangulation station and the two ground points must form a strong triangle in which the ground side and all three angles are measured.

With the advent of the automobile, city surveyors have been faced with a growing hazard. Traffic density on city streets has increased continuously in recent years, accompanied by an increase in the speed of traffic. This combination of greater mass and higher

Fig. 9-7. Taping along a city street.
(Courtesy Los Angeles County, Calif.)

velocity is a constant and serious menace to the safety of survey personnel whose work must often be performed on streets and highways. Because of the increasingly dangerous working conditions, survey parties have to consider the problem of self-preservation. See Figure 9-7 for the safety measures employed by the crews of the Los Angeles County Surveyor.

Cities must maintain up-to-date maps for many different purposes. The types of maps kept for the Los Angeles metropolitan area, with some of the scales used, are:

	PURPOSE	SCALE
City:	1. General city	1 in. = 1000 ft
	2. Councilmanic districts	1 in. = 1000 ft
	3. Street maintenance	1 in. = 1000 ft
	4. Annexation	1 in. = 1 mile
	5. City district (with streets, tracts, lots, etc.)	1 in. = 100 ft
	6. Cadastral (based on county subdivision of state plane-coordinate system)	1 in. = 100 ft
	7. Drainage	1 in. = 400 ft
	8. Sewer "Y" records	1 in. = 50 ft

County:
1. Cadastral (show location, shape and dimension of all parcels of real estate, the status of dedication of all public streets and thoroughfares)
2. Condemnation and appraisal
3. Precinct
4. Tax Assessor
5. Index

Modern photogrammetry and aerial photography are often used for detailing and keeping up-to-date the many types of maps required in the efficient operation and planning of our cities. These methods are discussed in Chapter 14.

A major portion of the city surveyor's work is the layout and checking of construction. These surveys require immediate and continuing effort to keep ahead of street and utility expansion. Construction surveys are discussed in Chapter 15.

Chapter 10

〰〰〰〰〰〰〰〰〰〰〰〰〰〰〰〰〰〰〰〰〰〰〰〰〰

SUBDIVISION OF PUBLIC LANDS

THE SYSTEM of surveying the public lands of the United States represents a type of control survey almost as old as our nation. It is based upon a rectangular system of measurement planned by a committee appointed by the Continental Congress in 1784 and accepted by an ordinance passed by that body in 1785. That it was well conceived is evidenced by the fact that the original procedures have not been extensively modified from that time to the present.[11]

The public land area subdivided under the system includes the Territory of Alaska; the states of Florida, Alabama, and Mississippi; and all states, except Texas, north and west of the Ohio and Mississippi Rivers.

Most of the land surveys in the thirteen original colonies and Tennessee and Kentucky were made as separate closed traverses. Distance and direction were measured between points bounding a given area. No overall control system existed. Sometimes bodies of water or other natural landmarks were used to define ownership boundaries. Surveys of this general character are described as *metes* and *bounds* surveys.

The survey determines the length and direction of boundary lines and the legal description is made in terms of those lengths and directions. Two examples of metes and bounds survey descriptions follow:

> **1.** Beginning at a point which is the N.E. corner of the land of Joseph Hill and is marked by an iron pin. From said pin a 10-inch oak tree bears S 20 degrees W 20 links and a chisel mark (×) on the face of a cliff bears N 30 degrees E 18 links. The tree is blazed and marked B.T.; thence, N 80 degrees W along the northerly line of the property of the said Joseph Hill, 20 ch. 40 lks. (20.40 ch.) to the N.W. corner of Joseph Hill's land; thence N 10 degrees E 30 chains to a stone 12 × 12 × 30 inches; thence, S 80 degrees E 20 chains to a 20 × 20 × 30-inch stone;

178

thence, S 10 degrees W 30 chains to point of beginning, containing 60 acres, more or less.

  2. Beginning at a point marked with a concrete monument located 25.42 feet east and 325.86 feet south of the intersection of the center lines of Burns Avenue and 12th Street in the City of ... , County of ... , State of ...; N 88°36' E along the north property line of Burns Avenue a distance of 1140.26 feet to an iron pin; N 02°10' E a distance of 1216.20 feet to an iron pin; S 88°30' W a distance of 1139.20 feet; S 03°10' W a distance of 1216.00 feet to point of beginning. Containing 32 acres, more or less.

While all surveys and recorded plats should bear a date, this is extremely important in a description similar to number 1. Without a date the ownership reference might not have any significance. In addition to this, magnetic bearings could not be checked because the declination change would be unknown.

The use of State Plane Coordinates (Article 9-15) to make property descriptions would in most cases be more direct and less complicated than metes and bounds descriptions.

Texas has a method of subdivision, similar to the United States system of surveying the public lands, but influenced by procedures of the Spanish settlers prior to the time of annexation.

Surveying and granting of *original* title to lands within all states bounded by the Atlantic, except Florida, and in the states of Pennsylvania, West Virginia, Tennessee, Kentucky, and Texas, is under the jurisdiction of the respective state governments rather than the national government.

In dealing with land subdivision or resurveys, engineers and surveyors have a legal responsibility to exercise the care and judgment expected of members of any learned profession. Because those in private practice may be held liable by the courts for any proved incompetence, it is necessary always to proceed with complete knowledge of past and present rules regarding land subdivision.

The legality of boundaries as established which are under dispute must be decided by courts of law. The surveyor functions only as an expert witness and has no power to make decisions in a case.

Following the enactment into law of the rectangular surveying system, "devised with the object of marking upon the ground and fixing for all time legal subdivision for purposes of description and disposal of the public domain . . . ," it became necessary to create an administering agency as the settlement of the West increased.

The General Land Office, now the Bureau of Land Management, was organized in 1812 primarily for the purpose of selling the public lands to pay the debts of the Revolutionary War. Surveys were necessary before the lands could be identified and described.

The work was urgent because the demand for the western land was high. Because of this demand and because of the value of the land compared with the cost of surveying, accurate work was not required. Also, instruments of that time were crude compared to those of today.

Control points were either marked with wooden stakes; pits containing buried charcoal and surrounded by mounds of earth; or by stones bearing chisel marks, indicating their position in the system. Time has destroyed many of these marks.

The early surveying was done by private contractors. There were no rules for inspecting their work which led to some fraudulent surveys and widely varying standards of precision.

Now the major work of the U. S. Bureau of Land Management in connection with land subdivision consists of the following:

1. Surveying and monumenting lands in the Public Domain not previously surveyed.
2. Resurveys of both public and private lands where many of the original corners cannot be found.

10-1. Outline of the system. The procedure for subdividing the public lands has as its basic control a system of coordinates.

Obviously this cannot be a truly rectangular system, since the surface of the earth is not a plane. However, in order to provide for curvature and yet approach true rectangular coordinates, a method of correcting for direction is used at intervals near enough to one another to maintain, for most purposes, the definition of the basic unit of area of the system. This unit is called a *township* and is defined as a square tract of land 6 miles on a side.

The general scheme provides for the following:

1. The selection of points of beginning, called *initial points*, are located advantageously for extending the survey in separate areas. The geographic position of the initial point is established by astronomical observation.
2. Lines through the initial points and usually, although not necessarily, extending both north and south therefrom are run as true meridians and are called *principal meridians*. The principal meridian for any given initial point is identified either by number or by name.
3. Lines through the initial points at right angles to the principal meridian and usually, although not necessarily, extending both east and west from an initial point are called *base lines* and are run as

true parallels of latitude (curved lines). Some of them are designated by name, but most are identified by the principal meridian with which they are used.

4. *Guide meridians* run as true meridians at designated, equal intervals east and west from the principal meridians.

5. *Standard parallels*, sometimes called *correction lines*, run as true parallels of latitude at specified intervals from the base lines. The guide meridians and standard parallels bound quadrangles which are approximately square and are run at sufficiently frequent intervals to maintain that relationship. Normally, tracts bounded by guide meridians on the east and west and standard parallels on the north and south are either 24 or 30 miles on a side, except on the north (see Figure 10-6).

6. *Range lines* are run at 6-mile intervals between guide meridians. They are run as true meridians, continuous between standard parallels.

7. *Township lines* are straight lines running approximately east and west at 6-mile intervals between standard parallels. The township lines and range lines subdivide the 24-mile or 30-mile tracts into townships.

8. *Section lines* subdivide each township into 36 tracts called *sections*. These are approximately 1 mile on a side.

10-2. Detailed procedure. During the period from 1815 to 1855 details for the subdivision of public lands were found in a set of instructions by Mr. Edward Tiffin, then Surveyor General of the United States.

Since 1855 detailed directions have been published in *The Manual of Instructions for the Survey of Public Lands of the United States.*[12] Special instructions and revisions of the manual have been issued from time to time as changes in the prescribed procedure were made. Manuals have been published in 1855, 1881, 1890, 1902, 1930, and 1947. For specific questions on the subject of public land subdivision, the manual or instructions in effect at the time of the survey in question should be consulted.

Consideration must be given to the instructions in effect at the time of the original survey when any later work is undertaken in a particular area. For example, the instructions of Mr. Tiffin specified two sets of section corners on the west and north boundaries of each township. One set was established as the township boundaries were run and the others were placed as the township was subdivided into sections. This procedure was later changed and closing corners were established as outlined in Articles 10-4, 10-5, and 10-6. The earlier system is sometimes referred to as the *double corner system*.

Also, as an example, the first subdivision of public lands authorized by the ordinance of 1785 was made without a principal meridian or base line as was later specified.

10-3. Running the major lines. After the initial point has been located, the direction for the principal meridian through it is determined by astronomical observation.

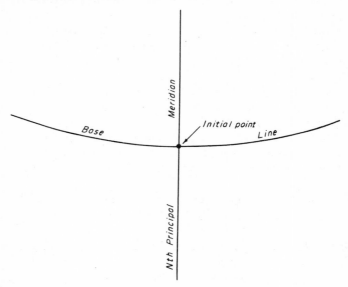

Fig. 10-1. Coordinate axis for public land surveys.

The principal meridian is extended from the initial point to the limits of the survey. As it is run all corners necessary for subdivision are placed along it. These corners include (1) quarter-section corners set at $\frac{1}{2}$-mile intervals; that is, between section corners; (2) section corners set at 1-mile intervals; and (3) township corners set at 6-mile intervals.

The base line is run as a true parallel of latitude from the initial point to the limits of the survey. All required corners are placed on it as it is run. Figure 10-1 shows the basic axes of the system.

There are three ways in which a base line may be run so that it will follow a parallel of latitude:

1. Set up at the initial point and turn off a right angle from the principal meridian. Extend that line for a half-mile. At that point turn
   off another right angle from the true meridian. Continue this procedure for the length of the base line. The series of connected straight
   lines will very nearly follow the curve of a true parallel.

2. At the initial point turn a right angle off the principal meridian and continue the line thus established for 6 miles. *Standard Field Tables*, obtainable from the U. S. Bureau of Land Management, gives the offset at half-mile intervals from this line to the true parallel for various latitudes.

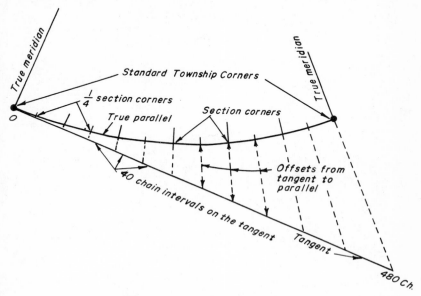

Fig. 10-2. True parallel constructed by tangent offset method.

Figure 10-2 illustrates this method of establishing a parallel of latitude. It is called the *tangent method*.

3. The *secant* method which is similar to the tangent method except that an angle slightly less than 90 degrees is turned off the meridian. The result is a straight line located as shown in Figure 10-3.

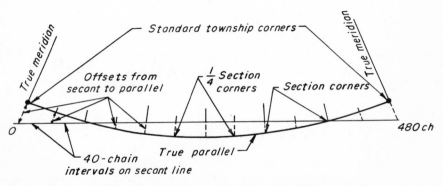

Fig. 10-3. True parallel constructed by secant offset method.

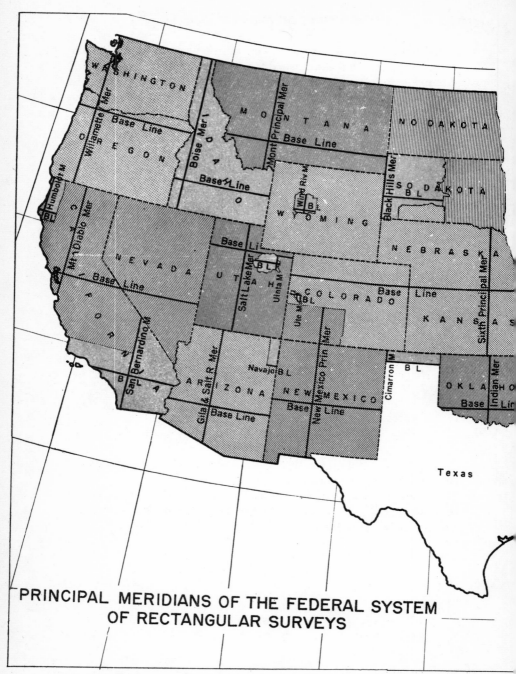

Fig. 10-4. Principal meridians and base lines in the United States.

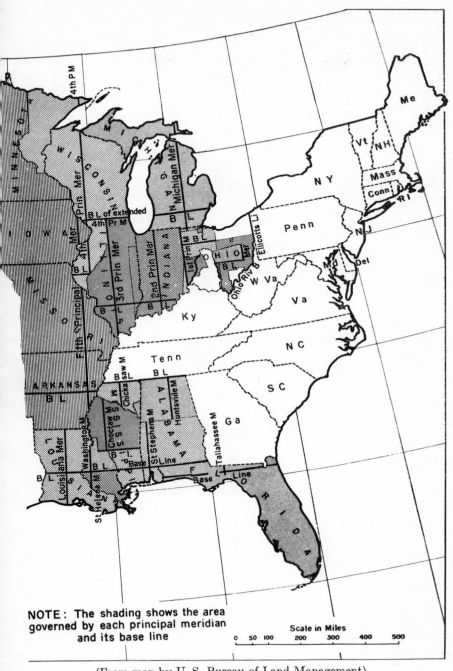

NOTE: The shading shows the area
governed by each principal meridian
and its base line

Scale in Miles

0   50 100   200   300   400   500

(From map by U. S. Bureau of Land Management)

185

Because the rate of curvature of the parallel differs with latitude, the angle to be measured off the meridian and the offsets from the secant line to the curved parallel will vary with latitude. These values are also provided in field tables.

Existing initial points, principal meridians, and base lines in the United States are shown in Figure 10-4.

Those already established in Alaska are shown in Figure 10.5.

Fig. 10-5. Principal meridians and base lines in Alaska. (From map by U. S. Bureau of Land Management)

10-4. 24-Mile tracts. As has been noted, the tracts which are formed by the first step in subdivision following the laying out of the major axes of the system may not all have the same dimensions. The most common dimensions are 24 or 30 miles. For convenience, throughout the balance of this discussion they will be referred to as 24-mile tracts.

From the 24-mile points (township corners) along the principal meridian, lines are run as true parallels for the extent of the survey. All corners are placed on these lines as they are run. These are the standard parallels or correction lines, numbered according to their position with respect to the base line. For example, 1st Standard Parallel North, 2nd Standard Parallel North, 1st Standard Parallel South, and so on.

Beginning at the 24-mile corners on the southernmost standard parallel in the area to be subdivided (the base line if the principal meridian does not extend south of the initial point), lines are run north as true meridians until they intersect the next standard parallel to the north. At that point a *closing* township corner is

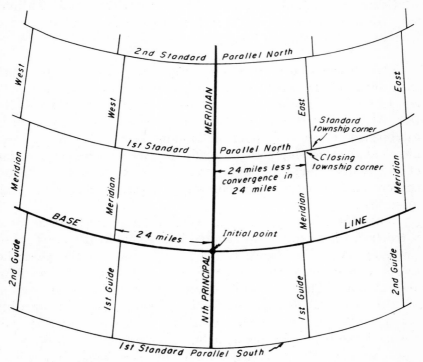

Fig. 10-6. Subdivision into 24-mile tracts.

established and the distance to the corresponding corner already in place (standard township corner) is recorded.

These lines are called *guide meridians*. All necessary corners are placed on them as they are run.

After a closing corner has been established the guide meridian is *corrected* for convergence by moving to the standard township corner and continuing a true meridian from that point until the next standard parallel to the north is intersected. Another closing township corner is established there. The same procedure continues until the northern boundary of the area to be surveyed has been reached.

The standard parallels and guide meridians subdivide the area into tracts approximately 24 miles on a side. See Figure 10-6.

It should now be apparent why standard parallels are sometimes called correction lines.

Guide meridians are designated as *1st Guide Meridian East* (of principal meridian), *1st Guide Meridian West*, and so on, in a manner similar to the numbering of standard parallels.

Even though guide meridians are continuous for only 24 miles, they are considered to be continuous to the limits of the survey insofar as their number designations are concerned.

10-5. Subdivision into townships. Beginning at the southeast corner of the southwest township in a 24-mile tract, a line is run true north for 6 miles. All necessary corners are placed as it is run. At 6 miles north of the beginning point, a township corner is established. From that point a random line is run to the west aimed at the township corner already in place on the west boundary of the 24-mile tract. As the random line is run, temporary section corners and quarter-section corners ($\frac{1}{4}$ *corners*) are set at $\frac{1}{2}$-mile intervals.

When the township corner at which the random line was aimed is reached, the falling of the random line is noted (how far it missed township corner in place). If the falling is within the prescribed limits, a line connecting the two township corners is calculated and run back. The corners are moved over onto the connecting line.

The procedure is repeated for the second and third townships north of the beginning point. From the township corner 18 miles north of the beginning point, a line is continued north on a true meridian until the standard parallel or base line is intersected. At that point a closing township corner is placed and the distance to the corresponding standard corner noted.

Notice that the prescribed method of measuring in the corners throws error to the west and north half-mile of each 24-mile tract. This concept of *pushing* error to the west and north is consistently followed throughout further subdivision.

The line forming the eastern boundary of the four townships bounded by the procedure just outlined is called a *range line*. The next two range lines in the township are run in a similar manner.

After the third range line has been run, random lines are run to the west from each township corner in place on the guide meridian which is the east boundary of the 24-mile tract. As before, temporary corners are placed on the random line and moved over onto the corrected line.

Figure 10-7 shows 24-mile tracts subdivided into townships.

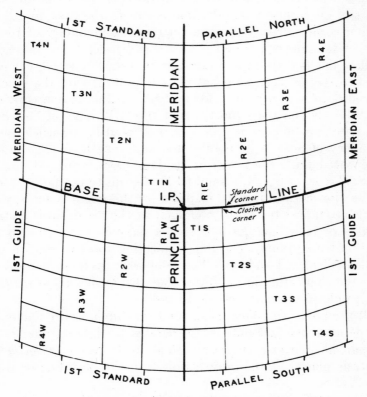

Fig. 10-7. Subdivision of 24-mile tracts.

10-6. Subdivision into sections. The final step in subdivision carried out by the Federal Government is the marking out of sections in each township. All townships have 36 sections, each approximately 1 mile square.

Quarter-section corners are placed on the boundaries of each section, but the actual subdivision into quarter sections must be carried on by county, state, or private surveyors.

In subdividing a township, the east and south boundaries are retraced for one mile, beginning at the southeast corner of the township. This is done to check the previous work and to check the instrument with the one previously used.

Beginning at the section corner one mile west of the southeast corner of the township (S.W. cor., Sec. 36), a line is run north for one mile parallel to the east boundary of the township. A $\frac{1}{4}$ corner is placed at one-half mile and a section corner at one mile. From this section corner a random line is run to the east, aimed at the section corner already in place on the east boundary of the township. A temporary $\frac{1}{4}$ corner is placed at $\frac{1}{2}$ mile. If the falling of the random line is within the prescribed limits, a line which will connect the two section corners is calculated. As it is run, the $\frac{1}{4}$ corner is moved onto it at a point midway between the section corners.

A line is continued north from the N.W. cor. of Sec. 36 with any necessary change in direction indicated by whether the north boundary of Sec. 36 is more or less than one mile. The procedure is repeated until the first five sections have been laid out. From the S.W. cor. of Sec. 1, a random line is run to the north, aimed at the section corner already in place on the north boundary of the township, unless the north boundary of the township is a standard parallel or base line. As it is run, a temporary $\frac{1}{4}$ corner is placed at the $5\frac{1}{2}$-mile point. The line connecting the two section corners is then calculated and run. The temporary $\frac{1}{4}$ corner is moved over onto the connecting line. Notice that this pushes the error into the last $\frac{1}{2}$ mile to the north of the township.

If the northern boundary of the township is a base line or standard parallel, the last mile is run parallel to the east boundary, the permanent quarter-corner is placed at 40 chains and a *closing section corner* is placed at the intersection with the base line or standard parallel.

The subdivision proceeds westerly across the township in the same way until the N.W. cor. of Sec. 32 is reached. See Figure 10-8.

From this corner a random line is also run to the west, aimed at the section corner already in place on the west boundary of the township. If the falling of the random line is within the prescribed limits, the $\frac{1}{4}$ corner set temporarily at $\frac{1}{2}$ mile as the random line was run is moved onto the line connecting the two section corners. (Error thrown to the west.) The remaining sections along the west boundary of the township are laid out in a similar way.

Figure 10-8 shows a township divided into sections. The numbering system for sections is also shown.

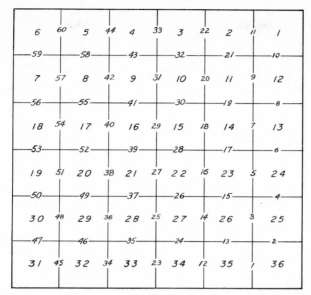

Fig. 10-8. Subdivision of township. Smaller figures indicate sequence of running lines.

10-7. Subdivision of sections. As indicated in Article 10-6, the Government does not survey beyond the subdivision into sections. They do, however, place the $\frac{1}{4}$ corners on the boundary of each section. General rules, in keeping with the rules for subdividing larger parcels, are specified for subdividing into quarter sections (160-acre plats) and quarter-quarter sections (40-acre plats).

Figure 10-9 shows the subdivision of Sections 5, 6, 7, and 8. These four sections cover all conditions within a township except the occurrence of *meander lines*. Meandering will be discussed in the next article.

The numbered parcels along the north boundaries of Sections 5 and 6 and along the west boundaries of Sections 6 and 7 are called *lots*. The term *lot* is used to designate any parcel of land which is irregular in shape or area.

10-8. Meandering. The details for meandering are also given in the *Manual of Instruction for the Survey of the Public Lands of the United States*.[12] Only some of the general concepts will be given here.

All navigable bodies of water, as well as those of three or more chains in "right angle width," are required to be meandered; also

○   *Section corners*
X   *Quarter section corners*

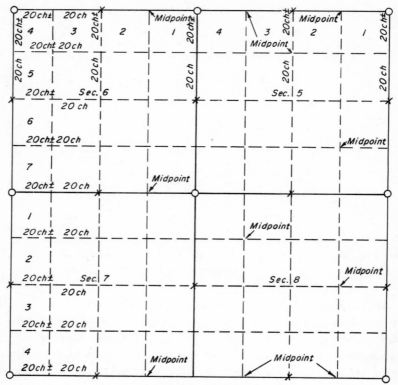

Fig. 10-9. Subdivision of sections.

Lakes covering 25 acres or more and islands (except those formed after the state was admitted to the Union) in any meanderable body of water.

Meander lines are a series of connected straight lines which define the sinuosities of a bank or shore line at mean high water elevation. They are not run as boundary lines and therefore when the bed of the body of water concerned changes, the high-water line and the ownership of adjoining land changes also.

Meander corners are set at the intersection of all regularly surveyed lines with the body of water or island. A traverse of the high-water line is then run to connect the meander corners.

In the subdivision of sections crossed by meander lines the procedure outlined in Article 10-7 is used for all full quarter-quarter sections ($\frac{1}{16}$th of a section). Those quarter-quarter sections rendered

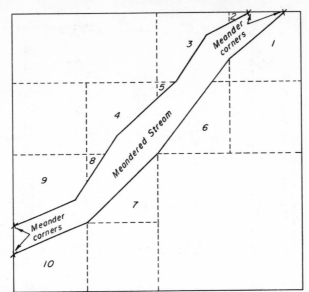

Fig. 10-10. Lots in a section crossed by a meanderable stream.

fractional by a meander line are designated as lots and numbered as indicated in Figure 10-10.

10-9. Witness corners. When the location for any regularly placed corner falls in an inaccessible place, such as an unmeandered body of water, a marsh, or a precipitous cliff where the corner could not be occupied, a witness corner is established.

Usually only one witness corner is established on one of the regular surveyed lines leading into the corner, if it can be placed within 10 chains of the location of the corner. If a place which can be marked and occupied on a surveyed line cannot be found within 10 chains distance, the witness corner may be located in any direction within 5 chains of the position of the corner witnessed.

10-10. Surveys prior to 1910. The contract system for subdivision of public lands was discontinued in 1910. Prior to that time there were many poorly made surveys resulting from inadequate instruments, low value on much of the land being surveyed, and careless work to avoid losing money at the price bid for a particular job. In addition, there were cases of actual fraud. Claims were made for work never actually done, but for which field notes were forged and submitted to collect the contract price for the work claimed.

MAP OF

DEPENDENT RESURVEY OF T.10N., R.38W., PERKINS COUNTY, NEBR.

Survey completed July 15, 1930.
Surveyed by H.B Lawson, Deputy State Surveyor.

• = Corners found.
○ = Corners restored.
Scale, 2 inches = 1 mile.

Sec. 1, Sec. 2, Sec. 3, Sec. 4, Sec. 5, Sec. 6
Sec. 7, Sec. 8, Sec. 9, Sec. 10, Sec. 11, Sec. 12
Sec. 13, Sec. 14, Sec. 15, Sec. 16, Sec. 17, Sec. 18

N.2°.25'W. 79.25
N.2°.25'W. 79.23
N.2°.25'W. 79.29

S.89°.11'W. 80.20
N.89°.07'E. 80.40
N.89°.05'E. 80.44

N.2°.14'W. 39.74½ 79.74½
N.2°.11'W. 73.49
N.2°.44'W. 73.49

S.89°.11'W. 80.20
N.89°.51'E. 80.20
S.89°.50'E. 80.44

N.2°.14'W. 39.33 78.85
N.1°.47'W. 78.64
N.3°.19'W. 78.85

S.83°.11'W. 80.20
N.89°.06'E. 80.54
N.88°.03'E. 80.70

N.2°.13'W. 39.08 79.02
N.1°.31'W. 73.58
N.3°.45'W. 73.88

S.89°.11'W. 80.20
S.89°.48'E. 80.18
S.86°.07'E. 80.44

N.2°.16'W. 38.18 76.20
N.1°.25'W. 76.04
N.7°.48'W. 38.08 40.09 N.1°.04'W.

S.89°.49'W. 81.42
N.88°.06'E. 80.54
N.89°.00'E. 80.74

N.2°.34'W. 38.78 77.21
N.1°.16'W. 74.82
N.0°.07'W. 37.41

S.88°.49'W. 40.71 82.34
S.88°.52'W. 40.65 81.89
S.86°.57'W. 40.29 81.17

41.63
41.26 40.88

N.3°.22'W. 38.51
N.3°.03'W. 38.63
N.1°.49'W. 77.54
N.2°.16'W. 38.49
N.3°.41'W. 39.82

N.1°.33'W. 39.85 N.2°.16'W.

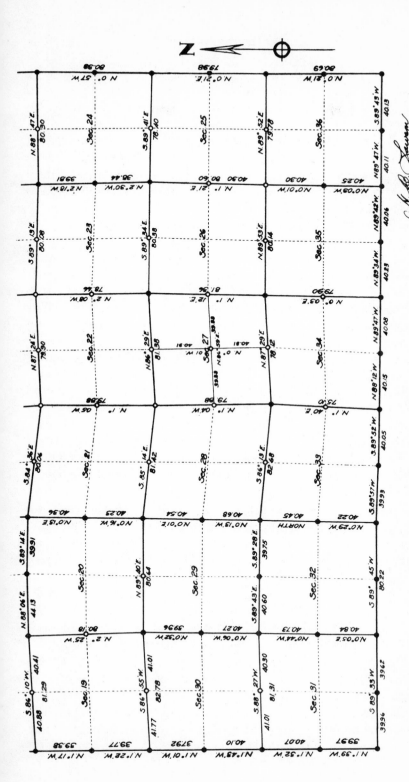

Fig. 10-11. Plat of dependent resurvey of a township by a deputy state surveyor. (Courtesy State Surveyor of Nebraska)

Had there been an adequate system of inspection, undoubtedly the quality of early surveys would have been better. From 1890 to 1910, however, inspection procedures improved, resulting in better surveys during that period.

In most cases inaccuracies in old surveys cannot be corrected if evidence of the original location of the land corners still exists. The law states that corners once established, designated, and used to mark land boundaries cannot be changed when there exist valid property rights based upon them. This is true, no matter how gross the error in positioning the marker in the original survey.

10-11. Modern land (cadastral) surveys. The modern cadastral survey under the Bureau of Land Management, U. S. Department of the Interior, functions to "mark on the ground the boundaries of public land for disposal and administrative purposes." The work may be divided into two general categories: new surveys and resurveys.

In 1950 there were approximately 116,000,000 acres of public domain in the continental United States which had not been surveyed. The rectangular system of subdivision in Alaska covered less than one per cent of the total area.

Resurveys are necessary in many areas to locate and identify those corner markers which still remain, and to re-establish those corners for which markers are not found. Usually, a large amount of work is necessary to ascertain that the re-established corner is as near to the location of the original as possible.

Wrought-iron pipes with brass disks fastened to the tops are placed to monument the land corners in modern surveys. The brass cap is appropriately marked to identify its position in the system.

Resurveys are divided into two types: the *dependent resurvey* and the *independent resurvey*.

The dependent resurvey is made to restore the original conditions according to (1) existing corners of the original survey, (2) the records of the original field notes and plat, and (3) acceptable evidence of the original location of the corners which are missing.

Existing corners are located and identified and missing corners are restored by proportional measurements based upon records of the original survey.

In some states dependent resurveys may be made by the state surveyor or his deputy upon a referendum vote of a majority of the parties concerned that the resurvey be made.

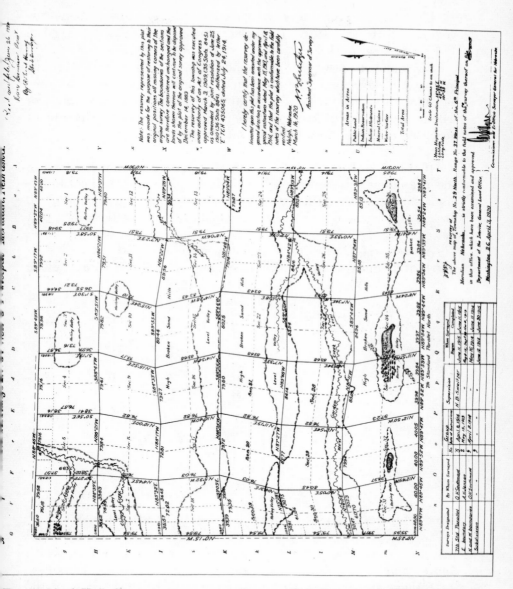

Fig. 10-12. A U. S. Government resurvey. (Courtesy U. S. Bureau of Land Management)

Figure 10-11 shows a township resurveyed by a deputy state surveyor.

Figure 10-12 shows a resurvey made by U. S. Government surveyors in 1914 and 1915. The township was originally surveyed in 1883.

Independent resurveys are made when, over large areas, the original survey cannot be identified with any degree of certainty as represented by the originally approved plat and field notes, or when restoration of corners based upon existing monuments or accepted locations does not give satisfactory results.

10-12. Land description. The rectangular system outlined in the preceding articles forms the basis for land description. Reference is made to the principal meridian controlling the area involved and to the range and tier of townships in which the described plat lies.

A range of townships is one township in width and extends north and south to the limits of the survey referred to any given

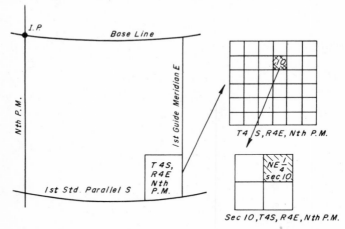

Fig. 10-13. Location of NE¼, Sec. 10, T 4 S, R 4 E, Nth P.M.

principal meridian. A tier of townships is one township in width and extends to the limits of the survey in an east-west direction.

Ranges are numbered consecutively both east and west of the principal meridian. Tiers are numbered consecutively both north and south from the base line. For example, any township which has as its eastern boundary the First Guide Meridian East of the Nth Principal Meridian is in Range 4 East (R 4 E). Any township which has as its southern boundary the First Standard Parallel South of a given base line is in Tier 4 South or Township 4 South (T 4 S).

The description for smaller tracts follows this scheme, always with the area being described listed at the beginning of the description.

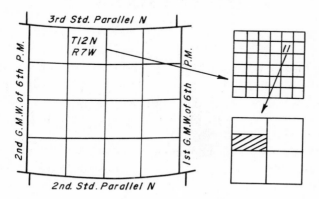

Fig. 10-14. Location of S½, NW¼, Sec. 11, T 12 N, R 7 W, 6th P.M.

Section 10 in the township just discussed would be described as follows: Sec. 10, T 4 S, R 4 E, *N*th P.M. The northeast quarter of that section would be described as the NE¼, Sec. 10, T 4 S, R 4 E, *N*th P.M. Figure 10-13 shows the location of the tract just described.

Figure 10-14 pictorially locates the following described tract of land: S½, NW¼, Sec. 11, T 12 N, R 7 W, 6th P.M., containing 80 acres, more or less.

Chapter 11

~~~~~~

TRAVERSES

THE BASIC idea of traversing was introduced, and open and closed traverses were defined, in Chapters 5 and 6 primarily to present applications for the use of the compass and transit. This chapter will consider the field work involved in a traverse and its relationship to an engineering survey.

In running a traverse, the measurement of distance and direction is integrated into a complete survey, having several important functions.

The combination of measurements of distance and direction gathered in traversing provides the essential two dimensional data for determining land areas and for providing horizontal control; that is, the relative location of points in the horizontal plane. To this information may be added the results of a level net covering the same general location, thus completing the data for the three dimensional representation of a section of the earth's surface.

The open traverse will provide the control for highway route surveys, railroads, canals, pipelines, or other projects where activity is confined to a comparatively long and narrow strip. The closed traverse is essential for area determination and may be used for control for mapping, laying out of real estate developments, power developments, arsenals, large industrial plants, and similar developments. The closed traverse has the advantage of providing a check on angle and distance measurements because the last side returns to the starting point.

As noted in Chapter 9, the traverse may be used in direct connection with triangulation nets. Where the terrain is easily accessible and relatively flat or rolling, first order traversing may be more advantageous in extending a control net than triangulation (which necessitates building high sighting towers). However, the traverse usually aids primary control of high order by supplying a lower order of control for a specific engineering project.

Each station (angle point) on a traverse must be visible to the station on either side and should be completely referenced by measured ties. A convenient check is provided by relating the traverse data to surveys already completed in the area, either public land surveys or a state plane coordinate system.

The precision usually specified for traverses requires the use of the transit and steel tape. However, any combination of angle-distance measuring equipment may be used. For example, transit-stadia, compass-tape, plane table (see Chapter 13), or, for approximate results, the pocket compass and pacing. As always, it is the job of the engineer to select method and equipment in terms of economy versus required precision. In the following discussion, it is assumed that transit and tape are being used.

11-1. The interior angle traverse. The use of interior angles indicates a closed traverse. To run the traverse, the transit is set up at each station on the polygon and interior angles are measured with sufficient repetitions to provide the desired precision. Dis-

INTERIOR ANGLE TRAVERSE

K.&.E. Transit #1065, Dec. 20, 1954, Clear, Cool 50°F. — ⊼ C. Nordstrom, I. R. Wegner, N. A. Richards

STA. AT	TO	DIST.	INTERIOR ANGLE SINGLE	DOUBLE	MEAN	MAG. BEAR.	CALC. BEAR.
1	5						
	2	263.22	90°05'	180°11'	90°05'	N11½°W	N11°20'W
2	1						
	3	244.32	90°16'	180°34'	90°17'	N78½°E	N78°23'E
3	2						
	4	456.42	166°53'	333°46'	166°53'	S88°E	S88°30'E
4	3						
	5	164.16	103°16'	206°30'	103°15'	S12°E	S11°45'E
5	4						
	1	690.53	89°29'	178°58'	89°29'	S78½°W	S78°45'W
					539°59'		

Σ Interior Angles
(n-2) 180° = 540°00'

Angular Error of Closure
Max. Allowable
30" √n = 01' 06"

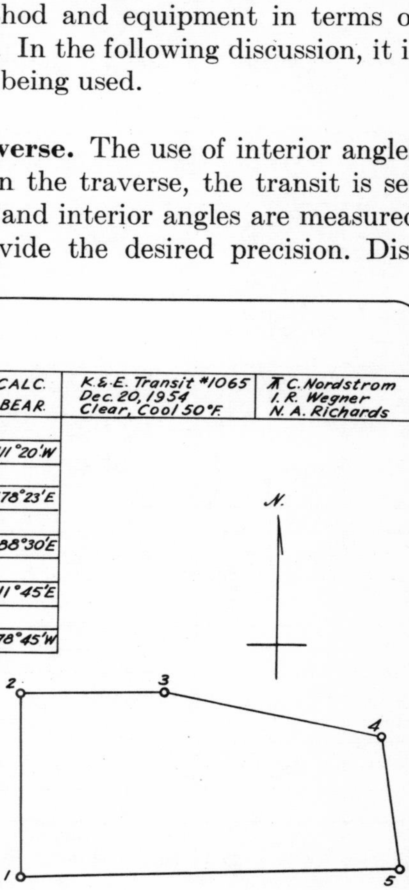

Fig. 11-1. Field notes for interior angle traverse.

tances between stations are taped to a precision consistent with that used in the angle measurements. See Article 3-6.

In running any traverse, distances may be measured either at the same time as the angles or as a separate step in the operation.

The interior angle traverse provides a convenient check on the accuracy of the angular measurements, because the sum of the interior angles of any closed polygon must equal $(n-2)$ times 180 degrees, where n is the number of sides in the polygon. Figure 11-1 shows a form of notes for a closed interior-angle traverse survey. Traverse computations are discussed in the next chapter.

11-2. Angle to the right traverse. This procedure, differing from the interior-angle traverse only in the method of turning angles,

STA.		DIST.	ANGLES			MAG.	CALC.	K. & E. Transit #1065	R. C. Nordstrom
AT	TO		SINGLE	DOUBLE	MEAN	BEAR.	BEAR.	Dec. 20, 1954 Clear, Cool 50°F	I. R. Wegner N. A. Richards
1	5								
	2	263.22	269°54'	539°50'	269°55'	N11½°W	N11°20'W		
2	1								
	3	244.32	269°43'	539°26'	269°43'	N78½°E	N78°23'E.		
3	2								
	4	456.42	193°06'	386°14'	193°07'	S88°E	S88°30'E		
4	3								
	5	164.16	256°46'	513°30'	256°45'	S12°E	S11°45'E		
5	4								
	1	690.53	270°30'	541°00'	270°30'	S78½°W	S78°45'W		

ANGLE TO RIGHT TRAVERSE

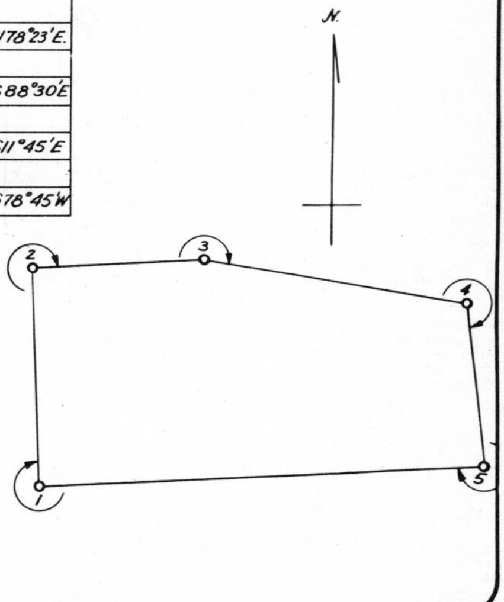

Fig. 11-2. Field notes for angle to the right traverse.

may be adapted to either a closed or open traverse. All angles are measured in a clockwise direction after the transit has been oriented by a backsight to the preceding station. Figure 11-2 shows a typical note form for this type of traverse.

11-3. Azimuth traverse. The azimuth traverse provides a simple definition of the direction of a line not inherent in the other methods. Each angular measurement yields a direction for the line ahead which is consistent with our natural sense of orientation. The azimuth of each line in the traverse is determined from the preceding line by setting the *A* vernier on the back azimuth of the preceding line (back azimuth of a line is its azimuth plus or minus 180 degrees). With the *A* vernier set, a backsight is taken on the preceding station. The instrument is then turned on its upper motion to sight the next station. The azimuth of the line to the next station will be recorded on the horizontal plate. To initiate this traverse, it is necessary to have a reference meridian, either true, magnetic, or assumed. See Article 5-2.

AZIMUTH TRAVERSE

STA. AT	TO	DIST.	A Z.	MAG. BEAR.	CALC. BEAR.
1	5		78°45'		
	2	263.22	348°40'	N11½°W	N11°20'W
2	1		168°40'		
	3	244.32	78°23'	N78½E	N78°23'E
3	2		258°23'		
	4	456.42	91°30'	S88°E	S88°30'E
4	3		271°30'		
	5	164.16	168°15'	S12°E	S11°45'E
5	4		348°15'		
	1	690.53	258°43'	S78½°W	S78°45'W

K.&E. TRANSIT #1065　　　R. C. NORDSTROM
DEC. 20, 1954　　　　　　 I. R. NEGNER
CLEAR, COOL 50°F.　　　　N. A. RICHARDS

Reference : N-point, clockwise

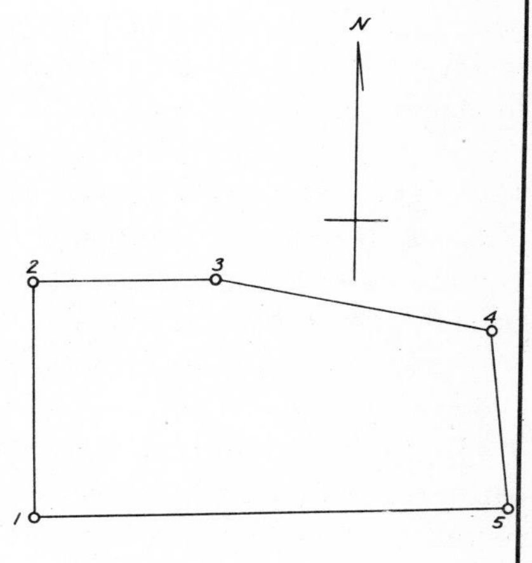

Fig. 11-3. Field notes for azimuth traverse.

The angular error in a closed azimuth traverse is checked by again setting up on the first station and using the backsight to the last station to establish, for the second time, the azimuth of the first side of the traverse. The difference between this azimuth and the initial azimuth of this line is an indication of the angular error in the traverse. Figure 11-3 shows a note form for this type of traverse.

In the second line of the notes, the azimuth recorded from station 1 to station 2 is 348°40′. This angle with 180 degrees subtracted from it is the value that must be set on the *A* vernier of the instrument when backsighting on station 1. The instrument is then turned on the upper motion and the reading of 78°23′ is obtained from the *A* vernier. This angle is the azimuth of the leg from station 2 to station 3. It will be noted that the measured azimuth of the final leg, station 5 to station 1, is in error by 02′. This represents the angular error in the traverse.

11-4. Deflection angle traverse. The deflection angle traverse is used extensively where the open traverse is required; for example, for locating a highway or railway, or for other route surveys. This traverse, as the name implies, measures the deflection angle of each course or leg from the direction of the preceding leg. The angle measured at each station must be designated either right (R) or left (L) in order to completely define the direction of the next course. A disadvantage of this system is the extreme care necessary when working with small angles, in order to avoid making a mistake in the designation of right or left.

To measure the deflection angle, the telescope is plunged and a backsight taken to the preceding station with the vernier set at zero. The telescope is then returned to the normal position and the angle is measured by turning the transit right or left on its upper motion to sight the next station. The deflection angle, when measured, is read, recorded, and designated as measured either to the right or to the left.

If the line of sight is not in adjustment (see Chapter 8), it will cause an error in any deflection angle measured. This may be corrected by double centering and taking the mean of the two angles measured.

A set of notes for the deflection angle traverse appears in Figure 11-4. The notes are for a closed traverse which provides a check on the angular accuracy, because the algebraic sum of the deflection angles should equal 360 degrees.

Because a similar check on the angular accuracy is not possible with the open traverse, field checking of the angular measurements as they are made becomes increasingly important. Angular accuracy on an open traverse may be checked by observing Polaris or the sun

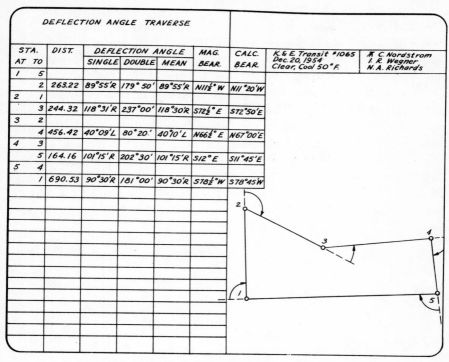

DEFLECTION ANGLE TRAVERSE								K.&E. Transit #1065 Dec. 20, 1954 Clear, Cool 50°F.	Ŧ C. Nordstrom I. R. Wegner N. A. Richards
STA.		DIST.	DEFLECTION ANGLE			MAG.	CALC.		
AT	TO		SINGLE	DOUBLE	MEAN	BEAR.	BEAR.		
1	5								
	2	263.22	89°55'R	179°50'	89°55'R	N11½°W	N11°20'W		
2	1								
	3	244.32	118°31'R	237°00'	118°30'R	S72½°E	S72°50'E		
3	2								
	4	456.42	40°09'L	80°20.'	40°10'L	N66½°E	N67°00'E		
4	3								
	5	164.16	101°15'R	202°30'	101°15'R	S12°E	S11°45'E		
5	4								
	1	690.53	90°30'R	181°00'	90°30'R	S78½°W	S78°45'W		

Fig. 11-4. Field notes for deflection angle traverse.

to establish a true meridian at intermediate points and at each end of the traverse. A check may also be provided by tying in with established lines from previous surveys.

11-5. Random lines. Many times it becomes necessary to establish a straight line between two points not visible from one another. An application of the traverse concept known as *running a random line* makes this possible.

Random lines are of two general types: (1) one continuous

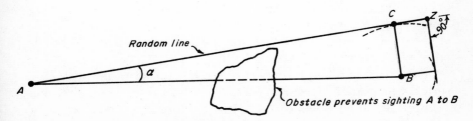

Fig. 11-5. Random line with swing offsets. Swing offset gives accurate value for *Z–C*.

straight line run from point A in the general direction of point B until the latter is visible (see Figure 11-5). (2) A series of connected straight lines none of which run in the same direction, sometimes referred to as a *random traverse* (see Figure 11-6).

The first type consists of an open traverse of two sides, A–C and C–B, Figure 11-5, which meet in a right angle. In the figure, the missing side needed to close the triangle is side A–B, whose length and direction are required.

The right angle at point C in Figure 11-5 is constructed in the field by holding the zero of a steel tape on point B while the tape is swung in an arc. When a minimum reading is obtained by a transit set up on, and sighting along, the random line A–Z, the tape is per-

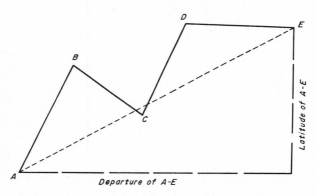

Fig. 11-6. Random traverse.

pendicular to line A–Z. This is called the *swing offset* method. If the random line is too far from point A for use of the swing offset, the connecting line to B is run from any point on line A–Z and computations are based upon a triangle with two sides and the included angle being known.

Once the lengths and directions of sides A–C and C–B are known, the computation of the length and direction of the line connecting points A and B can be made.

This type of random line has specific application in the subdivision of public lands. See Article 10-5.

Often, to avoid heavy timber, rough terrain, or other obstacles, a series of lines are run from one of the points in the general direction of the other, finally connecting with it. Here the second type of random line finds its application. It also consists of an open traverse. The line whose length and direction are sought is the missing line which would form a closed traverse (the dotted line A–E in Figure 11-6).

The computation for the length and direction of A–E is based upon a determination of how far point E is east or west from point A and of how far it is north or south from point A. The concepts and procedure necessary to do this are detailed in the next chapter, Article 12-11.

Chapter 12

~~~~~~

OFFICE COMPUTATIONS:
TRAVERSES AND
SIMPLE TRIANGULATION

THE OFFICE computations required for all surveys have many features in common. In general, the formalization of computation leads to greater accuracy. For that reason, different forms have been devised for tabulating computations. Essentially, they provide an arrangement for a systematic approach to results. In practice, each office will use the system most convenient in its particular work. Those making computations should avoid routine, thoughtless calculations, always checking for the logic of answers and for the possibility of mistakes in original data and calculations.

This chapter will discuss the computation of closed traverses, random lines, and small triangulation systems. Triangulation adjustment and computation was outlined in Chapter 9; for a detailed discussion, refer to a text on advanced surveying[6] or publications of the U. S. Coast and Geodetic Survey.[7]

When making office computations, various devices, such as the mechanical or electrical calculator, aid in expediting the work. The slide rule may be used, but in general does not yield the required accuracy. As mentioned before, the fastest and most efficient methods that will give the required accuracy should be used.

The complete computation is usually made by two or more men. The first makes all of the necessary computations for the project, and each man following acts as a checker to determine any mistakes.

12-1. Area computations. In most surveys the area calculated is the horizontal projection of the area rather than the actual surface of the land. The field work employed for the determination of area consists of a series of angular and linear measurements, defining the outline of the area concerned and forming a closed traverse.

The methods for office computation are: (1) plotting the traverse to scale and measuring the enclosed area directly with a polar planimeter, used where only approximate results are required, or for checking purposes; (2) subdividing the area into a series of triangles, determining the area of each of the triangles, and adding areas; (3) computation of the area using the coordinates of the individual points of the traverse, termed the *coordinate* method; and (4) computation of the area by means of the balanced latitude and calculated double meridian distance of each course, termed the *D.M.D.* method.

12-2. Adjusting the traverse and computing bearings. Before any computation for area or control location is made, the data for a closed traverse is adjusted so that in terms of angles only, the traverse does close. In simplifying the discussion up to this point, it has been assumed that the field data provided perfect results. This is not true, although by chance, compensating errors may cause the angles to appear to be without error.

The balancing of a traverse begins with the adjustment of the angles. This may be done in the field or as the first step in the office computation. The angles may be checked by noting whether the interior angles of the closed traverse total $(n - 2)$ times 180 degrees, where n is the number of sides in the traverse. The algebraic sum of deflection angles on a closed traverse should equal 360 degrees. If the error is found to be within the allowable limits based upon the required precision, it is distributed through the angles of the traverse to meet the theoretical sum.

This may be done by logically applying any one of the following suggestions or any combination of the three: (1) change angles adjacent to the short sides of the traverse; (2) change values ci single angles so that the single angle and the mean of the repeated angle still check within the prescribed limit; for example, when the single angle is 20°20′, and the double angle is 40°39′, change the single angle to 20°19′ (see Article 6-8); (3) change angles according to judgment; for example, angles where field conditions make accurate sighting difficult.

In balancing, individual angle changes should be made in increments of the least count of the instrument vernier so that the balanced angle values do not imply an accuracy greater than the instrument will give.

If the angular error is more than is consistent with the required precision, the measurements must be checked in the field until the incorrect angular values are located and correctly determined.

After the angular adjustments have been made, the bearings are computed. The bearing of each side is computed by use of the known or assumed bearing of one side and the measured angles between successive sides. The starting bearing should always be computed as the last step by using the computed bearing of the last side. Unless the result is the same as the bearing which was used to begin computations, there is a mistake in the calculations which must be found before proceeding.

12-3. Latitudes and departures.
The latitude (Lat.) of a line or course is its projection onto the reference meridian (north-south line). The numerical value for the latitude of a line or course is the length of the line or course times the cosine of its bearing angle.

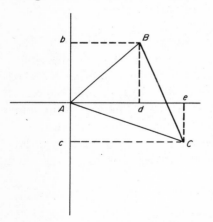

If a line bears northerly, its latitude is positive. If it bears southerly, its latitude is negative.

The departure (Dep.) of a line is its projection onto a line at right angles to the reference meridian. It is numerically equal to the length of the line times the sine of its bearing angle. If a line bears easterly, its departure is positive. If it bears westerly, its departure is negative.

For example, the latitude of AB

Fig. 12-1. Latitudes and departures.

in Figure 12-1 is Ab. The latitude of BC is $-bc$. The departure of AB is Ad. The departure of BC is de. The departure of CA is $-Cc$. From this it follows that the y coordinate of A is 0, of B is Ab, and of C is $Ab + (-bc)$. The x coordinate of A is 0, of B is Ad, and of C is $Ad + de$.

12-4. Error of closure and precision.
If one travels from a given point for any distance and by any conceivable path, but eventually returns to that point, he will have traveled as far north as

he did south and as far east as he did west. This means that theoretically the sum of all north latitudes for a traverse will be numerically equal to the sum of all south latitudes. The sum of all of the east departures will, for the same reason, be numerically equal to the sum of all west departures.

Since it is not possible to measure without error, the plus and minus latitudes for a closed traverse will not algebraically add to zero except by occasional chance when compensating errors act together in the right way. The same is true of the plus and minus departures.

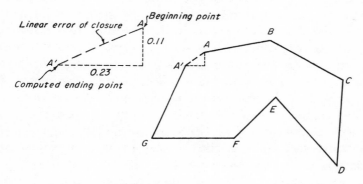

Fig. 12-2. Traverse with error of closure.

The difference between the plus and minus latitudes, called the *error in latitudes*, indicates how much the traverse computations fail to close in a north-south direction. The difference in plus and minus departures indicates how far the closure misses in an east-west direction.

Figure 12-2 shows the closure conditions on a traverse having the following computed values for the sum of latitudes and departures: South latitudes: $-1,732.15$ feet; North latitudes: $+1,732.04$ feet; West departures: $-2,631.43$ feet; East departures: $+2,631.20$ feet.

The line $A-A'$ represents the linear error of closure and is equal to

$$\sqrt{\text{(error in latitudes)}^2 + \text{(error in departures)}^2}$$

or $$\sqrt{(0.11)^2 + (0.23)^2} = 0.25 \text{ feet}$$

The ratio of linear error of closure to the perimeter of the traverse is the expression for precision of the survey. It is always written with the numerator expressed as one. Thus in the example, if we assume the perimeter of the traverse to be 3,260.42 feet, the precision of that survey is 0.25/3260.42, or 1 in 13,041. The 41 would be dropped and the precision reported as 1 in 13,000, or 1/13,000.

If the precision is within the required limits, the latitudes and departures are adjusted so that the plus and minus values are numerically equal. This is done by changing the latitudes and departures of some lines or of all lines according to one of three rules: (1) If certain lines are noted as being less accurately measured than others because of difficult field conditions, the latitudes and departures for those lines are changed in proportion to their magnitude so that the desired balance is attained; (2) If, probably, the discrepancies are caused as much by angular errors as by distance errors, the distribution of error is made according to a ratio known as the *compass rule*, which is that the correction to be applied to the latitude *or* departure of any course is to the total error in latitudes or departures as the length of that course is to the perimeter of the traverse; (3) If it is probable that discrepancies are caused primarily by distance errors rather than angular errors, the proportional corrections may be determined by the *transit rule*, which states that the correction to be applied to the latitude (or departure) of any course is to the total error in latitudes (or departures) as the latitude (or departure) of that course is to the sum of all latitudes (or departures) without regard to algebraic sign (absolute sum).

12-5. Plotting the traverse. The traverse is usually plotted to scale as a part of the computations for area, either so that it may be planimetered or may serve as a record when other means of computation are used.

Plotting may be done with a scale and protractor, or it may be done by measurements made from a base coordinate axis. The latter of these two methods is more accurate. Its use necessitates computing the x and y coordinates of each point (*station*) on the traverse. Coordinates for each point are determined by first computing the latitude and departure for each line in the traverse.

The computation of latitude and departure for each course, then, establishes a relationship between the traverse stations which may be used for (1) plotting, (2) establishing the stations as control points for extending the survey within the traverse or to adjacent territory, and (3) for the computation of the area enclosed by the traverse.

The latitudes and departures are given algebraic signs in accordance with where they project on the coordinate axis. For example, any line in either the N–W or N–E quadrant will project onto the positive end of the *Y*-axis. Thus, all north latitudes are positive and conversely, all south latitudes are negative. Any line in either the N–E or S–E quadrants will project onto the positive end of the *X*-axis. Thus, all east departures are positive and conversely, all west departures are negative.

The references for the coordinate system should be located through the most westerly and the most southerly points of the traverse. The difference between the calculated *y* coordinates for the last course must then equal the latitude of that course and the difference between the calculated *x* coordinates must equal the departure of the last course. This serves as a positive check on the computation of coordinates.

12-6. Double meridian distances. The area determination of a traverse by the double meridian distances method makes use of

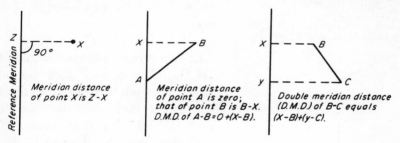

Fig. 12-3. Meridian distances.

balanced latitudes and departures. After the latitudes and departures have been balanced or adjusted, the next step is the determination of the double meridian distance of each line or course. The double meridian distance (D.M.D.) of a course is the sum of the meridian distances of its end points. The meridian distance of a point is the perpendicular distance from the reference meridian to that point. See Figure 12-3.

In computing the double meridian distances for a closed traverse it is important that the reference meridian be placed through the most westerly point of the traverse. Confusion will be avoided if the course leading out of the most westerly point be designated as the first course, regardless of station numbers.

The following three rules provide a means for computing the D.M.D. for each course:

1. The D.M.D. of the first course is equal to the balanced departure of that course.
2. The D.M.D. of any course is equal to the D.M.D. of the preceding course, plus the balanced departure of the preceding course, plus the balanced departure of the course itself (pay strict attention to algebraic signs).
3. The D.M.D. of the last course is numerically equal to the balanced departure of that course, but with the opposite sign. Use this rule as a check only. First apply Rule 2. If there is not a check by Rule 3, some mistake exists in the D.M.D. computations.

The reader should prove each of these rules by sketching a traverse and applying the Double Meridian Distance definition in conjunction with the definition for departure of a line. Notice that when the reference meridian is placed through the most westerly point of the traverse all D.M.D's will be positive. Departures must carry the sign indicated by the bearing of the lines.

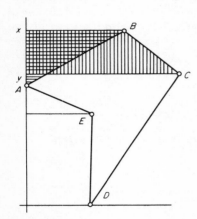

Fig. 12-4. Area within a traverse, D.M.D. method.

12-7. Area computation by D.M.D. The double area for any course is equal to the D.M.D. for that course multiplied by the balanced latitude for that course. To prove this, consider Figure 12-4. In the traverse A–B–C–D–E, the double area for the course A–B is represented by the triangle A–B–x and is equal to A–x, the latitude of A–B, multiplied by $(0 + B$–$x)$, the D.M.D. of A–B. Because this double area is positive, it is covered by horizontal lines. The double area for the course B–C is equal to its latitude $-xy$ times its D.M.D. $(x$–$B + y$–$C)$. It is represented by the trapezoid x–B–C–y. Since the latitude of B–C is south, this double area is negative and the lines covering the area of this trapezoid are vertical. In this manner the remaining courses are calculated and the area covered by each of the courses is indicated. The areas covered with lines running in both directions are those which are canceled out when the individual areas of the courses are added algebraically. The area resulting from this computation is the area of the traverse. The use of the rules for algebraic signs will result in a traverse area which is negative. This does not alter the value of the numerical result, and the negative sign is ignored. With this one exception, strict attention to signs is absolutely necessary in the computation.

The double meridian distances rather than meridian distances are used for convenience in the application of the set of rules for area computation. The final answer is then obtained by dividing the calculated double area by two.

12-8. Numerical example. A numerical example is given in Figure 12-5 to further explain the computation for the area of an

COMPUTATIONS FOR CLOSED TRAVERSE 51-55

LINE	CALCULATED BEARINGS	DISTANCE	LATITUDES N.	S	DEPARTURES E	W	BALANCED LATS.	DEP.	D.M.D.	DOUBLE AREA +	−
51-52	N11°20'W	263.22	258.09			51.73		− 51.73	51.73	13353	
52-53	N78°23'E	244.32	49.20		239.32		+ 49.21	+239.31	239.31	11776	
53-54	S88°30'E	456.42		11.95	456.28		− 11.95	+456.26	934.88		11172
54-55	S11°45'E	164.16		160.72	33.43		−160.69	+ 33.43	1424.57		228900
55-51	S78°45'W	690.53		134.72		677.25	−134.70	−677.27	780.73		105120
		1818.65	307.29	307.29	729.03	728.98	0.	0.		25127	345192
				.29		.98					25129
				.10		.05				2	320063

Error of Closure $= \sqrt{(0.1)^2+(0.05)^2} = 0.11$
Precision $= \dfrac{0.11}{1818} = \dfrac{1}{16,000}$

160031
÷43560 =
3.67 acres

COMPUTATIONS OF LATITUDES AND DEPARTURES					
Line	51-52	52-53	53-54	54-55	55-51
Dep.	51.728	239.32	456.28	33.43	677.25
Log Dep.	1.71372	2.37897	2.65922	1.52414	2.83075
Sin. Brg.	9.29340	9.99101	9.99985	9.30887	9.99157
Log Dist.	2.42032	2.38796	2.65937	2.21527	2.83918
Cos. Brg.	9.99145	9.30398	8.41792	9.99060	9.29024
Log Lat.	2.41177	1.69194	1.07729	2.20607	2.12942
Lat.	258.09	49.195	11.948	160.72	134.72

Balanced by Transit Rule

Corr. to Lats.   Corr. to Deps.
$\dfrac{.10}{614.68} = \dfrac{.01}{61}$ $\dfrac{0.05}{1458.01} = \dfrac{.01}{294}$

51-52 .04   51-52 .00
52-53 .01   52-53 .01
53-54 .00   53-54 .02
54-55 .03   54-55 .00
55-51 .02   55-51 .02
       .10   .05

COMPUTATION OF DOUBLE AREA					
Line	51-52	52-53	53-54	54-55	55-51
Log Lat.	2.41184	1.69205	1.07737	2.20599	2.12937
Log D.M.D.	1.71374	2.37896	2.97076	3.15366	2.89249
Log D.A.	4.12558	4.07101	4.04813	5.35965	5.02186
D.A.	13353	11776	11172	228900	105120

Fig. 12-5. Calculation for area by D.M.D. method.

interior angle traverse, and to show a form in which the results may be tabulated and summarized. The steps taken in the calculation are as follows:

1. Balance the field angles so that their sum is $(n - 2)$ times 180 degrees.

2. Calculate the bearings for all of the courses from the adjusted field angles.

3. Calculate the latitudes and departures for each of the courses and record them in their proper columns as to sign.

4. Add the north and south latitudes and the east and west departures algebraically to determine error in Lats. (E_L) and error in Deps. (E_D).

5. Determine the error of closure.

$$\text{error of closure} = \sqrt{(E_L)^2 + (E_D)^2}$$

6. Determine the precision of the survey.

$$\text{precision} = \frac{\text{error of closure}}{\text{traverse perimeter}}, \quad \text{expressed} \ \frac{1}{\text{so many}}$$

7. Balance the latitudes and departures (use the transit rule).
8. Calculate the double meridian distances.
9. Calculate double area for each course (D.M.D. times balanced latitude). Record each in proper column as to sign.
10. Add plus and minus double areas algebraically. The result is double area of traverse, regardless of algebraic sign.
11. Divide double area by two to get area in square feet. Divide this result by 43,560 for area in acres.

12-9. Computing area by coordinates. Figure 12-6 shows a traverse, *A–B–C–D–E*, the area of which is to be determined by the method of coordinates.

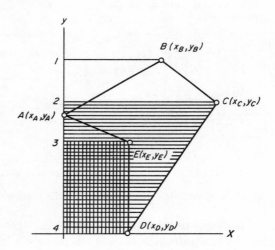

Fig. 12-6. Area within a traverse, coordinate method.

The use of coordinates in area determination is similar to the D.M.D. method; it involves finding the area of the individual triangles and trapezoids defined by the traverse polygon. For example, the trapezoid *D–E–3–4* as shown in the Figure 12-6, crosshatched with vertical lines.

The area of the complementary trapezoid from the line *D–C*,

(D–C–2–4) and covering a portion of the previous trapezoid, is shown by horizontal crosshatching. Notice that line C–D bears SW, and, therefore, its latitude is negative while the line D–E bears NE which makes its latitude positive. Since the latitude in each case is the altitude of the trapezoid concerned, each trapezoidal area will carry the sign of the latitude for the course involved. If the areas of trapezoids D–E–3–4 and D–C–2–4 are added algebraically, the portion of the area not canceled by the summation is primarily within the traverse boundaries. This illustrates what occurs when all trapezoidal and triangular segments of the shaded areas in Figure 12-6 are determined and added algebraically. The net result is that all areas outside the traverse are canceled out, leaving only the desired area. The summation of the areas may be expressed in the following formula:

area A–B–C–D–E =
+area D–E–3–4 + area E–A–3 + area A–B–1 − area B–C–2–1 − area C–D–4–2 =
$-\frac{1}{2}(x_B + x_C)\,(y_B - y_C)$ $-\frac{1}{2}(x_E + x_D)(y_E - y_D)$
$-\frac{1}{2}(x_C + x_D)\,(y_C - y_D)$ $+\frac{1}{2}(x_A + x_E)(y_A - y_E)$
                    $+\frac{1}{2}(x_B + x_A)(y_B - y_A)$.

It is advantageous to have the traverse represented in one quadrant so that the coordinates of all points may be expressed as positive. Where this is not done, the north ordinates are classified as positive and the south as negative, the east abscissa as positive and the west as negative.

A rule given in analytical geometry for the determination of the area of a closed polygon states: If the vertices of the figure are taken in order around the figure, the area is equal to one-half the sum of the products of each ordinate multiplied by the difference between the two adjacent abscissas always subtracting the preceding from the following abscissa.

This rule expressed algebraically for any figure, A–B–C–D–E, is

area = $\frac{1}{2}[y_B(x_C - x_A) + y_C(x_D - x_B) + y_D(x_E - x_C) + y_E(x_A - x_D) + y_A(x_B - x_E)]$.

12-10. Numerical example. Reference to Figure 12-7 indicates that in the application of the principles of the coordinate method the area of the traverse 51 through 55 is equal to the area of triangles: 51–52–d, plus 52–53–a, minus trapezoids 53–54–b–a, 54–55–c–b, and 55–51–d–c.

The substitution of these data in the expression for area by the coordinate method will provide the same answer as appears in the computation using double meridian distances, Figure 12-5.

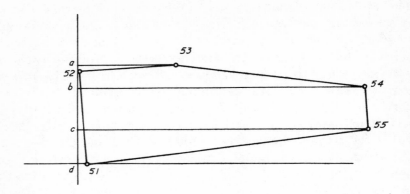

STA.	INTERIOR ANGLE	CALC BEARING	DIST.	BALANCED				COORDINATES	
				LATITUDES		DEPARTURES			
				N +	S −	E +	W −	y	z
51-52	90° 05'	N11°20'W	263.22	258.13			51.73	0	51.73
52-53	90° 17'	N78°23'E	244.32	49.21		239.31		258.13	0
53-54	166°53'	S88°30'E	456.42		11.95	456.26		307.34	239.31
54-55	103°15'	S11°45'E	164.16		160.69	33.43		295.39	695.57
55-51	89°30'	S78°45'W	690.53		134.70		677.27	134.70	729.00

Fig. 12-7. Computation of coordinates.

12-11. Random line computations. Figure 12-8 illustrates the method of computation for the closing of a random line or for determining the missing side of a closed traverse. The problem is to determine the direction and the length of the line 55–51. This may be accomplished by determining the latitude and departure for each course and adding them algebraically. The results give the latitude and departure for the missing side. The length and direction may then be determined by recognizing that the algebraic sum of the latitudes forms one side of a right triangle, the algebraic sum of the departures forms the other side and the closing line 55–51 forms its hypotenuse.

The same results can be accomplished by determining the coordinates of the individual stations and summating to get the coordinates of the last point on the random line or open traverse, point 55.

Obviously either method precludes the possibility of determining the error of closure check for precision as in a closed figure.

12-12. Missing parts. Occasionally it is not possible to determine by field observation the length of a side or the value of an

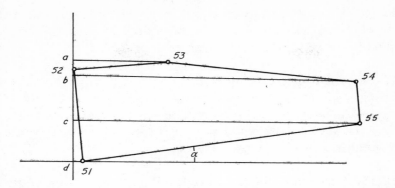

LINE	CALC. BEARING	DIST.	LATITUDES		DEPARTURES	
			N	S	E	W
51-52	N 11° 20' W	263.22	258.09			51.73
52-53	N 78° 23' E	244.32	49.20		239.32	
53-54	S 88° 30' E	456.42		11.95	456.28	
54-55	S 11° 45' E	164.16		160.72	33.43	
			307.29	172.67	729.03	51.73

$$Lat. \ 51\text{-}55 = 307.29 \qquad Dep. \ 51\text{-}55 = 729.03$$
$$\underline{\phantom{Lat. \ 51\text{-}55 = }\ 172.67} \qquad \qquad \underline{\phantom{Dep. \ 51\text{-}55 = }\ 51.73}$$
$$+ \ 134.62 \qquad\qquad\qquad + \ 677.30$$

$$Tan \ \alpha = \frac{134.62}{677.30} = 0.19875$$

$$\alpha = 11° 14' 30''$$

$$55\text{-}51 = \frac{677.30}{Cos \ \alpha} = 690.54 \ ft$$

$$Bearing \ 55\text{-}51 = S \ 78° 45' W$$

Fig. 12-8. Traverse with a missing side.

angle within a closed traverse. These missing parts may be computed if they do not exceed two in number. In order to make the calculations, it is necessary to assume that all available data is correct and without error. Any error that does exist is automatically thrown into the computed lengths or angles. Some of the more common measurements which can be determined are listed as follows: (1) the length of a missing side, (2) the value of a missing angle, (3) the length of a missing side and the value of a missing angle, (4) the lengths of two missing sides, and (5) the values of two missing angles.

12-13. A missing side. When it is necessary to determine the length of a missing side, the same procedure may be followed as outlined in Article 12-11 concerning random lines.

12-14. A missing angle. In the determination of the value of a missing angle of a closed traverse, it is necessary to use the geometric relationship for the interior angles of a polygon (the sum of the interior angles must equal $(n-2)$ times 180 degrees, where n is the number of sides in the polygon).

12-15. A missing side and angle. When the missing information includes both the length of a side and the value of an angle,

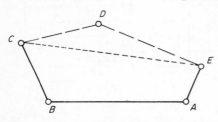

Fig. 12-9. Missing length and missing direction in adjacent sides.

the following procedure may be used. The polygon A-B-C-D-E shown in Figure 12-9 represents a traverse with the length of the line C-D being unknown and the direction of the line D-E unknown. The computation of these quantities may be made by forming a closed traverse using the substitute line C-E. The line C-E then represents the same situation as occurs in the determination of a missing side. The length of the line C-E is represented by the following expression:

$$L = \sqrt{(\Sigma \text{ Lat.})^2 + (\Sigma \text{ Dep.})^2},$$

where the latitudes and departures are derived from the polygon A-B-C-E. The tangent of the bearing angle is Σ Dep./Σ Lat.

Since the direction of the line C-D is known, the angle between the lines C-E and C-D may be determined. This information then allows the computation of the remaining two angles and the missing side of triangle C-D-E.

If the unknown quantities are so located that a triangle cannot be formed as in Figure 12-9, the

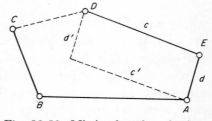

Fig. 12-10. Missing length and missing direction, sides not adjacent.

closed traverse must be rearranged so that the two unknown quantities are adjacent. Figure 12-10 shows the rearrangement of Figure 12-9 when the length of the line *C–D* is missing and the direction of the line *E–A* is missing. This rearrangement may be made if the side, when moved, is parallel to its former location.

12-16. Two missing sides. When the lengths of two adjoining sides are missing, calculation is almost the same as that in the preceding article. If the missing sides are the sides *C–D* and *D–E* of the traverse shown in Figure 12-9, a substitute side is again used to close the traverse and the same solution is followed, first determining the length of the substitute side *C–E* and then calculating the lengths of *C–D* and *D–E* by the sine law. If the two sides are not adjacent, the figure must be rearranged in a manner similar to that outlined in Article 12-15.

12-17. Two missing angles. When two angles of a closed traverse are missing, the same procedure may be followed in their determination as described in Article 12-16.

12-18. Locating large angular mistakes. A convenient and formalized method of locating large angular mistakes is helpful when

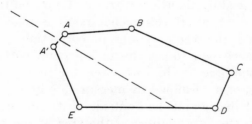

Fig. 12-11. Probable location of angular mistake.

the closed traverse being run contains a large number of sides. Angular mistakes in values of 10 to 20 degrees are easily located usually by one of two methods. In the first case, assume that a closed traverse containing a large number of sides (30 or more) was run around the high water line of a reservoir. A check in the summation of observed angles indicates an angular error of 10 to 20 degrees at some place within the traverse. This error may be located by calculating the magnetic bearings for all sides of the traverse. The comparison of the calculated bearings with the observed bearings will indicate the most logical location where a mistake has been made.

The second method involves the same type of traverse.* The traverse is first plotted to scale and the error of closure, represented by the length A–A' in Figure 12-11, is utilized in locating the most probable location of the angular mistake. To affect this solution, it is necessary to erect a perpendicular bisector to the line representing the error of closure. The perpendicular bisector should point approximately to the location where the mistake was made.

12-19. Polar planimeter. The polar planimeter is a mechanical device used to determine the area of any shape of figure, bounded by straight or curved lines, if the figure is plotted to a known scale. This device utilizes the relationship between the tracing arm which traces the outline and the connected recording wheel which records the area over which the tracing arm has traversed.

Figure 12-12 illustrates the various parts of the polar planimeter. These parts are: (1) tracing point, (2) tracing arm, (3) recording wheel, (4) anchor point with weight, (5) pole arm, (6) recording disk, and (7) vernier for recording wheel.

If in using the planimeter, the anchor point is placed inside the area to be measured, a correction must be made for the zero circle. This circle is traced by the tracing arm with no resulting movement of the recording wheel. If the anchor point is placed outside the area to be traced, the results require no correction.

When it is necessary to use the anchor point within the area to be measured, the area of the zero circle for that planimeter must either be known or determined by measuring a known area with the anchor arm first inside and then outside of its boundaries. The difference between the two readings is the area of the zero circle. To keep the anchor point outside the boundaries of an area, it may be necessary to temporarily subdivide it, measure the parts, and total the results.

In measuring an area with the planimeter, first calibrate the instrument by the measurement of an area of known value. If there is an adjustable tracing arm, the adjustment for direct reading with different plotting scales will usually be noted on the inside of the planimeter case. The setting of the tracing arm should be made and checked by measuring a rectangular or circular area of known size. For example, suppose we wish to measure an irregular area plotted to the scale of 1 inch equals 10 feet, with a planimeter having an

* Dana E. Low, "Finding Angle Reading Errors in Long Traverses," *Civil Engineering*, November, 1954.

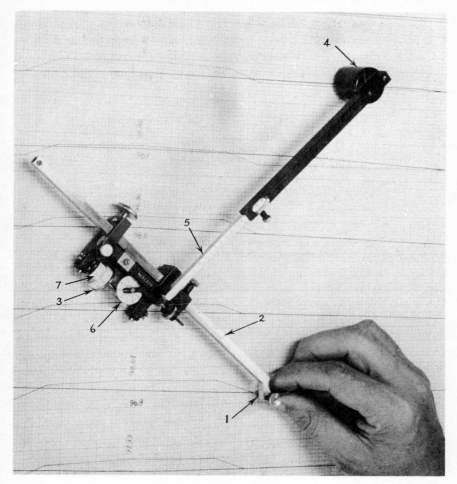

Fig. 12-12. Parts of a polar planimeter.

adjustable tracing arm. The tracing arm would first be set on 10 square inches. A 1-inch square would then be traced and the reading on the recording wheel noted. At the scale of one inch equals 10 feet, this reading should be one tenth of a revolution or 100 square feet. If the reading is not correct, the tracing arm may be adjusted to obtain the correct reading on the next trial or the reading on the recording wheel and disk may be noted and a corresponding correction applied to all subsequent readings.

In this example, it is assumed that the anchor point has been placed outside the area to be determined.

12-20. Triangulation. The same principles as outlined in Chapter 9 for control surveys by triangulation may often be applied on a smaller scale for determining inaccessible distances.

Figure 12-13 illustrates a solution to the problem of determining

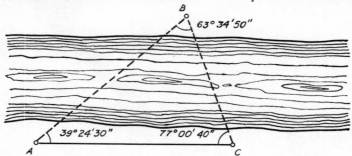

Fig. 12-13. Computation of inaccessible distance by triangulation.

the distance between points A and B along an inaccessible line. In this case the location A–C is selected to provide an easily measured distance to be used as the base line for the triangle A–B–C. This distance was laid out as 3,000.0 feet. Since the location of the point C could be selected, the distance could be made a whole number. The angle B–A–C was measured and found to be 39°24′30″. The angle B–C–A was measured as 77°00′40″. From this data the desired distance A–B may be computed by the use of the sine law.

The angle

$$A\text{–}B\text{–}C = 180°00'00'' - 39°24'30'' - 77°00'40''$$
$$= 63°34'50''$$

Therefore,

$$\frac{A\text{–}B}{\sin 77°00'40''} = \frac{3,000.0}{\sin 63°34'50''}$$

From this relationship, the value of 3,203.6 feet is found for the distance A–B.

Figure 12-14 shows a simple *chain* of two triangles where one of the sides of the first triangle is used as the base line. Although this example is for a relatively simple triangulation problem, the same principle applies for all others. The problem is to determine the distance from the points A and C to the inaccessible point, *tower*. For this situation, the measurement of the base line must be made along the line shown, because from A to B the terrain is flat and open, while accurate taping across the terrain from A to C would

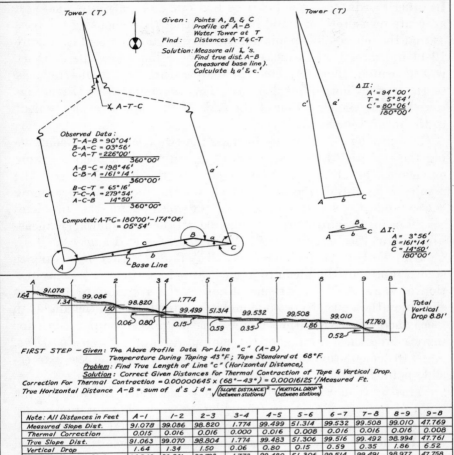

FIRST STEP — *Given*: The Above Profile Data For Line "c" (A–B)
Temperature During Taping 43°F; Tape Standard at 68°F.
Problem: Find True Length of Line "c" (Horizontal Distance).
Solution: Correct Given Distances For Thermal Contraction of Tape & Vertical Drop.
Correction For Thermal Contraction = 0.00000645 × (68°−43°) = 0.00016125'/Measured Ft.
True Horizontal Distance A–B = sum of d's j d = $\sqrt{\left(\text{SLOPE DISTANCE}\atop\text{between stations}\right)^2 - \left(\text{VERTICAL DROP}\atop\text{between stations}\right)^2}$

Note: All Distances in Feet	A–1	1–2	2–3	3–4	4–5	5–6	6–7	7–8	8–9	9–B
Measured Slope Dist.	91.078	99.086	98.820	1.774	99.499	51.3/4	99.532	99.508	99.010	47.769
Thermal Correction	0.015	0.016	0.016	0.000	0.016	0.008	0.016	0.016	0.016	0.008
True Slope Dist.	91.063	99.070	98.804	1.774	99.483	51.306	99.516	99.492	98.994	47.761
Vertical Drop	1.64	1.34	1.50	0.06	0.80	0.15	0.59	0.35	1.86	6.52
True Horizontal Dist.	91.048	99.061	98.793	1.773	99.480	51.306	99.514	99.491	98.977	47.758

True Horizontal Distance A – B ("c") = 787.201 Length of Base.

SECOND STEP — *Given*: ⅃'s of ΔI By Observation; Side c of ΔI From First Step; ⅃'s of ΔII By Observation.
Find: Side b of ΔI by Law of Sines; Sides a' & c' of ΔII by Law of Sines.

In ΔI:
$$\frac{b}{\sin B} = \frac{c}{\sin C}, \qquad b = \frac{c \sin B}{\sin C} = \frac{787.201 \times 0.32171}{0.25601} = 989.22 \ \text{Ft.} = b$$

In ΔII:
$$\frac{a'}{\sin A} = \frac{b}{\sin T}, \qquad a' = \frac{b \sin A}{\sin T} = \frac{989.221 \times 0.99756}{0.10279} = 9600.23 \ \text{Ft.} = a'$$

$$\frac{c'}{\sin C} = \frac{b}{\sin T}, \qquad c' = \frac{b \sin C}{\sin T} = \frac{989.221 \times 0.98511}{0.10279} = 9480.41 \ \text{Ft.} = c'$$

CONCLUSION: Distance From A to the Water Tower is 9480 Ft.
Distance From C to the Water Tower is 9600 Ft.

Fig. 12-14. A simple triangulation problem.

be impossible. Station *tower*, however, is not in view from point *B*. In other words, the base line was laid out along a route where an accurate measurement could be made rather than choosing the base so that the inaccessible point was visible from both ends of it. Figure 12-14 indicates that in measuring the base line the slope distance was measured, then corrected for temperature, and finally reduced to the correct horizontal distance. This necessitates level readings to determine the elevation of the ends of the tape at each segment of the measurement.

The problem is solved by forming the two triangles and computing the required distances. Where the computation becomes more extensive, the orderly tabulation of both the basic data and the results is essential. Figure 12-14 shows one method of arranging the computations and summary of the solution for this problem.

Steps for the entire problem may be outlined as follows: (1) measurement of the baseline *A–B*; (2) measurement of angles *B–A–C*, *C–A–T*, *T–A–B*, *A–B–C*, *C–B–A*, *B–C–T*, *T–C–A*, *A–C–B*; angles shown represent the mean of angles turned six times; (3) computation of angle *A–T–C*; (4) summation of the appropriate angles as shown on the figure to provide a check; adjustment of the angles to meet theoretical conditions before the distances computations for unmeasured sides are made; (5) computation of *auxiliary baseline*, *A–C*; (6) calculation of sides of the triangle containing the inaccessible point by means of the law of sines.

This particular geometrical layout was selected to illustrate the point of *strength of figure* in triangulation work. The interior angles in any system of figures used in triangulation should be between 30 and 150 degrees for accurate results. In this example the computed angle at station T (tower) is definitely out of these limits. The reader should vary the value of this angle slightly and recompute the distances *A*–tower and *C*–tower. This will indicate the relative effect when small angles are involved.

PROBLEMS

1. Compute the area to the nearest square foot for the traverse shown. Tabulate all data. Latitudes and departures are in feet.

Course	Balanced	
	Latitude	Departure
A–B	25.0 (N)	100.0 (E)
B–C	100.0 (S)	25.0 (E)
C–D	25.0 (S)	100.0 (W)
D–A	100.0 (N)	25.0 (W)

2. Compute area by the D.M.D. method for the following traverse. Make two calculations, one in which latitudes and departures are balanced by compass rule and the other in which balancing is by transit rule. Compute the precision of the survey.

Station	Angle-Lt	Distance	Bearing
1	90°00′	601.0	Due E
2	90°00′	302.0	Due S
3	150°00′	500.0	S 30°00′ W
4	76°35′	483.0	N 46°35′ W
5	133°25′	400.0	Due N

Note: Excessive error of closure will show difference between the methods of balancing.

3. Given the following data, compute length and bearing of *E–A*.

Station	Bearing	Distance
A–B	N 45°00′ E	1,000.00 ft
B–C	S 60°10′ E	105.26
C–D	N 32°25′ W	5,205.55
D–E	S 31°21′ W	2,323.75

4. Given the data shown and the fact that line *C–A* bears N 47°10′ E, place data in a complete form of field notes. Compute area of traverse by D.M.D. method placing data in tabular form.

Points	Angle	Distance
C–A–B	90°01′	52.10 ft
B–C–A	15°00′	195.21
A–B–C	75°00′	202.22

5. Compute the area of the traverse given. Use either the D.M.D. or coordinate method.

Station	Bearing	Distance
1–2	S 86°17′ W	267.23 ft
2–3	N 14°57′ W	228.15
3–4	N 00°54′ E	261.72
4–5	S 89°48′ E	134.53
5–6	S 02°03′ E	230.43
6–7	S 85°04′ E	174.45
7–8	S 01°18′ E	219.07

6. What is the purpose of balancing the angles, and latitudes and departures of a closed traverse?

7. Compute the area of the following closed traverse:

Line	Bearing	Distance
11–12	N 80°30′ W	465.25
12–13	N 16°27′ E	295.32
13–14	S 72°09′ E	259.33
14–15	N 77°10′ E	187.01
15–11	S 09°30′ W	326.63

8. The latitudes and departures of the sides of a triangular plot of land are given below. If the area of parcel is divided into two equal areas by a line running through point *A*, what is the bearing of this line?

Side	Latitude	Departure
A–B	N 200	E 100
B–C	S 300	E 100
C–A	N 100	W 200

9. Compute the area of the following closed traverses:

	TRAVERSE *A*		TRAVERSE *B*		TRAVERSE *C*	
Line	*Length*	*Bearing*	*Length*	*Bearing*	*Length*	*Bearing*
11–12	245.78	N 11°30′ W	450.96	N 07°47′ W	177.19	N 21°59′ W
12–13	186.92	N 10°57′ W	695.20	N 83°26′ E	226.20	N 13°00′ W
13–14	321.19	N 78°50′ E	247.50	S 06°00′ E	335.04	N 79°32′ E
14–15	371.26	N 78°26′ E	197.68	S 06°44′ E	381.41	N 78°51′ E
15–16	438.86	S 11°00′ E	323.87	S 83°00′ W	395.46	S 10°55′ E
16–11	690.55	S 79°05′ W	359.86	S 82°56′ W	674.14	S 78°48′ W

Chapter 13

~~~~~~

TOPOGRAPHIC SURVEYING

THE BASIC purpose of the topographic map, in addition to locating rivers, lakes, towns, houses, roads, and property lines, is to indicate the three dimensional relationships for the terrain of any given area of land. This is accomplished by the use of contour lines, color, shading, hachure marks, and relief models. The latter show the three dimensions to scale. In all of the others the relationship of elevations is symbolized. The use of contour lines in engineering has far exceeded the other methods.

Procedures for gathering information and presenting it in the form of a topographic map will be discussed as well as the uses of topographic maps in engineering.

Topographic maps may be classified according to the scale used in their preparation. The precision of the survey is determined by the scale and the principal use for which the map is intended. The classification includes large scale, intermediate scale, and small scale maps, for which the scales are: 1 inch equals 100 feet or less; 1 inch equals 100 feet to 1,000 feet; and 1 inch equals 1,000 feet and over.

13-1. Horizontal control. The contour lines on the map are based on a series of measurements made in the field. These measurements must be made with some basic framework to which to tie the detailed topographic data. For this reason, a horizontal control is necessary for all information gathered in the survey. This control is often provided by the use of a transit and tape traverse. The traverse provides the framework for the collection of topographic data. The precision of the traverse must be consistent with the desired precision of the finished topographic map. A good procedure is to select traverse points which are of value in locating and plotting the topographic data. If these points are easily identifiable on the ground, the making of ties and correlation with aerial photographs will be facilitated. For example, these points may be ends of ridge lines, tops of hills, or beginnings of valleys; or points near man-made features such as telephone lines, roads, or buildings.

Horizontal control for topographic maps is basically the same as the horizontal control discussed in Chapter 9. The control for small areas may be tied together by the use of coordinates. The control will be of more value if a standard system such as state plane coordinates is used. See Article 9-15.

13-2. Vertical control. Vertical control establishes a framework in which to plot elevation differences. This control is very important since the topographic map must indicate the relief or third dimension. Vertical control is discussed in Article 9-3.

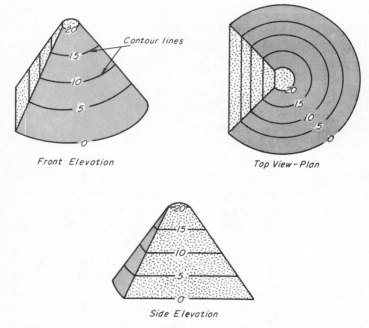

Fig. 13-1. Contour lines.

13-3. Contours. A contour is an imaginary line on the ground connecting points of equal elevation. Each contour line represents a given elevation and is drawn on the topographic map to accurately locate in plan all points having that elevation. Contour lines have certain characteristics. They must not touch each other or cross on the map except when representing a vertical or overhanging cliff. They are continuous within the limits of the map. When a contour crosses a stream, its representation will point upstream. The space between plotted contour lines indicates the slope of the ground in that section of the terrain. Figure 13-1 shows how contour lines follow around a hill, each staying at its own elevation. Now looking at the hill from above we see in the same figure the contours, represented on the two dimensional surface of a map. A typical contour map is shown in Figure 2-3. The addition of natural and man-made features such as trees, marshes, buildings, roads, and so on, located

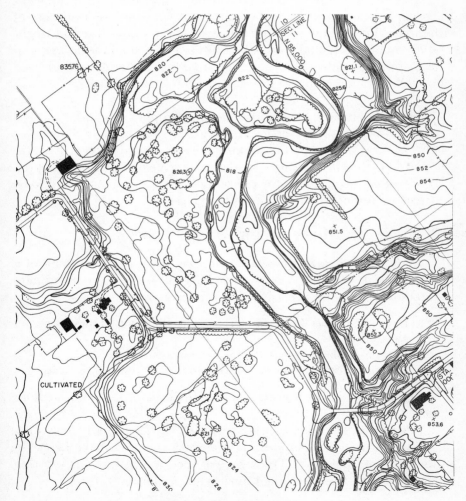

Fig. 13-2. A topographic map.

in plan makes the complete topographic map as shown in Figure 13-2. Some of the characteristics of contour lines are:

1. A uniform spacing between contours indicates a uniform slope of the terrain.
2. All contour lines close upon themselves either on or off the map.
3. The summit of a hill or the floor of a valley will be represented by a closed contour line on the map, unless it is located too near the edge of the sheet.
4. The horizontal distance between contour lines is proportional to the slope of the terrain.

The contour interval is the vertical distance between adjacent contours. The interval selected varies with the intended purpose of the map. For a large scale map in flat country, the interval might be as small as one-half foot. The interval for small scale maps of rough terrain might be in the order of 50 feet. The interval utilized in much of engineering work falls between 2 and 10 feet.

13-4. Accuracy. The allowable error in plan should be consistent with the allowable error in elevation. For topographic maps, one specification is that the permissible error in position of features in plan is to be within $\frac{1}{40}$ inch at final map scale of their true position. By the same specification, 90 per cent of all map elevations are to be correct within one-half of the contour interval.

METHODS OF OBTAINING CONTOURS

13–5. Coordinate system. In order to plot the contours of a given area of terrain, it is possible to utilize a grid or coordinate system. The general procedure is as follows:

1. Lay out the area on a grid system by establishing corner and perimeter stakes.
2. Determine elevations at the intersections of the grid lines.
3. Plot the points of known elevation to the desired scale in plan.

Figure 13-3 shows a grid layout with three of the contour lines plotted.

Starting at the edge of the area, each of the contour lines may be traced through the appropriate elevations which have been obtained by interpolation. The degree of accuracy attained in plotting will depend on the care taken during interpolation.

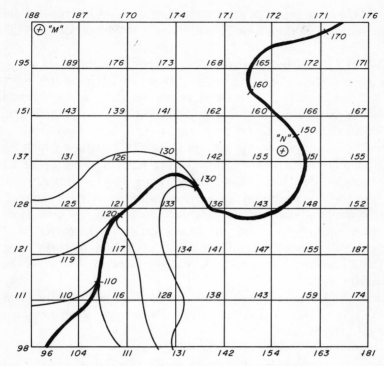

Fig. 13-3. Contours by coordinate system.

13-6. Trace contour method. Perhaps the most accurate procedure for locating contours is by the *trace contour method*, which has the advantage of accuracy, but the disadvantage of requiring more time in the field. The system consists of a series of shots taken along the same contour line from successive setups of the instrument. For example, if the transit and stadia rod are used, the instrument is set up in one location near the elevation of the contour to be traced. The height of instrument is obtained by means of a backsight to a station of known elevation. With this information, the rod reading is computed when the rod is on the contour to be traced. The rodman is then sent out along the general path that the contour will take. Points on the contour are found by trial. The location of points where the rod is held are determined by angle and stadia distance. In this manner, the entire length of the contour line may be traced out. The contour line is usually traced to the limit of vision and then the next contour line in the area is pursued until all the lines possible are taken from the one instrument setup. The instrument is then moved ahead and another section is worked.

13-7. Controlling points. The system with the most universal application is the controlling point system. Its basic principle is that the easily seen and easily defined points on the terrain will form a framework in which additional information may be placed or upon which interpolation may be made with confidence. Specifically, the controlling points are the points on the earth's surface which designate a change in the general slope of the terrain. The top of a hill, the ends of a ridge line, the beginning of a gully, the line of a valley floor, the top of a curb and the corresponding gutter are some of the places where the slope of the terrain changes. If the elevations of these locations are obtained, the configuration of the earth's surface can be shown in consistent detail. The advantage of this system is that the amount of detail gathered can easily be modified to provide the desired result.

As in the other systems, the instruments used to gather the information may be the transit with stadia or taped distances, or the plane table and alidade.

13-8. Cross profile. The *cross profile* method is a modification of the cross sectioning used in route surveys. Principally, it is used to define contours along a route or other narrow area of terrain. Data for plotting contours are obtained by determining elevations at points of changing ground slope on both sides of a center line. These points are then located in the horizontal plane. Another method of cross profiling is to locate the calculated rod reading for each contour. These points are located by trial and the distance is measured to each one.

13-9. Aerial photographs. During recent years the use of aerial photographs in the construction of topographic maps has expanded rapidly. With the equipment available, contours may be plotted from aerial photographs of the terrain with a minimum of ground survey for control. The advantages of this system are (1) reduction in cost by decreasing the required field work and (2) the obtaining of a photographic representation of the details of the area. See Chapter 14.

STADIA

The stadia method of surveying is a quick and efficient means of measuring distance, used extensively in topographic and other surveys. It is faster than taping and is often sufficiently accurate.

The stadia method determines distance by relative rod intercepts obtained by telescope and graduated rod as explained in Article 4-2. An ordinary level rod may be used. However, stadia rods or stadia boards as shown in Figure 13-4 are easier to read.

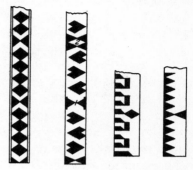

Fig. 13-4. Some types of stadia rods.

13-10. Stadia principle. Figure 13-5 indicates the basic principle of the stadia method. The stadia hairs are shown as points a and b; the distance between the hairs is i. The positions of the two stadia hairs on the stadia rod are A and B. The corresponding observed interval (rod intercept) is I. From

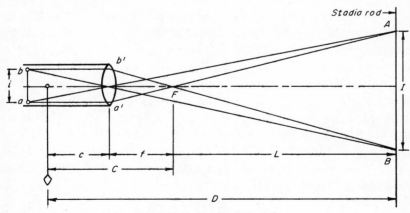

Fig. 13-5. Stadia principle.

a consideration of optics, it is apparent that the parallel rays starting from the stadia hairs, a and b, and passing through both the optical center and the principal focus of the lens results in the triangle shown. Since points a and A, and b and B are the conjugate foci and their distances from the optical center of the object measured along the optical axis are the conjugate focal distances, it may be shown that ab is equal to $a'b'$ and f/i is equal to L/I. The relationship f/i is a coefficient termed the *stadia interval factor* and is designated by the letter K. The stadia interval factor for any given instrument remains constant. The horizontal distance from the center of the instrument to the stadia rod may be computed by the following formula:

$$D = KI + (f + c) = KI + C$$

where C is the distance from the center of the instrument to principal focus. The value of C is composed of the focal distance f, which remains constant, and the distance c, which varies with the position of the objective. The distance c varies such a small amount that essentially it may be considered a constant. One foot is an approximate value of C for external focusing instruments. If the telescope is internal focusing, the value of C is either zero or small enough to be neglected.

Occasionally the engineer will need to use an instrument with an unknown stadia interval factor. Although this factor is usually 100, the interval factor should be checked by direct observation by measuring distances of 100 to 500 feet, usually in 100-foot increments, from the principal focus of the instrument. The stadia rod is then held over each position and the stadia interval read. The stadia interval factor may be determined by dividing the distance from the principal focus to each station by the corresponding stadia interval (*rod intercept*).

When making a reading of the stadia interval (vertical distance between stadia hairs as it appears on the rod), place the lower stadia hair on an even foot mark and make the stadia interval reading from the top stadia cross-hair. This will result in a more direct reading and reduce the possibility of a mistake. When feasible, to avoid the effect of heat waves, the reading on the lower stadia hair should not be made close to the ground.

13-11. Inclined sights. In actual practice, a stadia measurement often cannot be made as a horizontal measurement. When the line of sight is not horizontal, a correction must be applied to the observed distance in order to obtain the horizontal distance. Reference to Figure 13-6 indicates the principles involved in making an inclined stadia measurement. The reading $A-B$ indicated on the rod is too great, since the line of sight is not perpendicular to the rod.

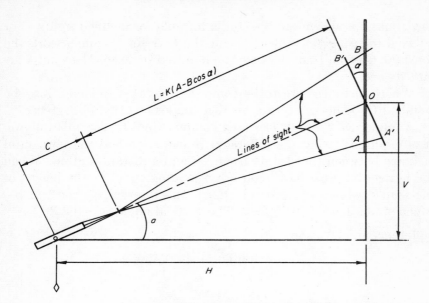

Fig. 13-6. Inclined sight to stadia rod.

If the line A'–B' is drawn perpendicular to the line of sight, the angle A'–O–A will be equal to the vertical angle of inclination of the telescope (a). Since the angle between the line passing through the principal focus and intercepting the points A'–B' is quite small, the line A'–B' may be considered to be at right angles to the line of sight with no appreciable error. The distance A'–B', which would be intercepted on the rod if the rod were held perpendicular to the line of sight, is then equal to A–B cos a. The distance from the center of the instrument to the intersection of the line of sight with the rod equal $K(A$–$B \cos a) + C$. The horizontal component of this inclined distance is

$$H = K(A\text{–}B \cos^2 a) + C \cos a$$

Replace A–B, the rod intercept, by I and

$$H = K(I \cos^2 a) + C \cos a \tag{13-1}$$

This is the expression for obtaining the horizontal distance from the center of the instrument to the intersection of the center of the line of sight with the stadia rod. The vertical component

$$V = KI \cos a \sin a + (C \sin a)$$

may be restated

$$V = \tfrac{1}{2}KI \sin 2a + (C \sin a) \tag{13-2}$$

The equations shown are the stadia formula for inclined sights. For internal focusing instruments, omit the C term. In much work the constant C is omitted, because the required precision does not warrant its use.

Where distances are to be computed to feet the sights may be assumed to be horizontal for vertical angles less than 3 degrees.

A numerical example of stadia computations by formula follows. It is required to find the difference in elevation and the horizontal distance between the station occupied and a distant station. When the horizontal cross-hair is on a rod reading equal to the height of the transit above the ground (H.I.), the interval on the rod between stadia hairs is 6.25 feet. The vertical angle is $-(02°30')$.

Difference in elevation:

$$V = \tfrac{1}{2}\ 100(6.25)\ \sin 05°00'$$
$$= 27.2 \text{ ft}$$

Horizontal distance:

$$H = 100(6.25)(\cos 02°30')^2$$
$$= 625 \text{ ft}$$

If, in the above example, the H.I. were 5.00, but the horizontal cross-hair were set at 8.00 feet on the rod, the difference in elevation would be computed as before, but on the basis of a larger·vertical angle. This result would then have to be reduced by the quantity $8.00 - 5.00$ to get the difference in elevation of the ground points.

13-12. Stadia reduction. In practice, it is inconvenient to use the formula expressed in Article 13-11. Most engineers turn to the use of tables, diagrams, Beaman's stadia arc, the stadia slide rule, or a self-reducing device built into the transit or alidade telescope.

Table A in the appendix shows the horizontal and vertical distances for a stadia distance of 100 feet at vertical angles up to 30°.

One convenient method of directly reading the horizontal and vertical distance is by use of the Beaman stadia arc. This device, attached to the vertical circle of the transit or alidade is graduated in per cent of slope to give readings for the direct computation of vertical and horizontal distance from the rod intercept.

The stadia slide rule has the usual scale of numbers consisting of the logarithms of the distances. In addition, there is one scale having values of log cos² a and another having values of log $\frac{1}{2}$ sin $2a$. The rule provides a rapid means of stadia reduction for obtaining horizontal and vertical distance from rod intercepts taken at any angle, with sufficiently accurate results for most purposes.

The self-reducing stadia instrument is of European design. Readings are made on a vertical rod. However, in addition to two short conventional stadia lines, two pairs of curved lines appear in the field of view of the telescope. The outer pair of lines are curved in accordance with the expression cos² a, and the inner pair in accordance with the expression sin a cos a. An arrangement of prisms within the telescope rotates, causing these lines to be automatically adjusted to the proper spacing for the vertical angle being sighted. Thus, the corrected vertical and horizontal distance for inclined sights can be obtained directly by noting the interval on the rod intercepted by the appropriate pair of curved lines and multiplying this value by a constant.

13-13. Errors. The more common errors in stadia surveys are caused by: (1) incorrect stadia interval, the instrumentman not having observed the stadia interval correctly; (2) use of a rod having inaccurate graduations; (3) a rodman not holding the rod plumb, thus giving incorrect observed stadia interval; and (4) a systematic error, introduced in the readings when the stadia interval factor has been assumed and not checked.

13-14. Precision. In making single observations for distances of 100 to 1,500 feet, a precision of 1/500 can be obtained if the vertical angles are relatively small and care is exercised in plumbing the rod. If vertical angles are read to the nearest five minutes, the precision for elevation determination is approximately one foot of elevation per 1,000 feet horizontal distance.

PLANE TABLE SURVEYS

13-15. Plane table. The plane table is composed of a drawing board mounted on a tripod so that it can be set up in the field and leveled. Observations are made by an instrument called the *alidade*. The plane table must be mounted on a tripod which allows rotation of the board in the horizontal plane after leveling.

Figure 13-7 shows a plane table in use. The instrument through which the observer is looking is the alidade.

Fig. 13-7. A plane table in use.

13-16. Alidades. The alidade is a combination of a straight edge and a sighting device. The simplest form is the *triangular boxwood scale*. The operator sights along the top edge of the scale and draws the line of sight along the side of the scale. Slightly more refined is the *peep-sight alidade*, consisting of peep-sights mounted on a straight edge so that the line of sight is parallel to the straight edge. Finally there is the engineer's alidade with its transit-type telescope mounted on a straight edge. This telescope may be rotated in a vertical plane to measure vertical angles. See Figure 13-7.

13-17. Use of the plane table. In the use of the plane table, the table must be set up, leveled, and oriented with care. The table, if set up at waist height, will allow the surveyor to bend over it easily without leaning on any part of it. For small scale maps, the map point representing the station occupied need not be set exactly over the station on the ground. In large scale maps, however, the exact point on the map must be placed over the station on the ground by use of a plumb-bob.

The orientation of the plane table is generally accomplished by sighting on points of known location. The board may be oriented by reference to magnetic north, using a compass attached to the alidade. The use of the magnetic needle, however, is usually restricted to small scale, rough mapping.

Orientation by backsighting is done by sighting along a line previously plotted on the board. The plane table is set up over one end of the line and leveled. The alidade is then placed along the plotted line on the table; the entire board is rotated until the first station appears in the telescope, and the orientation is complete.

Orientation by the *three point problem* is possible when the station to be occupied has not yet been located on the map. There must be, however, three visible stations which have been located on the map. With the three known points and the use of resection (Article 13-23), it is possible by a trial process to locate the occupied station on the map.

When only two stations are visible from the occupied, unlocated station, the *two point problem* must be used. This consists of making observations on the two visible stations from two locations near the desired station. From the information obtained, it is possible to orient the table and to locate the occupied station.

13-18. Topographic detail. After the board has been set up and oriented, the topographic detail is collected by one of the following means: radiation, traversing, intersection, resection, three point problem, and two point problem.

13-19. Radiation. With the table located at one station, details of the surrounding terrain may be obtained by rotating the alidade around the plotted position of the occupied station. Sights are taken on the objects to be plotted and a ray or line is drawn along the straight edge toward the object. A succession of such rays from the occupied station with stadia readings to points sighted will define the position of items to be located.

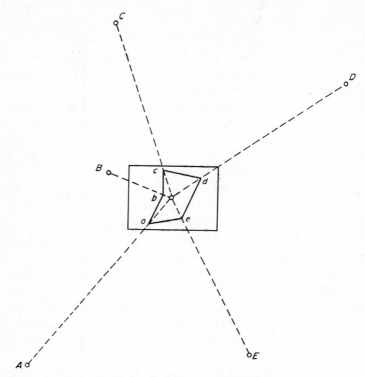

Fig. 13-8. Principle of radiation with plane table.

When the distance has been determined, the point is plotted on the ray at the scale of the map. Figure 13-8 illustrates this principle.

13-20. Traversing. The topographic details may also be determined by traversing from station to station with the plane table. Figure 13-9 illustrates the process by which the table is moved successively from station one to station five to form a completed traverse.

By the application of radiation at each of the stations, additional information could be obtained. In the figure, the board might be oriented by magnetic compass at station one. Rays are then drawn to stations five and two. With the table set at station two, the board is oriented by backsighting to station one. This process is followed through the balance of the traverse. The dotted lines on the figure represent sights taken to check the accuracy of the traverse at stations other than at the adjacent stations.

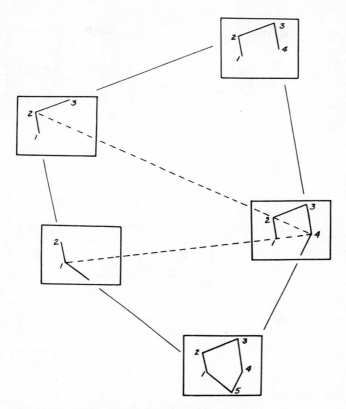

Fig. 13-9. A plane table traverse.

13-21. Intersection. By means of intersection, topographic detail may be completed on stations not actually occupied. This is done by sighting on the same station from two different stations. The intersection of the constructed rays represents the location of the desired stations on the board. The principle is the same as the checks shown in Figure 13-9. Figure 13-10 shows how this information may be used in the location of the stations three, four, and five, which are inaccessible. The use of intersection combined with resection is graphical triangulation.

13-22. Resection. Resection, Figure 13-11, is used to locate the position on the map of an occupied station. The process requires that the board be oriented, and backsights taken with the alidade. The straight edge is placed so that it passes through the plotted

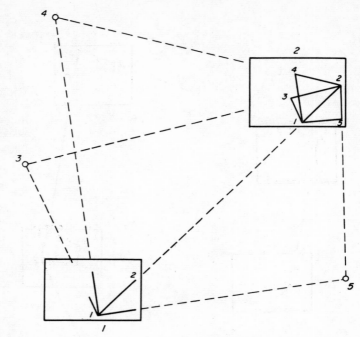

Fig. 13-10. Location of stations by intersection.

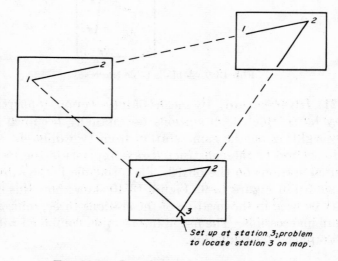

Set up at station 3; problem
to locate station 3 on map.

Fig. 13-11. Location of station by resection.

location of the point being sighted. A ray of indefinite length is drawn along this direction. The process is repeated for another station of known location and the intersection of the two rays locates the occupied station.

13-23. Profiles from contour maps. One convenient feature of the contour map is that the profile of any cross section on the map may be determined from it. If the profile of the line 1-2, shown

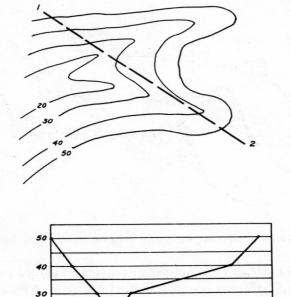

Fig. 13-12. A profile from a contour map.

in Figure 13-12, is to be plotted, the elevations for the intersections of that line and the contour lines may be plotted on the profile sheet as shown. This process provides information that can be used in the determination of grades and in estimating earthwork quantities for any construction along line 1-2.

13-24. Earthwork quantities. There are two convenient methods for estimating earthwork quantities by use of contour maps. One is by use of the profile as discussed in the previous article to obtain adjacent end areas and thereby the volume of earthwork (see

Article 15-12). The other method is by comparison of existing contours of the surface concerned with contours of the desired surface plotted on the same map.

The horizontal planes formed by the adjacent contours provide the information for the estimation of the earthwork. In Figure 13-13 the existing contours are shown as solid lines and the desired contours by dashed lines.

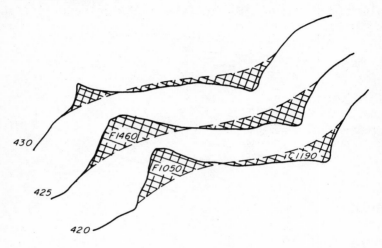

Fig. 13-13. Estimating earthwork volumes from contour lines.

The cross-hatched areas represent horizontal planes bounded by the corresponding existing and proposed contours. The area designated as F 1,050 sq ft indicates that the area between these two contours at elevation 420 feet is 1,050 square feet, and it is in fill. The volume of the fill between these contours and the next pair at elevation 425 feet would be approximately equal to the contour interval, 5 feet, multiplied by $(1,050 + 1,460)/2$.

When the cut or fill runs out between contours, the volume from the last section to the point of zero cut or fill will be a pyramid.

PROBLEMS

1. Plot Figure 13-3 and draw in the remainder of the contours. Plot profile of line "*M*"-"*N*".

2. Compute the difference in elevation and the horizontal distance between Station *A* and the following points in a stadia survey. Assume $f + c = 1$.

Station	Rod interval	Vertical angle
Inst. at A		
B	2.50 ft	01°23′
C	7.63	04°17′
D	5.20 (half stad.)	15°55′
E	5.60 (half stad.)	02°42′
F	7.63	10°52′

Use stadia formulas for computing. All readings to H.I. (5.0 feet).

3. Same as Problem two except use stadia reduction tables to obtain results.

4. Solve for Station *B* in Problem two if horizontal cross-hair is at 2.00 feet on the rod. Solve for Station *D* if it is at the 6.00-foot point.

5. Given rectangular area 5,280 by 2,640 feet, elevation at center of area 542 feet, elevation of corners *A*, *B*, *C*, *D* being 205, 306, 698 and, 411 feet, respectively. Plot contours at 10-foot intervals. The line *A–B* equals 5,280 feet.

Chapter 14

~~~~~~

AERIAL SURVEYING

THE STUDY of terrain features and conditions by aerial photography has developed from a limited military beginning until its use today to expedite a variety of engineering work.

The terms *aerial photography, aerial surveying,* and *aerial photogrammetry* are used synonymously to designate the taking of photographs from the air, showing a portion of the earth's surface.

Aerial cameras are mounted in the aircraft so that in flight the axis of the lens is vertical or at a known angle of obliquity. The exposure is made through an opening in the plane's fusilage. Figure 14-1 shows an aerial camera mounted in a plastic-nosed plane.

In terrestrial photogrammetry, the forerunner of aerial photogrammetry, photographs of the same area are taken from different camera ground stations with the axis of the camera lens approximately horizontal, and the cameras mounted on tripods. From the companion photographs the relationship of points in both the horizontal and vertical planes can be determined. Control angles are measured by a theodolite mounted on top of the camera (*phototheodolite*) or by a theodolite which replaces the camera on the tripod.

A French army officer, Capt. A. Laussedat, first conceived the possibilities of photogrammetry. In 1851 he compiled map data from measurements taken from photographs. A Canadian named Deville took stereoscopic pairs of photographs with a phototheodolite nearly fifty years later and devised a way of drawing maps from these photographs.

The coming of the airplane provided an ideal situation for camera position, but aerial photography has the disadvantage of not permitting the direct determination of the length of base between two different camera positions as done in the case of terrestrial photogrammetry. In addition, the problem arises of variation in (1) camera altitude, (2) elevation of ground points, and (3) angle of exposure of the photographs.

Fig. 14-1. Camera installation in the nose of a special plane. (Courtesy Abrams Aerial Survey Corp.)

The solutions to these problems were begun during World War I with the development of instruments and techniques to make the use of aerial photographs practicable for mapping purposes. Developments have continued until now, with proper ground control, aerial surveys will yield precise mapping data.

The requirements of the National Map Accuracy Standards, which have been adopted by many agencies as specifications for maps made from aerial photographs, call for 90 per cent of all map elevations to be correct within one-half the contour interval. For horizontal position the requirement is that all well defined map features be within $\frac{1}{40}$ inch at final map scale of their true position. These limits are known as *standard map accuracy* for maps plotted by photogrammetric methods and procedures. They can be satisfied in open areas, but where trees, shadows, or other objects partially obscure ground detail, the requirements must be lowered in order to be met.

Improvements in aerial equipment, materials, and techniques by research and experience have developed with the discovery of new uses and requirements for aerial photography. Camera lenses have been improved to reduce distortion, with the ultimate goal a lens free from distortion. Roll film to replace the earlier glass plates has simplified the photographing operation. The disadvantage of unequal distortion caused by film shrinkage has been largely overcome by the development of a more stable film base. Glass plates are still used, however, when dimensional stability of the negative is of extreme importance.

In the office, the development of techniques and equipment for rectifying negatives for tilt, and the utilization of stereo views to produce the third dimension has increased the accuracy of horizontal and vertical distance determinations from aerial photographs.

14-1. Lenses for aerial cameras. Figure 14-2 shows schematically the principle of the aerial camera lens. The distance from

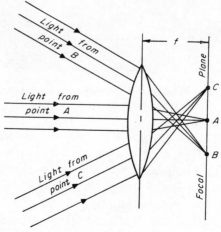

Fig. 14-2. Light rays from a distant point passing through a lens.

camera to ground is so large in comparison to the lens diameter that light rays from an object on the ground are essentially parallel as they reach the lens and meet to form the image at the focal plane of the lens. The distance from the lens to its focal plane is fixed.

That is, aerial cameras are of fixed focus rather than being focused for object distance as in the case of ordinary cameras.

The rays of light from the distant objects *a*, *b*, and *c*, Figure 14-2, are refracted through the lens and theoretically meet at its focal plane. The focal plane is behind the lens a distance equal to the focal length *f* of the lens. The focal length is also known as the *principal distance*.

The failure of a lens to refract light rays so that they meet in a point at a distance *f* behind the lens is known as *aberration*, and produces a blurred and distorted image.

To reduce aberration, lenses are made up of several pieces of glass, each one having a slightly different index of refraction. Thus, the simple lens shown in Figure 14-2 is not the type found in aerial cameras.

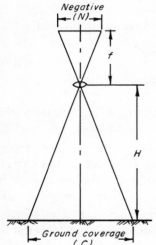

Fig. 14-3. Relationship between ground coverage and other factors.

The principal requirements for a good aerial camera lens are (1) speed, i.e., ability to admit enough light to permit a short exposure time; (2) freedom from significant aberration; and (3) a wide angle of coverage.

The principal distance or focal length of the lenses used in aerial cameras varies from 4 to 24 inches, with the average being about 8 inches. Figure 14-3 shows the relationship between focal length of lens, camera elevation above an assumed horizontal reference plane, and the size of the negative being exposed.

14-2. Types of aerial photographs.

Photographs taken from the air may be classified as vertical, oblique, or composite. The first of these is taken with the axis of the camera as nearly vertical as practicable and presents a picture of the ground corresponding to a map. It covers less area for a given camera lens and camera altitude than either of the other types.

The oblique photograph is taken with the camera axis out of the vertical by some predetermined amount, causing a scale distortion as shown in Figure 14-4; greater coverage is obtained than by a vertical exposure.

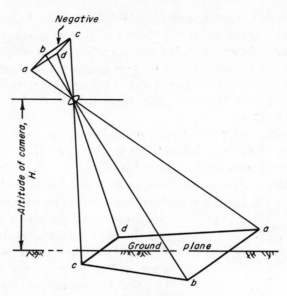

Fig. 14-4. Oblique photograph.

An oblique negative can be rectified by projecting it onto a horizontal plane by a special camera called a *transforming printer*. This has the same effect as stretching one edge of the square or rectangular negative until it has the same shape as the ground area covered by the oblique photograph. This procedure, called *rectifying*, produces a true scale on the rectified photograph, neglecting the effect of ground point elevation differences, or tilt of the camera from its assumed position at time of exposure. Negatives may also be rectified for tilt by first computing the angle of tilt.

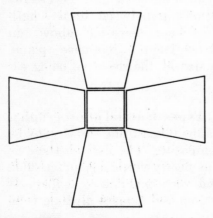

Fig. 14-5. Outline of vertical print surrounded by four rectified prints.

A composite photograph is made up of a vertical and a group of oblique photographs, or of a group of oblique photographs. These are made simultaneously with a camera having several lenses. Figure 14-5 shows the shape of a rectified composite photograph.

14-3. Cameras. The simplest type of aerial camera is the *single-lens* camera. It has no basic variation from an ordinary camera, although to produce photographs suitable for mapping purposes it must conform to rigid specifications.

When more coverage is desired than can be obtained with a single-lens camera, a group of lenses with properly related angles of obliquity are mounted in one frame. These cameras are called *multiple-lens* cameras. They produce the composite photographs discussed in the preceding article.

The number of lenses in a multi-lens camera depends upon the coverage desired, although there is a practical upper limit. The complexity of construction is increased with each additional lens, but an increase of lenses reduces the amount of ground control required for plotting and the amount of flying necessary to cover a given area.

Captain Theodore Scheimpflug constructed a multiple-lens camera in Austria in 1904, but the first one to be extensively used was developed in 1918 by Major James W. Bagley, Corps of Engineers, U. S. Army, and had three lenses.

Cameras with four and five lenses are extensively used and the U. S. Coast and Geodetic Survey has constructed and used a nine-lens camera.

Another type of camera known as the *Sonne Continuous Strip* aerial camera was developed about 1950. It is intended for aerial surveys made for obtaining a continuous, large-scale photograph of strips of terrain.

In using this camera the aircraft is flown at low altitude and high speed. The film is drawn across a narrow slit in a light barrier located just in front of the focal plane of the lens. The film moves at the same velocity as that at which the image crosses the focal plane. The result is a strip of exposed negative of any desired length which has no *skips* or *overlaps*, all of which has been exposed vertically.

14-4. Determining ground coverage and scale. Aerial cameras are so constructed that the focal plane of the lens is in coincidence with the plane of the film. For all practical purposes the necessary relationships for determining coverage and scale can be obtained by considering the focal length f of the lens to represent the distance between the lens and the film.

Figure 14-6 shows the relationship between the negative, the camera lens, and any plane being photographed. Let H represent

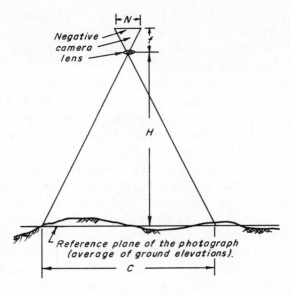

Fig. 14-6

the height of the camera lens above this plane, and f the focal length
of the camera. If the dimension of the negative is N, the distance C,
covered on the plane being photographed, is determined by the ratio

$$\frac{f}{H} = \frac{N}{C} \tag{14-1}$$

From this relationship it follows that the ratio of the size of the
negative to the size of the area photographed is f/H. This is one
means of expressing scale. That is, if $f = 10$ inches and the camera
lens is 7,000 feet above a plane being photographed, the picture scale
will be 0.833/7,000. This is expressed as a scale of 1 to 8,400.

The scale may also be expressed as the distance, in feet, on the
photographed plane represented by 1 inch on the negative. If the
ratio of Equation (14-1) is revised on this basis, we have

$$\frac{f}{H} = \frac{1}{12S} \tag{14-2}$$

in which S represents the scale. The scale relationship by this ratio
is 1 inch $= H/12f$. The scale in the preceding example then is
1 inch $= 700$ feet.

The relationships outlined are true only when all of the area
being photographed lies in the same horizontal plane, which is never

the case, of course, when the earth's surface is being photographed.

In many instances a satisfactory approximate scale may be obtained by assuming that all photographed points lie in a reference plane located at an elevation equal to the mean elevation of the area being photographed.

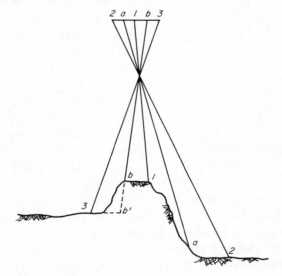

Fig. 14-7. Distances 2*a*, *a*1, 1*b*, and *b*3 are all equal on the negative. The distances they represent on the ground are variable.

Figure 14-7 shows how photograph scale is affected by variations in ground elevation.

To compute the ground coverage per photograph, the relationship expressed in the ratio presented in Equation (14-1) is used. For example, if the camera has a principal distance of 8 inches and a 7- by 9-inch negative, the ground coverage for an H of 8,000 feet will be 8,000(0.75)/0.667, or 9,000 feet in the 9-inch direction on the negative. The coverage in the 7-inch direction on the negative will be 8,000(0.583)/0.667, or 7,000 feet.

14-5. Overlap. To insure complete coverage, there should be some overlap of the area covered by each aerial photograph when more than one is taken in succession. Furthermore, when topographic mapping is to be done from the photographs, there must be sufficient overlap along the flight line (*end overlap*) to make stereoscopic viewing possible.

The perception of depth or relief is obtained by simultaneously viewing, through a stereoscope, two overlapping photographs which show the same objects taken from different camera viewpoints.

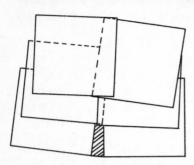

Fig. 14-8. Cross-hatched area not covered photographically because of insufficient side overlap.

The greater the overlap the less will be the relief, or three dimensional effect. An overlap of 60 per cent will give a slightly exaggerated relief, but is widely used in photographing flat to rolling terrain.

The overlap of photographs from two adjacent flight strips (*side overlap*) varies from 10 to 40 per cent, depending upon the purpose of the project and upon whether the aircraft has equipment to keep it automatically on flight lines parallel throughout their length.

Without special equipment it is difficult for a pilot to fly a straight course. Insufficient side overlap might then result in a pattern of coverage as shown in Figure 14-8.

When the desired amount of picture overlap has been determined, the computation of distance between exposures along a flight line and the distance between flight lines may be computed for any given camera altitude by again considering Equation (14-1).

Suppose a camera with a 9- by 9-inch negative and a 9-inch principal distance is to be used at an altitude of 9,000 feet above the terrain being photographed. For a 40 per cent overlap the distance between flight lines on the scale of the negative would then be $9 - (0.4 \times 9)$, or 5.4 inches. On the ground this would be $9,000(5.4)/12(0.75)$, or 5,400 feet between flight lines.

The distance between exposures for 60 per cent overlap would be $9 - (0.6 \times 9)$, or 3.6 inches on the negative. This would represent 3,600 feet on the ground.

The desired side overlap is obtained by the spacing of flight lines. The desired end overlap is obtained either with a *view finder* or an *intervalometer*.

A view finder is optically designed to cover the same image as the camera negative. Lines are drawn on it at the desired interval (3.6 inches in the example just given). An exposure is made when an object on the ground coincides with the first line, another when the same object coincides with the second line, and so on.

An *intervalometer* is used to properly space the exposures. This consists essentially of a timing device which makes exposures at constant time intervals, based on the speed of the aircraft. For example, at 60 per cent overlap the time interval is such that during it the camera will have traveled a distance equal to 40 per cent of the ground coverage of the camera at that altitude of flight.

In taking photographs, the film is passed across the focal plate of the camera by winding it from one spool to another. The portion of the film to be exposed for one photograph is held flat by pressure from a vacuum plate. When the exposure is made, the pressure is released and the film rolled ahead, leaving unused film in position for the next exposure.

14-6. Planning an aerial survey. In planning an aerial survey, the intended use of the photographs and the area to be covered must be determined so that a scale and camera may be selected.

Then the flight plan is made, by designating the scale and the amount of overlap desired. With these values known, the interval between flight lines and exposures can be determined.

If a map of the area is available the flight lines are drawn on it to indicate the paths that the aircraft is to take in *flying* the area. If no official map exists, a sketch map may be made or the pilot may fly lines connecting identifiable ground points.

14-7. Aerial photographs in engineering. Aerial photographs for engineering uses may be divided into four general categories: (1) wide coverage photographs to aid in reconnaissance for the preliminary location of highways, power installations, pipe lines, or other engineering works; used either singly or in groups as a substitute for a topographic map of the area; (2) strip photographs without overlap that aid in studying such things as highway traffic conditions and in making highway studies relative to pavement surface condition; (3) overlapping photographs to be trimmed, fitted and mounted to form a pictorial map (*aerial mosaics*), used in city and regional planning, land use studies, and flood and erosion control studies; (4) overlapping photographs used to construct planimetric maps or topographic maps, stereoscopic plotting instruments are used in connection with the latter so that the third dimension (elevation) can be measured and contour lines plotted.

14-8. Ground control. While wide coverage photographs may in one sense be considered maps, some framework of points of known relative positions is needed around which details in the photographs are plotted to obtain results of sufficient accuracy to be termed a map.

This is true even in the case of the mosaic, a pictorial map, formed by piecing together the photographs so that the ground details are continuous, without any breaks or gaps. For accuracy of position of photographed detail, however, it is necessary to bring the prints to a uniform scale and to form the mosaic so that key points (*control points*) appearing in the photographs coincide with these same points as plotted from the ground control survey. The pictorial map con-

Fig. 14-9. Making a mosaic. (Courtesy Fairchild Aerial Surveys, Inc.)

structed in this way is known as a *controlled mosaic*. Figure 14-9 shows the process of trimming and fitting to make a mosaic.

The network of ground points of known location and elevation that form the basis for any mapping work is called the *control*. When mapping from aerial photographs, it is called the *ground control*. The points are known as *control stations* or *control points*.

Ground control may be run either before or after the photographs are taken. If it is run before, the control points must be identifiable in the photographs. They should be so located that the position of two to four identifiable points in every photograph can be determined. The number of secondary control points per photograph will depend upon the type of map to be made and the accuracy required for the finished product.

If the photographs are taken before ground control is run, the approximate locations for control points are circled on prints which are then taken to the field where points within these circles are tied in by ground survey.

The methods of establishing control for aerial surveys are the same as those for establishing control for any other type of survey.

14-9. Working up data from the photographs. After the film has been processed, the negatives are numbered in the order in

Fig. 14-10. Setting up an assembly of prints for photographing to make a photo index. (Courtesy Abrams Aerial Survey Corp.)

which they were exposed. Prints are made from these and assembled to form an index map. The assembly is made so that the ground detail in each picture occupies as nearly as possible its true relative position. This is done by matching the photographs approximately to control points plotted on the index map base, or if a map of the area involved is available, detail on the prints is matched with that shown on the map.

Usually the assembled prints are then photographed to provide a permanent record of the index. Figure 14-10 shows the preparation of an index map for copying.

An index map serves the following functions:

1. Indicates photographic coverage of the particular area to which it applies.
2. Serves to make possible the rapid selection of any particular negative or negatives from the file as needed.

A section of an index map being copied is shown in Figure 14-11.

14-10. Orienting the prints. Variations in the scale of aerial photographs, or different parts of the same photograph, may be

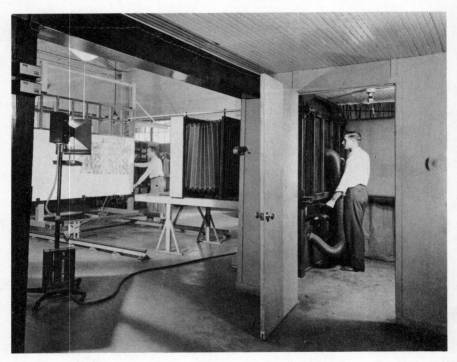

Fig. 14-11. Copy camera used in making a photo index of an aerial survey. (Courtesy Abrams Aerial Survey Corp.)

caused by camera tilt, difference in ground elevations, or variations in camera height. In the preparation of line maps from these photographs, adjustment for scale differences may be made in several ways.

14-11. Matching control. The simplest procedure for constructing a planimetric map from aerial photographs is to plot the control points on a transparent map sheet to the scale of the photographs. The control points on the map sheet are then matched with these same points on the print and the details are traced onto the transparent sheet.

If there is much displacement, caused by relief or tilt, it may be necessary to fit one part of the print at a time to the control. The portion of the matching print is traced; then the print is shifted for a better match in other areas before these parts are traced.

Often several negatives having different scales must be used in producing a map. Prints from these negatives are brought to the same scale by enlargement or reduction. These prints of common scale are called *ratioed prints*.

14-12. Radial line plot. In this method it is assumed that the photographs are truly vertical and that any angles measured about the central point of the photograph will represent the actual horizontal angle.

Fig. 14-12. Collimation marks at each edge of print.

This central point is called the *principal point* of the photograph. When a camera is properly adjusted, lines drawn from the register marks, or collimation marks, appearing on each edge of the negative, will intersect at the principal point of the photograph. See Figure 14-12.

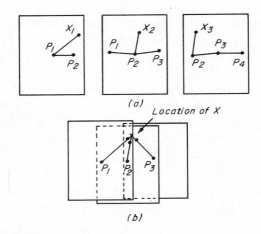

Fig. 14-13. Locating points by intersection of radial lines from principal point.

Fig. 14-14. A slotted template assembly. (Courtesy Fairchild Aerial Surveys, Inc.)

The radial line plot, sometimes called *radial line triangulation*, consists of drawing lines from the principal points of the photographs to control points and prominent objects in the photographs.

It is assumed that tilt angles are small (less than 3 degrees); therefore, angles made at the principal point are true horizontal angles. Because of overlap, the principal points of each print will

Fig. 14-15. A stereocartograph for plotting from aerial photographs.
(Courtesy Abrams Aerial Survey Corp.)

appear on adjacent prints as will control points and points of detail. The principal points are located and lines drawn between them. Lines from each principal point are also drawn to the object or point to be located as shown in Figure 14-13(a). The principal points on overlapping prints are then placed over each other to coincide as shown in Figure 14-13(b). The intersection of the lines radiating from the respective principal points shows the true location of the point in question. If the lines do not intersect in a common point, it indicates that one or more of the pictures may be distorted by tilt. If the discrepancy is serious enough, some negatives may have to be discarded or prints from them corrected.

The intersection of radial lines to ground control points and picture controls such as road intersections, streams and buildings, are traced onto a transparent sheet called the *map sheet*. The remaining details are filled in to form the completed line map or planimetric map.

14-13. Slotted templates. This is a mechanical method of adjusting the picture detail to conform to plotted ground control.

Fig. 14-16. Plotting by means of the multiplex. (Courtesy Michael Baker, Jr., Air Maps, Inc.)

Templates of cardboard or other heavy material are cut to the size of each print. The principal point and all control points are established on the templates by pricking through the prints with a needle. By means of a special cutter, short slots are cut in the templates along the radial passing through the various points, and a hole is punched through the point corresponding to the principal point of the print. The templates are then fastened together by small pins passing through the slots. The slots allow the templates to move in relation to the pins, thus adjusting themselves to rigid ground control automatically. Figure 14-14 shows a slotted template assembly.

14-14. Plotting contours. Once the planimetric map has been made, contours may be drawn on it by the regular ground surveying

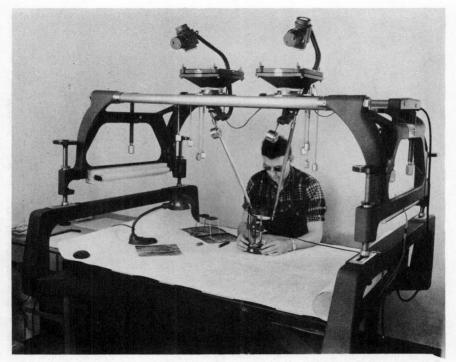

Fig. 14-17. The Kelsh Plotter in use. (Courtesy Michael Baker, Jr., Air Maps, Inc.)

methods of plane table or stadia as outlined in Chapter 13. This, however, does not utilize the possibilities of aerial photographs to the fullest extent.

By making use of stereoscopic viewing of overlapping photographs, contours can be plotted without going to the field.

Assuming that the overlapping photographs for forming a stereopair are available, the plotting of contours from them requires a viewing system, a measuring device and a means of drawing or tracing.

Several different instruments are available for these purposes. Some are large and costly, but make possible the accurate plotting of contour intervals of 5 feet or less. Figure 14-15 illustrates this type of machine.

Figures 14-16 and 14-17 illustrate other types of less costly plotting equipment that is still quite accurate.

Figure 14-18 shows one of the stereo-pair used with the Kelsh

Fig. 14-18. One of the stereo-pair used to produce map shown in Fig. 14-19. (Courtesy Michael Baker, Jr., Air Maps, Inc.)

Plotter to compile the 2-foot interval contour map shown in Figure 14-19.

Several types of relatively simple plotting instruments have been developed which give results precise enough for work requiring contour intervals of 10 feet or over. Figure 14-20 shows an instrument in this category.

The functioning of all of these plotting instruments depends upon the formation of the *spatial model*. This is the three dimensional image formed in the mind of the observer as he stereoscopically views the two pictures of the same object.

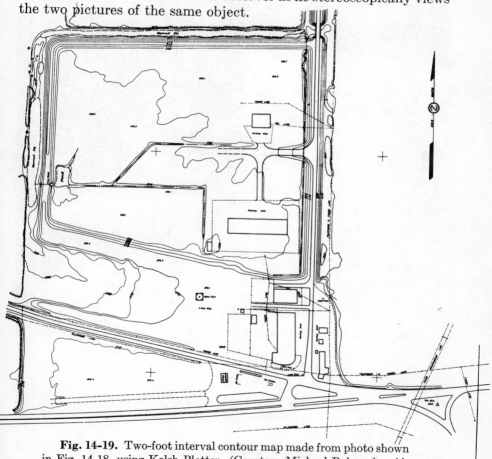

Fig. 14-19. Two-foot interval contour map made from photo shown in Fig. 14-18, using Kelsh Plotter. (Courtesy Michael Baker, Jr., Air Maps, Inc.)

In the field of view of each instrument, a small dot or a pinpoint of light appears, sometimes called the *floating dot*. The dot is actually two dots, being viewed stereoscopically and fusing to produce the third dimension in the mind of the observer. Viewing the dot in the third dimension causes it to appear to float, either above, below or on the surface of the landscape, also being viewed three

Fig. 14-20. Plotting contours from stereo-pair with the Stereocomparator.

dimensionally. The dot is set so that it appears to touch the surface at some point of known elevation (*vertical control point*), and the tracing arm of the equipment is set at that point on the map sheet. By moving the dot over the landscape image so that it continues to appear to float on the surface of the ground, the tracing pencil will follow a contour line representing that elevation.

14-15. Applications. A few of the possible applications of aerial surveys have been mentioned in Chapter 2. There are many others, and practical applications will doubtless increase with time.

Figures 14-21, 14-22, and 14-23 show the picture, topographic map made from a stereo-pair, and the final design for a city subdivision.

Figure 14-24 shows a 9- by 60-foot mosaic made up of an assembly of 9- by 4-foot panels. These photographs cover 26 miles

Fig. 14-21. One of stereo-pair used to produce map shown in Fig. 14-22. (Courtesy Abrams Aerial Survey Corp.)

of roadway and the area for 2 miles on either side. The advantages of this *layout* in estimating the problems of widening the existing highway or relocating it across less developed areas are apparent. Planning in connection with grade separations and access roads would also be facilitated.

A part of a photo alignment map as used by the pipe line industry is shown in Figure 14-25.

The photographs are printed on a map surface film so that data

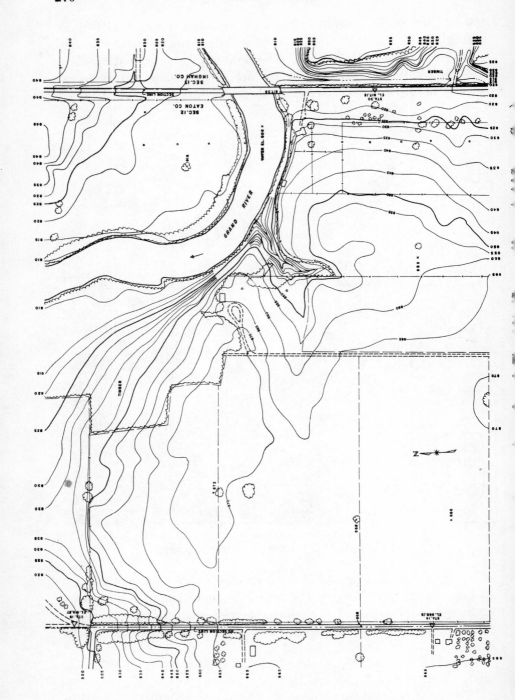

can be lettered in. The dashed lines in the picture indicate the pipe lines of other companies.

An interesting, though not routine, use for an aerial survey is that of determining the volume of large piles of stored material such as coal or pulpwood. Figure 14-26 shows one of the stereo pictures

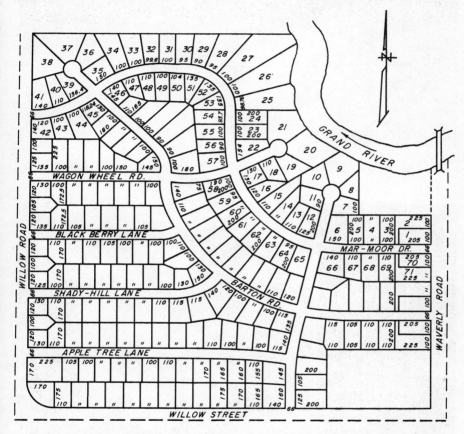

Fig. 14-23. Design of subdivision from map in Fig. 14-22. With contour map available lots can be laid out to take advantage of terrain variations. (Courtesy Abrams Aerial Survey Corp.)

of a coal pile. Figure 14-27 shows the *topographic map* for coal-pile inventory.

Fig. 14-24. "King size" mosaic for use in highway planning. (Courtesy Abrams Aerial Survey Corp.)

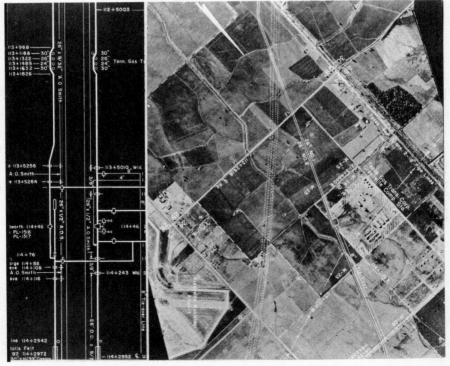

Fig. 14-25. Picture showing part of a photo alignment map as used by the pipeline industry. The photos are printed on a map surface film so that data can be lettered in. From the film, photo or blueprint copies can be made. (Courtesy Abrams Aerial Survey Corp.)

Fig. 14-26. One of stereo-pair of coal pile photograph. Contour map of the pile as shown in Fig. 14-27 was made from the pair of aerial photos. (Courtesy Abrams Aerial Survey Corp.)

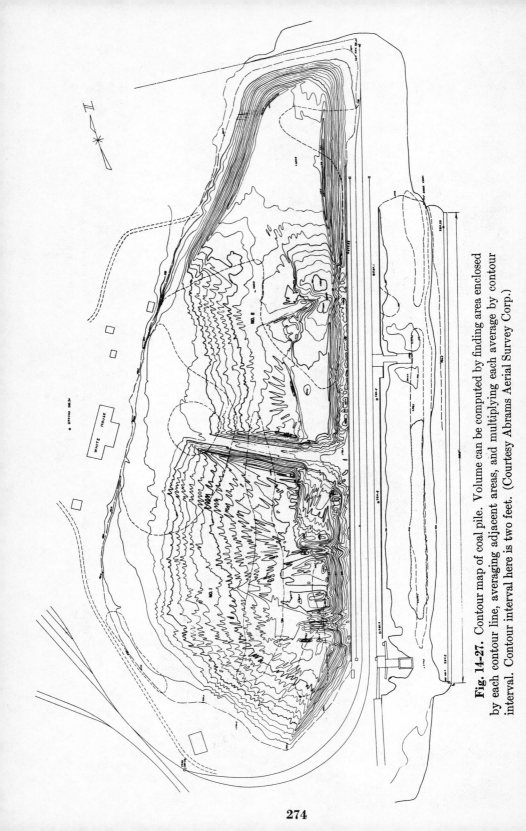

Fig. 14-27. Contour map of coal pile. Volume can be computed by finding area enclosed by each contour line, averaging adjacent areas, and multiplying each average by contour interval. Contour interval here is two feet. (Courtesy Abrams Aerial Survey Corp.)

PROBLEMS

1. At what height should a camera having a 9- by 9-inch negative and $f = 8.00$ inches be flown so that each exposure covers 8,000 feet of ground distance?

2. Compute the altitude of flight, distance along the ground between exposures, and the ground distance between flight lines with the following information known: Desired scale 1 to 10,000. Overlaps 25 and 60 per cent. Camera has 9- by 9-inch negative and 8.25-inch principal distance.

3. A photograph is taken from a height of 4,000 feet above the datum plane, with a camera having a 6-inch principal distance. What is the scale of the photograph in terms of the datum? What is the scale for an area of terrain in the photograph which is 700 feet above the datum? What is the scale for an area 300 feet below the datum?

Chapter 15

CONSTRUCTION SURVEYS

To BUILD according to the specifications and plans for any project, contractors must have reference lines and points established in the field.

These reference lines and points must be usable and convenient, close to the work, yet out of the way of construction operations. The layout engineer should have a good comprehension of the building sequence and of the methods to be used for a particular project. Because the construction industry is highly competitive and techniques are continually being improved, excellent liaison is needed between the layout engineer and the project superintendent.

Surveying is an integral part of the building process, not a merely tolerated secondary operation. Proper planning and execution of the surveying work can speed the construction and prevent costly mistakes, contributing as much to a profitable project as proper design of concrete formwork and efficient methods of fabricating materials.

High accuracy is required for construction surveys, and the allowable tolerances are low. For example, it may be necessary to build walls within $\frac{1}{8}$ inch of true alignment, and floor elevations within $\frac{1}{8}$ or $\frac{1}{16}$ inch of design elevation. For small buildings these tolerances do not require exceptionally high precision, but the short distances do make attention to detail, with frequent, independent checking, necessary.

15-1. Industrial site control. On one hand, site control is not a construction survey; on the other, it is the beginning of all construction surveys necessary to insure proper location and erection of the many buildings and other facilities for development of industrial locations.

High order surveying and mapping are required for the economic development of large industrial sites. The most feasible control is one based on the plane coordinate system of the state (see Article 9-15).

Under current regulations, the U. S. Coast and Geodetic Survey can extend its control network to any private site, the only expense to the owner being the actual cost of the survey and related computations.

The initial cost of establishing control for coordinating an entire project, or series of projects, into a common system will be higher than for an isolated survey. However, surveying costs for later extensions and additions will be much less.

High quality control is essential to the proper development of maps that correlate field construction with office plans. Adequate control must be available to coordinate and protect all installations on, above, or beneath the ground as additions, removals and rearrangements occur. The total cost of a control system based upon state plane coordinates might be less than the cost of one mistake caused by inadequate control.

Some of the advantages of using a state coordinate system as the basis for industrial site control, or for controlling any major construction are:

1. A single standard system will be developed as control is filled in and extended.
2. Records and descriptions will be on a common basis; as work is expanded, a progressive network will be established which will reduce the required surveying for future expansion and additions to the original construction.
3. Descriptions for irregular parcels of real property are simplified.
4. Accurate control is attained over large areas by the use of plane surveying methods.
5. The annoyances and added chances for mistakes, inherent in attempting to use unrelated, arbitrary control systems, are avoided.
6. Continued use will eventually result in mutual consistence between all surveys within a state.

15-2. Layout. Once the primary control for a project has been established, the locations of units within the system must be determined.

The procedure of properly positioning field construction may be termed *layout.* It may take any form from the relatively simple positioning of a building foundation, considering the four corners of a lot, to the most intricate arrangement of interrelated buildings, utility lines, streets, roads and other facilities.

Surveying methods provide the tool for all layout work as well as providing the control which makes proper layout possible.

15-3. Buildings. When the boundaries of the site have been determined, the specific location for a building or buildings must be set out in a way that the points of reference can be maintained throughout the construction.

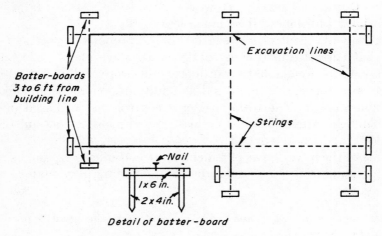

Fig. 15-1. Batter boards for building layout.

If excavation is required, as is usually the case, stakes should be set at the corners and other control points on the excavation lines. These temporary points identify where work is to begin, but must be removed as excavation gets under way. Therefore, sufficient reference must be provided for the re-establishment of the lines in order to place the footings and walls after excavation is complete. For small buildings, batterboards are used for this purpose, as illustrated in Figure 15-1.

For larger buildings, reference points must be established where they can be preserved. Lines are then re-established by transit sights as construction work progresses. The transit may also be used to plumb the steel framework or the forms for concrete.

It may be necessary to set reference points within a building as it is being constructed so that machinery or prefabricated piping layouts can be properly located after the building has been enclosed. This may be done by setting brass reference bolts or disks in the floor and at other points before the completed walls prevent long sights to the accurately positioned reference points outside of the building.

Bench marks must also be established and preserved to provide vertical control.

Optical tooling instruments and techniques (see Chapter 16) can be used to position turbine shafts or large machines that must be very accurately placed within a building.

Fig. 15-2. Partially completed water storage tank.

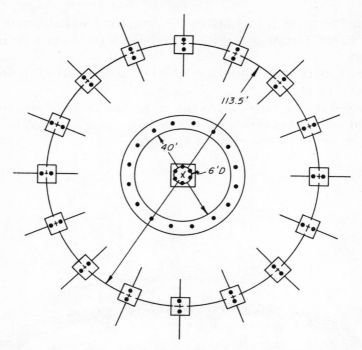

Fig. 15-3. Plan of anchor-bolt layout for water storage tank.

Fig. 15-4. Partially completed base of water tank.

Fig. 15-5. Checking tunnel alignment. (Courtesy Naylor Pipe Co.)

15-4. Anchor-bolt layout for elevated water tank. The layout for the foundation of an elevated water storage tank illustrates an example of the application of surveying techniques to construction measurements. Figure 15-2 shows a tank during construction.

Figure 15-3 shows a schematic diagram for positioning the anchor bolts which were embedded in the concrete base. For this tank 54 bolts were required either $1\frac{1}{2}$ or $2\frac{1}{2}$ inches in diameter and 6 or 8 feet in length.

The steel base plates for the tank were shaped and drilled at a fabrication plant, making it necessary to position the anchor bolts within $\frac{1}{16}$ inch so that the plates would fit. This was accomplished by careful angle and distance measurement.

Figure 15-4 shows the partially completed base with a transit set up near the center.

Fig. 15-6. Spad.

15-5. Tunnels. The control of tunnel construction requires very careful work. It consists of transferring alignment and elevation references from the surface to the tunnel and then carrying alignment and elevations forward as construction progresses.

Tunnels are usually driven simultaneously from two points: the two portals. In some instances, vertical shafts will be sunk to allow construction to begin at intermediate points, and progress in either or both directions. For these separate operations to meet and produce a single bore that is correct at all points in grade and line, requires a high degree of accuracy in the measurements controlling them. Particular care must be taken in the use of short reference lines which must often be used and extended to hundreds of times their lengths.

Figure 15-5 shows a transit in use for tunnel construction control. Note that the instrument is set up under a plumb-bob suspended from above. Points are placed in the roof by driving a wooden pin into a drill hole and then driving a metal hook called a *spad* into it. See Figure 15-6.

It is usually necessary to place points in the tunnel roof because

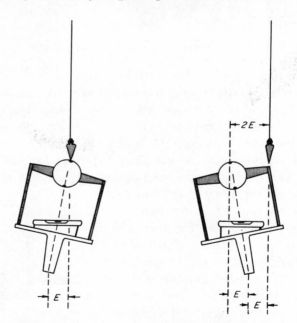

Fig. 15-7. Instrument under a point with the plate bubble out of adjustment.

the floor may be covered by water. Also, the overhead points are out of the way of construction traffic; points on the floor are almost sure to be disturbed. Points for elevation control are usually placed in the roof or walls of the tunnel.

When set up under a point rather than over it, the error caused by the plate bubbles being out of adjustment is exaggerated when the instrument is turned about its vertical axis and releveled. Figure 15-7 illustrates this for a rotation of 180 degrees.

The diameter and concentricity of the tunnel may be checked by a device called a *sunflower*. This equipment will also provide measurements for determining the cross-sectional area at any point. Figure 15-8 illustrates the sunflower.

15-6. Bridges. Construction surveys for bridges may involve extensive surveys. Figue 15-9 shows a method of staking out a small bridge. For large bridges, control

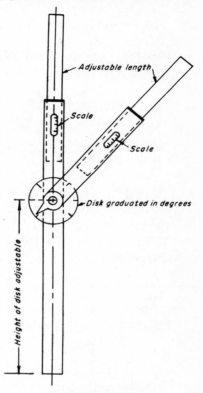

Fig. 15-8. Sunflower.

must be established for the plotting of borings to investigate foundation conditions, and later for the location of abutments and piers. These locations must be accurate, since spanning members are usually prefabricated and field erection will be possible only if all dimensions are precise. A triangulation system will provide the precise control required.

15-7. Route surveys. Surveys for the location and construction of facilities which continue across country for some distance, such as railroads, highways or pipelines, are called *route surveys*. As discussed in Chapter 2, the reconnaissance survey and the preliminary survey determine the approximate location of the center line of the project. Figure 15-10 shows a form of notes for a preliminary route survey.

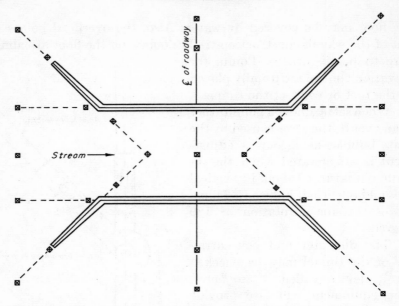

Fig. 15-9. Layout for a small bridge assuming stream diversion during construction.

PRELIMINARY – ACCESS ROAD FOR ATOMIC ENERGY PLANT						CLEAR, HOT	July 30, 1956 Haines – Δ & Notes Bell – Hd. Ch. Martin – R. Ch. Work – Chief
STA.	DEFLECT RT.	ANGLE LT.	MAG. BEARING	CALC. BEARING			
38 + 17		28° 17'	N28°15'W			□←70.0→□←70.0→□←38+17 P.I. ←70.0→□←70.0→□	
21 + 18						21+18 × WOVEN WIRE FENCE	
18 + 20		17° 14'	N0° 30'E.			□ 18+20 P. I.	
						Cultivated sta. 18 to 30	
10 + 30						J. C. Hill Barn 10+30 ⊢30'⊣ 50'	
						Wooded Sta. 5 to 17	
5 +00	1° 20'		N17°30'E			□←70.0→□←70.0→□←5+00 P.I. ←70.0→□←70.0→□	
3 + 70						STREAM 3+70 50' APPROX.	
0 +00			N16°15'E			□←60.0→□←60.0→□ 0+00 P.O.T. ←60.0→□←60.0→□	

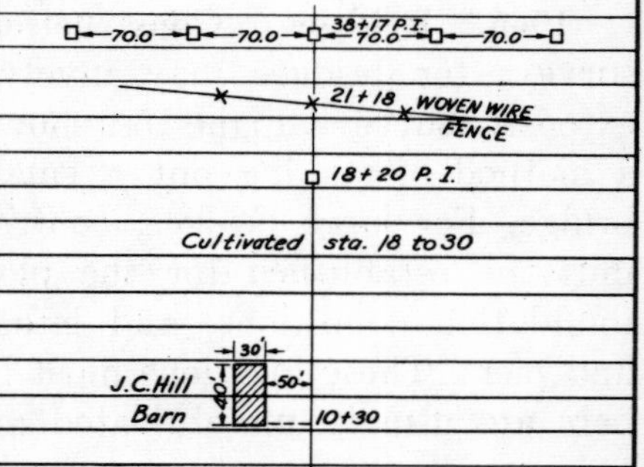

Fig. 15-10. Field notes for preliminary road location.

Notice that the notes in Figure 15-10 are kept from the bottom of the page up. This is common practice so that the sketch on the opposite page will be properly oriented as the notekeeper faces ahead along the survey. The center line is sketched as though it were a straight, continuous line. Angle points are recorded by station, but no attempt is made to lay off the changes in direction in the sketch.

A section of the center line which is continuous in any direction is called a *tangent*. The point where two sections of center line of different directions intersect is called a P.I. (*point of intersection*). If the deflection angle at a P.I. is more than a degree or two, a curve is used in highway or railroad construction to connect the two tangents. These are referred to as *horizontal curves*, or *simple curves*. Two connected curves of different radii form a *compound curve*.

15-8. Horizontal curves. Horizontal curves are circular and are defined either by their radius or by degree of curvature. The degree of curvature is the angle subtended at the center by the radii from each end of a *chord* or an *arc* of 100 feet. In practice, both the chord and the arc definitions are used.

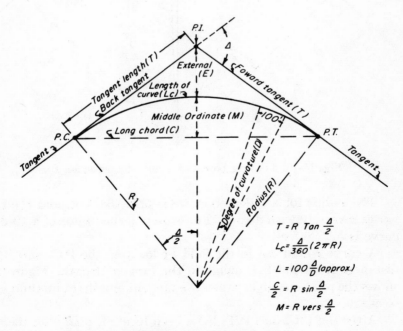

$$T = R \, \mathrm{Tan} \, \frac{\Delta}{2}$$

$$L_c = \frac{\Delta}{360} (2\pi R)$$

$$L = 100 \frac{\Delta}{D} \text{(approx.)}$$

$$\frac{C}{2} = R \sin \frac{\Delta}{2}$$

$$M = R \, \mathrm{vers} \, \frac{\Delta}{2}$$

Fig. 15-11. Elements of a simple curve.

The point along a center line, progressing with the stationing, where the tangent meets the curve is called the P.C. (*point of curvature*). The point at the opposite end of the curve where it meets the other tangent is called the P.T. (*point of tangency*). Figure 15-11 shows a horizontal curve and the nomenclature in common use.

The station number of the P.C. is the P.I. station minus tangent length. The P.T. station number is the P.C. station plus the length of the curve.

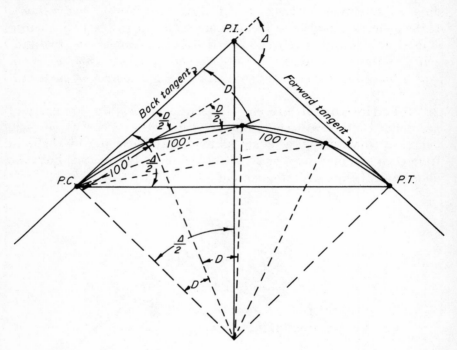

Fig. 15-12. Locating points on a curve by deflection angles.

The radius for a 1-degree curve is 5,729.58 feet, and the radius varies inversely with degree. For example, the radius of a 10-degree curve is 572.96 feet.

A curve is laid out in the field by locating the P.C. and P.T. at distances from the P.I. equal to the tangent length. Figure 15-11 shows the relationship between the tangent length, radius and length of curve.

After the P.C. and P.T. have been located, points on the curve may be located by measuring deflection angles from the P.I. as shown in Figure 15-12.

The deflection for each 100 foot chord is equal to the degree of curvature divided by 2. Deflections for shorter chords are directly proportional.

Curves of short radius may be laid out by actual radial measurements. Measuring offsets from the tangent may also be used to advantage in some cases to locate points on a curve.

STA.	POINT	Deflect.	Mag. Bearing	Calc. Bearing	Curve Data	
LOCATION – ACCESS ROAD FOR ATOMIC ENERGY PLANT					Cloudy, Cool	Nov. 10, 1956 Haines-△ & ▱ Bell – H. ch. Martin – R. ch. Work – Chief
59+00	P.O.T.					P.O.T. ▭—70'—▭—70'—▭—70'—▭—70'—▭
39+74⁹³	P. T.	14°15'	N30°30'W		P.I.38+09⁶⁷	P. T.
39		11°17'			Δ=28°30'Lt.	
38		7°17"			D=8°00'	
37		3°17'			T=181.89	
36+17⁷⁸	P. C.				L=356.25	P.C.
					R=716.20	
21+55¹²	P. T.	10°10'	N1°30'W			P.T. ▭—70'—▭—70'—▭—70'—▭—70'—▭
21		9°20'				
20		7°50'				
19		6°20'				
18		4°50'			P.I.18+20	
17		3°20'			Δ=20°20'Lt.	
16		1°50'			D=3°00'	
15		0°20'			T=342.50	
14+77⁵⁰	P. C.				L=677.67	P.C. ▭—70'—▭—70'—▭—70'—▭—70'—▭
					R=1909.86	
5+00	P. I.		N19°00'E		Δ2°10'Rt. No Curve	P.I.
3+70	₵ 500-ft. stream					
0+00	P.O.T		N16°15'E			0+00

Fig. 15-13. Field notes for road location survey.

Textbooks on route surveying give procedures for using both horizontal and vertical curves.[13] They also contain tables which give relationships between various curve components.

Figure 15-13 shows a form of notes for a location survey with data for horizontal curves. The curves are indicated symbolically on the sketch.

15-9. Vertical curves. Curves are also used to connect tangents in the vertical plane; that is, where the rate of grade of the route changes. These are especially necessary in railroad or highway construction to provide for riding comfort and safety.

Vertical curves are parabolic rather than circular. Figure 15-14 shows a vertical curve.

From the basic properties of a parabola it can be shown that the curve will pass midway between point *B* and the P.I. Offsets from

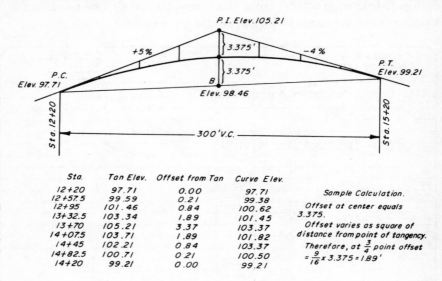

Sta.	Tan Elev.	Offset from Tan	Curve Elev.	
12+20	97.71	0.00	97.71	Sample Calculation.
12+57.5	99.59	0.21	99.38	
12+95	101.46	0.84	100.62	Offset at center equals
13+32.5	103.34	1.89	101.45	3.375.
13+70	105.21	3.37	103.37	Offset varies as square of
14+07.5	103.71	1.89	101.82	distance from point of tangency.
14+45	102.21	0.84	103.37	Therefore, at $\frac{3}{4}$ point offset
14+82.5	100.71	0.21	100.50	$= \frac{9}{16} \times 3.375 = 1.89'$
14+20	99.21	0.00	99.21	

Fig. 15-14. Vertical curve principle and calculations.

the tangent to the curve vary as the square of the distance from the point of tangency. The table in the figure shows elevations computed for points on the vertical curve.

15-10. Grades. The word *grade*, as used in construction, has two meanings: (1) grade or rate of grade, meaning the rise or fall in feet per 100 feet; and (2) the grade of a building foundation or other point on a structure, meaning the elevation of that point with respect to the plane of reference being used.

In constructing a road, sewer line, pipe line, railroad, or similar project, the finished structure will be built to a certain grade line. That is, it will follow a straight line in the vertical plane between control points of predetermined elevations.

Stakes must be set to guide the construction to the proper grade. This necessitates computing the difference between the elevation of the natural ground and the desired elevation for the finished product.

In the field, the relative position of the grade line is located by determining what the rod reading from any given H.I. would be if the rod could be held on the finished grade. This value for any point is known as the *grade rod* for that point. Figure 15-15 shows the three possible field conditions for computing grade rod, and the cut or fill necessary to reach the grade.

Once the grade rod for a particular location is known, a stake may be driven to grade by driving it until the reading on a rod held on top of it is equal to grade rod. If it would be necessary to bury the stake or make it an impractical length in order that its top can

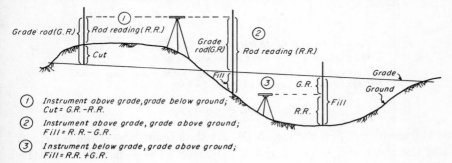

Fig. 15-15. Three possible relationships between grade rod, rod reading, and cut or fill required.

be set at grade, it is driven to a convenient height above the ground and the cut or fill necessary to get from the stake top to grade is marked on it. When a stake can be driven to grade, its top is often blued with keel (lumber crayon). These stakes are referred to as *blue tops*. Blue tops are set along both edges of a highway or railway grade when the construction is near the required elevation. They serve to define the roadbed width and aid in the finish grading.

15-11. Slope stakes. When the sides of the excavation or embankment are built on a slope, as on such projects as canals, roads and railroads, stakes, called *slope stakes*, are set at the point where the slope of the construction meets the original ground. Here they serve to guide the construction and with care can be preserved through the duration of the grading work.

The slope stakes are located at each station and at any other desired points along the center line. Their positions out from the center line are located by trial. With the grade rod for the station known, the rod is moved out at right angles to the center line until the distance out to the rod is equal to one-half the width of the roadbed plus the quantity, rate of side slope times the cut or fill

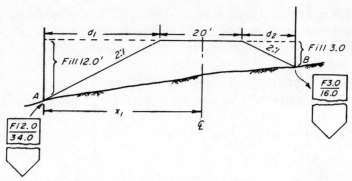

Suppose fill at left =12.0 ft; then d_1 =24.0, and x_1 must equal $24 + \frac{20}{2}$ or 34.0'. If it is not, slope will not be 2:1.

Rod must be moved in or out a small amount until indicated fill at A is such that x_1 = fill (slope) + $\frac{20}{2}$.

Fig. 15-16. Slope stakes.

at the shoulder. See Figure 15-16. At that point, the stake is driven and the cut or fill to reach grade elevation at the shoulder, and the distance out from the center line are marked on it as shown in the figure.

The rate of side slope is expressed as the horizontal distance to the vertical distance; for example, a 3 to 1 slope indicates a slope

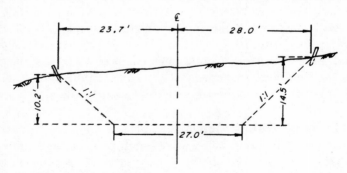

Fig. 15-17. Slope stake locations for canal.

of 3 feet horizontal for each foot of vertical rise or fall. The expression is also written 3 : 1, and 3 on 1.

Figure 15-17 shows the planned cross-section of a canal with the slope stakes in position.

15-12. Computing earthwork. Before the beginning of construction on any project involving earth moving, the shape of the original ground must be determined. This is necessary to compute the volume of material to be added or removed. Called *cross-sectioning*, it consists of determining elevations at control points over the surface involved. Cross-sections taken before construction are called *original cross-sections*. Those taken after completed construction are called *final cross-sections*.

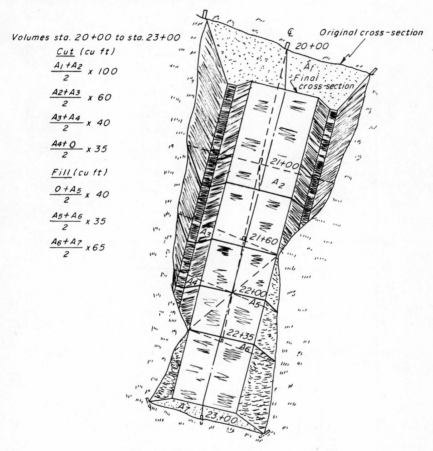

Volumes sta. 20+00 to sta. 23+00

Cut (cu ft)

$$\frac{A_1+A_2}{2} \times 100$$

$$\frac{A_2+A_3}{2} \times 60$$

$$\frac{A_3+A_4}{2} \times 40$$

$$\frac{A_4+0}{2} \times 35$$

Fill (cu ft)

$$\frac{0+A_5}{2} \times 40$$

$$\frac{A_5+A_6}{2} \times 35$$

$$\frac{A_6+A_7}{2} \times 65$$

Fig. 15-18. Earthwork quantity determination.

Earthwork quantities may be obtained by computing or measuring with a planimeter the area between the original and final cross-sections at adjacent stations on the project. See Figure 15-18. These areas are then averaged and multiplied by the distance between them. This will give the approximate volume of the prism of earth in question. Figure 3-2 shows a planimeter being used to determine end areas. Figure 15-19 shows the computation of the area of a cross-section (end area) from known cuts at points where the ground slope changes and the known distances out to those points.

The method described above is called the *average end-area method.* Where the cost of excavation is high, or if a more exact determina-

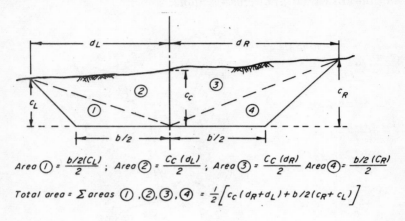

$$\text{Area} \ ① = \frac{b/2(c_L)}{2} \ ; \quad \text{Area} \ ② = \frac{c_c \ (d_L)}{2} \ ; \quad \text{Area} \ ③ = \frac{c_c \ (d_R)}{2} \quad \text{Area} \ ④ = \frac{b/2 \ (c_R)}{2}$$

$$\text{Total area} = \Sigma \ \text{areas} \ ①,②,③,④ = \frac{1}{2}\left[c_c \ (d_R + d_L) + b/2 (c_R + c_L)\right]$$

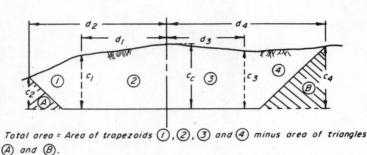

Total area = Area of trapezoids ①, ②, ③ and ④ minus area of triangles Ⓐ and Ⓑ.

Fig. 15-19. Computing end areas.

tion of volume is desired, the prismoidal formula may be used. This formula is

$$V = \frac{L}{6} \ (A_1 + 4M + A_2) \qquad\qquad (15\text{-}1)$$

in which, V is the volume of the prism, L its length, A_1 and A_2 are the respective end areas, and M is the area at the midpoint of the prism (usually not equal to the mean of the end areas).

After the quantities of excavation (*cut*) and embankment (*fill*) have been determined, a mass diagram is sometimes used to aid in solving problems of length and direction of haul and balancing quantities of cut and fill. The *mass diagram* is made by plotting the cumulative algebraic sum of cut and fill between stations as the ordinate, and the distance along the center-line or stations as abscissa. The resulting graphical representation is similar to hydrographs used in stream discharge studies.

For a more complete and detailed discussion on all problems connected with curves and earthwork a book on route surveying should be consulted.[13,14]

15-13. Sewer lines. The flow in storm sewers and sanitary sewers is ordinarily by gravity. Therefore, the grade of the completed line is very important.

The rate of grade of a sewer is expressed as that of a line which follows the bottom (*invert*) of the pipe or tile. This line is also referred to as the flowline. The grade is usually uniform from one manhole (M.H.) to the next.

Figure 15-20 shows a form of notes for establishing sewer grade for construction.

SEWER GRADES								8
OAK GROVE AVE. – SHATTUCK ST.					APRIL 8, 1947			D. OLSON ☐
STA.	B. S.	H. I.	F. S.	ELEV. INVERT.	GRADE ROD @ 2.0'ABOVE INVERT	CLEAR & COOL NATURAL GROUND		R. DIETZ ∧
		207.00				℄ ROD	℄ ELEV.	G. SARGENT ∅
13+00				183.96	3.04	3.9	203.1	
+25				184.02	2.98	3.9	203.1	
+50				184.07	2.93	4.0	203.0	
+75				184.13	2.87	4.1	203.1	
14+00				184.18	2.82	4.2	202.8	
+18	(OUTLET) M.H.#13			184.22	2.78	4.2	202.8	
+18	(INLET)			184.47	2.53	4.4	202.6	
+25				184.50	2.50	4.5	202.5	
+50				184.59	2.41	4.5	202.5	
+75				184.68	2.32	4.7	202.3	
15+00	M.H.#12			187.77	2.23	4.8	202.2	INTERSECTION W/ CENTER ST.

(annotations in GRADE ROD column: *15" PIPE S = 0.0022* between stations 13+25 and 13+75; *12" PIPE S = 0.0036* between stations 14+75 and 15+00)

Fig. 15-20. Field notes for establishing sewer grade.

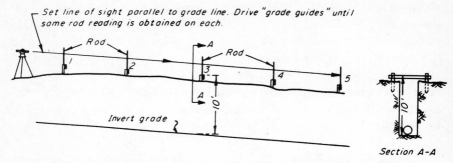

Fig. 15-21. Setting sewer or pipeline to specified grade.

Figure 15-21 shows one method of measurement to establish flow-line grade for laying the pipe.

Construction surveys for pipe lines are similar to those for sewers, although grades are not as important where the flow is under pressure.

15-14. Summary. As pointed out in Chapter 2, surveying is required for all types of construction work. The discussion in Chapter 15 has cited only a few examples, including some of the principles and methods that would apply also to types of construction not mentioned. For example, a survey for the construction of a power line would be similar to that for a highway, except that no curves or earthwork computations would be necessary. However, soil borings should be made and located so that conditions to be met in constructing towers or setting poles would be known.

Where a power line must span a ravine or where spans of considerable distance are necessary for any reason, methods similar to those for bridge construction may be used. The cables are usually cut to specified lengths in the shop and insulators attached. Accurate field control is then necessary to insure proper fit of the prefabricated units.

The ingenuity of the engineer in the field is continually being taxed. He must devise efficient ways of meeting variations in survey requirements which are sure to occur from project to project.

PROBLEMS

1. Complete the following level notes. Sights marked − (minus) were taken with the rod inverted and held on the roof of the tunnel.

Station	B.S.	H.I.	F.S.	Elevation	Description
B.M.$_A$	4.47			465.25	Drill steel near west portal
T.P. 1			3.79		Bolt in floor
	4.54				
T.P. 2			$-(4.11)$		Spad in roof
	$-(3.98)$				
T.P. 3			3.87		Bolt in floor
	3.83				
T.P. 4			$-(4.53)$		Spad in roof
	$-(4.01)$				
B.M.$_B$			4.63		Bolt in floor.

2. Given the following information, compute the volume of cut between stations $9 + 00$ and $16 + 20$.

Station	End Area, sq ft
$9 + 00$	$523.6\ c$
$10 + 00$	$154.8\ c$
$10 + 60$	$87.6\ c$
$11 + 00$	$109.9\ c$
$12 + 00$	$120.0\ c$
$13 + 00$	$150.8\ c$
$14 + 00$	$208.5\ c$
$15 + 00$	$176.3\ c$
$16 + 00$	$205.5\ c$
$16 + 20$	$385.4\ c$

Volumes of earthwork are commonly expressed in cubic yards.

3. Grade elevation Sta. $12 + 00 = 152.71$ feet. Rate of grade is $-(4\%)$. Compute the grade rod at Sta. $20 + 40$ for an H.I. of 125.62 feet. Compute the cut at center line if the ground rod there is 0.8 feet.

4. Compute the tangent length for a 10-degree curve having a deflection angle at the P.I. $(\triangle)$ of $36°10'$. Compute the P.C. and P.T. station numbers if the P.I. Sta. is $35 + 75.5$.

Chapter 16

OPTICAL TOOLING*

THE PHENOMENAL expansion of aircraft production during World War II was made possible by the conversion of civilian manufacturing facilities to feed hastily constructed assembly plants. The nature of this expansion meant that various parts and sub-assemblies made at one location must fit perfectly with others made at another location once they all reached an assembly plant. The need for the components to be interchangeable also meant that a high order of precision must be maintained in all operations. To accomplish this, jigs which were many times larger than anything previously used had to be erected. The dimensions of these large structures had to be the same for all production lines.

During the war-production period most American factories were using master gauges, some of them extremely large, with none too satisfactory results. Third-order surveying equipment of the type ordinarily used for construction surveys was also being used for controlling the erection of jigs.

The British, who were transporting sub-assemblies from Canada to assembly plants in England, pioneered in the field of optical methods of dimension control during this same period and achieved satisfactory assembly and interchangeability of parts with the use of alignment telescopes and collimators.

In 1946, the U. S. Air Force initiated a study of the British measuring methods. This study resulted in a cooperative project involving machine tool, aircraft, and surveying equipment companies. The purpose was to build a coordinate-setting machine for the control of large jigs. This instrument was built under the direction of the U. S. Coast and Geodetic Survey. Coordinates of key

* By permission, the material in this chapter is based on the *Optical Tooling Manual*, Keuffel & Esser Co., Hoboken, N. J., 1952.

points are located on jigs by the use of the optical lines of sight and precise tapes incorporated into this machine.

With the stimulus provided by war needs and the later requirements for even greater precision in shaping aircraft components, as sizes and flight speeds increase, there has developed another art in the field of precision measurement. It is called *optical tooling*.

16-1. Optical tooling defined. Optical tooling is a measuring technique which uses modified surveying instruments and methods for attaining the very high precision in alignment and distance measurements required in building large mock-ups, jigs or structures. It is also used in the erection and alignment of large machine tools and has a definite place in the setting of turbines, cyclotrons, and other large, high-speed rotating machines which must be accurately positioned.

The machinist with his gauge blocks, micrometer calipers and surface plates can make high order measurements up to lengths of five feet. In the field of surveying there have been developed instruments, techniques, and experience relative to precision measurements of lengths over 200 feet. Optical tooling is the art of measuring with high precision in the intermediate range: between the fields of the surveyor and the machinist. Although the range of optical tooling has been extended to 3,000 feet by using special targets, its main applications has been in the range indicated.

16-2. Optical tooling instruments. The demands for high precision measurement in industry by means of optical devices created a need for instruments other than the regular surveying instruments used in the early stages of this development.

The advantages of having straight and weightless reference lines from which to work is obvious. The horizontal and vertical lines of sight of surveying instruments give these, but to increase the precision attainable, special instruments are necessary.

Since 1952, optical tooling instruments have been available through American instrument manufactures. Keuffel & Esser Company was the first to produce a complete line of them.[15]

These instruments establish with high precision the reference lines and horizontal and vertical planes exactly where they are wanted. With them, lines of sight can be moved parallel to themselves, either horizontally or vertically within a tolerance of 0.001 inch. Following is a list of the basic instruments:

1. *Optical micrometer:* for moving the line of sight or reference plane parallel to itself horizontally or vertically.
2. *Optical tooling scales:* for providing a highly legible precision target at every tenth of an inch. From it measurements are made with the optical micrometer to 0.001 inch.
3. *Precise level:* for establishing horizontal planes at any required height.
4. *Jig transit:* for establishing vertical planes precisely where required.
5. *Jig alignment telescope:* for providing permanent reference lines.

16-3. Optical micrometers. These attachments for levels and transits make use of the phenomena of refraction of light for measuring directly to 0.001 inch on scales calibrated only to 0.1 inch.

Fig. 16-1. Optical micrometer for very precise leveling and alignment. When attached to levels, transits, and jig transit measures to 0.001 inch.

Essentially, an optical micrometer is a disk of optical glass with flat parallel faces. It is mounted in a tube which is attached to the telescope of either a transit or level in place of the sunshade. This added weight on the objective end of a telescope must be balanced by a counterweight placed near the eyepiece end.

As the graduated drum is turned (see Figure 16-1) the glass disk inside the tube is rotated about its own axis and the line of sight is moved parallel to itself. The device can be installed so that the line of sight moves up and down for leveling or left and right for lateral displacement. The drum is graduated so that it records the shift of the line of sight to 0.001 inch.

Figure 16-2 illustrates the principle of this device.

The accuracy of the optical micrometer is dependent upon the flatness of the two sides of the glass disk and upon the two faces being parallel to each other. When these conditions are met the glass is referred to as an *optical flat.* This means that the variations in the surface are less than one wave length of light or are within

$\frac{1}{20}$ millionth of an inch of being a true plane. The calibration of the micrometer is carried out in an optical laboratory.

Sights are taken on a steel scale graduated to tenths of an inch. The upper part of Figure 16-2 shows the line of sight in its zero or normal position. The micrometer drum is graduated in both directions from zero to 100. To avoid using the wrong direction the drum should first be turned to zero. It is then turned so that the line of

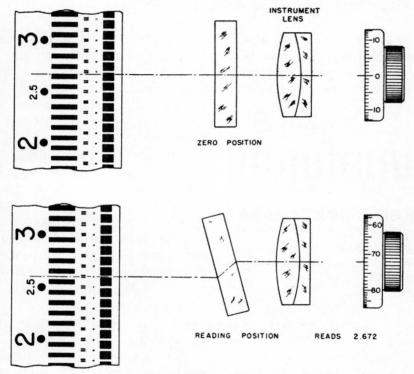

Fig. 16-2. The principle of the optical micrometer.

sight moves toward the smaller of the two scale numbers between which it falls. In Figure 16-2 the line of sight falls between 2.6 and 2.7 when the micrometer is set at zero. The micrometer drum, therefore, is turned so that the line of sight moves toward 2.6. Turning is stopped when the cross line falls midway between this set of black lines. The drum always records how far the line of sight has moved from its zero position, in this case 72 thousandths of an inch. Thus the reading is 2.6 + 72 thousandths or 2.672 inches.

If these directions are followed, a steel scale that is used to measure downward will also be read without error. The micrometer drum is set at zero and the line of sight is moved toward the zero end of the steel scale. An additive reading will be obtained, regardless of whether the steel scale is up, down, left, or right.

All readings in one plane must be taken without moving the micrometer housing on the telescope. If it is moved, all readings must be checked, since this attachment cannot be positioned on the telescope within its reading tolerance of 0.001 inch.

16-4. Optical tooling scales. The most accurate setting of a cross line (cross-hair) can be made between two black lines on a white surface, provided the white areas between the lines and the cross line are properly proportioned. Accordingly, for a given width of cross line, a certain spacing of lines will serve over a limited range of distances.

Fig. 16-3. Optical tooling scale provides precision target with graduations of 0.1 inch.

Cross lines in good sighting telescopes vary in width from 2 to 3 seconds of arc. When cross lines of this width are used, a white space within the range of 8 to 22 seconds between two graduations on a scale gives a probable pointing error of 0.15 second or less under laboratory conditions.

Scales of hardened tool steel are manufactured by the Keuffel & Esser Company in lengths of 10, 20 and 40 inches. These scales are divided to tenths of an inch (see Figure 16-3). At each tenth of an inch, there are four pairs of lines with different separations for sights of different lengths. The sight is made with the cross line of the instrument placed between two black marks selected from one of the four rows, depending upon the length of sight.

The width of the white space in the four sets of lines vary:

> 0.004 inch for sights up to about 7 feet.
> 0.010 inch for sights of from 7 to 20 feet.
> 0.025 inch for sights of from 20 to 50 feet.
> 0.060 inch for sights of from 50 to 130 feet.

Scale levels are available to hold the scales in proper position. Two circular bubbles, one to keep the scale vertical and the other to keep it horizontal, are attached to a bracket which holds the scale. A scale can be held so that the face is either at right angle or tilted at 45 degrees to the line of sight. When an optical tooling scale is inserted in the scale level in the 45° position and the cross lines appear to cut diagonally across the graduation pattern on the scale, this indicates that the scale is either tilted in a vertical plane or inclined toward or away from the observer in a horizontal plane. Small magnetic blocks are also used to properly position the scales on metal surfaces. These magnetic blocks will speed up operations when a number of shots are needed.

16-5. Optical tooling tapes. The tapes used in optical tooling are precision steel tapes with accurate graduations spaced every 10 inches rather than every foot. The graduations are made to be read under the magnification of a transit. Under controlled conditions, no graduation will vary more than 0.005 inch from its true position, and no 10-inch length will vary more than 0.003 inch.

16-6. Precise level. A horizontal reference plane is established in optical tooling work with a tilting dumpy level. These are the

Fig. 16-4. Precise level with an optical micrometer.

same instruments that are in use for precise leveling work in surveying. The only differences are in the attachments, optical tooling scales and micrometers, which read to 0.001 inch rather than the 0.001 of a foot that would be adequate in surveying.

Precise leveling in optical tooling work ordinarily involves a number of observations from one set-up. Since the reading is to 0.001 inch, the height of the instrument should not change during the observations. The instrument shown in Figure 16-4 has two features which eliminate the error caused by varying height of the line of sight: (1) It has four leveling screws which prevent the instrument from changing height when the leveling screws are turned. (2) The telescope is pivoted about a horizontal axis, which intersects the vertical axis of the instrument. Because of these features, the height of the telescope axle above its support does not change as the telescope is rotated, even if the center spindle is not vertical. Since the height of the telescope axle is fixed and does not change when the

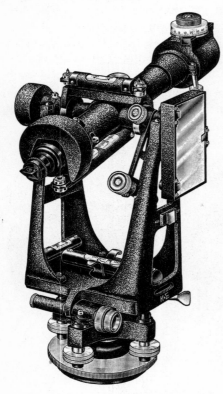

telescope is precisely leveled with the tilting screw, the horizontal plane swept by the precisely leveled line of sight is always the same distance above the ground.

If the telescope is tilted about a point other than the vertical axis of the instrument, it is necessary to center the coincidence bubble with the leveling screws, a time consuming job. With a three-screw instrument, if after a sight is taken, one screw is moved, the height of the instrument is changed, and it is necessary to repeat all the readings taken from that set-up.

16-7. Jig transit. A stripped down transit is used in optical tooling to establish vertical references planes. This instrument, a *jig transit*, differs from a standard surveying transit in that it

Fig. 16-5. Jig transit establishes planes precisely wherever required. The erecting telescope has a minimum focus of 3 feet from instrument center.

has no vertical or horizontal circles since it is used to define vertical planes, not to measure angles. Another principal difference is that the plate bubble which is perpendicular to the telescope is as sensitive as the telescope bubble. When this plate bubble is centered, the vertical plane established by the line of sight is vertical. Figure 16-5 shows a jig transit with an axle mirror in place. To balance the mirror a counterweight is attached to the other end of the horizontal axis of the telescope. The use of the axle mirror is explained in Article 16-8.

Note the detachable striding level on the horizontal axis of the telescope. This device will give a check, independent of other instrument adjustments, on the plane of the line of sight being vertical. If the bubble will remain in the same position in its vial when the striding level is reversed, the plane is vertical. A measuring button appears in Figure 16-5 which is 2.500 inches below the center of the mirror and 3.250 inches from the vertical axis of the instrument. This gives an accurate point for making measurements to the instrument or the line of sight. Deviations from the vertical reference plane of the jig transit can be measured readily when an optical micrometer is attached to the instrument. The procedure is the same as described in Article 16-3, but in this case the optically flat disk is rotated about a vertical axis which shifts the line of sight laterally either right or left.

The micrometer and its counterweight near the eyepiece end of the telescope are also shown in Figure 16-5.

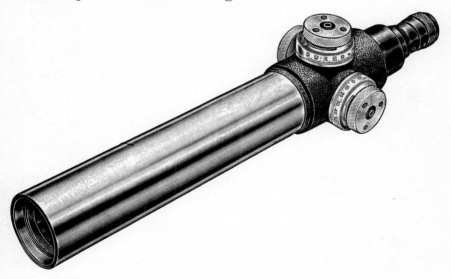

Fig. 16-6. Jig alignment telescope establishes permanent reference lines. The erecting telescope can be focused from infinity to a point actually in contact with the objective lens.

16-8. Jig alignment telescope. The *jig alignment telescope* provides an optical reference line of great accuracy on a jig or on any structure where measurements are to be made. Unlike the other instruments discussed, this one has been developed especially for optical tooling. The barrel of the telescope is a precisely machined cylinder of hardened tool steel with a chrome surface. The optical axis of the instrument is exactly centered in the telescope barrel so that when the telescope is positioned in a jig, the line of sight is also positioned. Figure 16-6 shows an alignment telescope. Notice the three knobs near the eyepiece. One of these knobs, the one nearest the eyepiece, is for focusing on the target. The other two are graduated drums which control the optical micrometers built into the telescope. Another feature of this instrument is a built-in auto-reflection target. (Article 16-9)

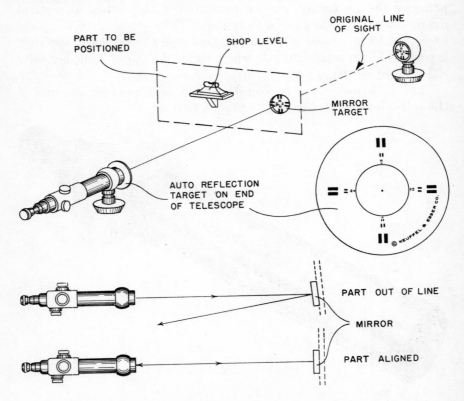

Fig. 16-7. Positioning by auto-reflection and a shop level.

16-9. Auto-reflection mirror and target. Optical tooling applies two basic principles of optics to shop measurements in addition to the principles involved in surveying. One, the principle of refraction, has been noted as the basis of the optical micrometer. The second principle, the reflection of light, is utilized to precisely position parts on reference lines and to set off accurate right angles.

When the problem is to position a part, as illustrated in Figure 16-7, first, the alignment telescope and a target are positioned in spherical bearings to establish the reference line. A mirror is attached to the part to be positioned and the part is placed between the telescope and the original target. These mirrors must be front surfaced and optically flat to give the necessary accuracy. When the line of sight of the telescope hits the mirror it will be reflected

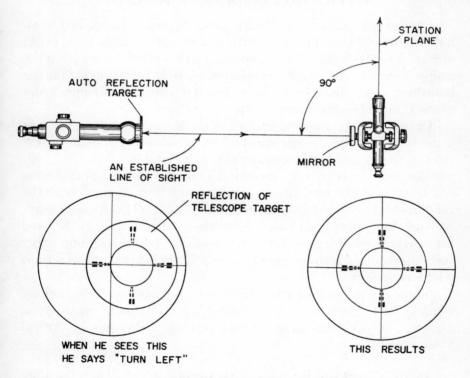

Fig. 16-8. To establish a plane perpendicular to the line of sight of the jig transit telescope: The operator sees the reflection of the target mounted on the end of the alignment telescope, and the jig transit is turned until the reflection of the target appears on the cross lines of the alignment telescope.

away at an angle if the mirror is not perpendicular to the line of sight (the angle of incidence equaling the angle of reflection). The mirror target placed on the part being positioned must be on line and perpendicular to the line of sight, so that the observer may look through the telescope and see the cross-hairs of the instrument centered on the reflection of the auto-reflection target mounted on his instrument. As can be seen from Figure 16-7, there is only one possible position of-the part, which will meet the three required conditions.

The auto-reflection principle can be used to set up a jig transit perpendicular to the horizontal line of sight of a jig alignment telescope. See Figure 16-8.

APPLICATION OF OPTICAL TOOLING

Optical tooling instruments and procedures can be applied to an unlimited number of problems within their normal measuring range of from 5 to 200 feet. By using special targets which incorporate the proper target to cross-hair size relation (Article 16-4), guided missile launching tracks have been checked to 0.001 inch in alignment and grade throughout their lengths up to 3,000 feet.

Optical tooling was first applied in the aircraft industry, but has since been adapted to machine tool erection and checking. Its expanded use in other engineering fields is inevitable.

The primary reason for including a chapter on optical tooling is not to expand the province of the surveyor, but to emphasize the fundamental nature of his measuring principles: (1) the use of gravity and the optical line of sight as reference directions, (2) the need for constant checking of the instruments by telescoping and other techniques, and (3) the study of errors and application of corrections where necessary.

Three optical tooling procedures will be explained: (1) checking flatness with precise level, (2) checking straightness with a jig transit, and (3) positioning airplane fuselage bulkheads by optical tooling methods.

16-10. Checking flatness with precise level. The procedure for use of the precise level, optical micrometer, and optical tooling scales for checking the flatness of a surface is illustrated in Figure 16-9.

1: Set up the level opposite the surface to be checked so that the telescope is about 6 inches higher than the surface.

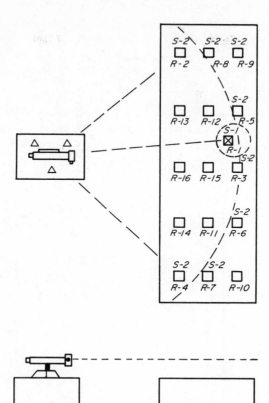

Fig. 16-9. Checking flatness of a machine bed. Note the sequence of shots and the attempt to balance the length of sights.

2. Clamp a 10-inch optical target scale to a magnetic V-block and place at "R-1." This scale, "S-1," remains in this position until all readings are taken at this instrument set-up.

3. Carefully level the instrument. Where a great many readings are to be taken from one set-up, it is wise to proceed as follows: (a) Carefully level the instrument with bull's-eye bubble. (b) Turn slow motion level dial to "0." (c) With telescope over one set of leveling screws, bring coincidence bubble to center with the leveling screws. Repeat over other set of leveling screws. This operation requires care and patience, but will save a great deal of time as only a slight adjustment of the slow motion level dial will then be required at the different position readings.

4. Take reading on scale S-1 at position R-1. In taking all readings, set optical micrometer at zero, bring target scale and cross-hair into sharp focus, check bubble, with the micrometer bring cross-hair

down to even graduation on the scale, check bubble, record reading of scale and micrometer. Repeat procedure three times at each target position, the average of the three is the reading for this position.

5. Clamp another 10-inch optical target scale, S-2, to a V-block and place on position R-2; repeat procedure No. 4; proceed to positions R-3, R-4, etc., until all readings are recorded.

6. At frequent intervals between position readings, take a check reading on scale, S-1 at position R-1. This check will indicate any shift in the *height of instrument* or the target surface.

7. Plot all "R" points to determine the flatness of the surface.

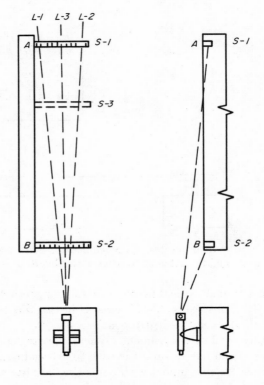

Fig. 16-10. Checking straightness with a jig transit. *L*-1 and *L*-2 are trial readings and *L*-3 represents equal readings on scales *S*-1 and *S*-2.

16-11. Checking for straightness with jig transit. The procedure for measuring deviations from a vertical plane with the jig transit, optical micrometer and target scale is illustrated in Figure 16-10. The necessary steps to do this are:

1. Set optical target scales S-1 and S-2 perpendicular to edge *A–B*.
2. Set up jig transit so that telescope is at least 6 inches above the scales.
3. Carefully level instrument and check with striding level.
4. With optical micrometer at zero, rotate transit on horizontal axis and take reading on scales S-1 and S-2, until the same reading to the closest 0.10 inch is obtained on both scales.
5. Clamp instrument and carefully check horizontal axis with the striding level.

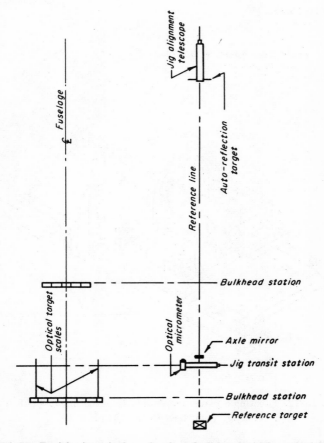

Fig. 16-11. Positioning airplane fuselage bulkheads with optical tooling instruments.

6. Now take reading with micrometer and rotate instrument with the slow motion screw until the same reading to 0.001 inch is obtained on scales S-1 and S-2. The jig transit is now parallel to edge *A–B*.
7. To check this positioning of the instrument, set micrometer reading of Step 6 on the opposite side of zero. Unclamp the instrument, rotate 180 degrees, plunge the telescope and set scale reading from step 6 on S-2. S-1 should read the same.
8. By using a third optical target scale, S-3, readings can be taken along edge *A–B* to check the straightness.
9. Scales S-1 and S-2 should be left in their original position for check references until all readings are taken from this set-up.
10. In taking all readings, be sure target scale and cross-hairs remain in sharp focus.

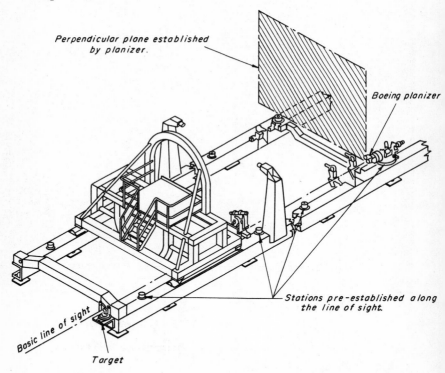

Fig. 16-12. Erecting a plane perpendicular to the line of sight midway on a jig. (Courtesy Boeing Airplane Co.)

16-12. Positioning airplane fuselage bulkheads. The procedure used for positioning aircraft structural parts to close tolerances is shown in Figure 16-11. The problem illustrated here is to set each bulkhead at a given distance from the reference line from a specified station along that reference line and then to bring the bulkhead into a vertical plane.

Fig. 16-13. Building a jig for airplane production. (Courtesy Boeing Airplane Co.)

The system used by the Boeing Airplane Company to erect perpendicular planes midway on a jig is shown in Figure 16-12. Station planes (vertical planes, perpendicular to the center line of the jig) are established by an optical tooling technique called *planizing*, which requires the use of an optical square attached to the end of an alignment telescope. The penta-prism in the optical square deviates the line-of-sight 90 degrees from the telescope axis. The square and the telescope can be rotated a full 360 degrees, making it possible to view and measure displacement by means of a scale or offset target in any position in a station plane.

Figure 16-13 shows some of the measuring involved in the building of a jig for the Boeing B-47 production program.

SELECTED REFERENCES

1. *Monroe Figuring Methods for Civil Engineering*, Monroe Calculating Machine Company, Inc., Orange, N. J., February, 1954.

2. Stearn, Joseph L., "Some Fundamentals of Error Theory," *The Journal, Coast and Geodetic Survey*, June, 1953.

3. Beers, Yardley, *Introduction to the Theory of Errors*, Addison-Wesley Publishing Co., Inc., Cambridge, Mass., 1953.

4. *Ephemerus* (published annually):
   - (a) C. L. Berger & Sons, Inc., Boston, Mass.
   - (b) W. & L. E. Gurley, Troy, N. Y.
   - (c) Keuffel & Esser Co., Hoboken, N. J.

5. *American Ephemerus and Nautical Almanac*, U. S. Government Printing Office, Washington, D. C.

6. Whitmore, George D., *Advanced Surveying and Mapping*, International Textbook Co., Scranton, Pa., 1949.

7. *Manual of First-Order Triangulation*, U. S. Coast and Geodetic Survey, U. S. Government Printing Office, Washington, D. C.

8. Sharp, H. Oakley, *Geodetic Control Surveys*, John Wiley & Sons, Inc., New York, N. Y., 2nd ed., 1943.

9. *Application of the Theory of Least Squares to the Adjustment of Triangulation*, U. S. Coast and Geodetic Survey, U. S. Government Printing Office, Washington, D. C.

10. "Technical Procedure for City Surveys," *Manual of Engineering Practice No. 10*, ASCE, New York, N. Y., 1934.

11. "Land Subdivision," *Manual of Engineering Practice No. 16*, ASCE, New York, N. Y., 1939.

12. *Manual of Instruction for the Survey of Public Lands of the United States*, U. S. Government Printing Office, Washington, D. C.

13. Skelton, Russell R., *Route Surveys*, McGraw-Hill Book Company, Inc., New York, N. Y.

14. Allen, C. Frank, *Railroad Curves and Earthwork*, McGraw-Hill Book Company, Inc., New York, N. Y.

15. *Optical Tooling Manual*, Keuffel & Esser Co., Hoboken, N. J.

APPENDIX

LIST OF TABLES

TABLE A—STADIA REDUCTIONS

Minutes	0° Hor. Dist.	0° Diff. Elev.	1° Hor. Dist.	1° Diff. Elev.	2° Hor. Dist.	2° Diff. Elev.	3° Hor. Dist.	3° Diff. Elev.
0	100.00	.00	99.97	1.74	99.88	3.49	99.73	5.23
2	100.00	.06	99.97	1.80	99.87	3.55	99.72	5.28
4	100.00	.12	99.97	1.86	99.87	3.60	99.71	5.34
6	100.00	.17	99.96	1.92	99.87	3.66	99.71	5.40
8	100.00	.23	99.96	1.98	99.86	3.72	99.70	5.46
10	100.00	.29	99.96	2.04	99.86	3.78	99.69	5.52
12	100.00	.35	99.96	2.09	99.85	3.84	99.69	5.57
14	100.00	.41	99.95	2.15	99.85	3.89	99.68	5.63
16	100.00	.47	99.95	2.21	99.84	3.95	99.68	5.69
18	100.00	.52	99.95	2.27	99.84	4.01	99.67	5.75
20	100.00	.58	99.95	2.33	99.83	4.07	99.66	5.80
22	100.00	.64	99.94	2.38	99.83	4.13	99.66	5.86
24	100.00	.70	99.94	2.44	99.82	4.18	99.65	5.92
26	99.99	.76	99.94	2.50	99.82	4.24	99.64	5.98
28	99.99	.81	99.93	2.56	99.81	4.30	99.63	6.04
30	99.99	.87	99.93	2.62	99.81	4.36	99.63	6.09
32	99.99	.93	99.93	2.67	99.80	4.42	99.62	6.15
34	99.99	.99	99.93	2.73	99.80	4.47	99.61	6.21
36	99.99	1.05	99.92	2.79	99.79	4.53	99.61	6.27
38	99.99	1.11	99.92	2.85	99.79	4.59	99.60	6.32
40	99.99	1.16	99.92	2.91	99.78	4.65	99.59	6.38
42	99.99	1.22	99.91	2.97	99.78	4.71	99.58	6.44
44	99.98	1.28	99.91	3.02	99.77	4.76	99.58	6.50
46	99.98	1.34	99.90	3.08	99.77	4.82	99.57	6.56
48	99.98	1.40	99.90	3.14	99.76	4.88	99.56	6.61
50	99.98	1.45	99.90	3.20	99.76	4.94	99.55	6.67
52	99.98	1.51	99.89	3.26	99.75	4.99	99.55	6.73
54	99.98	1.57	99.89	3.31	99.74	5.05	99.54	6.79
56	99.97	1.63	99.89	3.37	99.74	5.11	99.53	6.84
58	99.97	1.69	99.88	3.43	99.73	5.17	99.52	6.90
60	99.97	1.74	99.88	3.49	99.73	5.23	99.51	6.96
$C = .75$	.75	.01	.75	.02	.75	.03	.75	.05
$C = 1.00$	1.00	.01	1.00	.03	1.00	.04	1.00	.06
$C = 1.25$	1.25	.02	1.25	.03	1.25	.05	1.25	.08

Tables on pages 317-417 are reprinted from Harry Bouchard, Surveying, 3rd. ed. (Scranton: International Textbook Company, 1947), by permission of the publisher.

Minutes	4°		5°		6°		7°	
	Hor. Dist.	Diff. Elev.	Hor. Dist.	Diff. Elev.	Hor. Dist.	Diff. Elev.	Hor. Dist.	Diff. Elev.
0	99.51	6.96	99.24	8.68	98.91	10.40	98.51	12.10
2	99.51	7.02	99.23	8.74	98.90	10.45	98.50	12.15
4	99.50	7.07	99.22	8.80	98.88	10.51	98.49	12.21
6	99.49	7.13	99.21	8.85	98.87	10.57	98.47	12.27
8	99.48	7.19	99.20	8.91	98.86	10.62	98.46	12.32
10	99.47	7.25	99.19	8.97	98.85	10.68	98.44	12.38
12	99.46	7.30	99.18	9.03	98.83	10.74	98.43	12.43
14	99.46	7.36	99.17	9.08	98.82	10.79	98.41	12.49
16	99.45	7.42	99.16	9.14	98.81	10.85	98.40	12.55
18	99.44	7.48	99.15	9.20	98.80	10.91	98.39	12.60
20	99.43	7.53	99.14	9.25	98.78	10.96	98.37	12.66
22	99.42	7.59	99.13	9.31	98.77	11.02	98.36	12.72
24	99.41	7.65	99.11	9.37	98.76	11.08	98.34	12.77
26	99.40	7.71	99.10	9.43	98.74	11.13	98.33	12.83
28	99.39	7.76	99.09	9.48	98.73	11.19	98.31	12.88
30	99.38	7.82	99.08	9.54	98.72	11.25	98.30	12.94
32	99.38	7.88	99.07	9.60	98.71	11.30	98.28	13.00
34	99.37	7.94	99.06	9.65	98.69	11.36	98.27	13.05
36	99.36	7.99	99.05	9.71	98.68	11.42	98.25	13.11
38	99.35	8.05	99.04	9.77	98.67	11.47	98.24	13.17
40	99.34	8.11	99.03	9.83	98.65	11.53	98.22	13.22
42	99.33	8.17	99.01	9.88	98.64	11.59	98.20	13.28
44	99.32	8.22	99.00	9.94	98.63	11.64	98.19	13.33
46	99.31	8.28	98.99	10.00	98.61	11.70	98.17	13.39
48	99.30	8.34	98.98	10.05	98.60	11.76	98.16	13.45
50	99.29	8.40	98.97	10.11	98.58	11.81	98.14	13.50
52	99.28	8.45	98.96	10.17	98.57	11.87	98.13	13.56
54	99.27	8.51	98.94	10.22	98.56	11.93	98.11	13.61
56	99.26	8.57	98.93	10.28	98.54	11.98	98.10	13.67
58	99.25	8.63	98.92	10.34	98.53	12.04	98.08	13.73
60	99.24	8.68	98.91	10.40	98.51	12.10	98.06	13.78
C = .75	.75	.06	.75	.07	.75	.08	.74	.10
C = 1.00	1.00	.08	1.00	.10	.99	.11	.99	.13
C = 1.25	1.25	.10	1.24	.12	1.24	.14	1.24	.16

TABLE A—STADIA REDUCTIONS

Minutes	8°		9°		10°		11°	
	Hor. Dist.	Diff. Elev.	Hor. Dist.	Diff. Elev.	Hor. Dist.	Diff. Elev.	Hor. Dist.	Diff. Elev.
0	98.06	13.78	97.55	15.45	96.98	17.10	96.36	18.73
2	98.05	13.84	97.53	15.51	96.96	17.16	96.34	18.78
4	98.03	13.89	97.52	15.56	96.94	17.21	96.32	18.84
6	98.01	13.95	97.50	15.62	96.92	17.26	96.29	18.89
8	98.00	14.01	97.48	15.67	96.90	17.32	96.27	18.95
10	97.98	14.06	97.46	15.73	96.88	17.37	96.25	19.00
12	97.97	14.12	97.44	15.78	96.86	17.43	96.23	19.05
14	97.95	14.17	97.43	15.84	96.84	17.48	96.21	19.11
16	97.93	14.23	97.41	15.89	96.82	17.54	96.18	19.16
18	97.92	14.28	97.39	15.95	96.80	17.59	96.16	19.21
20	97.90	14.34	97.37	16.00	96.78	17.65	96.14	19.27
22	97.88	14.40	97.35	16.06	96.76	17.70	96.12	19.32
24	97.87	14.45	97.33	16.11	96.74	17.76	96.09	19.38
26	97.85	14.51	97.31	16.17	96.72	17.81	96.07	19.43
28	97.83	14.56	97.29	16.22	96.70	17.86	96.05	19.48
30	97.82	14.62	97.28	16.28	96.68	17.92	96.03	19.54
32	97.80	14.67	97.26	16.33	96.66	17.97	96.00	19.59
34	97.78	14.73	97.24	16.39	96.64	18.03	95.98	19.64
36	97.76	14.79	97.22	16.44	96.62	18.08	95.96	19.70
38	97.75	14.84	97.20	16.50	96.60	18.14	95.93	19.75
40	97.73	14.90	97.18	16.55	96.57	18.19	95.91	19.80
42	97.71	14.95	97.16	16.61	96.55	18.24	95.89	19.86
44	97.69	15.01	97.14	16.66	96.53	18.30	95.86	19.91
46	97.68	15.06	97.12	16.72	96.51	18.35	95.84	19.96
48	97.66	15.12	97.10	16.77	96.49	18.41	95.82	20.02
50	97.64	15.17	97.08	16.83	96.47	18.46	95.79	20.07
52	97.62	15.23	97.06	16.88	96.45	18.51	95.77	20.12
54	97.61	15.28	97.04	16.94	96.42	18.57	95.75	20.18
56	97.59	15.34	97.02	16.99	96.40	18.62	95.72	20.23
58	97.57	15.40	97.00	17.05	96.38	18.68	95.70	20.28
60	97.55	15.45	96.98	17.10	96.36	18.73	95.68	20.34
$C = .75$	.74	.11	.74	.12	.74	.14	.73	.15
$C = 1.00$	.99	.15	.99	.17	.98	.18	.98	.20
$C = 1.25$	1.24	.18	1.23	.21	1.23	.23	1.22	.25

TABLE A—STADIA REDUCTIONS

Minutes	12° Hor. Dist.	12° Diff. Elev.	13° Hor. Dist.	13° Diff. Elev.	14° Hor. Dist.	14° Diff. Elev.	15° Hor. Dist.	15° Diff. Elev.
0	95.68	20.34	94.94	21.92	94.15	23.47	93.30	25.00
2	95.65	20.39	94.91	21.97	94.12	23.52	93.27	25.05
4	95.63	20.44	94.89	22.02	94.09	23.58	93.24	25.10
6	95.61	20.50	94.86	22.08	94.07	23.63	93.21	25.15
8	95.58	20.55	94.84	22.13	94.04	23.68	93.18	25.20
10	95.56	20.60	94.81	22.18	94.01	23.73	93.16	25.25
12	95.53	20.66	94.79	22.23	93.98	23.78	93.13	25.30
14	95.51	20.71	94.76	22.28	93.95	23.83	93.10	25.35
16	95.49	20.76	94.73	22.34	93.93	23.88	93.07	25.40
18	95.46	20.81	94.71	22.39	93.90	23.93	93.04	25.45
20	95.44	20.87	94.68	22.44	93.87	23.99	93.01	25.50
22	95.41	20.92	94.66	22.49	93.84	24.04	92.98	25.55
24	95.39	20.97	94.63	22.54	93.82	24.09	92.95	25.60
26	95.36	21.03	94.60	22.60	93.79	24.14	92.92	25.65
28	95.34	21.08	94.58	22.65	93.76	24.19	92.89	25.70
30	95.32	21.13	94.55	22.70	93.73	24.24	92.86	25.75
32	95.29	21.18	94.52	22.75	93.70	24.29	92.83	25.80
34	95.27	21.24	94.50	22.80	93.67	24.34	92.80	25.85
36	95.24	21.29	94.47	22.85	93.65	24.39	92.77	25.90
38	95.22	21.34	94.44	22.91	93.62	24.44	92.74	25.95
40	95.19	21.39	94.42	22.96	93.59	24.49	92.71	26.00
42	95.17	21.45	94.39	23.01	93.56	24.55	92.68	26.05
44	95.14	21.50	94.36	23.06	93.53	24.60	92.65	26.10
46	95.12	21.55	94.34	23.11	93.50	24.65	92.62	26.15
48	95.09	21.60	94.31	23.16	93.47	24.70	92.59	26.20
50	95.07	21.66	94.28	23.22	93.45	24.75	92.56	26.25
52	95.04	21.71	94.26	23.27	93.42	24.80	92.53	26.30
54	95.02	21.76	94.23	23.32	93.39	24.85	92.49	26.35
56	94.99	21.81	94.20	23.37	93.36	24.90	92.46	26.40
58	94.97	21.87	94.17	23.42	93.33	24.95	92.43	26.45
60	94.94	21.92	94.15	23.47	93.30	25.00	92.40	26.50
C = .75	.73	.16	.73	.18	.73	.19	.72	.20
C = 1.00	.98	.22	.97	.23	.97	.25	.96	.27
C = 1.25	1.22	.27	1.22	.29	1.21	.31	1.20	.33

TABLE A—STADIA REDUCTIONS

Minutes	16°		17°		18°		19°	
	Hor. Dist.	Diff. Elev.	Hor. Dist.	Diff. Elev.	Hor. Dist.	Diff. Elev.	Hor. Dist.	Diff. Elev.
0	92.40	26.50	91.45	27.96	90.45	29.39	89.40	30.78
2	92.37	26.55	91.42	28.01	90.42	29.44	89.36	30.83
4	92.34	26.59	91.39	28.06	90.38	29.48	89.33	30.87
6	92.31	26.64	91.35	28.10	90.35	29.53	89.29	30.92
8	92.28	26.69	91.32	28.15	90.31	29.58	89.26	30.97
10	92.25	26.74	91.29	28.20	90.28	29.62	89.22	31.01
12	92.22	26.79	91.26	28.25	90.24	29.67	89.18	31.06
14	92.19	26.84	91.22	28.30	90.21	29.72	89.15	31.10
16	92.15	26.89	91.19	28.34	90.18	29.76	89.11	31.15
18	92.12	26.94	91.16	28.39	90.14	29.81	89.08	31.19
20	92.09	26.99	91.12	28.44	90.11	29.86	89.04	31.24
22	92.06	27.04	91.09	28.49	90.07	29.90	89.00	31.28
24	92.03	27.09	91.06	28.54	90.04	29.95	88.97	31.33
26	92.00	27.13	91.02	28.58	90.00	30.00	88.93	31.38
28	91.97	27.18	90.99	28.63	89.97	30.04	88.89	31.42
30	91.93	27.23	90.96	28.68	89.93	30.09	88.86	31.47
32	91.90	27.28	90.92	28.73	89.90	30.14	88.82	31.51
34	91.87	27.33	90.89	28.77	89.86	30.18	88.78	31.56
36	91.84	27.38	90.86	28.82	89.83	30.23	88.75	31.60
38	91.81	27.43	90.82	28.87	89.79	30.28	88.71	31.65
40	91.77	27.48	90.79	28.92	89.76	30.32	88.67	31.69
42	91.74	27.52	90.76	28.96	89.72	30.37	88.64	31.74
44	91.71	27.57	90.72	29.01	89.69	30.41	88.60	31.78
46	91.68	27.62	90.69	29.06	89.65	30.46	88.56	31.83
48	91.65	27.67	90.66	29.11	89.61	30.51	88.53	31.87
50	91.61	27.72	90.62	29.15	89.58	30.55	88.49	31.92
52	91.58	27.77	90.59	29.20	89.54	30.60	88.45	31.96
54	91.55	27.81	90.55	29.25	89.51	30.65	88.41	32.01
56	91.52	27.86	90.52	29.30	89.47	30.69	88.38	32.05
58	91.48	27.91	90.49	29.34	89.44	30.74	88.34	32.09
60	91.45	27.96	90.45	29.39	89.40	30.78	88.30	32.14
C = .75	.72	.21	.72	.23	.71	.24	.71	.25
C = 1.00	.96	.28	.95	.30	.95	.32	.94	.33
C = 1.25	1.20	.36	1.19	.38	1.19	.40	1.18	.42

TABLE A—STADIA REDUCTIONS

Minutes	20° Hor. Dist.	20° Diff. Elev.	21° Hor. Dist.	21° Diff. Elev.	22° Hor. Dist.	22° Diff. Elev.	23° Hor. Dist.	23° Diff. Elev.
0	88.30	32.14	87.16	33.46	85.97	34.73	84.73	35.97
2	88.26	32.18	87.12	33.50	85.93	34.77	84.69	36.01
4	88.23	32.23	87.08	33.54	85.89	34.82	84.65	36.05
6	88.19	32.27	87.04	33.59	85.85	34.86	84.61	36.09
8	88.15	32.32	87.00	33.63	85.80	34.90	84.57	36.13
10	88.11	32.36	86.96	33.67	85.76	34.94	84.52	36.17
12	88.08	32.41	86.92	33.72	85.72	34.98	84.48	36.21
14	88.04	32.45	86.88	33.76	85.68	35.02	84.44	36.25
16	88.00	32.49	86.84	33.80	85.64	35.07	84.40	36.29
18	87.96	32.54	86.80	33.84	85.60	35.11	84.35	36.33
20	87.93	32.58	86.77	33.89	85.56	35.15	84.31	36.37
22	87.89	32.63	86.73	33.93	85.52	35.19	84.27	36.41
24	87.85	32.67	86.69	33.97	85.48	35.23	84.23	36.45
26	87.81	32.72	86.65	34.01	85.44	35.27	84.18	36.49
28	87.77	32.76	86.61	34.06	85.40	35.31	84.14	36.53
30	87.74	32.80	86.57	34.10	85.36	35.36	84.10	36.57
32	87.70	32.85	86.53	34.14	85.31	35.40	84.06	36.61
34	87.66	32.89	86.49	34.18	85.27	35.44	84.01	36.65
36	87.62	32.93	86.45	34.23	85.23	35.48	83.97	36.69
38	87.58	32.98	86.41	34.27	85.19	35.52	83.93	36.73
40	87.54	33.02	86.37	34.31	85.15	35.56	83.89	36.77
42	87.51	33.07	86.33	34.35	85.11	35.60	83.84	36.80
44	87.47	33.11	86.29	34.40	85.07	35.64	83.80	36.84
46	87.43	33.15	86.25	34.44	85.02	35.68	83.76	36.88
48	87.39	33.20	86.21	34.48	84.98	35.72	83.72	36.92
50	87.35	33.24	86.17	34.52	84.94	35.76	83.67	36.96
52	87.31	33.28	86.13	34.57	84.90	35.80	83.63	37.00
54	87.27	33.33	86.09	34.61	84.86	35.85	83.59	37.04
56	87.24	33.37	86.05	34.65	84.82	35.89	83.54	37.08
58	87.20	33.41	86.01	34.69	84.77	35.93	83.50	37.12
60	87.16	33.46	85.97	34.73	84.73	35.97	83.46	37.16
C = .75	.70	.26	.70	.27	.69	.29	.69	.30
C = 1.00	.94	.35	.93	.37	.92	.38	.92	.40
C = 1.25	1.17	.44	1.16	.46	1.15	.48	1.15	.50

TABLE A—STADIA REDUCTIONS

Minutes	24° Hor. Dist.	24° Diff. Elev.	25° Hor. Dist.	25° Diff. Elev.	26° Hor. Dist.	26° Diff. Elev.	27° Hor. Dist.	27° Diff. Elev.
0	83.46	37.16	82.14	38.30	80.78	39.40	79.39	40.45
2	83.41	37.20	82.09	38.34	80.74	39.44	79.34	40.49
4	83.37	37.23	82.05	38.38	80.69	39.47	79.30	40.52
6	83.33	37.27	82.01	38.41	80.65	39.51	79.25	40.55
8	83.28	37.31	81.96	38.45	80.60	39.54	79.20	40.59
10	83.24	37.35	81.92	38.49	80.55	39.58	79.15	40.62
12	83.20	37.39	81.87	38.53	80.51	39.61	79.11	40.66
14	83.15	37.43	81.83	38.56	80.46	39.65	79.06	40.69
16	83.11	37.47	81.78	38.60	80.41	39.69	79.01	40.72
18	83.07	37.51	81.74	38.64	80.37	39.72	78.96	40.76
20	83.02	37.54	81.69	38.67	80.32	39.76	78.92	40.79
22	82.98	37.58	81.65	38.71	80.28	39.79	78.87	40.82
24	82.93	37.62	81.60	38.75	80.23	39.83	78.82	40.86
26	82.89	37.66	81.56	38.78	80.18	39.86	78.77	40.89
28	82.85	37.70	81.51	38.82	80.14	39.90	78.73	40.92
30	82.80	37.74	81.47	38.86	80.09	39.93	78.68	40.96
32	82.76	37.77	81.42	38.89	80.04	39.97	78.63	40.99
34	82.72	37.81	81.38	38.93	80.00	40.00	78.58	41.02
36	82.67	37.85	81.33	38.97	79.95	40.04	78.54	41.06
38	82.63	37.89	81.28	39.00	79.90	40.07	78.49	41.09
40	82.58	37.93	81.24	39.04	79.86	40.11	78.44	41.12
42	82.54	37.96	81.19	39.08	79.81	40.14	78.39	41.16
44	82.49	38.00	81.15	39.11	79.76	40.18	78.34	41.19
46	82.45	38.04	81.10	39.15	79.72	40.21	78.30	41.22
48	82.41	38.08	81.06	39.18	79.67	40.24	78.25	41.26
50	82.36	38.11	81.01	39.22	79.62	40.28	78.20	41.29
52	82.32	38.15	80.97	39.26	79.58	40.31	78.15	41.32
54	82.27	38.19	80.92	39.29	79.53	40.35	78.10	41.35
56	82.23	38.23	80.87	39.33	79.48	40.38	78.06	41.39
58	82.18	38.26	80.83	39.36	79.44	40.42	78.01	41.42
60	82.14	38.30	80.78	39.40	79.39	40.45	77.96	41.45
C = .75	.68	.31	.68	.32	.67	.33	.67	.35
C = 1.00	.91	.41	.90	.43	.89	.45	.89	.46
C = 1.25	1.14	.52	1.13	.54	1.12	.56	1.11	.58

323

Minutes	28°		29°		30°	
	Hor. Dist.	Diff. Elev.	Hor. Dist.	Diff. Elev.	Hor. Dist.	Diff. Elev.
0	77.96	41.45	76.50	42.40	75.00	43.30
2	77.91	41.48	76.45	42.43	74.95	43.33
4	77.86	41.52	76.40	42.46	74.90	43.36
6	77.81	41.55	76 35	42.49	74.85	43.39
8	77.77	41.58	76.30	42.53	74.80	43.42
10	77.72	41.61	76.25	42.56	74.75	43.45
12	77.67	41.65	76.20	42.59	74.70	43.47
14	77.62	41.68	76.15	42.62	74.65	43.50
16	77.57	41.71	76.10	42.65	74.60	43.53
18	77.52	41.74	76.05	42.68	74.55	43.56
20	77.48	41.77	76.00	42.71	74.49	43.59
22	77.42	41.81	75.95	42.74	74.44	43.62
24	77.38	41.84	75.90	42.77	74.39	43.65
26	77.33	41.87	75.85	42.80	74.34	43.67
28	77.28	41.90	75.80	42.83	74.29	43.70
30	77.23	41.93	75.75	42.86	74.24	43.73
32	77.18	41.97	75.70	42.89	74.19	43.76
34	77.13	42.00	75.65	42.92	74.14	43.79
36	77.09	42.03	75.60	42.95	74.09	43.82
38	77.04	42.06	75.55	42.98	74.04	43.84
40	76.99	42.09	75.50	43.01	73.99	43.87
42	76.94	42.12	75.45	43.04	73.93	43.90
44	76.89	42.15	75.40	43.07	73.88	43.93
46	76.84	42.19	75.35	43.10	73.83	43.95
48	76.79	42.22	75.30	43.13	73.78	43.98
50	76.74	42.25	75.25	43.16	73.73	44.01
52	76.69	42.28	75.20	43.18	73.68	44.04
54	76.64	42.31	75.15	43.21	73.63	44.07
56	76.59	42.34	75.10	43.24	73.58	44.09
58	76.55	42.37	75.05	43.27	73.52	44.12
60	76.50	42.40	75.00	43.30	73.47	44.15
$C = .75$	.66	.36	.65	.37	.65	.38
$C = 1.00$	.88	.48	.87	.49	.86	.51
$C = 1.25$	1.10	.60	1.09	.62	1.08	.63

TABLE B—LOGARITHMS OF NUMBERS

N.	0	1	2	3	4	5	6	7	8	9	Diff.
100	000000	0434	0868	1301	1734	2166	2598	3029	3461	3891	432
101	4321	4751	5181	5609	6038	6466	6894	7321	7748	8174	428
102	8600	9026	9451	9876	*0300	*0724	*1147	*1570	*1993	*2415	424
103	012837	3259	3680	4100	4521	4940	5360	5779	6197	6616	420
104	7033	7451	7868	8284	8700	9116	9532	9947	*0361	*0775	416
105	021189	1603	2016	2428	2841	3252	3664	4075	4486	4896	412
106	5306	5715	6125	6533	6942	7350	7757	8164	8571	8978	408
107	9384	9789	*0195	*0600	*1004	*1408	*1812	*2216	*2619	*3021	404
108	033424	3826	4227	4628	5029	5430	5830	6230	6629	7028	400
109	7426	7825	8223	8620	9017	9414	9811	*0207	*0602	*0998	397

PROPORTIONAL PARTS

Diff.	1	2	3	4	5	6	7	8	9	Diff.
434	43	87	130	174	217	260	304	347	391	434
433	43	87	130	173	217	260	303	346	390	433
432	43	86	130	173	216	259	302	346	389	432
431	43	86	129	172	216	259	302	345	388	431
430	43	86	129	172	215	258	301	344	387	430
429	43	86	129	172	215	257	300	343	386	429
428	43	86	128	171	214	257	300	342	385	428
427	43	85	128	171	214	256	299	342	384	427
426	43	85	128	170	213	256	298	341	383	426
425	43	85	128	170	213	255	298	340	383	425
424	42	85	127	170	212	254	297	339	382	424
423	42	85	127	169	212	254	296	338	381	423
422	42	84	127	169	211	253	295	338	380	422
421	42	84	126	168	211	253	295	337	379	421
420	42	84	126	168	210	252	294	336	378	420
419	42	84	126	168	210	251	293	335	377	419
418	42	84	125	167	209	251	293	334	376	418
417	42	83	125	167	209	250	292	334	375	417
416	42	83	125	166	208	250	291	333	374	416
415	42	83	125	166	208	249	291	332	374	415
414	41	83	124	166	207	248	290	331	373	414
413	41	83	124	165	207	248	289	330	372	413
412	41	82	124	165	206	247	288	330	371	412
411	41	82	123	164	206	247	288	329	370	411
410	41	82	123	164	205	246	287	328	369	410
409	41	82	123	164	205	245	286	327	368	409
408	41	82	122	163	204	245	286	326	367	408
407	41	81	122	163	204	244	285	326	366	407
406	41	81	122	162	203	244	284	325	365	406
405	41	81	122	162	203	243	284	324	365	405
404	40	81	121	162	202	242	283	323	364	404
403	40	81	121	161	202	242	282	322	363	403
402	40	80	121	161	201	241	281	322	362	402
401	40	80	120	160	201	241	281	321	361	401
400	40	80	120	160	200	240	280	320	360	400
399	40	80	120	160	200	239	279	319	359	399
398	40	80	119	159	199	239	279	318	358	398
397	40	79	119	159	199	238	278	318	357	397
396	40	79	119	158	198	238	277	317	356	396
395	40	79	119	158	198	237	277	316	356	395
394	39	79	118	158	197	236	276	315	355	394
393	39	79	118	157	197	236	275	314	354	393
392	39	78	118	157	196	235	274	314	353	392
391	39	78	117	156	196	235	274	313	352	391
390	39	78	117	156	195	234	273	312	351	390
389	39	78	117	156	195	233	272	311	350	389
388	39	78	116	155	194	233	272	310	349	388

TABLE B—LOGARITHMS OF NUMBERS

N.	0	1	2	3	4	5	6	7	8	9	Diff.
110	041393	1787	2182	2576	2969	3362	3755	4148	4540	4932	393
111	5323	5714	6105	6495	6885	7275	7664	8053	8442	8830	390
112	9218	9606	9993	*0380	*0766	*1153	*1538	*1924	*2309	*2694	386
113	053078	3463	3846	4230	4613	4996	5378	5760	6142	6524	383
114	6905	7286	7666	8046	8426	8805	9185	9563	9942	*0320	379
115	060698	1075	1452	1829	2206	2582	2958	3333	3709	4083	376
116	4458	4832	5206	5580	5953	6326	6699	7071	7443	7815	373
117	8186	8557	8928	9298	9668	*0038	*0407	*0776	*1145	*1514	370
118	071882	2250	2617	2985	3352	3718	4085	4451	4816	5182	366
119	5547	5912	6276	6640	7004	7368	7731	8094	8457	8819	363
120	079181	9543	9904	*0266	*0626	*0987	*1347	*1707	*2067	*2426	360
121	082785	3144	3503	3861	4219	4576	4934	5291	5647	6004	357
122	6360	6716	7071	7426	7781	8136	8490	8845	9198	9552	355
123	9905	*0258	*0611	*0963	*1315	*1667	*2018	*2370	*2721	*3071	352
124	093422	3772	4122	4471	4820	5169	5518	5866	6215	6562	349

PROPORTIONAL PARTS

Diff.	1	2	3	4	5	6	7	8	9	Diff.
387	39	77	116	155	194	232	271	310	348	387
386	39	77	116	154	193	232	270	309	347	386
385	39	77	116	154	193	231	270	308	347	385
384	38	77	115	154	192	230	269	307	346	384
383	38	77	115	153	192	230	268	306	345	383
382	38	76	115	153	191	229	267	306	344	382
381	38	76	114	152	191	229	267	305	343	381
380	38	76	114	152	190	228	266	304	342	380
379	38	76	114	152	190	227	265	303	341	379
378	38	76	113	151	189	227	265	302	340	378
377	38	75	113	151	189	226	264	302	339	377
376	38	75	113	150	188	226	263	301	338	376
375	38	75	113	150	188	225	263	300	338	375
374	37	75	112	150	187	224	262	299	337	374
373	37	75	112	149	187	224	261	298	336	373
372	37	74	112	149	186	223	260	298	335	372
371	37	74	111	148	186	223	260	297	334	371
370	37	74	111	148	185	222	259	296	333	370
369	37	74	111	148	185	221	258	295	332	369
368	37	74	110	147	184	221	258	294	331	368
367	37	73	110	147	184	220	257	294	330	367
366	37	73	110	146	183	220	256	293	329	366
365	37	73	110	146	183	219	256	292	329	365
364	36	73	109	146	182	218	255	291	328	364
363	36	73	109	145	182	218	254	290	327	363
362	36	72	109	145	181	217	253	290	326	362
361	36	72	108	144	181	217	253	289	325	361
360	36	72	108	144	180	216	252	288	324	360
359	36	72	108	144	180	215	251	287	323	359
358	36	72	107	143	179	215	251	286	322	358
357	36	71	107	143	179	214	250	286	321	357
356	36	71	107	142	178	214	249	285	320	356
355	36	71	107	142	178	213	249	284	320	355
354	35	71	106	142	177	212	248	283	319	354
353	35	71	106	141	177	212	247	282	318	353
352	35	70	106	141	176	211	246	282	317	352
351	35	70	105	140	176	211	246	281	316	351
350	35	70	105	140	175	210	245	280	315	350
349	35	70	105	140	175	209	244	279	314	349
348	35	70	104	139	174	209	244	278	313	348
347	35	69	104	139	174	208	243	278	312	347

TABLE B—LOGARITHMS OF NUMBERS

N.	0	1	2	3	4	5	6	7	8	9	Diff.
125	096910	7257	7604	7951	8298	8644	8990	9335	9681	*0026	346
126	100371	0715	1059	1403	1747	2091	2434	2777	3119	3462	343
127	3804	4146	4487	4828	5169	5510	5851	6191	6531	6871	341
128	7210	7549	7888	8227	8565	8903	9241	9579	9916	*0253	338
129	110590	0926	1263	1599	1934	2270	2605	2940	3275	3609	335
130	113943	4277	4611	4944	5278	5611	5943	6276	6608	6940	333
131	7271	7603	7934	8265	8595	8926	9256	9586	9915	*0245	330
132	120574	0903	1231	1560	1888	2216	2544	2871	3198	3525	328
133	3852	4178	4504	4830	5156	5481	5806	6131	6456	6781	325
134	7105	7429	7753	8076	8399	8722	9045	9368	9690	*0012	323
135	130334	0655	0977	1298	1619	1939	2260	2580	2900	3219	321
136	3539	3858	4177	4496	4814	5133	5451	5769	6086	6403	318
137	6721	7037	7354	7671	7987	8303	8618	8934	9249	9564	316
138	9879	*0194	*0508	*0822	*1136	*1450	*1763	*2076	*2389	*2702	314
139	143015	3327	3639	3951	4263	4574	4885	5196	5507	5818	311

PROPORTIONAL PARTS

Diff.	1	2	3	4	5	6	7	8	9	Diff.
347	35	69	104	139	174	208	243	278	312	347
346	35	69	104	138	173	208	242	277	311	346
345	35	69	104	138	173	207	242	276	311	345
344	34	69	103	138	172	206	241	275	310	344
343	34	69	103	137	172	206	240	274	309	343
342	34	68	103	137	171	205	239	274	308	342
341	34	68	102	136	171	205	239	273	307	341
340	34	68	102	136	170	204	238	272	306	340
339	34	68	102	136	170	203	237	271	305	339
338	34	68	101	135	169	203	237	270	304	338
337	34	67	101	135	169	202	236	270	303	337
336	34	67	101	134	168	202	235	269	302	336
335	34	67	101	134	168	201	235	268	302	335
334	33	67	100	134	167	200	234	267	301	334
333	33	67	100	133	167	200	233	266	300	333
332	33	66	100	133	166	199	232	266	299	332
331	33	66	99	132	166	199	232	265	298	331
330	33	66	99	132	165	198	231	264	297	330
329	33	66	99	132	165	197	230	263	296	329
328	33	66	98	131	164	197	230	262	295	328
327	33	65	98	131	164	196	229	262	294	327
326	33	65	98	130	163	196	228	261	293	326
325	33	65	98	130	163	195	228	260	293	325
324	32	65	97	130	162	194	227	259	292	324
323	32	65	97	129	162	194	226	258	291	323
322	32	64	97	129	161	193	225	258	290	322
321	32	64	96	128	161	193	225	257	289	321
320	32	64	96	128	160	192	224	256	288	320
319	32	64	96	128	160	191	223	255	287	319
318	32	64	95	127	159	191	223	254	286	318
317	32	63	95	127	159	190	222	254	285	317
316	32	63	95	126	158	190	221	253	284	316
315	32	63	95	126	158	189	221	252	284	315
314	31	63	94	126	157	188	220	251	283	314
313	31	63	94	125	157	188	219	250	282	313
312	31	62	94	125	156	187	218	250	281	312
311	31	62	93	124	156	187	218	249	280	311
310	31	62	93	124	155	186	217	248	279	310
309	31	62	93	124	155	185	216	247	278	309
308	31	62	92	123	154	185	216	246	277	308
307	31	61	92	123	154	184	215	246	276	307

N.	0	1	2	3	4	5	6	7	8	9	Diff.
140	146128	6438	6748	7058	7367	7676	7985	8294	8603	8911	309
141	9219	9527	9835	*0142	*0449	*0756	*1063	*1370	*1676	*1982	307
142	152288	2594	2900	3205	3510	3815	4120	4424	4728	5032	305
143	5336	5640	5943	6246	6549	6852	7154	7457	7759	8061	303
144	8362	8664	8965	9266	9567	9868	*0168	*0469	*0769	*1068	301
145	161368	1667	1967	2266	2564	2863	3161	3460	3758	4055	299
146	4353	4650	4947	5244	5541	5838	6134	6430	6726	7022	297
147	7317	7613	7908	8203	8497	8792	9086	9380	9674	9968	295
148	170262	0555	0848	1141	1434	1726	2019	2311	2603	2895	293
149	3186	3478	3769	4060	4351	4641	4932	5222	5512	5802	291
150	176091	6381	6670	6959	7248	7536	7825	8113	8401	8689	289
151	8977	9264	9552	9839	*0126	*0413	*0699	*0986	*1272	*1558	287
152	181844	2129	2415	2700	2985	3270	3555	3839	4123	4407	285
153	4691	4975	5259	5542	5825	6108	6391	6674	6956	7239	283
154	7521	7803	8084	8366	8647	8928	9209	9490	9771	*0051	281
155	190332	0612	0892	1171	1451	1730	2010	2289	2567	2846	279
156	3125	3403	3681	3959	4237	4514	4792	5069	5346	5623	278
157	5900	6176	6453	6729	7005	7281	7556	7832	8107	8382	276
158	8657	8932	9206	9481	9755	*0029	*0303	*0577	*0850	*1124	274
159	201397	1670	1943	2216	2488	2761	3033	3305	3577	3848	272

PROPORTIONAL PARTS

Diff.	1	2	3	4	5	6	7	8	9	Diff.
306	31	61	92	122	153	184	214	245	275	306
305	31	61	92	122	153	183	214	244	275	305
304	30	61	91	122	152	182	213	243	274	304
303	30	61	91	121	152	182	212	242	273	303
302	30	60	91	121	151	181	211	242	272	302
301	30	60	90	120	151	181	211	241	271	301
300	30	60	90	120	150	180	210	240	270	300
299	30	60	90	120	150	179	209	239	269	299
298	30	60	89	119	149	179	209	238	268	298
297	30	59	89	119	149	178	208	238	267	297
296	30	59	89	118	148	178	207	237	266	296
295	30	59	89	118	148	177	207	236	266	295
294	29	59	88	118	147	176	206	235	265	294
293	29	59	88	117	147	176	205	234	264	293
292	29	58	88	117	146	175	204	234	263	292
291	29	58	87	116	146	175	204	233	262	291
290	29	58	87	116	145	174	203	232	261	290
289	29	58	87	116	145	173	202	231	260	289
288	29	58	86	115	144	173	202	230	259	288
287	29	57	86	115	144	172	201	230	258	287
286	29	57	86	114	143	172	200	229	257	286
285	29	57	86	114	143	171	200	228	257	285
284	28	57	85	114	142	170	199	227	256	284
283	28	57	85	113	142	170	198	226	255	283
282	28	56	85	113	141	169	197	226	254	282
281	28	56	84	112	141	169	197	225	253	281
280	28	56	84	112	140	168	196	224	252	280
279	28	56	84	112	140	167	195	223	251	279
278	28	56	83	111	139	167	195	222	250	278
277	28	55	83	111	139	166	194	222	249	277
276	28	55	83	110	138	166	193	221	248	276
275	28	55	83	110	138	165	193	220	248	275
274	27	55	82	110	137	164	192	219	247	274
273	27	55	82	109	137	164	191	218	246	273
272	27	54	82	109	136	163	190	218	245	272
271	27	54	81	108	136	163	190	217	244	271

TABLE B—LOGARITHMS OF NUMBERS

No. 179—Log. 255

N.	0	1	2	3	4	5	6	7	8	9	Diff.
160	204120	4391	4663	4934	5204	5475	5746	6016	6286	6556	271
161	6826	7096	7365	7634	7904	8173	8441	8710	8979	9247	269
162	9515	9783	*0051	*0319	*0586	*0853	*1121	*1388	*1654	*1921	267
163	212188	2454	2720	2986	3252	3518	3783	4049	4314	4579	266
164	4844	5109	5373	5638	5902	6166	6430	6694	6957	7221	264
165	217484	7747	8010	8273	8536	8798	9060	9323	9585	9846	262
166	220108	0370	0631	0892	1153	1414	1675	1936	2196	2456	261
167	2716	2976	3236	3496	3755	4015	4274	4533	4792	5051	259
168	5309	5568	5826	6084	6342	6600	6858	7115	7372	7630	258
169	7887	8144	8400	8657	8913	9170	9426	9682	9938	*0193	256
170	230449	0704	0960	1215	1470	1724	1979	2234	2488	2742	255
171	2996	3250	3504	3757	4011	4264	4517	4770	5023	5276	253
172	5528	5781	6033	6285	6537	6789	7041	7292	7544	7795	252
173	8046	8297	8548	8799	9049	9299	9550	9800	*0050	*0300	250
174	240549	0799	1048	1297	1546	1795	2044	2293	2541	2790	249
175	243038	3286	3534	3782	4030	4277	4525	4772	5019	5266	248
176	5513	5759	6006	6252	6499	6745	6991	7237	7482	7728	246
177	7973	8219	8464	8709	8954	9198	9443	9687	9932	*0176	245
178	250420	0664	0908	1151	1395	1638	1881	2125	2368	2610	243
179	2853	3096	3338	3580	3822	4064	4306	4548	4790	5031	242

PROPORTIONAL PARTS

Diff.	1	2	3	4	5	6	7	8	9	Diff.
272	27	54	82	109	136	163	190	218	245	272
271	27	54	81	108	136	163	190	217	244	271
270	27	54	81	108	135	162	189	216	243	270
269	27	54	81	108	135	161	188	215	242	269
268	27	54	80	107	134	161	188	214	241	268
267	27	53	80	107	134	160	187	214	240	267
266	27	53	80	106	133	160	186	213	239	266
265	27	53	80	106	133	159	186	212	239	265
264	26	53	79	106	132	158	185	211	238	264
263	26	53	79	105	132	158	184	210	237	263
262	26	52	79	105	131	157	183	210	236	262
261	26	52	78	104	131	157	183	209	235	261
260	26	52	78	104	130	156	182	208	234	260
259	26	52	78	104	130	155	181	207	233	259
258	26	52	77	103	129	155	181	206	232	258
257	26	51	77	103	129	154	180	206	231	257
256	26	51	77	102	128	154	179	205	230	256
255	26	51	77	102	128	153	179	204	230	255
254	25	51	76	102	127	152	178	203	229	254
253	25	51	76	101	127	152	177	202	228	253
252	25	50	76	101	126	151	176	202	227	252
251	25	50	75	100	126	151	176	201	226	251
250	25	50	75	100	125	150	175	200	225	250
249	25	50	75	100	125	149	174	199	224	249
248	25	50	74	99	124	149	174	198	223	248
247	25	49	74	99	124	148	173	198	222	247
246	25	49	74	98	123	148	172	197	221	246
245	25	49	74	98	123	147	172	196	221	245
244	24	49	73	98	122	146	171	195	220	244
243	24	49	73	97	122	146	170	194	219	243
242	24	48	73	97	121	145	169	194	218	242
241	24	48	72	96	121	145	169	193	217	241
240	24	48	72	96	120	144	168	192	216	240

329

N.	0	1	2	3	4	5	6	7	8	9	Diff.
180	255273	5514	5755	5996	6237	6477	6718	6958	7198	7439	241
181	7679	7918	8158	8398	8637	8877	9116	9355	9594	9833	239
182	260071	0310	0548	0787	1025	1263	1501	1739	1976	2214	238
183	2451	2688	2925	3162	3399	3636	3873	4109	4346	4582	237
184	4818	5054	5290	5525	5761	5996	6232	6467	6702	6937	235
185	267172	7406	7641	7875	8110	8344	8578	8812	9046	9279	234
186	9513	9746	9980	*0213	*0446	*0679	*0912	*1144	*1377	*1609	233
187	271842	2074	2306	2538	2770	3001	3233	3464	3696	3927	232
188	4158	4389	4620	4850	5081	5311	5542	5772	6002	6232	230
189	6462	6692	6921	7151	7380	7609	7838	8067	8296	8525	229
190	278754	8982	9211	9439	9667	9895	*0123	*0351	*0578	*0806	228
191	281033	1261	1488	1715	1942	2169	2396	2622	2849	3075	227
192	3301	3527	3753	3979	4205	4431	4656	4882	5107	5332	226
193	5557	5782	6007	6232	6456	6681	6905	7130	7354	7578	225
194	7802	8026	8249	8473	8696	8920	9143	9366	9589	9812	223
195	290035	0257	0480	0702	0925	1147	1369	1591	1813	2034	222
196	2256	2478	2699	2920	3141	3363	3584	3804	4025	4246	221
197	4466	4687	4907	5127	5347	5567	5787	6007	6226	6446	220
198	6665	6884	7104	7323	7542	7761	7979	8198	8416	8635	219
199	8853	9071	9289	9507	9725	9943	*0161	*0378	*0595	*0813	218
200	301030	1247	1464	1681	1898	2114	2331	2547	2764	2980	217
201	3196	3412	3628	3844	4059	4275	4491	4706	4921	5136	216
202	5351	5566	5781	5996	6211	6425	6639	6854	7068	7282	215
203	7496	7710	7924	8137	8351	8564	8778	8991	9204	9417	213
204	9630	9843	*0056	*0268	*0481	*0693	*0906	*1118	*1330	*1542	212

PROPORTIONAL PARTS

Diff.	1	2	3	4	5	6	7	8	9	Diff.
239	24	48	72	96	120	143	167	191	215	239
238	24	48	71	95	119	143	167	190	214	238
237	24	47	71	95	119	142	166	190	213	237
236	24	47	71	94	118	142	165	189	212	236
235	24	47	71	94	118	141	165	188	212	235
234	23	47	70	94	117	140	164	187	211	234
233	23	47	70	93	117	140	163	186	210	233
232	23	46	70	93	116	139	162	186	209	232
231	23	46	69	92	116	139	162	185	208	231
230	23	46	69	92	115	138	161	184	207	230
229	23	46	69	92	115	137	160	183	206	229
228	23	46	68	91	114	137	160	182	205	228
227	23	45	68	91	114	136	159	182	204	227
226	23	45	68	90	113	136	158	181	203	226
225	23	45	68	90	113	135	158	180	203	225
224	22	45	67	90	112	134	157	179	202	224
223	22	45	67	89	112	134	156	178	201	223
222	22	44	67	89	111	133	155	178	200	222
221	22	44	66	88	111	133	155	177	199	221
220	22	44	66	88	110	132	154	176	198	220
219	22	44	66	88	110	131	153	175	197	219
218	22	44	65	87	109	131	153	174	196	218
217	22	43	65	87	109	130	152	174	195	217
216	22	43	65	86	108	130	151	173	194	216
215	22	43	65	86	108	129	151	172	194	215
214	21	43	64	86	107	128	150	171	193	214
213	21	43	64	85	107	128	149	170	192	213
212	21	42	64	85	106	127	148	170	191	212

N.	0	1	2	3	4	5	6	7	8	9	Diff.
205	311754	1966	2177	2389	2600	2812	3023	3234	3445	3656	211
206	3867	4078	4289	4499	4710	4920	5130	5340	5551	5760	210
207	5970	6180	6390	6599	6809	7018	7227	7436	7646	7854	209
208	8063	8272	8481	8689	8898	9106	9314	9522	9730	9938	208
209	320146	0354	0562	0769	0977	1184	1391	1598	1805	2012	207
210	322219	2426	2633	2839	3046	3252	3458	3665	3871	4077	206
211	4282	4488	4694	4899	5105	5310	5516	5721	5926	6131	205
212	6336	6541	6745	6950	7155	7359	7563	7767	7972	8176	204
213	8380	8583	8787	8991	9194	9398	9601	9805	*0008	*0211	203
214	330414	0617	0819	1022	1225	1427	1630	1832	2034	2236	202
215	332438	2640	2842	3044	3246	3447	3649	3850	4051	4253	202
216	4454	4655	4856	5057	5257	5458	5658	5859	6059	6260	201
217	6460	6660	6860	7060	7260	7459	7659	7858	8058	8257	200
218	8456	8656	8855	9054	9253	9451	9650	9849	*0047	*0246	199
219	340444	0642	0841	1039	1237	1435	1632	1830	2028	2225	198
220	342423	2620	2817	3014	3212	3409	3606	3802	3999	4196	197
221	4392	4589	4785	4981	5178	5374	5570	5766	5962	6157	196
222	6353	6549	6744	6939	7135	7330	7525	7720	7915	8110	195
223	8305	8500	8694	8889	9083	9278	9472	9666	9860	*0054	194
224	350248	0442	0636	0829	1023	1216	1410	1603	1796	1989	193
225	352183	2375	2568	2761	2954	3147	3339	3532	3724	3916	193
226	4108	4301	4493	4685	4876	5068	5260	5452	5643	5834	192
227	6026	6217	6408	6599	6790	6981	7172	7363	7554	7744	191
228	7935	8125	8316	8506	8696	8886	9076	9266	9456	9646	190
229	9835	*0025	*0215	*0404	*0593	*0783	*0972	*1161	*1350	*1539	189
230	361728	1917	2105	2294	2482	2671	2859	3048	3236	3424	188
231	3612	3800	3988	4176	4363	4551	4739	4926	5113	5301	188
232	5488	5675	5862	6049	6236	6423	6610	6796	6983	7169	187
233	7356	7542	7729	7915	8101	8287	8473	8659	8845	9030	186
234	9216	9401	9587	9772	9958	*0143	*0328	*0513	*0698	*0883	185

PROPORTIONAL PARTS

Diff.	1	2	3	4	5	6	7	8	9	Diff.
212	21	42	64	85	106	127	148	170	191	212
211	21	42	63	84	106	127	148	169	190	211
210	21	42	63	84	105	126	147	168	189	210
209	21	42	63	84	105	125	146	167	188	209
208	21	42	62	83	104	125	146	166	187	208
207	21	41	62	83	104	124	145	166	186	207
206	21	41	62	82	103	124	144	165	185	206
205	21	41	62	82	103	123	144	164	185	205
204	20	41	61	82	102	122	143	163	184	204
203	20	41	61	81	102	122	142	162	183	203
202	20	40	61	81	101	121	141	162	182	202
201	20	40	60	80	101	121	141	161	181	201
200	20	40	60	80	100	120	140	160	180	200
199	20	40	60	80	100	119	139	159	179	199
198	20	40	59	79	99	119	139	158	178	198
197	20	39	59	79	99	118	138	158	177	197
196	20	39	59	78	98	118	137	157	176	196
195	20	39	59	78	98	117	137	156	176	195
194	19	39	58	78	97	116	136	155	175	194
193	19	39	58	77	97	116	135	154	174	193
192	19	38	58	77	96	115	134	154	173	192
191	19	38	57	76	96	115	134	153	172	191
190	19	38	57	76	95	114	133	152	171	190
189	19	38	57	76	95	113	132	151	170	189
188	19	38	56	75	94	113	132	150	169	188

N.	0	1	2	3	4	5	6	7	8	9	Diff.
235	371068	1253	1437	1622	1806	1991	2175	2360	2544	2728	184
236	2912	3096	3280	3464	3647	3831	4015	4198	4382	4565	184
237	4748	4932	5115	5298	5481	5664	5846	6029	6212	6394	183
238	6577	6759	6942	7124	7306	7488	7670	7852	8034	8216	182
239	8398	8580	8761	8943	9124	9306	9487	9668	9849	*0030	181
240	380211	0392	0573	0754	0934	1115	1296	1476	1656	1837	181
241	2017	2197	2377	2557	2737	2917	3097	3277	3456	3636	180
242	3815	3995	4174	4353	4533	4712	4891	5070	5249	5428	179
243	5606	5785	5964	6142	6321	6499	6677	6856	7034	7212	178
244	7390	7568	7746	7923	8101	8279	8456	8634	8811	8989	178
245	389166	9343	9520	9698	9875	*0051	*0228	*0405	*0582	*0759	177
246	390935	1112	1288	1464	1641	1817	1993	2169	2345	2521	176
247	2697	2873	3048	3224	3400	3575	3751	3926	4101	4277	176
248	4452	4627	4802	4977	5152	5326	5501	5676	5850	6025	175
249	6199	6374	6548	6722	6896	7071	7245	7419	7592	7766	174
250	397940	8114	8287	8461	8634	8808	8981	9154	9328	9501	173
251	9674	9847	*0020	*0192	*0365	*0538	*0711	*0883	*1056	*1228	173
252	401401	1573	1745	1917	2089	2261	2433	2605	2777	2949	172
253	3121	3292	3464	3635	3807	3978	4149	4320	4492	4663	171
254	4834	5005	5176	5346	5517	5688	5858	6029	6199	6370	171
255	406540	6710	6881	7051	7221	7391	7561	7731	7901	8070	170
256	8240	8410	8579	8749	8918	9087	9257	9426	9595	9764	169
257	9933	*0102	*0271	*0440	*0609	*0777	*0946	*1114	*1283	*1451	169
258	411620	1788	1956	2124	2293	2461	2629	2796	2964	3132	168
259	3300	3467	3635	3803	3970	4137	4305	4472	4639	4806	167
260	414973	5140	5307	5474	5641	5808	5974	6141	6308	6474	167
261	6641	6807	6973	7139	7306	7472	7638	7804	7970	8135	166
262	8301	8467	8633	8798	8964	9129	9295	9460	9625	9791	165
263	9956	*0121	*0286	*0451	*0616	*0781	*0945	*1110	*1275	*1439	165
264	421604	1768	1933	2097	2261	2426	2590	2754	2918	3082	164

PROPORTIONAL PARTS

Diff.	1	2	3	4	5	6	7	8	9	Diff.
187	19	37	56	75	94	112	131	150	168	187
186	19	37	56	74	93	112	130	149	167	186
185	19	37	56	74	93	111	130	148	167	185
184	18	37	55	74	92	110	129	147	166	184
183	18	37	55	73	92	110	128	146	165	183
182	18	36	55	73	91	109	127	146	164	182
181	18	36	54	72	91	109	127	145	163	181
180	18	36	54	72	90	108	126	144	162	180
179	18	36	54	72	90	107	125	143	161	179
178	18	36	53	71	89	107	125	142	160	178
177	18	35	53	71	89	106	124	142	159	177
176	18	35	53	70	88	106	123	141	158	176
175	18	35	53	70	88	105	123	140	158	175
174	17	35	52	70	87	104	122	139	157	174
173	17	35	52	69	87	104	121	138	156	173
172	17	34	52	69	86	103	120	138	155	172
171	17	34	51	68	86	103	120	137	154	171
170	17	34	51	68	85	102	119	136	153	170
169	17	34	51	68	85	101	118	135	152	169
168	17	34	50	67	84	101	118	134	151	168
167	17	33	50	67	84	100	117	134	150	167
166	17	33	50	66	83	100	116	133	149	166
165	17	33	50	66	83	99	116	132	149	165
164	16	33	49	66	82	98	115	131	148	164

N.	0	1	2	3	4	5	6	7	8	9	Diff.
265	423246	3410	3574	3737	3901	4065	4228	4392	4555	4718	164
266	4882	5045	5208	5371	5534	5697	5860	6023	6186	6349	163
267	6511	6674	6836	6999	7161	7324	7486	7648	7811	7973	162
268	8135	8297	8459	8621	8783	8944	9106	9268	9429	9591	162
269	9752	9914	*0075	*0236	*0398	*0559	*0720	*0881	*1042	*1203	161
270	431364	1525	1685	1846	2007	2167	2328	2488	2649	2809	161
271	2969	3130	3290	3450	3610	3770	3930	4090	4249	4409	160
272	4569	4729	4888	5048	5207	5367	5526	5685	5844	6004	159
273	6163	6322	6481	6640	6799	6957	7116	7275	7433	7592	159
274	7751	7909	8067	8226	8384	8542	8701	8859	9017	9175	158
275	439333	9491	9648	9806	9964	*0122	*0279	*0437	*0594	*0752	158
276	440909	1066	1224	1381	1538	1695	1852	2009	2166	2323	157
277	2480	2637	2793	2950	3106	3263	3419	3576	3732	3889	157
278	4045	4201	4357	4513	4669	4825	4981	5137	5293	5449	156
279	5604	5760	5915	6071	6226	6382	6537	6692	6848	7003	155
280	447158	7313	7468	7623	7778	7933	8088	8242	8397	8552	155
281	8706	8861	9015	9170	9324	9478	9633	9787	9941	*0095	154
282	450249	0403	0557	0711	0865	1018	1172	1326	1479	1633	154
283	1786	1940	2093	2247	2400	2553	2706	2859	3012	3165	153
284	3318	3471	3624	3777	3930	4082	4235	4387	4540	4692	153
285	454845	4997	5150	5302	5454	5606	5758	5910	6062	6214	152
286	6366	6518	6670	6821	6973	7125	7276	7428	7579	7731	152
287	7882	8033	8184	8336	8487	8638	8789	8940	9091	9242	151
288	9392	9543	9694	9845	9995	*0146	*0296	*0447	*0597	*0748	151
289	460898	1048	1198	1348	1499	1649	1799	1948	2098	2248	150
290	462398	2548	2697	2847	2997	3146	3296	3445	3594	3744	150
291	3893	4042	4191	4340	4490	4639	4788	4936	5085	5234	149
292	5383	5532	5680	5829	5977	6126	6274	6423	6571	6719	149
293	6868	7016	7164	7312	7460	7608	7756	7904	8052	8200	148
294	8347	8495	8643	8790	8938	9085	9233	9380	9527	9675	148
295	469822	9969	*0116	*0263	*0410	*0557	*0704	*0851	*0998	*1145	147
296	471292	1438	1585	1732	1878	2025	2171	2318	2464	2610	146
297	2756	2903	3049	3195	3341	3487	3633	3779	3925	4071	146
298	4216	4362	4508	4653	4799	4944	5090	5235	5381	5526	146
299	5671	5816	5962	6107	6252	6397	6542	6687	6832	6976	145

PROPORTIONAL PARTS

Diff.	1	2	3	4	5	6	7	8	9	Diff.
164	16	33	49	66	82	98	115	131	148	164
163	16	33	49	65	82	98	114	130	147	163
162	16	32	49	65	81	97	113	130	146	162
161	16	32	48	64	81	97	113	129	145	161
160	16	32	48	64	80	96	112	128	144	160
159	16	32	48	64	80	95	111	127	143	159
158	16	32	47	63	79	95	111	126	142	158
157	16	31	47	63	79	94	110	126	141	157
156	16	31	47	62	78	94	109	125	140	156
155	16	31	47	62	78	93	109	124	140	155
154	15	31	46	62	77	92	108	123	139	154
153	15	31	46	61	77	92	107	122	138	153
152	15	30	46	61	76	91	106	122	137	152
151	15	30	45	60	76	91	106	121	136	151
150	15	30	45	60	75	90	105	120	135	150
149	15	30	45	60	75	89	104	119	134	149
148	15	30	44	59	74	89	104	118	133	148
147	15	29	44	59	74	88	103	118	132	147
146	15	29	44	58	73	88	102	117	131	146
145	15	29	44	58	73	87	102	116	131	145
144	14	29	43	58	72	86	101	115	130	144
143	14	29	43	57	72	86	100	114	129	143

N.	0	1	2	3	4	5	6	7	8	9	Diff.
300	477121	7266	7411	7555	7700	7844	7989	8133	8278	8422	145
301	8566	8711	8855	8999	9143	9287	9431	9575	9719	9863	144
302	480007	0151'	0294	0438	0582	0725	0869	1012	1156	1299	144
303	1443	1586	1729	1872	2016	2159	2302	2445	2588	2731	143
304	2874	3016	3159	3302	3445	3587	3730	3872	4015	4157	143
305	484300	4442	4585	4727	4869	5011	5153	5295	5437	5579	142
306	5721	5863	6005	6147	6289	6430	6572	6714	6855	6997	142
307	7138	7280	7421	7563	7704	7845	7986	8127	8269	8410	141
308	8551	8692	8833	8974	9114	9255	9396	9537	9677	9818	141
309	9958	*0099	*0239	*0380	*0520	*0661	*0801	*0941	*1081	*1222	140
310	491362	1502	1642	1782	1922	2062	2201	2341	2481	2621	140
311	2760	2900	3040	3179	3319	3458	3597	3737	3876	4015	139
312	4155	4294	4433	4572	4711	4850	4989	5128	5267	5406	139
313	5544	5683	5822	5960	6099	6238	6376	6515	6653	6791	139
314	6930	7068	7206	7344	7483	7621	7759	7897	8035	8173	138
315	498311	8448	8586	8724	8862	8999	9137	9275	9412	9550	138
316	9687	9824	9962	*0099	*0236	*0374	*0511	*0648	*0785	*0922	137
317	501059	1196	1333	1470	1607	1744	1880	2017	2154	2291	137
318	2427	2564	2700	2837	2973	3109	3246	3382	3518	3655	136
319	3791	3927	4063	4199	4335	4471	4607	4743	4878	5014	136
320	505150	5286	5421	5557	5693	5828	5964	6099	6234	6370	136
321	6505	6640	6776	6911	7046	7181	7316	7451	7586	7721	135
322	7856	7991	8126	8260	8395	8530	8664	8799	8934	9068	135
323	9203	9337	9471	9606	9740	9874	*0009	*0143	*0277	*0411	134
324	510545	0679	0813	0947	1081	1215	1349	1482	1616	1750	134
325	511883	2017	2151	2284	2418	2551	2684	2818	2951	3084	133
326	3218	3351	3484	3617	3750	3883	4016	4149	4282	4415	133
327	4548	4681	4813	4946	5079	5211	5344	5476	5609	5741	133
328	5874	6006	6139	6271	6403	6535	6668	6800	6932	7064	132
329	7196	7328	7460	7592	7724	7855	7987	8119	8251	8382	132
330	518514	8646	8777	8909	9040	9171	9303	9434	9566	9697	131
331	9828	9959	*0090	*0221	*0353	*0484	*0615	*0745	*0876	*1007	131
332	521138	1269	1400	1530	1661	1792	1922	2053	2183	2314	131
333	2444	2575	2705	2835	2966	3096	3226	3356	3486	3616	130
334	3746	3876	4006	4136	4266	4396	4526	4656	4785	4915	130
335	525045	5174	5304	5434	5563	5693	5822	5951	6081	6210	129
336	6339	6469	6598	6727	6856	6985	7114	7243	7372	7501	129
337	7630	7759	7888	8016	8145	8274	8402	8531	8660	8788	129
338	8917	9045	9174	9302	9430	9559	9687	9815	9943	*0072	128
339	530200	0328	0456	0584	0712	0840	0968	1096	1223	1351	128

PROPORTIONAL PARTS

Diff.	1	2	3	4	5	6	7	8	9	Diff.
142	14	28	43	57	71	85	99	114	128	142
141	14	28	42	56	71	85	99	113	127	141
140	14	28	42	56	70	84	98	112	126	140
139	14	28	42	56	70	83	97	111	125	139
138	14	28	41	55	69	83	97	110	124	138
137	14	27	41	55	69	82	96	110	123	137
136	14	27	41	54	68	82	95	109	122	136
135	14	27	41	54	68	81	95	108	122	135
134	13	27	40	54	67	80	94	107	121	134
133	13	27	40	53	67	80	93	106	120	133
132	13	26	40	53	66	79	92	106	119	132
131	13	26	39	52	66	79	92	105	118	131
130	13	26	39	52	65	78	91	104	117	130
129	13	26	39	52	65	77	90	103	116	129
128	13	26	38	51	64	77	90	102	115	128
127	13	25	38	51	64	76	89	102	114	127

TABLE B—LOGARITHMS OF NUMBERS

No. 340—Log. 531   No. 379—Log. 579

N.	0	1	2	3	4	5	6	7	8	9	Diff.
340	531479	1607	1734	1862	1990	2117	2245	2372	2500	2627	128
341	2754	2882	3009	3136	3264	3391	3518	3645	3772	3899	127
342	4026	4153	4280	4407	4534	4661	4787	4914	5041	5167	127
343	5294	5421	5547	5674	5800	5927	6053	6180	6306	6432	126
344	6558	6685	6811	6937	7063	7189	7315	7441	7567	7693	126
345	537819	7945	8071	8197	8322	8448	8574	8699	8825	8951	126
346	9076	9202	9327	9452	9578	9703	9829	9954	*0079	*0204	125
347	540329	0455	0580	0705	0830	0955	1080	1205	1330	1454	125
348	1579	1704	1829	1953	2078	2203	2327	2452	2576	2701	125
349	2825	2950	3074	3199	3323	3447	3571	3696	3820	3944	124
350	544068	4192	4316	4440	4564	4688	4812	4936	5060	5183	124
351	5307	5431	5555	5678	5802	5925	6049	6172	6296	6419	124
352	6543	6666	6789	6913	7036	7159	7282	7405	7529	7652	123
353	7775	7898	8021	8144	8267	8389	8512	8635	8758	8881	123
354	9003	9126	9249	9371	9494	9616	9739	9861	9984	*0106	123
355	550228	0351	0473	0595	0717	0840	0962	1084	1206	1328	122
356	1450	1572	1694	1816	1938	2060	2181	2303	2425	2547	122
357	2668	2790	2911	3033	3155	3276	3398	3519	3640	3762	121
358	3883	4004	4126	4247	4368	4489	4610	4731	4852	4973	121
359	5094	5215	5336	5457	5578	5699	5820	5940	6061	6182	121
360	556303	6423	6544	6664	6785	6905	7026	7146	7267	7387	120
361	7507	7627	7748	7868	7988	8108	8228	8349	8469	8589	120
362	8709	8829	8948	9068	9188	9308	9428	9548	9667	9787	120
363	9907	*0026	*0146	*0265	*0385	*0504	*0624	*0743	*0863	*0982	119
364	561101	1221	1340	1459	1578	1698	1817	1936	2055	2174	119
365	562293	2412	2531	2650	2769	2887	3006	3125	3244	3362	119
366	3481	3600	3718	3837	3955	4074	4192	4311	4429	4548	119
367	4666	4784	4903	5021	5139	5257	5376	5494	5612	5730	118
368	5848	5966	6084	6202	6320	6437	6555	6673	6791	6909	118
369	7026	7144	7262	7379	7497	7614	7732	7849	7967	8084	118
370	568202	8319	8436	8554	8671	8788	8905	9023	9140	9257	117
371	9374	9491	9608	9725	9842	9959	*0076	*0193	*0309	*0426	117
372	570543	0660	0776	0893	1010	1126	1243	1359	1476	1592	117
373	1709	1825	1942	2058	2174	2291	2407	2523	2639	2755	116
374	2872	2988	3104	3220	3336	3452	3568	3684	3800	3915	116
375	574031	4147	4263	4379	4494	4610	4726	4841	4957	5072	116
376	5188	5303	5419	5534	5650	5765	5880	5996	6111	6226	115
377	6341	6457	6572	6687	6802	6917	7032	7147	7262	7377	115
378	7492	7607	7722	7836	7951	8066	8181	8295	8410	8525	115
379	8639	8754	8868	8983	9097	9212	9326	9441	9555	9669	114

PROPORTIONAL PARTS

Diff.	1	2	3	4	5	6	7	8	9	Diff.
128	13	26	38	51	64	77	90	102	115	128
127	13	25	38	51	64	76	89	102	114	127
126	13	25	38	50	63	76	88	101	113	126
125	13	25	38	50	63	75	88	100	113	125
124	12	25	37	50	62	74	87	99	112	124
123	12	25	37	49	62	74	86	98	111	123
122	12	24	37	49	61	73	85	98	110	122
121	12	24	36	48	61	73	85	97	109	121
120	12	24	36	48	60	72	84	96	108	120
119	12	24	36	48	60	71	83	95	107	119
118	12	24	35	47	59	71	83	94	106	118
117	12	23	35	47	59	70	82	94	105	117
116	12	23	35	46	58	70	81	93	104	116

TABLE B—LOGARITHMS OF NUMBERS

N.	0	1	2	3	4	5	6	7	8	9	Diff.
380	579784	9898	*0012	*0126	*0241	*0355	*0469	*0583	*0697	*0811	114
381	580925	1039	1153	1267	1381	1495	1608	1722	1836	1950	114
382	2063	2177	2291	2404	2518	2631	2745	2858	2972	3085	114
383	3199	3312	3426	3539	3652	3765	3879	3992	4105	4218	113
384	4331	4444	4557	4670	4783	4896	5009	5122	5235	5348	113
385	585461	5574	5686	5799	5912	6024	6137	6250	6362	6475	113
386	6587	6700	6812	6925	7037	7149	7262	7374	7486	7599	112
387	7711	7823	7935	8047	8160	8272	8384	8496	8608	8720	112
388	8832	8944	9056	9167	9279	9391	9503	9615	9726	9838	112
389	9950	*0061	*0173	*0284	*0396	*0507	*0619	*0730	*0842	*0953	112
390	591065	1176	1287	1399	1510	1621	1732	1843	1955	2066	111
391	2177	2288	2399	2510	2621	2732	2843	2954	3064	3175	111
392	3286	3397	3508	3618	3729	3840	3950	4061	4171	4282	111
393	4393	4503	4614	4724	4834	4945	5055	5165	5276	5386	110
394	5496	5606	5717	5827	5937	6047	6157	6267	6377	6487	110
395	596597	6707	6817	6927	7037	7146	7256	7366	7476	7586	110
396	7695	7805	7914	8024	8134	8243	8353	8462	8572	8681	110
397	8791	8900	9009	9119	9228	9337	9446	9556	9665	9774	109
398	9883	9992	*0101	*0210	*0319	*0428	*0537	*0646	*0755	*0864	109
399	600973	1082	1191	1299	1408	1517	1625	1734	1843	1951	109
400	602060	2169	2277	2386	2494	2603	2711	2819	2928	3036	108
401	3144	3253	3361	3469	3577	3686	3794	3902	4010	4118	108
402	4226	4334	4442	4550	4658	4766	4874	4982	5089	5197	108
403	5305	5413	5521	5628	5736	5844	5951	6059	6166	6274	108
404	6381	6489	6596	6704	6811	6919	7026	7133	7241	7348	107
405	607455	7562	7669	7777	7884	7991	8098	8205	8312	8419	107
406	8526	8633	8740	8847	8954	9061	9167	9274	9381	9488	107
407	9594	9701	9808	9914	*0021	*0128	*0234	*0341	*0447	*0554	107
408	610660	0767	0873	0979	1086	1192	1298	1405	1511	1617	106
409	1723	1829	1936	2042	2148	2254	2360	2466	2572	2678	106
410	612784	2890	2996	3102	3207	3313	3419	3525	3630	3736	106
411	3842	3947	4053	4159	4264	4370	4475	4581	4686	4792	106
412	4897	5003	5108	5213	5319	5424	5529	5634	5740	5845	105
413	5950	6055	6160	6265	6370	6476	6581	6686	6790	6895	105
414	7000	7105	7210	7315	7420	7525	7629	7734	7839	7943	105
415	618048	8153	8257	8362	8466	8571	8676	8780	8884	8989	105
416	9093	9198	9302	9406	9511	9615	9719	9824	9928	*0032	104
417	620136	0240	0344	0448	0552	0656	0760	0864	0968	1072	104
418	1176	1280	1384	1488	1592	1695	1799	1903	2007	2110	104
419	2214	2318	2421	2525	2628	2732	2835	2939	3042	3146	104

PROPORTIONAL PARTS

Diff.	1	2	3	4	5	6	7	8	9	Diff.
115	12	23	35	46	58	69	81	92	104	115
114	11	23	34	46	57	68	80	91	103	114
113	11	23	34	45	57	68	79	90	102	113
112	11	22	34	45	56	67	78	90	101	112
111	11	22	33	44	56	67	78	89	100	111
110	11	22	33	44	55	66	77	88	99	110
109	11	22	33	44	55	65	76	87	98	109
108	11	22	32	43	54	65	76	86	97	108
107	11	21	32	43	54	64	75	86	96	107
106	11	21	32	42	53	64	74	85	95	106
105	11	21	32	42	53	63	74	84	95	105
104	10	21	31	42	52	62	73	83	94	104
103	10	21	31	41	52	62	72	82	93	103

N.	0	1	2	3	4	5	6	7	8	9	Diff.
420	623249	3353	3456	3559	3663	3766	3869	3973	4076	4179	103
421	4282	4385	4488	4591	4695	4798	4901	5004	5107	5210	103
422	5312	5415	5518	5621	5724	5827	5929	6032	6135	6238	103
423	6340	6443	6546	6648	6751	6853	6956	7058	7161	7263	103
424	7366	7468	7571	7673	7775	7878	7980	8082	8185	8287	102
425	628389	8491	8593	8695	8797	8900	9002	9104	9206	9308	102
426	9410	9512	9613	9715	9817	9919	*0021	*0123	*0224	*0326	102
427	630428	0530	0631	0733	0835	0936	1038	1139	1241	1342	102
428	1444	1545	1647	1748	1849	1951	2052	2153	2255	2356	101
429	2457	2559	2660	2761	2862	2963	3064	3165	3266	3367	101
430	633468	3569	3670	3771	3872	3973	4074	4175	4276	4376	101
431	4477	4578	4679	4779	4880	4981	5081	5182	5283	5383	101
432	5484	5584	5685	5785	5886	5986	6087	6187	6287	6388	100
433	6488	6588	6688	6789	6889	6989	7089	7189	7290	7390	100
434	7490	7590	7690	7790	7890	7990	8090	8190	8290	8389	100
435	638489	8589	8689	8789	8888	8988	9088	9188	9287	9387	100
436	9486	9586	9686	9785	9885	9984	*0084	*0183	*0283	*0382	99
437	640481	0581	0680	0779	0879	0978	1077	1177	1276	1375	99
438	1474	1573	1672	1771	1871	1970	2069	2168	2267	2366	99
439	2465	2563	2662	2761	2860	2959	3058	3156	3255	3354	99
440	643453	3551	3650	3749	3847	3946	4044	4143	4242	4340	98
441	4439	4537	4636	4734	4832	4931	5029	5127	5226	5324	98
442	5422	5521	5619	5717	5815	5913	6011	6110	6208	6306	98
443	6404	6502	6600	6698	6796	6894	6992	7089	7187	72ₒₒ	98
444	7383	7481	7579	7676	7774	7872	7969	8067	8165	8262	98
445	648360	8458	8555	8653	8750	8848	8945	9043	9140	9237	97
446	9335	9432	9530	9627	9724	9821	9919	*0016	*0113	*0210	97
447	650308	0405	0502	0599	0696	0793	0890	0987	1084	1181	97
448	1278	1375	1472	1569	1666	1762	1859	1956	2053	2150	97
449	2246	2343	2440	2536	2633	2730	2826	2923	3019	3116	97
450	653213	3309	3405	3502	3598	3695	3791	3888	3984	4080	96
451	4177	4273	4369	4465	4562	4658	4754	4850	4946	5042	96
452	5138	5235	5331	5427	5523	5619	5715	5810	5906	6002	96
453	6098	6194	6290	6386	6482	6577	6673	6769	6864	6960	96
454	7056	7152	7247	7343	7438	7534	7629	7725	7820	7916	96
455	658011	8107	8202	8298	8393	8488	8584	8679	8774	8870	95
456	8965	9060	9155	9250	9346	9441	9536	9631	9726	9821	95
457	9916	*0011	*0106	*0201	*0296	*0391	*0486	*0581	*0676	*0771	95
458	660865	0960	1055	1150	1245	1339	1434	1529	1623	1718	95
459	1813	1907	2002	2096	2191	2286	2380	2475	2569	2663	95
460	662758	2852	2947	3041	3135	3230	3324	3418	3512	3607	94
461	3701	3795	3889	3983	4078	4172	4266	4360	4454	4548	94
462	4642	4736	4830	4924	5018	5112	5206	5299	5393	5487	94
463	5581	5675	5769	5862	5956	6050	6143	6237	6331	6424	94
464	6518	6612	6705	6799	6892	6986	7079	7173	7266	7360	94

PROPORTIONAL PARTS

Diff.	1	2	3	4	5	6	7	8	9	Diff.
104	10	21	31	42	52	62	73	83	94	104
103	10	21	31	41	52	62	72	82	93	103
102	10	20	31	41	51	61	71	82	92	102
101	10	20	30	40	51	61	71	81	91	101
100	10	20	30	40	50	60	70	80	90	100
99	10	20	30	40	50	59	69	79	89	99
98	10	20	29	39	49	59	69	78	88	98
97	10	19	29	39	49	58	68	78	87	97
96	10	19	29	38	48	58	67	77	86	96
95	10	19	29	38	48	57	67	76	86	95

TABLE B—LOGARITHMS OF NUMBERS

N.	0	1	2	3	4	5	6	7	8	9	Diff.
465	667453	7546	7640	7733	7826	7920	8013	8106	8199	8293	93
466	8386	8479	8572	8665	8759	8852	8945	9038	9131	9224	93
467	9317	9410	9503	9596	9689	9782	9875	9967	*0060	*0153	93
468	670246	0339	0431	0524	0617	0710	0802	0895	0988	1080	93
469	1173	1265	1358	1451	1543	1636	1728	1821	1913	2005	93
470	672098	2190	2283	2375	2467	2560	2652	2744	2836	2929	92
471	3021	3113	3205	3297	3390	3482	3574	3666	3758	3850	92
472	3942	4034	4126	4218	4310	4402	4494	4586	4677	4769	92
473	4861	4953	5045	5137	5228	5320	5412	5503	5595	5687	92
474	5778	5870	5962	6053	6145	6236	6328	6419	6511	6602	92
475	676694	6785	6876	6968	7059	7151	7242	7333	7424	7516	91
476	7607	7698	7789	7881	7972	8063	8154	8245	8336	8427	91
477	8518	8609	8700	8791	8882	8973	9064	9155	9246	9337	91
478	9428	9519	9610	9700	9791	9882	9973	*0063	*0154	*0245	91
479	680336	0426	0517	0607	0698	0789	0879	0970	1060	1151	91
480	681241	1332	1422	1513	1603	1693	1784	1874	1964	2055	90
481	2145	2235	2326	2416	2506	2596	2686	2777	2867	2957	90
482	3047	3137	3227	3317	3407	3497	3587	3677	3767	3857	90
483	3947	4037	4127	4217	4307	4396	4486	4576	4666	4756	90
484	4845	4935	5025	5114	5204	5294	5383	5473	5563	5652	90
485	685742	5831	5921	6010	6100	6189	6279	6368	6458	6547	89
486	6636	6726	6815	6904	6994	7083	7172	7261	7351	7440	89
487	7529	7618	7707	7796	7886	7975	8064	8153	8242	8331	89
488	8420	8509	8598	8687	8776	8865	8953	9042	9131	9220	89
489	9309	9398	9486	9575	9664	9753	9841	9930	*0019	*0107	89
490	690196	0285	0373	0462	0550	0639	0728	0816	0905	0993	89
491	1081	1170	1258	1347	1435	1524	1612	1700	1789	1877	88
492	1965	2053	2142	2230	2318	2406	2494	2583	2671	2759	88
493	2847	2935	3023	3111	3199	3287	3375	3463	3551	3639	88
494	3727	3815	3903	3991	4078	4166	4254	4342	4430	4517	88
495	694605	4693	4781	4868	4956	5044	5131	5219	5307	5394	88
496	5482	5569	5657	5744	5832	5919	6007	6094	6182	6269	87
497	6356	6444	6531	6618	6706	6793	6880	6968	7055	7142	87
498	7229	7317	7404	7491	7578	7665	7752	7839	7926	8014	87
499	8101	8188	8275	8362	8449	8535	8622	8709	8796	8883	87
500	698970	9057	9144	9231	9317	9404	9491	9578	9664	9751	87
501	9838	9924	*0011	*0098	*0184	*0271	*0358	*0444	*0531	*0617	87
502	700704	0790	0877	0963	1050	1136	1222	1309	1395	1482	86
503	1568	1654	1741	1827	1913	1999	2086	2172	2258	2344	86
504	2431	2517	2603	2689	2775	2861	2947	3033	3119	3205	86
505	703291	3377	3463	3549	3635	3721	3807	3893	3979	4065	86
506	4151	4236	4322	4408	4494	4579	4665	4751	4837	4922	86
507	5008	5094	5179	5265	5350	5436	5522	5607	5693	5778	86
508	5864	5949	6035	6120	6206	6291	6376	6462	6547	6632	85
509	6718	6803	6888	6974	7059	7144	7229	7315	7400	7485	85

PROPORTIONAL PARTS

Diff.	1	2	3	4	5	6	7	8	9	Diff.
94	9	19	28	38	47	56	66	75	85	94
93	9	19	28	37	47	56	65	74	84	93
92	9	18	28	37	46	55	64	74	83	92
91	9	18	27	36	46	55	64	73	82	91
90	9	18	27	36	45	54	63	72	81	90
89	9	18	27	36	45	53	62	71	80	89
88	9	18	26	35	44	53	62	70	79	88
87	9	17	26	35	44	52	61	70	78	87
86	9	17	26	34	43	52	60	69	77	86
85	9	17	26	34	43	51	60	68	77	85

N.	0	1	2	3	4	5	6	7	8	9	Diff.
510	707570	7655	7740	7826	7911	7996	8081	8166	8251	8336	85
511	8421	8506	8591	8676	8761	8846	8931	9015	9100	9185	85
512	9270	9355	9440	9524	9609	9694	9779	9863	9948	*0033	85
513	710117	0202	0287	0371	0456	0540	0625	0710	0794	0879	85
514	0963	1048	1132	1217	1301	1385	1470	1554	1639	1723	84
515	711807	1892	1976	2060	2144	2229	2313	2397	2481	2566	84
516	2650	2734	2818	2902	2986	3070	3154	3238	3323	3407	84
517	3491	3575	3659	3742	3826	3910	3994	4078	4162	4246	84
518	4330	4414	4497	4581	4665	4749	4833	4916	5000	5084	84
519	5167	5251	5335	5418	5502	5586	5669	5753	5836	5920	84
520	716003	6087	6170	6254	6337	6421	6504	6588	6671	6754	83
521	6838	6921	7004	7088	7171	7254	7338	7421	7504	7587	83
522	7671	7754	7837	7920	8003	8086	8169	8253	8336	8419	83
523	8502	8585	8668	8751	8834	8917	9000	9083	9165	9248	83
524	9331	9414	9497	9580	9663	9745	9828	9911	9994	*0077	83
525	720159	0242	0325	0407	0490	0573	0655	0738	0821	0903	83
526	0986	1068	1151	1233	1316	1398	1481	1563	1646	1728	82
527	1811	1893	1975	2058	2140	2222	2305	2387	2469	2552	82
528	2634	2716	2798	2881	2963	3045	3127	3209	3291	3374	82
529	3456	3538	3620	3702	3784	3866	3948	4030	4112	4194	82
530	724276	4358	4440	4522	4604	4685	4767	4849	4931	5013	82
531	5095	5176	5258	5340	5422	5503	5585	5667	5748	5830	82
532	5912	5993	6075	6156	6238	6320	6401	6483	6564	6646	82
533	6727	6809	6890	6972	7053	7134	7216	7297	7379	7460	81
534	7541	7623	7704	7785	7866	7948	8029	8110	8191	8273	81
535	728354	8435	8516	8597	8678	8759	8841	8922	9003	9084	81
536	9165	9246	9327	9408	9489	9570	9651	9732	9813	9893	81
537	9974	*0055	*0136	*0217	*0298	*0378	*0459	*0540	*0621	*0702	81
538	730782	0863	0944	1024	1105	1186	1266	1347	1428	1508	81
539	1589	1669	1750	1830	1911	1991	2072	2152	2233	2313	81
540	732394	2474	2555	2635	2715	2796	2876	2956	3037	3117	80
541	3197	3278	3358	3438	3518	3598	3679	3759	3839	3919	80
542	3999	4079	4160	4240	4320	4400	4480	4560	4640	4720	80
543	4800	4880	4960	5040	5120	5200	5279	5359	5439	5519	80
544	5599	5679	5759	5838	5918	5998	6078	6157	6237	6317	80
545	736397	6476	6556	6635	6715	6795	6874	6954	7034	7113	80
546	7193	7272	7352	7431	7511	7590	7670	7749	7829	7908	79
547	7987	8067	8146	8225	8305	8384	8463	8543	8622	8701	79
548	8781	8860	8939	9018	9097	9177	9256	9335	9414	9493	79
549	9572	9651	9731	9810	9889	9968	*0047	*0126	*0205	*0284	79
550	740363	0442	0521	0600	0678	0757	0836	0915	0994	1073	79
551	1152	1230	1309	1388	1467	1546	1624	1703	1782	1860	79
552	1939	2018	2096	2175	2254	2332	2411	2489	2568	2647	79
553	2725	2804	2882	2961	3039	3118	3196	3275	3353	3431	78
554	3510	3588	3667	3745	3823	3902	3980	4058	4136	4215	78

PROPORTIONAL PARTS

Diff.	1	2	3	4	5	6	7	8	9	Diff.
86	9	17	26	34	43	52	60	69	77	86
85	9	17	26	34	43	51	60	68	77	85
84	8	17	25	34	42	50	59	67	76	84
83	8	17	25	33	42	50	58	66	75	83
82	8	16	25	33	41	49	57	66	74	82
81	8	16	24	32	41	49	57	65	73	81
80	8	16	24	32	40	48	56	64	72	80
79	8	16	24	32	40	47	55	63	71	79

TABLE B—LOGARITHMS OF NUMBERS

No. 555—Log. 744   No. 599—Log. 778

N.	0	1	2	3	4	5	6	7	8	9	Diff.
555	744293	4371	4449	4528	4606	4684	4762	4840	4919	4997	78
556	5075	5158	5231	5309	5387	5465	5543	5621	5699	5777	78
557	5855	5933	6011	6089	6167	6245	6323	6401	6479	6556	78
558	6634	6712	6790	6868	6945	7023	7101	7179	7256	7334	78
559	7412	7489	7567	7645	7722	7800	7878	7955	8033	8110	78
560	748188	8266	8343	8421	8498	8576	8653	8731	8808	8885	77
561	8963	9040	9118	9195	9272	9350	9427	9504	9582	9659	77
562	9736	9814	9891	9968	*0045	*0123	*0200	*0277	*0354	*0431	77
563	750508	0586	0663	0740	0817	0894	0971	1048	1125	1202	77
564	1279	1356	1433	1510	1587	1664	1741	1818	1895	1972	77
565	752048	2125	2202	2279	2356	2433	2509	2586	2663	2740	77
566	2816	2893	2970	3047	3123	3200	3277	3353	3430	3506	77
567	3583	3660	3736	3813	3889	3966	4042	4119	4195	4272	77
568	4348	4425	4501	4578	4654	4730	4807	4883	4960	5036	76
569	5112	5189	5265	5341	5417	5494	5570	5646	5722	5799	76
570	755875	5951	6027	6103	6180	6256	6332	6408	6484	6560	76
571	6636	6712	6788	6864	6940	7016	7092	7168	7244	7320	76
572	7396	7472	7548	7624	7700	7775	7851	7927	8003	8079	76
573	8155	8230	8306	8382	8458	8533	8609	8685	8761	8836	76
574	8912	8988	9063	9139	9214	9290	9366	9441	9517	9592	76
575	759668	9743	9819	9894	9970	*0045	*0121	*0196	*0272	*0347	75
576	760422	0498	0573	0649	0724	0799	0875	0950	1025	1101	75
577	1176	1251	1326	1402	1477	1552	1627	1702	1778	1853	75
578	1928	2003	2078	2153	2228	2303	2378	2453	2529	2604	75
579	2679	2754	2829	2904	2978	3053	3128	3203	3278	3353	75
580	763428	3503	3578	3653	3727	3802	3877	3952	4027	4101	75
581	4176	4251	4326	4400	4475	4550	4624	4699	4774	4848	75
582	4923	4998	5072	5147	5221	5296	5370	5445	5520	5594	75
583	5669	5743	5818	5892	5966	6041	6115	6190	6264	6338	74
584	6413	6487	6562	6636	6710	6785	6859	6933	7007	7082	74
585	767156	7230	7304	7379	7453	7527	7601	7675	7749	7823	74
586	7898	7972	8046	8120	8194	8268	8342	8416	8490	8564	74
587	8638	8712	8786	8860	8934	9008	9082	9156	9230	9303	74
588	9377	9451	9525	9599	9673	9746	9820	9894	9968	*0042	74
589	770115	0189	0263	0336	0410	0484	0557	0631	0705	0778	74
590	770852	0926	0999	1073	1146	1220	1293	1367	1440	1514	74
591	1587	1661	1734	1808	1881	1955	2028	2102	2175	2248	73
592	2322	2395	2468	2542	2615	2688	2762	2835	2908	2981	73
593	3055	3128	3201	3274	3348	3421	3494	3567	3640	3713	73
594	3786	3860	3933	4006	4079	4152	4225	4298	4371	4444	73
595	774517	4590	4663	4736	4809	4882	4955	5028	5100	5173	73
596	5246	5319	5392	5465	5538	5610	5683	5756	5829	5902	73
597	5974	6047	6120	6193	6265	6338	6411	6483	6556	6629	73
598	6701	6774	6846	6919	6992	7064	7137	7209	7282	7354	73
599	7427	7499	7572	7644	7717	7789	7862	7934	8006	8079	72

PROPORTIONAL PARTS

Diff.	1	2	3	4	5	6	7	8	9	Diff.
78	8	16	23	31	39	47	55	62	70	78
77	8	15	23	31	39	46	54	62	69	77
76	8	15	23	30	38	46	53	61	68	76
75	8	15	23	30	38	45	53	60	68	75
74	7	15	22	30	37	44	52	59	67	74
73	7	15	22	29	37	44	51	58	66	73
72	7	14	22	29	36	43	50	58	65	72

No. 600—Log. 778   No. 649—Log. 812

N.	0	1	2	3	4	5	6	7	8	9	Diff.
600	778151	8224	8296	8368	8441	8513	8585	8658	8730	8802	72
601	8874	8947	9019	9091	9163	9236	9308	9380	9452	9524	72
602	9596	9669	9741	9813	9885	9957	*0029	*0101	*0173	*0245	72
603	780317	0389	0461	0533	0605	0677	0749	0821	0893	0965	72
604	1037	1109	1181	1253	1324	1396	1468	1540	1612	1684	72
605	781755	1827	1899	1971	2042	2114	2186	2258	2329	2401	72
606	2473	2544	2616	2688	2759	2831	2902	2974	3046	3117	72
607	3189	3260	3332	3403	3475	3546	3618	3689	3761	3832	71
608	3904	3975	4046	4118	4189	4261	4332	4403	4475	4546	71
609	4617	4689	4760	4831	4902	4974	5045	5116	5187	5259	71
610	785330	5401	5472	5543	5615	5686	5757	5828	5899	5970	71
611	6041	6112	6183	6254	6325	6396	6467	6538	6609	6680	71
612	6751	6822	6893	6964	7035	7106	7177	7248	7319	7390	71
613	7460	7531	7602	7673	7744	7815	7885	7956	8027	8098	71
614	8168	8239	8310	8381	8451	8522	8593	8663	8734	8804	71
615	788875	8946	9016	9087	9157	9228	9299	9369	9440	9510	71
616	9581	9651	9722	9792	9863	9933	*0004	*0074	*0144	*0215	70
617	790285	0356	0426	0496	0567	0637	0707	0778	0848	0918	70
618	0988	1059	1129	1199	1269	1340	1410	1480	1550	1620	70
619	1691	1761	1831	1901	1971	2041	2111	2181	2252	2322	70
620	792392	2462	2532	2602	2672	2742	2812	2882	2952	3022	70
621	3092	3162	3231	3301	3371	3441	3511	3581	3651	3721	70
622	3790	3860	3930	4000	4070	4139	4209	4279	4349	4418	70
623	4488	4558	4627	4697	4767	4836	4906	4976	5045	5115	70
624	5185	5254	5324	5393	5463	5532	5602	5672	5741	5811	70
625	795880	5949	6019	6088	6158	6227	6297	6366	6436	6505	69
626	6574	6644	6713	6782	6852	6921	6990	7060	7129	7198	69
627	7268	7337	7406	7475	7545	7614	7683	7752	7821	7890	69
628	7960	8029	8098	8167	8236	8305	8374	8443	8513	8582	69
629	8651	8720	8789	8858	8927	8996	9065	9134	9203	9272	69
630	799341	9409	9478	9547	9616	9685	9754	9823	9892	9961	69
631	800029	0098	0167	0236	0305	0373	0442	0511	0580	0648	69
632	0717	0786	0854	0923	0992	1061	1129	1198	1266	1335	69
633	1404	1472	1541	1609	1678	1747	1815	1884	1952	2021	69
634	2089	2158	2226	2295	2363	2432	2500	2568	2637	2705	68
635	802774	2842	2910	2979	3047	3116	3184	3252	3321	3389	68
636	3457	3525	3594	3662	3730	3798	3867	3935	4003	4071	68
637	4139	4208	4276	4344	4412	4480	4548	4616	4685	4753	68
638	4821	4889	4957	5025	5093	5161	5229	5297	5365	5433	68
639	5501	5569	5637	5705	5773	5841	5908	5976	6044	6112	68
640	806180	6248	6316	6384	6451	6519	6587	6655	6723	6790	68
641	6858	6926	6994	7061	7129	7197	7264	7332	7400	7467	68
642	7535	7603	7670	7738	7806	7873	7941	8008	8076	8143	68
643	8211	8279	8346	8414	8481	8549	8616	8684	8751	8818	67
644	8886	8953	9021	9088	9156	9223	9290	9358	9425	9492	67
645	809560	9627	9694	9762	9829	9896	9964	*0031	*0098	*0165	67
646	810233	0300	0367	0434	0501	0569	0636	0703	0770	0837	67
647	0904	0971	1039	1106	1173	1240	1307	1374	1441	1508	67
648	1575	1642	1709	1776	1843	1910	1977	2044	2111	2178	67
649	2245	2312	2379	2445	2512	2579	2646	2713	2780	2847	67

PROPORTIONAL PARTS

Diff.	1	2	3	4	5	6	7	8	9	Diff.
73	7	15	22	29	37	44	51	58	66	73
72	7	14	22	29	36	43	50	58	65	72
71	7	14	21	28	36	43	50	57	64	71
70	7	14	21	28	35	42	49	56	63	70
69	7	14	21	28	35	41	48	55	62	69
68	7	14	20	27	34	41	48	54	61	68

TABLE B—LOGARITHMS OF NUMBERS

No. 650—Log. 812   No. 699—Log. 845

N.	0	1	2	3	4	5	6	7	8	9	Diff.
650	812913	2980	3047	3114	3181	3247	3314	3381	3448	3514	67
651	3581	3648	3714	3781	3848	3914	3981	4048	4114	4181	67
652	4248	4314	4381	4447	4514	4581	4647	4714	4780	4847	67
653	4913	4980	5046	5113	5179	5246	5312	5378	5445	5511	66
654	5578	5644	5711	5777	5843	5910	5976	6042	6109	6175	66
655	816241	6308	6374	6440	6506	6573	6639	6705	6771	6838	66
656	6904	6970	7036	7102	7169	7235	7301	7367	7433	7499	66
657	7565	7631	7698	7764	7830	7896	7962	8028	8094	8160	66
658	8226	8292	8358	8424	8490	8556	8622	8688	8754	8820	66
659	8885	8951	9017	9083	9149	9215	9281	9346	9412	9478	66
660	819544	9610	9676	9741	9807	9873	9939	*0004	*0070	*0136	66
661	820201	0267	0333	0399	0464	0530	0595	0661	0727	0792	66
662	0858	0924	0989	1055	1120	1186	1251	1317	1382	1448	66
663	1514	1579	1645	1710	1775	1841	1906	1972	2037	2103	65
664	2168	2233	2299	2364	2430	2495	2560	2626	2691	2756	65
665	822822	2887	2952	3018	3083	3148	3213	3279	3344	3409	65
666	3474	3539	3605	3670	3735	3800	3865	3930	3996	4061	65
667	4126	4191	4256	4321	4386	4451	4516	4581	4646	4711	65
668	4776	4841	4906	4971	5036	5101	5166	5231	5296	5361	65
669	5426	5491	5556	5621	5686	5751	5815	5880	5945	6010	65
670	826075	6140	6204	6269	6334	6399	6464	6528	6593	6658	65
671	6723	6787	6852	6917	6981	7046	7111	7175	7240	7305	65
672	7369	7434	7499	7563	7628	7692	7757	7821	7886	7951	65
673	8015	8080	8144	8209	8273	8338	8402	8467	8531	8595	64
674	8660	8724	8789	8853	8918	8982	9046	9111	9175	9239	64
675	829304	9368	9432	9497	9561	9625	9690	9754	9818	9882	64
676	9947	*0011	*0075	*0139	*0204	*0268	*0332	*0396	*0460	*0525	64
677	830589	0653	0717	0781	0845	0909	0973	1037	1102	1166	64
678	1230	1294	1358	1422	1486	1550	1614	1678	1742	1806	64
679	1870	1934	1998	2062	2126	2189	2253	2317	2381	2445	64
680	832509	2573	2637	2700	2764	2828	2892	2956	3020	3083	64
681	3147	3211	3275	3338	3402	3466	3530	3593	3657	3721	64
682	3784	3848	3912	3975	4039	4103	4166	4230	4294	4357	64
683	4421	4484	4548	4611	4675	4739	4802	4866	4929	4993	64
684	5056	5120	5183	5247	5310	5373	5437	5500	5564	5627	63
685	835691	5754	5817	5881	5944	6007	6071	6134	6197	6261	63
686	6324	6387	6451	6514	6577	6641	6704	6767	6830	6894	63
687	6957	7020	7083	7146	7210	7273	7336	7399	7462	7525	63
688	7588	7652	7715	7778	7841	7904	7967	8030	8093	8156	63
689	8219	8282	8345	8408	8471	8534	8597	8660	8723	8786	63
690	838849	8912	8975	9038	9101	9164	9227	9289	9352	9415	63
691	9478	9541	9604	9667	9729	9792	9855	9918	9981	*0043	63
692	840106	0169	0232	0294	0357	0420	0482	0545	0608	0671	63
693	0733	0796	0859	0921	0984	1046	1109	1172	1234	1297	63
694	1359	1422	1485	1547	1610	1672	1735	1797	1860	1922	63
695	841985	2047	2110	2172	2235	2297	2360	2422	2484	2547	62
696	2609	2672	2734	2796	2859	2921	2983	3046	3108	3170	62
697	3233	3295	3357	3420	3482	3544	3606	3669	3731	3793	62
698	3855	3918	3980	4042	4104	4166	4229	4291	4353	4415	62
699	4477	4539	4601	4664	4726	4788	4850	4912	4974	5036	62

PROPORTIONAL PARTS

Diff.	1	2	3	4	5	6	7	8	9	Diff.
67	7	13	20	27	34	40	47	54	60	67
66	7	13	20	26	33	40	46	53	59	66
65	7	13	20	26	33	39	46	52	59	65
64	6	13	19	26	32	38	45	51	58	64
63	6	13	19	25	32	38	44	50	57	63
62	6	12	19	25	31	37	43	50	56	62

N.	0	1	2	3	4	5	6	7	8	9	Diff.
700	845098	5160	5222	5284	5346	5408	5470	5532	5594	5656	62
701	5718	5780	5842	5904	5966	6028	6090	6151	6213	6275	62
702	6337	6399	6461	6523	6585	6646	6708	6770	6832	6894	62
703	6955	7017	7079	7141	7202	7264	7326	7388	7449	7511	62
704	7573	7634	7696	7758	7819	7881	7943	8004	8066	8128	62
705	848189	8251	8312	8374	8435	8497	8559	8620	8682	8743	62
706	8805	8866	8928	8989	9051	9112	9174	9235	9297	9358	61
707	9419	9481	9542	9604	9665	9726	9788	9849	9911	9972	61
708	850033	0095	0156	0217	0279	0340	0401	0462	0524	0585	61
709	0646	0707	0769	0830	0891	0952	1014	1075	1136	1197	61
710	851258	1320	1381	1442	1503	1564	1625	1686	1747	1809	61
711	1870	1931	1992	2053	2114	2175	2236	2297	2358	2419	61
712	2480	2541	2602	2663	2724	2785	2846	2907	2968	3029	61
713	3090	3150	3211	3272	3333	3394	3455	3516	3577	3637	61
714	3698	3759	3820	3881	3941	4002	4063	4124	4185	4245	61
715	854306	4367	4428	4488	4549	4610	4670	4731	4792	4852	61
716	4913	4974	5034	5095	5156	5216	5277	5337	5398	5459	61
717	5519	5580	5640	5701	5761	5822	5882	5943	6003	6064	61
718	6124	6185	6245	6306	6366	6427	6487	6548	6608	6668	60
719	6729	6789	6850	6910	6970	7031	7091	7152	7212	7272	60
720	857332	7393	7453	7513	7574	7634	7694	7755	7815	7875	60
721	7935	7995	8056	8116	8176	8236	8297	8357	8417	8477	60
722	8537	8597	8657	8718	8778	8838	8898	8958	9018	9078	60
723	9138	9198	9258	9318	9379	9439	9499	9559	9619	9679	60
724	9739	9799	9859	9918	9978	*0038	*0098	*0158	*0218	*0278	60
725	860338	0398	0458	0518	0578	0637	0697	0757	0817	0877	60
726	0937	0996	1056	1116	1176	1236	1295	1355	1415	1475	60
727	1534	1594	1654	1714	1773	1833	1893	1952	2012	2072	60
728	2131	2191	2251	2310	2370	2430	2489	2549	2608	2668	60
729	2728	2787	2847	2906	2966	3025	3085	3144	3204	3263	60
730	863323	3382	3442	3501	3561	3620	3680	3739	3799	3858	59
731	3917	3977	4036	4096	4155	4214	4274	4333	4392	4452	59
732	4511	4570	4630	4689	4748	4808	4867	4926	4985	5045	59
733	5104	5163	5222	5282	5341	5400	5459	5519	5578	5637	59
734	5696	5755	5814	5874	5933	5992	6051	6110	6169	6228	59
735	866287	6346	6405	6465	6524	6583	6642	6701	6760	6819	59
736	6878	6937	6996	7055	7114	7173	7232	7291	7350	7409	59
737	7467	7526	7585	7644	7703	7762	7821	7880	7939	7998	59
738	8056	8115	8174	8233	8292	8350	8409	8468	8527	8586	59
739	8644	8703	8762	8821	8879	8938	8997	9056	9114	9173	59
740	869232	9290	9349	9408	9466	9525	9584	9642	9701	9760	59
741	9818	9877	9935	9994	*0053	*0111	*0170	*0228	*0287	*0345	59
742	870404	0462	0521	0579	0638	0696	0755	0813	0872	0930	58
743	0989	1047	1106	1164	1223	1281	1339	1398	1456	1515	58
744	1573	1631	1690	1748	1806	1865	1923	1981	2040	2098	58
745	872156	2215	2273	2331	2389	2448	2506	2564	2622	2681	58
746	2739	2797	2855	2913	2972	3030	3088	3146	3204	3262	58
747	3321	3379	3437	3495	3553	3611	3669	3727	3785	3844	58
748	3902	3960	4018	4076	4134	4192	4250	4308	4366	4424	58
749	4482	4540	4598	4656	4714	4772	4830	4888	4945	5003	58

PROPORTIONAL PARTS

Diff.	1	2	3	4	5	6	7	8	9	Diff.
62	6	12	19	25	31	37	43	50	56	62
61	6	12	18	24	31	37	43	49	55	61
60	6	12	18	24	30	36	42	48	54	60
59	6	12	18	24	30	35	41	47	53	59
58	6	12	17	23	29	35	41	46	52	58

N.	0	1	2	3	4	5	6	7	8	9	Diff.
750	875061	5119	5177	5235	5293	5351	5409	5466	5524	5582	58
751	5640	5698	5756	5813	5871	5929	5987	6045	6102	6160	58
752	6218	6276	6333	6391	6449	6507	6564	6622	6680	6737	58
753	6795	6853	6910	6968	7026	7083	7141	7199	7256	7314	58
754	7371	7429	7487	7544	7602	7659	7717	7774	7832	7889	58
755	877947	8004	8062	8119	8177	8234	8292	8349	8407	8464	57
756	8522	8579	8637	8694	8752	8809	8866	8924	8981	9039	57
757	9096	9153	9211	9268	9325	9383	9440	9497	9555	9612	57
758	9669	9726	9784	9841	9898	9956	*0013	*0070	*0127	*0185	57
759	880242	0299	0356	0413	0471	0528	0585	0642	0699	0756	57
760	880814	0871	0928	0985	1042	1099	1156	1213	1271	1328	57
761	1385	1442	1499	1556	1613	1670	1727	1784	1841	1898	57
762	1955	2012	2069	2126	2183	2240	2297	2354	2411	2468	57
763	2525	2581	2638	2695	2752	2809	2866	2923	2980	3037	57
764	3093	3150	3207	3264	3321	3377	3434	3491	3548	3605	57
765	883661	3718	3775	3832	3888	3945	4002	4059	4115	4172	57
766	4229	4285	4342	4399	4455	4512	4569	4625	4682	4739	57
767	4795	4852	4909	4965	5022	5078	5135	5192	5248	5305	57
768	5361	5418	5474	5531	5587	5644	5700	5757	5813	5870	57
769	5926	5983	6039	6096	6152	6209	6265	6321	6378	6434	56
770	886491	6547	6604	6660	6716	6773	6829	6885	6942	6998	56
771	7054	7111	7167	7223	7280	7336	7392	7449	7505	7561	56
772	7617	7674	7730	7786	7842	7898	7955	8011	8067	8123	56
773	8179	8236	8292	8348	8404	8460	8516	8573	8629	8685	56
774	8741	8797	8853	8909	8965	9021	9077	9134	9190	9246	56
775	889302	9358	9414	9470	9526	9582	9638	9694	9750	9806	56
776	9862	9918	9974	*0030	*0086	*0141	*0197	*0253	*0309	*0365	56
777	890421	0477	0533	0589	0645	0700	0756	0812	0868	0924	56
778	0980	1035	1091	1147	1203	1259	1314	1370	1426	1482	56
779	1537	1593	1649	1705	1760	1816	1872	1928	1983	2039	56
780	892095	2150	2206	2262	2317	2373	2429	2484	2540	2595	56
781	2651	2707	2762	2818	2873	2929	2985	3040	3096	3151	56
782	3207	3262	3318	3373	3429	3484	3540	3595	3651	3706	56
783	3762	3817	3873	3928	3984	4039	4094	4150	4205	4261	55
784	4316	4371	4427	4482	4538	4593	4648	4704	4759	4814	55
785	894870	4925	4980	5036	5091	5146	5201	5257	5312	5367	55
786	5423	5478	5533	5588	5644	5699	5754	5809	5864	5920	55
787	5975	6030	6085	6140	6195	6251	6306	6361	6416	6471	55
788	6526	6581	6636	6692	6747	6802	6857	6912	6967	7022	55
789	7077	7132	7187	7242	7297	7352	7407	7462	7517	7572	55
790	897627	7682	7737	7792	7847	7902	7957	8012	8067	8122	55
791	8176	8231	8286	8341	8396	8451	8506	8561	8615	8670	55
792	8725	8780	8835	8890	8944	8999	9054	9109	9164	9218	55
793	9273	9328	9383	9437	9492	9547	9602	9656	9711	9766	55
794	9821	9875	9930	9985	*0039	*0094	*0149	*0203	*0258	*0312	55
795	900367	0422	0476	0531	0586	0640	0695	0749	0804	0859	55
796	0913	0968	1022	1077	1131	1186	1240	1295	1349	1404	55
797	1458	1513	1567	1622	1676	1731	1785	1840	1894	1948	54
798	2003	2057	2112	2166	2221	2275	2329	2384	2438	2492	54
799	2547	2601	2655	2710	2764	2818	2873	2927	2981	3036	54

PROPORTIONAL PARTS

Diff.	1	2	3	4	5	6	7	8	9	Diff.
57	6	11	17	23	29	34	40	46	51	57
56	6	11	17	22	28	34	39	45	50	56
55	6	11	17	22	28	33	39	44	50	55
54	5	11	16	22	27	32	38	43	49	54

No. 800—Log. 903   No. 849—Log. 929

N.	0	1	2	3	4	5	6	7	8	9	Diff.
800	903090	3144	3199	3253	3307	3361	3416	3470	3524	3578	54
801	3633	3687	3741	3795	3849	3904	3958	4012	4066	4120	54
802	4174	4229	4283	4337	4391	4445	4499	4553	4607	4661	54
803	4716	4770	4824	4878	4932	4986	5040	5094	5148	5202	54
804	5256	5310	5364	5418	5472	5526	5580	5634	5688	5742	54
805	905796	5850	5904	5958	6012	6066	6119	6173	6227	6281	54
806	6335	6389	6443	6497	6551	6604	6658	6712	6766	6820	54
807	6874	6927	6981	7035	7089	7143	7196	7250	7304	7358	54
808	7411	7465	7519	7573	7626	7680	7734	7787	7841	7895	54
809	7949	8002	8056	8110	8163	8217	8270	8324	8378	8431	54
810	908485	8539	8592	8646	8699	8753	8807	8860	8914	8967	54
811	9021	9074	9128	9181	9235	9289	9342	9396	9449	9503	54
812	9556	9610	9663	9716	9770	9823	9877	9930	9984	*0037	53
813	910091	0144	0197	0251	0304	0358	0411	0464	0518	0571	53
814	0624	0678	0731	0784	0838	0891	0944	0998	1051	1104	53
815	911158	1211	1264	1317	1371	1424	1477	1530	1584	1637	53
816	1690	1743	1797	1850	1903	1956	2009	2063	2116	2169	53
817	2222	2275	2328	2381	2435	2488	2541	2594	2647	2700	53
818	2753	2806	2859	2913	2966	3019	3072	3125	3178	3231	53
819	3284	3337	3390	3443	3496	3549	3602	3655	3708	3761	53
820	913814	3867	3920	3973	4026	4079	4132	4184	4237	4290	53
821	4343	4396	4449	4502	4555	4608	4660	4713	4766	4819	53
822	4872	4925	4977	5030	5083	5136	5189	5241	5294	5347	53
823	5400	5453	5505	5558	5611	5664	5716	5769	5822	5875	53
824	5927	5980	6033	6085	6138	6191	6243	6296	6349	6401	53
825	916454	6507	6559	6612	6664	6717	6770	6822	6875	6927	53
826	6980	7033	7085	7138	7190	7243	7295	7348	7400	7453	53
827	7506	7558	7611	7663	7716	7768	7820	7873	7925	7978	52
828	8030	8083	8135	8188	8240	8293	8345	8397	8450	8502	52
829	8555	8607	8659	8712	8764	8816	8869	8921	8973	9026	52
830	919078	9130	9183	9235	9287	9340	9392	9444	9496	9549	52
831	9601	9653	9706	9758	9810	9862	9914	9967	*0019	*0071	52
832	920123	0176	0228	0280	0332	0384	0436	0489	0541	0593	52
833	0645	0697	0749	0801	0853	0906	0958	1010	1062	1114	52
834	1166	1218	1270	1322	1374	1426	1478	1530	1582	1634	52
835	921686	1738	1790	1842	1894	1946	1998	2050	2102	2154	52
836	2206	2258	2310	2362	2414	2466	2518	2570	2622	2674	52
837	2725	2777	2829	2881	2933	2985	3037	3089	3140	3192	52
838	3244	3296	3348	3399	3451	3503	3555	3607	3658	3710	52
839	3762	3814	3865	3917	3969	4021	4072	4124	4176	4228	52
840	924279	4331	4383	4434	4486	4538	4589	4641	4693	4744	52
841	4796	4848	4899	4951	5003	5054	5106	5157	5209	5261	52
842	5312	5364	5415	5467	5518	5570	5621	5673	5725	5776	52
843	5828	5879	5931	5982	6034	6085	6137	6188	6240	6291	51
844	6342	6394	6445	6497	6548	6600	6651	6702	6754	6805	51
845	926857	6908	6959	7011	7062	7114	7165	7216	7268	7319	51
846	7370	7422	7473	7524	7576	7627	7678	7730	7781	7832	51
847	7883	7935	7986	8037	8088	8140	8191	8242	8293	8345	51
848	8396	8447	8498	8549	8601	8652	8703	8754	8805	8857	51
849	8908	8959	9010	9061	9112	9163	9215	9266	9317	9368	51

PROPORTIONAL PARTS

Diff.	1	2	3	4	5	6	7	8	9	Diff.
55	6	11	17	22	28	33	39	44	50	55
54	5	11	16	22	27	32	38	43	49	54
53	5	11	16	21	27	32	37	42	48	53
52	5	10	16	21	26	31	36	42	47	52

TABLE B—LOGARITHMS OF NUMBERS

N.	0	1	2	3	4	5	6	7	8	9	Diff.
850	929419	9470	9521	9572	9623	9674	9725	9776	9827	9879	51
851	9930	9981	*0032	*0083	*0134	*0185	*0236	*0287	*0338	*0389	51
852	930440	0491	0542	0592	0643	0694	0745	0796	0847	0898	51
853	0949	1000	1051	1102	1153	1204	1254	1305	1356	1407	51
854	1458	1509	1560	1610	1661	1712	1763	1814	1865	1915	51
855	931966	2017	2068	2118	2169	2220	2271	2322	2372	2423	51
856	2474	2524	2575	2626	2677	2727	2778	2829	2879	2930	51
857	2981	3031	3082	3133	3183	3234	3285	3335	3386	3437	51
858	3487	3538	3589	3639	3690	3740	3791	3841	3892	3943	51
859	3993	4044	4094	4145	4195	4246	4296	4347	4397	4448	51
860	934498	4549	4599	4650	4700	4751	4801	4852	4902	4953	50
861	5003	5054	5104	5154	5205	5255	5306	5356	5406	5457	50
862	5507	5558	5608	5658	5709	5759	5809	5860	5910	5960	50
863	6011	6061	6111	6162	6212	6262	6313	6363	6413	6463	50
864	6514	6564	6614	6665	6715	6765	6815	6865	6916	6966	50
865	937016	7066	7117	7167	7217	7267	7317	7367	7418	7468	50
866	7518	7568	7618	7668	7718	7769	7819	7869	7919	7969	50
867	8019	8069	8119	8169	8219	8269	8320	8370	8420	8470	50
868	8520	8570	8620	8670	8720	8770	8820	8870	8920	8970	50
869	9020	9070	9120	9170	9220	9270	9320	9369	9419	9469	50
870	939519	9569	9619	9669	9719	9769	9819	9869	9918	9968	50
871	940018	0068	0118	0168	0218	0267	0317	0367	0417	0467	50
872	0516	0566	0616	0666	0716	0765	0815	0865	0915	0964	50
873	1014	1064	1114	1163	1213	1263	1313	1362	1412	1462	50
874	1511	1561	1611	1660	1710	1760	1809	1859	1909	1958	50
875	942008	2058	2107	2157	2207	2256	2306	2355	2405	2455	50
876	2504	2554	2603	2653	2702	2752	2801	2851	2901	2950	50
877	3000	3049	3099	3148	3198	3247	3297	3346	3396	3445	49
878	3495	3544	3593	3643	3692	3742	3791	3841	3890	3939	49
879	3989	4038	4088	4137	4186	4236	4285	4335	4384	4433	49
880	944483	4532	4581	4631	4680	4729	4779	4828	4877	4927	49
881	4976	5025	5074	5124	5173	5222	5272	5321	5370	5419	49
882	5469	5518	5567	5616	5665	5715	5764	5813	5862	5912	49
883	5961	6010	6059	6108	6157	6207	6256	6305	6354	6403	49
884	6452	6501	6551	6600	6649	6698	6747	6796	6845	6894	49
885	946943	6992	7041	7090	7140	7189	7238	7287	7336	7385	49
886	7434	7483	7532	7581	7630	7679	7728	7777	7826	7875	49
887	7924	7973	8022	8070	8119	8168	8217	8266	8315	8364	49
888	8413	8462	8511	8560	8609	8657	8706	8755	8804	8853	49
889	8902	8951	8999	9048	9097	9146	9195	9244	9292	9341	49
890	949390	9439	9488	9536	9585	9634	9683	9731	9780	9829	49
891	9878	9926	9975	*0024	*0073	*0121	*0170	*0219	*0267	*0316	49
892	950365	0414	0462	0511	0560	0608	0657	0706	0754	0803	49
893	0851	0900	0949	0997	1046	1095	1143	1192	1240	1289	49
894	1338	1386	1435	1483	1532	1580	1629	1677	1726	1775	49
895	951823	1872	1920	1969	2017	2066	2114	2163	2211	2260	48
896	2308	2356	2405	2453	2502	2550	2599	2647	2696	2744	48
897	2792	2841	2889	2938	2986	3034	3083	3131	3180	3228	48
898	3276	3325	3373	3421	3470	3518	3566	3615	3663	3711	48
899	3760	3808	3856	3905	3953	4001	4049	4098	4146	4194	48

PROPORTIONAL PARTS

Diff.	1	2	3	4	5	6	7	8	9	Diff.
51	5	10	15	20	26	31	36	41	46	51
50	5	10	15	20	25	30	35	40	45	50
49	5	10	15	20	25	29	34	39	44	49
48	5	10	14	19	24	29	34	38	43	48

TABLE B—LOGARITHMS OF NUMBERS

N.	0	1	2	3	4	5	6	7	8	9	Diff.
900	954243	4291	4339	4387	4435	4484	4532	4580	4628	4677	48
901	4725	4773	4821	4869	4918	4966	5014	5062	5110	5158	48
902	5207	5255	5303	5351	5399	5447	5495	5543	5592	5640	48
903	5688	5736	5784	5832	5880	5928	5976	6024	6072	6120	48
904	6168	6216	6265	6313	6361	6409	6457	6505	6553	6601	48
905	956649	6697	6745	6793	6840	6888	6936	6984	7032	7080	48
906	7128	7176	7224	7272	7320	7368	7416	7464	7512	7559	48
907	7607	7655	7703	7751	7799	7847	7894	7942	7990	8038	48
908	8086	8134	8181	8229	8277	8325	8373	8421	8468	8516	48
909	8564	8612	8659	8707	8755	8803	8850	8898	8946	8994	48
910	959041	9089	9137	9185	9232	9280	9328	9375	9423	9471	48
911	9518	9566	9614	9661	9709	9757	9804	9852	9900	9947	48
912	9995	*0042	*0090	*0138	*0185	*0233	*0280	*0328	*0376	*0423	48
913	960471	0518	0566	0613	0661	0709	0756	0804	0851	0899	48
914	0946	0994	1041	1089	1136	1184	1231	1279	1326	1374	48
915	961421	1469	1516	1563	1611	1658	1706	1753	1801	1848	47
916	1895	1943	1990	2038	2085	2132	2180	2227	2275	2322	47
917	2369	2417	2464	2511	2559	2606	2653	2701	2748	2795	47
918	2843	2890	2937	2985	3032	3079	3126	3174	3221	3268	47
919	3316	3363	3410	3457	3504	3552	3599	3646	3693	3741	47
920	963788	3835	3882	3929	3977	4024	4071	4118	4165	4212	47
921	4260	4307	4354	4401	4448	4495	4542	4590	4637	4684	47
922	4731	4778	4825	4872	4919	4966	5013	5061	5108	5155	47
923	5202	5249	5296	5343	5390	5437	5484	5531	5578	5625	47
924	5672	5719	5766	5813	5860	5907	5954	6001	6048	6095	47
925	966142	6189	6236	6283	6329	6376	6423	6470	6517	6564	47
926	6611	6658	6705	6752	6799	6845	6892	6939	6986	7033	47
927	7080	7127	7173	7220	7267	7314	7361	7408	7454	7501	47
928	7548	7595	7642	7688	7735	7782	7829	7875	7922	7969	47
929	8016	8062	8109	8156	8203	8249	8296	8343	8390	8436	47
930	968483	8530	8576	8623	8670	8716	8763	8810	8856	8903	47
931	8950	8996	9043	9090	9136	9183	9229	9276	9323	9369	47
932	9416	9463	9509	9556	9602	9649	9695	9742	9789	9835	47
933	9882	9928	9975	*0021	*0068	*0114	*0161	*0207	*0254	*0300	47
934	970347	0393	0440	0486	0533	0579	0626	0672	0719	0765	46
935	970812	0858	0904	0951	0997	1044	1090	1137	1183	1229	46
936	1276	1322	1369	1415	1461	1508	1554	1601	1647	1693	46
937	1740	1786	1832	1879	1925	1971	2018	2064	2110	2157	46
938	2203	2249	2295	2342	2388	2434	2481	2527	2573	2619	46
939	2666	2712	2758	2804	2851	2897	2943	2989	3035	3082	46
940	973128	3174	3220	3266	3313	3359	3405	3451	3497	3543	46
941	3590	3636	3682	3728	3774	3820	3866	3913	3959	4005	46
942	4051	4097	4143	4189	4235	4281	4327	4374	4420	4466	46
943	4512	4558	4604	4650	4696	4742	4788	4834	4880	4926	46
944	4972	5018	5064	5110	5156	5202	5248	5294	5340	5386	46
945	975432	5478	5524	5570	5616	5662	5707	5753	5799	5845	46
946	5891	5937	5983	6029	6075	6121	6167	6212	6258	6304	46
947	6350	6396	6442	6488	6533	6579	6625	6671	6717	6763	46
948	6808	6854	6900	6946	6992	7037	7083	7129	7175	7220	46
949	7266	7312	7358	7403	7449	7495	7541	7586	7632	7678	46

PROPORTIONAL PARTS

Diff.	1	2	3	4	5	6	7	8	9	Diff.
49	5	10	15	20	25	29	34	39	44	49
48	5	10	14	19	24	29	34	38	43	48
47	5	9	14	19	24	28	33	38	42	47
46	5	9	14	18	23	28	32	37	41	46

N.	0	1	2	3	4	5	6	7	8	9	Diff.
950	977724	7769	7815	7861	7906	7952	7998	8043	8089	8135	46
951	8181	8226	8272	8317	8363	8409	8454	8500	8546	8591	46
952	8637	8683	8728	8774	8819	8865	8911	8956	9002	9047	46
953	9093	9138	9184	9230	9275	9321	9366	9412	9457	9503	46
954	9548	9594	9639	9685	9730	9776	9821	9867	9912	9958	46
955	980003	0049	0094	0140	0185	0231	0276	0322	0367	0412	45
956	0458	0503	0549	0594	0640	0685	0730	0776	0821	0867	45
957	0912	0957	1003	1048	1093	1139	1184	1229	1275	1320	45
958	1366	1411	1456	1501	1547	1592	1637	1683	1728	1773	45
959	1819	1864	1909	1954	2000	2045	2090	2135	2181	2226	45
960	982271	2316	2362	2407	2452	2497	2543	2588	2633	2678	45
961	2723	2769	2814	2859	2904	2949	2994	3040	3085	3130	45
962	3175	3220	3265	3310	3356	3401	3446	3491	3536	3581	45
963	3626	3671	3716	3762	3807	3852	3897	3942	3987	4032	45
964	4077	4122	4167	4212	4257	4302	4347	4392	4437	4482	45
965	984527	4572	4617	4662	4707	4752	4797	4842	4887	4932	45
966	4977	5022	5067	5112	5157	5202	5247	5292	5337	5382	45
967	5426	5471	5516	5561	5606	5651	5696	5741	5786	5830	45
968	5875	5920	5965	6010	6055	6100	6144	6189	6234	6279	45
969	6324	6369	6413	6458	6503	6548	6593	6637	6682	6727	45
970	986772	6817	6861	6906	6951	6996	7040	7085	7130	7175	45
971	7219	7264	7309	7353	7398	7443	7488	7532	7577	7622	45
972	7666	7711	7756	7800	7845	7890	7934	7979	8024	8068	45
973	8113	8157	8202	8247	8291	8336	8381	8425	8470	8514	45
974	8559	8604	8648	8693	8737	8782	8826	8871	8916	8960	45
975	989605	9049	9094	9138	9183	9227	9272	9316	9361	9405	45
976	9450	9494	9539	9583	9628	9672	9717	9761	9806	9850	44
977	9895	9939	9983	*0028	*0072	*0117	*0161	*0206	*0250	*0294	44
978	990339	0383	0428	0472	0516	0561	0605	0650	0694	0738	44
979	0783	0827	0871	0916	0960	1004	1049	1093	1137	1182	44
980	991226	1270	1315	1359	1403	1448	1492	1536	1580	1625	44
981	1669	1713	1758	1802	1846	1890	1935	1979	2023	2067	44
982	2111	2156	2200	2244	2288	2333	2377	2421	2465	2509	44
983	2554	2598	2642	2686	2730	2774	2819	2863	2907	2951	44
984	2995	3039	3083	3127	3172	3216	3260	3304	3348	3392	44
985	993436	3480	3524	3568	3613	3657	3701	3745	3789	3833	44
986	3877	3921	3965	4009	4053	4097	4141	4185	4229	4273	44
987	4317	4361	4405	4449	4493	4537	4581	4625	4669	4713	44
988	4757	4801	4845	4889	4933	4977	5021	5065	5108	5152	44
989	5196	5240	5284	5328	5372	5416	5460	5504	5547	5591	44
990	995635	5679	5723	5767	5811	5854	5898	5942	5986	6030	44
991	6074	6117	6161	6205	6249	6293	6337	6380	6424	6468	44
992	6512	6555	6599	6643	6687	6731	6774	6818	6862	6906	44
993	6949	6993	7037	7080	7124	7168	7212	7255	7299	7343	44
994	7386	7430	7474	7517	7561	7605	7648	7692	7736	7779	44
995	997823	7867	7910	7954	7998	8041	8085	8129	8172	8216	44
996	8259	8303	8347	8390	8434	8477	8521	8564	8608	8652	44
997	8695	8739	8782	8826	8869	8913	8956	9000	9043	9087	44
998	9131	9174	9218	9261	9305	9348	9392	9435	9479	9522	44
999	9565	9609	9652	9696	9739	9783	9826	9870	9913	9957	43

PROPORTIONAL PARTS

Diff.	1	2	3	4	5	6	7	8	9	Diff.
46	5	9	14	18	23	28	32	37	41	46
45	5	9	14	18	23	27	32	36	41	45
44	4	9	13	18	22	26	31	35	40	44
43	4	9	13	17	22	26	30	34	39	43

TABLE C—LOGARITHMIC SIN., COS., TAN., AND COT.

179°

M.	Sin.	D. 1".	Cos.	D. 1".	Tan.	D. 1".	Cot.	
0	− Inf.		10.000000		− Inf.		+ Inf.	60
1	6.463726	5017.17	.000000	.00	6.463726	5017.17	3.536274	59
2	.764756	2934.85	.000000	.00	.764756	2934.85	.235244	58
3	.940847	2082.32	.000000	.00	.940847	2082.32	.059153	57
4	7.065786	1615.17	.000000	.00	7.065786	1615.17	2.934214	56
5	7.162696	1319.68	10.000000	.00	7.162696	1319.70	2.837304	55
6	.241877	1115.78	9.999999	.02	.241878	1115.78	.758122	54
7	.308824	966.53	.999999	.00	.308825	966.53	.691175	53
8	.366816	852.53	.999999	.00	.366817	852.55	.633183	52
9	.417968	762.63	.999999	.00	.417970	762.62	.582030	51
10	7.463726	689.87	9.999998	.02	7.463727	689.88	2.536273	50
11	.505118	629.80	.999998	.00	.505120	629.82	.494880	49
12	.542906	579.37	.999997	.02	.542909	579.38	.457091	48
13	.577668	536.42	.999997	.00	.577672	536.42	.422328	47
14	.609853	499.38	.999996	.02	.609857	499.38	.390143	46
15	7.639816	467.15	9.999996	.00	7.639820	467.15	2.360180	45
16	.667845	438.80	.999995	.02	.667849	438.83	.332151	44
17	.694173	413.73	.999995	.00	.694179	413.73	.305821	43
18	.718997	391.35	.999994	.02	.719003	391.35	.280997	42
19	.742478	371.28	.999993	.02	.742484	371.28	.257516	41
20	7.764754	353.15	9.999993	.02	7.764761	353.17	2.235239	40
21	.785943	336.72	.999992	.02	.785951	336.73	.214049	39
22	.806146	321.75	.999991	.02	.806155	321.75	.193845	38
23	.825451	308.05	.999990	.02	.825460	308.07	.174540	37
24	.843934	295.47	.999989	.00	.843944	295.50	.156056	36
25	7.861662	283.88	9.999989	.02	7.861674	283.90	2.138326	35
26	.878695	273.17	.999988	.02	.878708	273.18	.121292	34
27	.895085	263.23	.999987	.02	.895099	263.25	.104901	33
28	.910879	254.00	.999986	.02	.910894	254.00	.089106	32
29	.926119	245.38	.999985	.03	.926134	245.40	.073866	31
30	7.940842	237.33	9.999983	.02	7.940858	237.37	2.059142	30
31	.955082	229.80	.999982	.02	.955100	229.82	.044900	29
32	.968870	222.72	.999981	.02	.968889	222.73	.031111	28
33	.982233	216.08	.999980	.02	.982253	216.10	.017747	27
34	.995198	209.82	.999979	.03	.995219	209.83	.004781	26
35	8.007787	203.90	9.999977	.02	8.007809	203.92	1.992191	25
36	.020021	198.30	.999976	.03	.020044	198.35	.979956	24
37	.031919	193.03	.999975	.03	.031945	193.03	.968055	23
38	.043501	188.00	.999973	.02	.043527	188.03	.956473	22
39	.054781	183.25	.999972	.02	.054809	183.28	.945191	21
40	8.065776	178.73	9.999971	.03	8.065806	178.75	1.934194	20
41	.076500	174.42	.999969	.02	.076531	174.43	.923469	19
42	.086965	170.30	.999968	.03	.086997	170.33	.913003	18
43	.097183	166.40	.999966	.03	.097217	166.43	.902783	17
44	.107167	162.65	.999964	.02	.107203	162.67	.892797	16
45	8.116926	159.08	9.999963	.03	8.116963	159.12	1.883037	15
46	.126471	155.65	.999961	.03	.126510	155.68	.873490	14
47	.135810	152.38	.999959	.02	.135851	152.42	.864149	13
48	.144953	149.23	.999958	.03	.144996	149.27	.855004	12
49	.153907	146.23	.999956	.03	.153952	146.25	.846048	11
50	8.162681	143.32	9.999954	.03	8.162727	143.35	1.837273	10
51	.171280	140.55	.999952	.03	.171328	140.58	.828672	9
52	.179713	137.87	.999950	.03	.179763	137.88	.820237	8
53	.187985	135.28	.999948	.03	.188036	135.33	.811964	7
54	.196102	132.80	.999946	.03	.196156	132.83	.803844	6
55	8.204070	130.42	9.999944	.03	8.204126	130.45	1.795874	5
56	.211895	128.10	.999942	.03	.211953	128.13	.788047	4
57	.219581	125.88	.999940	.03	.219641	125.90	.780359	3
58	.227134	123.72	.999938	.03	.227195	123.77	.772805	2
59	.234557	121.63	.999936	.03	.234621	121.67	.765379	1
60	8.241855		9.999934		8.241921		1.758079	0
	Cos.	D. 1".	Sin.	D. 1".	Cot.	D. 1".	Tan.	M.

90° 89°

349

TABLE C—LOGARITHMIC SINES,

1° 178°

M.	Sin.	D. 1″.	Cos.	D. 1″.	Tan.	D. 1″	Cot.	
0	8.241855	119.63	9.999934	.03	8.241921	119.68	1.758079	60
1	.249033	117.68	.999932	.05	.249102	117.72	.750898	59
2	.256094	115.80	.999929	.03	.256165	115.83	.743835	58
3	.263042	113.98	.999927	.03	.263115	114.02	.736885	57
4	.269881	112.22	.999925	.05	.269956	112.25	.730044	56
5	8.276614	110.48	9.999922	.03	8.276691	110.53	1.723309	55
6	.283243	108.83	.999920	.03	.283323	108.88	.716677	54
7	.289773	107.23	.999918	.05	.289856	107.27	.710144	53
8	.296207	105.65	.999915	.03	.296292	105.70	.703708	52
9	.302546	104.13	.999913	.05	.302634	104.17	.697366	51
10	8.308794	102.67	9.999910	.05	8.308884	102.70	1.691116	50
11	.314954	101.22	.999907	.03	.315046	101.27	.684954	49
12	.321027	99.82	.999905	.05	.321122	99.87	.678878	48
13	.327016	98.47	.999902	.05	.327114	98.52	.672886	47
14	.332924	97.15	.999899	.03	.333025	97.18	.666975	46
15	8.338753	95.85	9.999897	.05	8.338856	95.90	1.661144	45
16	.344504	94.62	.999894	.05	.344610	94.65	.655390	44
17	.350181	93.37	.999891	.05	.350289	93.43	.649711	43
18	.355783	92.20	.999888	.05	.355895	92.25	.644105	42
19	.361315	91.03	.999885	.05	.361430	91.08	.638570	41
20	8.366777	89.90	9.999882	.05	8.366895	89.95	1.633105	40
21	.372171	88.80	.999879	.05	.372292	88.83	.627708	39
22	.377499	87.72	.999876	.05	.377622	87.78	.622378	38
23	.382762	86.67	.999873	.05	.382889	86.72	.617111	37
24	.387962	85.65	.999870	.05	.388092	85.70	.611908	36
25	8.393101	84.63	9.999867	.05	8.393234	84.68	1.606766	35
26	.398179	83.67	.999864	.05	.398315	83.72	.601685	34
27	.403199	82.70	.999861	.05	.403338	82.77	.596662	33
28	.408161	81.78	.999858	.07	.408304	81.82	.591696	32
29	.413068	80.85	.999854	.05	.413213	80.92	.586787	31
30	8.417919	79.97	9.999851	.05	8.418068	80.02	1.581932	30
31	.422717	79.08	.999848	.07	.422869	79.15	.577131	29
32	.427462	78.23	.999844	.05	.427618	78.28	.572382	28
33	.432156	77.40	.999841	.05	.432315	77.45	.567685	27
34	.436800	76.57	.999838	.07	.436962	76.63	.563038	26
35	8.441394	75.78	9.999834	.05	8.441560	75.83	1.558440	25
36	.445941	74.98	.999831	.05	.446110	75.05	.553890	24
37	.450440	74.22	.999827	.05	.450613	74.28	.549387	23
38	.454893	73.47	.999824	.07	.455070	73.52	.544930	22
39	.459301	72.73	.999820	.07	.459481	72.80	.540519	21
40	8.463665	72.00	9.999816	.05	8.463849	72.05	1.536151	20
41	.467985	71.30	.999813	.07	.468172	71.37	.531828	19
42	.472263	70.58	.999809	.07	.472454	70.65	.527546	18
43	.476498	69.92	.999805	.07	.476693	69.98	.523307	17
44	.480693	69.25	.999801	.07	.480892	69.30	.519108	16
45	8.484848	68.58	9.999797	.05	8.485050	68.67	1.514950	15
46	.488963	67.95	.999794	.07	.489170	68.00	.510830	14
47	.493040	67.30	.999790	.07	.493250	67.38	.506750	13
48	.497078	66.70	.999786	.07	.497293	66.75	.502707	12
49	.501080	66.08	.999782	.07	.501298	66.15	.498702	11
50	8.505045	65.48	9.999778	.07	8.505267	65.55	1.494733	10
51	.508974	64.88	.999774	.08	.509200	64.97	.490800	9
52	.512867	64.32	.999769	.07	.513098	64.38	.486902	8
53	.516726	63.75	.999765	.07	.516961	63.82	.483039	7
54	.520551	63.20	.999761	.07	.520790	63.27	.479210	6
55	8.524343	62.65	9.999757	.07	8.524586	62.72	1.475414	5
56	.528102	62.10	.999753	.08	.528349	62.18	.471651	4
57	.531828	61.58	.999748	.07	.532080	61.65	.467920	3
58	.535523	61.05	.999744	.07	.535779	61.13	.464221	2
59	.539186	60.55	.999740	.08	.539447	60.62	.460553	1
60	8.542819		9.999735		8.543084		1.456916	0
	Cos.	D. 1″.	Sin.	D. 1″.	Cot.	D. 1″.	Tan.	M.

91° 88°

M.	Sin.	D. 1″.	Cos.	D. 1″.	Tan.	D. 1″.	Cot.	
0	8.542819	60.05	9.999735	.07	8.543084	60.12	1.456916	60
1	.546422	59.55	.999731	.08	.546691	59.62	.453309	59
2	.549995	59.07	.999726	.07	.550268	59.15	.449732	58
3	.553539	58.58	.999722	.08	.553817	58.65	.446183	57
4	.557054	58.10	.999717	.07	.557336	58.20	.442664	56
5	8.560540	57.65	9.999713	.08	8.560828	57.72	1.439172	55
6	.563999	57.20	.999708	.07	.564291	57.27	.435709	54
7	.567431	56.75	.999704	.08	.567727	56.83	.432273	53
8	.570836	56.30	.999699	.08	.571137	56.38	.428863	52
9	.574214	55.87	.999694	.08	.574520	55.95	.425480	51
10	8.577566	55.43	9.999689	.07	8.577877	55.52	1.422123	50
11	.580892	55.02	.999685	.08	.581208	55.10	.418792	49
12	.584193	54.60	.999680	.08	.584514	54.68	.415486	48
13	.587469	54.20	.999675	.08	.587795	54.27	.412205	47
14	.590721	53.78	.999670	.08	.591051	53.87	.408949	46
15	8.593948	53.40	9.999665	.08	8.594283	53.48	1.405717	45
16	.597152	53.00	.999660	.08	.597492	53.08	.402508	44
17	.600332	52.62	.999655	.08	.600677	52.70	.399323	43
18	.603489	52.23	.999650	.08	.603839	52.32	.396161	42
19	.606623	51.85	.999645	.08	.606978	51.93	.393022	41
20	8.609734	51.48	9.999640	.08	8.610094	51.58	1.389906	40
21	.612823	51.13	.999635	.10	.613189	51.22	.386811	39
22	.615891	50.77	.999629	.08	.616262	50.85	.383738	38
23	.618937	50.42	.999624	.08	.619313	50.50	.380687	37
24	.621962	50.05	.999619	.08	.622343	50.15	.377657	36
25	8.624965	49.72	9.999614	.10	8.625352	49.80	1.374648	35
26	.627948	49.38	.999608	.08	.628340	49.47	.371660	34
27	.630911	49.05	.999603	.10	.631308	49.13	.368692	33
28	.633854	48.70	.999597	.08	.634256	48.80	.365744	32
29	.636776	48.40	.999592	.10	.637184	48.48	.362816	31
30	8.639680	48.05	9.999586	.08	8.640093	48.15	1.359907	30
31	.642563	47.75	.999581	.10	.642982	47.85	.357018	29
32	.645428	47.43	.999575	.08	.645853	47.52	.354147	28
33	.648274	47.13	.999570	.10	.648704	47.22	.351296	27
34	.651102	46.82	.999564	.10	.651537	46.92	.348463	26
35	8.653911	46.52	9.999558	.08	8.654352	46.62	1.345648	25
36	.656702	46.22	.999553	.10	.657149	46.32	.342851	24
37	.659475	45.92	.999547	.10	.659928	46.02	.340072	23
38	.662230	45.63	.999541	.10	.662689	45.73	.337311	22
39	.664968	45.35	.999535	.10	.665433	45.45	.334567	21
40	8.667689	45.07	9.999529	.08	8.668160	45.17	1.331840	20
41	.670393	44.78	.999524	.10	.670870	44.88	.329130	19
42	.673080	44.52	.999518	.10	.673563	44.60	.326437	18
43	.675751	44.23	.999512	.10	.676239	44.35	.323761	17
44	.678405	43.97	.999506	.10	.678900	44.07	.321100	16
45	8.681043	43.70	9.999500	.12	8.681544	43.80	1.318456	15
46	.683665	43.45	.999493	.10	.684172	43.53	.315828	14
47	.686272	43.18	.999487	.10	.686784	43.28	.313216	13
48	.688863	42.92	.999481	.10	.689381	43.03	.310619	12
49	.691438	42.67	.999475	.10	.691963	42.77	.308037	11
50	8.693998	42.42	9.999469	.10	8.694529	42.53	1.305471	10
51	.696543	42.17	.999463	.12	.697081	42.27	.302919	9
52	.699073	41.93	.999456	.10	.699617	42.03	.300383	8
53	.701589	41.68	.999450	.12	.702139	41.78	.297861	7
54	.704090	41.45	.999443	.10	.704646	41.57	.295354	6
55	8.706577	41.20	9.999437	.10	8.707140	41.30	1.292860	5
56	.709049	40.97	.999431	.12	.709618	41.08	.290382	4
57	.711507	40.75	.999424	.10	.712083	40.85	.287917	3
58	.713952	40.52	.999418	.12	.714534	40.63	.285466	2
59	.716383	40.28	.999411	.12	.716972	40.40	.283028	1
60	8.718800		9.999404		8.719396		1.280604	0
	Cos.	D. 1″.	Sin.	D. 1″.	Cot.	D. 1″.	Tan.	M.

TABLE C—LOGARITHMIC SINES,

3° 176°

M.	Sin.	D. 1″.	Cos.	D. 1″.	Tan.	D. 1″.	Cot.	
0	8.718800	40.07	9.999404	.10	8.719396	40.17	1.280604	60
1	.721204	39.85	.999398	.12	.721806	39.97	.278194	59
2	.723595	39.62	.999391	.12	.724204	39.73	.275796	58
3	.725972	39.42	.999384	.12	.726588	39.52	.273412	57
4	.728337	39.18	.999378	.10	.728959	39.30	.271041	56
5	8.730688	38.98	9.999371	.12	8.731317	39.10	1.268683	55
6	.733027	38.78	.999364	.12	.733663	38.88	.266337	54
7	.735354	38.55	.999357	.12	.735996	38.68	.264004	53
8	.737667	38.37	.999350	.12	.738317	38.48	.261683	52
9	.739969	38.17	.999343	.12	.740626	38.27	.259374	51
10	8.742259	37.95	9.999336	.12	8.742922	38.08	1.257078	50
11	.744536	37.77	.999329	.12	.745207	37.87	.254793	49
12	.746802	37.55	.999322	.12	.747479	37.68	.252521	48
13	.749055	37.37	.999315	.12	.749740	37.48	.250260	47
14	.751297	37.18	.999308	.12	.751989	37.30	.248011	46
15	8.753528	36.98	9.999301	.12	8.754227	37.10	1.245773	45
16	.755747	36.80	.999294	.12	.756453	36.92	.243547	44
17	.757955	36.60	.999287	.13	.758668	36.73	.241332	43
18	.760151	36.43	.999279	.12	.760872	36.55	.239128	42
19	.762337	36.23	.999272	.12	.763065	36.35	.236935	41
20	8.764511	36.07	9.999265	.13	8.765246	36.18	1.234754	40
21	.766675	35.88	.999257	.12	.767417	36.02	.232583	39
22	.768828	35.70	.999250	.13	.769578	35.82	.230422	38
23	.770970	35.52	.999242	.12	.771727	35.65	.228273	37
24	.773101	35.37	.999235	.13	.773866	35.48	.226134	36
25	8.775223	35.17	9.999227	.12	8.775995	35.32	1.224005	35
26	.777333	35.02	.999220	.13	.778114	35.13	.221886	34
27	.779434	34.83	.999212	.12	.780222	34.97	.219778	33
28	.781524	34.68	.999205	.13	.782320	34.80	.217680	32
29	.783605	34.50	.999197	.13	.784408	34.63	.215592	31
30	8.785675	34.35	9.999189	.13	8.786486	34.47	1.213514	30
31	.787736	34.18	.999181	.12	.788554	34.32	.211446	29
32	.789787	34.02	.999174	.13	.790613	34.15	.209387	28
33	.791828	33.85	.999166	.13	.792662	33.98	.207338	27
34	.793859	33.70	.999158	.13	.794701	33.83	.205299	26
35	8.795881	33.55	9.999150	.13	8.796731	33.68	1.203269	25
36	.797894	33.38	.999142	.13	.798752	33.52	.201248	24
37	.799897	33.25	.999134	.13	.800763	33.37	.199237	23
38	.801892	33.07	.999126	.13	.802765	33.22	.197235	22
39	.803876	32.93	.999118	.13	.804758	33.07	.195242	21
40	8.805852	32.78	9.999110	.13	8.806742	32.92	1.193258	20
41	.807819	32.63	.999102	.13	.808717	32.77	.191283	19
42	.809777	32.48	.999094	.13	.810683	32.63	.189317	18
43	.811726	32.35	.999086	.15	.812641	32.47	.187359	17
44	.813667	32.20	.999077	.13	.814589	32.33	.185411	16
45	8.815599	32.05	9.999069	.13	8.816529	32.20	1.183471	15
46	.817522	31.90	.999061	.13	.818461	38.05	.181539	14
47	.819436	31.78	.999053	.15	.820384	31.90	.179616	13
48	.821343	31.62	.999044	.13	.822298	31.78	.177702	12
49	.823240	31.50	.999036	.15	.824205	31.63	.175795	11
50	8.825130	31.35	9.999027	.13	8.826103	31.48	1.173897	10
51	.827011	31.22	.999019	.15	.827992	31.37	.172008	9
52	.828884	31.08	.999010	.13	.829874	31.23	.170126	8
53	.830749	30.97	.999002	.15	.831748	31.08	.168252	7
54	.832607	30.82	.998993	.15	.833613	30.97	.166387	6
55	8.834456	30.68	9.998984	.13	8.835471	30.83	1.164529	5
56	.836297	30.55	.998976	.15	.837321	30.70	.162679	4
57	.838130	30.43	.998967	.15	.839163	30.58	.160837	3
58	.839956	30.30	.998958	.15	.840998	30.45	.159002	2
59	.841774	30.18	.998950	.13	.842825	30.32	.157175	1
60	8.843585		9.998941	.15	8.844644		1.155356	0
	Cos.	D. 1″.	Sin.	D. 1″.	Cot.	D. 1″.	Tan.	M.

COSINES, TANGENTS, AND COTANGENTS

M.	Sin.	D. 1″.	Cos.	D. 1″.	Tan.	D. 1″.	Cot.	
0	8.843585	30.03	9.998941	.15	8.844644	30.18	1.155356	60
1	.845387	29.93	.998932	.15	.846455	30.08	.153545	59
2	.847183	29.80	.998923	.15	.848260	29.95	.151740	58
3	.848971	29.67	.998914	.15	.850057	29.82	.149943	57
4	.850751	29.57	.998905	.15	.851846	29.70	.148154	56
5	8.852525	29.43	9.998896	.15	8.853628	29.58	1.146372	55
6	.854291	29.30	.998887	.15	.855403	29.47	.144597	54
7	.856049	29.20	.998878	.15	.857171	29.35	.142829	53
8	.857801	29.08	.998869	.15	.858932	29.23	.141068	52
9	.859546	28.95	.998860	.15	.860686	29.12	.139314	51
10	8.861283	28.85	9.998851	.17	8.862433	29.00	1.137567	50
11	.863014	28.73	.998841	.15	.864173	28.88	.135827	49
12	.864738	28.62	.998832	.15	.865906	28.77	.134094	48
13	.866455	28.50	.998823	.17	.867632	28.65	.132368	47
14	.868165	28.38	.998813	.15	.869351	28.55	.130649	46
15	8.869868	28.28	9.998804	.15	8.871064	28.43	1.128936	45
16	.871565	28.17	.998795	.17	.872770	28.32	.127230	44
17	.873255	28.05	.998785	.15	.874469	28.22	.125531	43
18	.874938	27.95	.998776	.17	.876162	28.12	.123838	42
19	.876615	27.83	.998766	.15	.877849	28.00	.122151	41
20	8.878285	27.73	9.998757	.17	8.879529	27.88	1.120471	40
21	.879949	27.63	.998747	.15	.881202	27.78	.118798	39
22	.881607	27.52	.998738	.17	.882869	27.68	.117131	38
23	.883258	27.42	.998728	.17	.884530	27.58	.115470	37
24	.884903	27.32	.998718	.17	.886185	27.47	.113815	36
25	8.886542	27.20	9.998708	.15	8.887833	27.38	1.112167	35
26	.888174	27.12	.998699	.17	.889476	27.27	.110524	34
27	.889801	27.00	.998689	.17	.891112	27.17	.108888	33
28	.891421	26.90	.998679	.17	.892742	27.07	.107258	32
29	.893035	26.80	.998669	.17	.894366	26.97	.105634	31
30	8.894643	26.72	9.998659	.17	8.895984	26.87	1.104016	30
31	.896246	26.60	.998649	.17	.897596	26.78	.102404	29
32	.897842	26.50	.998639	.17	.899203	26.67	.100797	28
33	.899432	26.42	.998629	.17	.900803	26.58	.099197	27
34	.901017	26.32	.998619	.17	.902398	26.48	.097602	26
35	8.902596	26.22	9.998609	.17	8.903987	26.38	1.096013	25
36	.904169	26.12	.998599	.17	.905570	26.28	.094430	24
37	.905736	26.02	.998589	.18	.907147	26.20	.092853	23
38	.907297	25.93	.998578	.17	.908719	26.10	.091281	22
39	.908853	25.85	.998568	.17	.910285	26.02	.089715	21
40	8.910404	25.75	9.998558	.17	8.911845	25.92	1.088154	20
41	.911949	25.65	.998548	.18	.913401	25.83	.086599	19
42	.913488	25.57	.998537	.17	.914951	25.73	.085049	18
43	.915022	25.47	.998527	.18	.916495	25.65	.083505	17
44	.916550	25.38	.998516	.17	.918034	25.57	.081966	16
45	8.918073	25.30	9.998506	.18	8.919568	25.47	1.080432	15
46	.919591	25.20	.998495	.17	.921096	25.38	.078904	14
47	.921103	25.12	.998485	.18	.922619	25.28	.077381	13
48	.922610	25.03	.998474	.17	.924136	25.22	.075864	12
49	.924112	24.95	.998464	.18	.925649	25.12	.074351	11
50	8.925609	24.85	9.998453	.18	8.927156	25.03	1.072844	10
51	.927100	24.78	.998442	.18	.928658	24.95	.071342	9
52	.928587	24.68	.998431	.17	.930155	24.87	.069845	8
53	.930068	24.60	.998421	.18	.931647	24.78	.068353	7
54	.931544	24.52	.998410	.18	.933134	24.70	.066866	6
55	8.933015	24.43	9.998399	.18	8.934616	24.62	1.065384	5
56	.934481	24.35	.998388	.18	.936093	24.53	.063907	4
57	.935942	24.27	.998377	.18	.937565	24.45	.062435	3
58	.937398	24.20	.998366	.18	.939032	24.37	.060968	2
59	.938850	24.10	.998355	.18	.940494	24.30	.059506	1
60	8.940296		9.998344		8.941952		1.058048	0
	Cos.	D. 1″.	Sin.	D. 1″.	Cot.	D. 1″.	Tan.	M.

TABLE C—LOGARITHMIC SINES,

M.	Sin.	D. 1″.	Cos.	D. 1″.	Tan.	D. 1″.	Cot.	
0	8.940296	24.03	9.998344	.18	8.941952	24.20	1.058048	60
1	.941738	23.93	.998333	.18	.943404	24.13	.056596	59
2	.943174	23.87	.998322	.18	.944852	24.05	.055148	58
3	.944606	23.80	.998311	.18	.946295	23.98	.053705	57
4	.946034	23.70	.998300	.18	.947734	23.90	.052266	56
5	8.947456	23.63	9.998289	.20	8.949168	23.82	1.050832	55
6	.948874	23.55	.998277	.18	.950597	23.73	.049403	54
7	.950287	23.48	.998266	.18	.952021	23.67	.047979	53
8	.951696	23.40	.998255	.20	.953441	23.58	.046559	52
9	.953100	23.32	.998243	.18	.954856	23.52	.045144	51
10	8.954499	23.25	9.998232	.20	8.956267	23.45	1.043733	50
11	.955894	23.17	.998220	.18	.957674	23.35	.042326	49
12	.957284	23.10	.998209	.20	.959075	23.30	.040925	48
13	.958670	23.03	.998197	.18	.960473	23.22	.039527	47
14	.960052	22.95	.998186	.20	.961866	23.15	.038134	46
15	8.961429	22.87	9.998174	.18	8.963255	23.07	1.036745	45
16	.962801	22.82	.998163	.20	.964639	23.00	.035361	44
17	.964170	22.73	.998151	.20	.966019	22.92	.033981	43
18	.965534	22.65	.998139	.18	.967394	22.87	.032606	42
19	.966893	22.60	.998128	.20	.968766	22.78	.031234	41
20	8.968249	22.52	9.998116	.20	8.970133	22.72	1.029867	40
21	.969600	22.45	.998104	.20	.971496	22.65	.028504	39
22	.970947	22.37	.998092	.20	.972855	22.57	.027145	38
23	.972289	22.32	.998080	.20	.974209	22.52	.025791	37
24	.973628	22.23	.998068	.20	.975560	22.43	.024440	36
25	8.974962	22.18	9.998056	.20	8.976906	22.37	1.023094	35
26	.976293	22.10	.998044	.20	.978248	22.30	.021752	34
27	.977619	22.03	.998032	.20	.979586	22.25	.020414	33
28	.978941	21.97	.998020	.20	.980921	22.17	.019079	32
29	.980259	21.90	.998008	.20	.982251	22.10	.017749	31
30	8.981573	21.83	9.997996	.20	8.983577	22.03	1.016423	30
31	.982883	21.77	.997984	.20	.984899	21.97	.015101	29
32	.984189	21.70	.997972	.22	.986217	21.92	.013783	28
33	.985491	21.63	.997959	.20	.987532	21.83	.012468	27
34	.986789	21.57	.997947	.20	.988842	21.78	.011158	26
35	8.988083	21.52	9.997935	.22	8.990149	21.70	1.009851	25
36	.989374	21.43	.997922	.20	.991451	21.65	.008549	24
37	.990660	21.38	.997910	.20	.992750	21.58	.007250	23
38	.991943	21.32	.997897	.22	.994045	21.53	.005955	22
39	.993222	21.25	.997885	.20	.995337	21.45	.004663	21
40	8.994497	21.18	9.997872	.22	8.996624	21.40	1.003376	20
41	.995768	21.13	.997860	.20	.997908	21.33	.002092	19
42	.997036	21.05	.997847	.22	.999188	21.28	.000812	18
43	.998299	21.02	.997835	.20	9.000465	21.22	0.999535	17
44	.999560	20.93	.997822	.22	.001738	21.15	.998262	16
45	9.000816	20.88	9.997809	.20	9.003007	21.08	0.996993	15
46	.002069	20.82	.997797	.22	.004272	21.03	.995728	14
47	.003318	20.75	.997784	.22	.005534	20.97	.994466	13
48	.004563	20.70	.997771	.22	.006792	20.92	.993208	12
49	.005805	20.65	.997758	.22	.008047	20.85	.991953	11
50	9.007044	20.57	9.997745	.22	9.009298	20.80	0.990702	10
51	.008278	20.53	.997732	.22	.010546	20.73	.989454	9
52	.009510	20.45	.997719	.22	.011790	20.68	.988210	8
53	.010737	20.42	.997706	.22	.013031	20.62	.986969	7
54	.011962	20.33	.997693	.22	.014268	20.57	.985732	6
55	9.013182	20.30	9.997680	.22	9.015502	20.50	0.984498	5
56	.014400	20.22	.997667	.22	.016732	20.45	.983268	4
57	.015613	20.18	.997654	.22	.017959	20.40	.982041	3
58	.016824	20.12	.997641	.22	.019183	20.33	.980817	2
59	.018031	20.07	.997628	.22	.020403	20.28	.979597	1
60	9.019235		9.997614	.23	9.021620		0.978380	0
	Cos.	D. 1″.	Sin.	D. 1″.	Cot.	D. 1″.	Tan.	M.

M.	Sin.	D. 1″.	Cos.	D. 1″.	Tan.	D. 1″.	Cot.	
0	9.019235	20.00	9.997614	.22	9.021620	20.23	0.978380	60
1	.020435	19.95	.997601	.22	.022834	20.17	.977166	59
2	.021632	19.88	.997588	.23	.024044	20.12	.975956	58
3	.022825	19.85	.997574	.22	.025251	20.07	.974749	57
4	.024016	19.78	.997561	.23	.026455	20.00	.973545	56
5	9.025203	19.72	9.997547	.22	9.027655	19.95	0.972345	55
6	.026386	19.68	.997534	.23	.028852	19.90	.971148	54
7	.027567	19.62	.997520	.22	.030046	19.85	.969954	53
8	.028744	19.57	.997507	.23	.031237	19.80	.968763	52
9	.029918	19.52	.997493	.22	.032425	19.73	.967575	51
10	9.031089	19.47	9.997480	.23	9.033609	19.70	0.966391	50
11	.032257	19.40	.997466	.23	.034791	19.63	.965209	49
12	.033421	19.35	.997452	.22	.035969	19.58	.964031	48
13	.034582	19.32	.997439	.23	.037144	19.53	.962856	47
14	.035741	19.25	.997425	.23	.038316	19.48	.961684	46
15	9.036896	19.20	9.997411	.23	9.039485	19.43	0.960515	45
16	.038048	19.15	.997397	.23	.040651	19.37	.959349	44
17	.039197	19.08	.997383	.23	.041813	19.33	.958187	43
18	.040342	19.05	.997369	.23	.042973	19.28	.957027	42
19	.041485	19.00	.997355	.23	.044130	19.23	.955870	41
20	9.042625	18.95	9.997341	.23	9.045284	19.17	0.954716	40
21	.043762	18.88	.997327	.23	.046434	19.13	.953566	39
22	.044895	18.85	.997313	.23	.047582	19.08	.952418	38
23	.046026	18.80	.997299	.23	.048727	19.03	.951273	37
24	.047154	18.75	.997285	.23	.049869	18.98	.950131	36
25	9.048279	18.68	9.997271	.23	9.051008	18.93	0.948992	35
26	.049400	18.65	.997257	.25	.052144	18.88	.947856	34
27	.050519	18.60	.997242	.23	.053277	18.83	.946723	33
28	.051635	18.57	.997228	.25	.054407	18.80	.945593	32
29	.052749	18.50	.997214	.23	.055535	18.73	.944465	31
30	9.053859	18.45	9.997199	.23	9.056659	18.70	0.943341	30
31	.054966	18.42	.997185	.25	.057781	18.65	.942219	29
32	.056071	18.35	.997170	.23	.058900	18.60	.941100	28
33	.057172	18.32	.997156	.25	.060016	18.57	.939984	27
34	.058271	18.27	.997141	.23	.061130	18.57	.938870	26
35	9.059367	18.22	9.997127	.25	9.062240	18.47	0.937760	25
36	.060460	18.18	.997112	.23	.063348	18.42	.936652	24
37	.061551	18.13	.997098	.25	.064453	18.38	.935547	23
38	.062639	18.08	.997083	.25	.065556	18.32	.934444	22
39	.063724	18.03	.997068	.25	.066655	18.28	.933345	21
40	9.064806	17.98	9.997053	.23	9.067752	18.23	0.932248	20
41	.065885	17.95	.997039	.25	.068846	18.20	.931154	19
42	.066962	17.90	.997024	.25	.069938	18.15	.930062	18
43	.068036	17.85	.997009	.25	.071027	18.10	.928973	17
44	.069107	17.82	.996994	.25	.072113	18.07	.927887	16
45	9.070176	17.77	9.996979	.25	9.073197	18.02	0.926803	15
46	.071242	17.73	.996964	.25	.074278	17.97	.925722	14
47	.072306	17.67	.996949	.25	.075356	17.93	.924644	13
48	.073366	17.63	.996934	.25	.076432	17.88	.923568	12
49	.074424	17.60	.996919	.25	.077505	17.85	.922495	11
50	9.075480	17.55	9.996904	.25	9.078576	17.80	0.921424	10
51	.076533	17.50	.996889	.25	.079644	17.77	.920356	9
52	.077583	17.47	.996874	.27	.080710	17.72	.919290	8
53	.078631	17.42	.996858	.25	.081773	17.67	.918227	7
54	.079676	17.38	.996843	.25	.082833	17.63	.917167	6
55	9.080719	17.33	9.996828	.27	9.083891	17.63	0.916109	5
56	.081759	17.30	.996812	.25	.084947	17.55	.915053	4
57	.082797	17.25	.996797	.25	.086000	17.50	.914000	3
58	.083832	17.20	.996782	.27	.087050	17.47	.912950	2
59	.084864	17.17	.996766	.25	.088098	17.43	.911902	1
60	9.085894		9.996751		9.089144		0.910856	0
	Cos.	D. 1″.	Sin.	D. 1″.	Cot.	D. 1″.	Tan.	M.

M.	Sin.	D. 1''.	Cos.	D. 1''.	Tan.	D. 1''.	Cot.	
0	9.085894	17.13	9.996751	.27	9.089144	17.38	0.910856	60
1	.086922	17.08	.996735	.25	.090187	17.35	.909813	59
2	.087947	17.05	.996720	.27	.091228	17.30	.908772	58
3	.088970	17.00	.996704	.27	.092266	17.27	.907734	57
4	.089990	16.97	.996688	.25	.093302	17.23	.906698	56
5	9.091008	16.93	9.996673	.27	9.094336	17.18	0.905664	55
6	.092024	16.88	.996657	.27	.095367	17.13	.904633	54
7	.093037	16.83	.996641	.27	.096395	17.12	.903605	53
8	.094047	16.82	.996625	.25	.097422	17.07	.902578	52
9	.095056	16.77	.996610	.27	.098446	17.03	.901554	51
10	9.096062	16.72	9.996594	.27	9.099468	16.98	0.900532	50
11	.097065	16.68	.996578	.27	.100487	16.95	.899513	49
12	.098066	16.65	.996562	.27	.101504	16.92	.898496	48
13	.099065	16.62	.996546	.27	.102519	16.88	.897481	47
14	.100062	16.57	.996530	.27	.103532	16.83	.896468	46
15	9.101056	16.53	9.996514	.27	9.104542	16.80	0.895458	45
16	.102048	16.48	.996498	.27	.105550	16.77	.894450	44
17	.103037	16.47	.996482	.28	.106556	16.72	.893444	43
18	.104025	16.42	.996465	.27	.107559	16.68	.892441	42
19	.105010	16.37	.996449	.27	.108560	16.65	.891440	41
20	9.105992	16.35	9.996433	.27	9.109559	16.62	0.890441	40
21	.106973	16.30	.996417	.28	.110556	16.58	.889444	39
22	.107951	16.27	.996400	.27	.111551	16.53	.888449	38
23	.108927	16.23	.996384	.27	.112543	16.50	.887457	37
24	.109901	16.20	.996368	.28	.113533	16.47	.886467	36
25	9.110873	16.15	9.996351	.27	9.114521	16.43	0.885479	35
26	.111842	16.12	.996335	.28	.115507	16.40	.884493	34
27	.112809	16.08	.996318	.27	.116491	16.35	.883509	33
28	.113774	16.05	.996302	.28	.117472	16.33	.882528	32
29	.114737	16.02	.996285	.27	.118452	16.28	.881548	31
30	9.115698	15.97	9.996269	.28	9.119429	16.25	0.880571	30
31	.116656	15.95	.996252	.28	.120404	16.22	.879596	29
32	.117613	15.90	.996235	.27	.121377	16.18	.878623	28
33	.118567	15.87	.996219	.28	.122348	16.15	.877652	27
34	.119519	15.83	.996202	.28	.123317	16.12	.876683	26
35	9.120469	15.80	9.996185	.28	9.124284	16.08	0.875716	25
36	.121417	15.75	.996168	.28	.125249	16.03	.874751	24
37	.122362	15.73	.996151	.28	.126211	16.02	.873789	23
38	.123306	15.70	.996134	.28	.127172	15.97	.872828	22
39	.124248	15.65	.996117	.28	.128130	15.95	.871870	21
40	9.125187	15.63	9.996100	.28	9.129087	15.90	0.870913	20
41	.126125	15.58	.996083	.28	.130041	15.88	.869959	19
42	.127060	15.55	.996066	.28	.130994	15.83	.869006	18
43	.127993	15.53	.996049	.28	.131944	15.82	.868056	17
44	.128925	15.48	.996032	.28	.132893	15.77	.867107	16
45	9.129854	15.45	9.996015	.28	9.133839	15.75	0.866161	15
46	.130781	15.42	.995998	.30	.134784	15.70	.865216	14
47	.131706	15.40	.995981	.28	.135726	15.68	.864274	13
48	.132630	15.35	.995963	.28	.136667	15.63	.863333	12
49	.133551	15.32	.995946	.30	.137605	15.62	.862395	11
50	9.134470	15.28	9.995928	.28	9.138542	15.57	0.861458	10
51	.135387	15.27	.995911	.28	.139476	15.55	.860524	9
52	.136303	15.22	.995894	.30	.140409	15.52	.859591	8
53	.137216	15.20	.995876	.28	.141340	15.48	.858660	7
54	.138128	15.15	.995859	.30	.142269	15.45	.857731	6
55	9.139037	15.12	9.995841	.30	9.143196	15.42	0.856804	5
56	.139944	15.10	.995823	.28	.144121	15.38	.855879	4
57	.140850	15.07	.995806	.30	.145044	15.37	.854956	3
58	.141754	15.02	.995788	.28	.145966	15.32	.854034	2
59	.142655	15.00	.995771	.30	.146885	15.30	.853115	1
60	9.143555		9.995753		9.147803		0.852197	0
	Cos.	D. 1''.	Sin.	D. 1''.	Cot.	D. 1''.	Tan.	M.

M.	Sin.	D. 1″.	Cos.	D. 1″.	Tan.	D. 1″.	Cot.	
0	9.143555	14.97	9.995753	.30	9.147803	15.25	0.852197	60
1	.144453	14.93	.995735	.30	.148718	15.23	.851282	59
2	.145349	14.90	.995717	.30	.149632	15.20	.850368	58
3	.146243	14.88	.995699	.30	.150544	15.17	.849456	57
4	.147136	14.83	.995681	.28	.151454	15.15	.848546	56
5	9.148026	14.82	9.995664	.30	9.152363	15.10	0.847637	55
6	.148915	14.78	.995646	.30	.153269	15.08	.846731	54
7	.149802	14.73	.995628	.30	.154174	15.05	.845826	53
8	.150686	14.72	.995610	.32	.155077	15.02	.844923	52
9	.151569	14.70	.995591	.30	.155978	14.98	.844022	51
10	9.152451	14.65	9.995573	.30	9.156877	14.97	0.843123	50
11	.153330	14.63	.995555	.30	.157775	14.93	.842225	49
12	.154208	14.58	.995537	.30	.158671	14.90	.841329	48
13	.155083	14.57	.995519	.30	.159565	14.87	.840435	47
14	.155957	14.55	.995501	.32	.160457	14.83	.839543	46
15	9.156830	14.50	9.995482	.30	9.161347	14.82	0.838653	45
16	.157700	14.48	.995464	.30	.162236	14.78	.837764	44
17	.158569	14.43	.995446	.32	.163123	14.75	.836877	43
18	.159435	14.43	.995427	.30	.164008	14.73	.835992	42
19	.160301	14.38	.995409	.32	.164892	14.70	.835108	41
20	9.161164	14.35	9.995390	.30	9.165774	14.67	0.834226	40
21	.162025	14.33	.995372	.32	.166654	14.63	.833346	39
22	.162885	14.30	.995353	.32	.167532	14.62	.832468	38
23	.163743	14.28	.995334	.30	.168409	14.58	.831591	37
24	.164600	14.23	.995316	.32	.169284	14.55	.830716	36
25	9.165454	14.22	9.995297	.32	9.170157	14.53	0.829843	35
26	.166307	14.20	.995278	.30	.171029	14.50	.828971	34
27	.167159	14.15	.995260	.32	.171899	14.47	.828101	33
28	.168008	14.13	.995241	.32	.172767	14.45	.827233	32
29	.168856	14.10	.995222	.32	.173634	14.42	.826366	31
30	9.169702	14.08	9.995203	.32	9.174499	14.38	0.825501	30
31	.170547	14.03	.995184	.32	.175362	14.37	.824638	29
32	.171389	14.02	.995165	.32	.176224	14.33	.823776	28
33	.172230	14.00	.995146	.32	.177084	14.30	.822916	27
34	.173070	13.97	.995127	.32	.177942	14.28	.822058	26
35	9.173908	13.93	9.995108	.32	9.178799	14.27	0.821201	25
36	.174744	13.90	.995089	.32	.179655	14.22	.820345	24
37	.175578	13.88	.995070	.32	.180508	14.20	.819492	23
38	.176411	13.85	.995051	.32	.181360	14.18	.818640	22
39	.177242	13.83	.995032	.32	.182211	14.13	.817789	21
40	9.178072	13.80	9.995013	.33	9.183059	14.13	0.816941	20
41	.178900	13.77	.994993	.32	.183907	14.08	.816093	19
42	.179726	13.75	.994974	.32	.184752	14.08	.815248	18
43	.180551	13.72	.994955	.33	.185597	14.03	.814403	17
44	.181374	13.70	.994935	.32	.186439	14.02	.813561	16
45	9.182196	13.67	9.994916	.33	9.187280	14.00	0.812720	15
46	.183016	13.63	.994896	.32	.188120	13.97	.811880	14
47	.183834	13.62	.994877	.33	.188958	13.93	.811042	13
48	.184651	13.58	.994857	.32	.189794	13.92	.810206	12
49	.185466	13.57	.994838	.33	.190629	13.88	.809371	11
50	9.186280	13.53	9.994818	.33	9.191462	13.87	0.808538	10
51	.187092	13.52	.994798	.32	.192294	13.83	.807706	9
52	.187903	13.48	.994779	.33	.193124	13.82	.806876	8
53	.188712	13.45	.994759	.33	.193953	13.78	.806047	7
54	.189519	13.43	.994739	.32	.194780	13.77	.805220	6
55	9.190325	13.42	9.994720	.33	9.195606	13.73	0.804394	5
56	.191130	13.38	.994700	.33	.196430	13.72	.803570	4
57	.191933	13.35	.994680	.33	.197253	13.68	.802747	3
58	.192734	13.33	.994660	.33	.198074	13.67	.801926	2
59	.193534	13.30	.994640	.33	.198894	13.65	.801106	1
60	9.194332		9.994620		9.199713		0.800287	0
	Cos.	D. 1″.	Sin.	D. 1″.	Cot.	D. 1″.	Tan.	M.

M.	Sin.	D. 1″.	Cos.	D. 1″.	Tan.	D. 1″.	Cot.	
0	9.194332	13.28	9.994620	.33	9.199713	13.60	0.800287	60
1	.195129	13.27	.994600	.33	.200529	13.60	.799471	59
2	.195925	13.23	.994580	.33	.201345	13.57	.798655	58
3	.196719	13.20	.994560	.33	.202159	13.53	.797841	57
4	.197511	13.18	.994540	.33	.202971	13.52	.797029	56
5	9.198302	13.15	9.994519	.33	9.203782	13.50	0.796218	55
6	.199091	13.13	.994499	.33	.204592	13.47	.795408	54
7	.199879	13.12	.994479	.33	.205400	13.45	.794600	53
8	.200666	13.08	.994459	.33	.206207	13.43	.793793	52
9	.201451	13.05	.994438	.35	.207013	13.40	.792987	51
10	9.202234	13.05	9.994418	.33	9.207817	13.37	0.792183	50
11	.203017	13.00	.994398	.33	.208619	13.35	.791381	49
12	.203797	13.00	.994377	.35	.209420	13.33	.790580	48
13	.204577	12.95	.994357	.33	.210220	13.30	.789780	47
14	.205354	12.95	.994336	.33	.211018	13.28	.788982	46
15	9.206131	12.92	9.994316	.33	9.211815	13.27	0.788185	45
16	.206906	12.88	.994295	.35	.212611	13.23	.787389	44
17	.207679	12.88	.994274	.35	.213405	13.22	.786595	43
18	.208452	12.83	.994254	.33	.214198	13.18	.785802	42
19	.209222	12.83	.994233	.35	.214989	13.18	.785011	41
20	9.209992	12.80	9.994212	.35	9.215780	13.13	0.784220	40
21	.210760	12.77	.994191	.35	.216568	13.13	.783432	39
22	.211526	12.75	.994171	.33	.217356	13.10	.782644	38
23	.212291	12.73	.994150	.35	.218142	13.07	.781858	37
24	.213055	12.72	.994129	.35	.218926	13.07	.781074	36
25	9.213818	12.68	9.994108	.35	9.219710	13.03	0.780290	35
26	.214579	12.65	.994087	.35	.220492	13.00	.779508	34
27	.215338	12.65	.994066	.35	.221272	13.00	.778728	33
28	.216097	12.62	.994045	.35	.222052	12.97	.777948	32
29	.216854	12.58	.994024	.35	.222830	12.95	.777170	31
30	9.217609	12.57	9.994003	.35	9.223607	12.92	0.776393	30
31	.218363	12.55	.993982	.37	.224382	12.90	.775618	29
32	.219116	12.53	.993960	.35	.225156	12.88	.774844	28
33	.219868	12.50	.993939	.35	.225929	12.85	.774071	27
34	.220618	12.48	.993918	.35	.226700	12.85	.773300	26
35	9.221367	12.47	9.993897	.37	9.227471	12.80	0.772529	25
36	.222115	12.43	.993875	.35	.228239	12.80	.771761	24
37	.222861	12.42	.993854	.37	.229007	12.77	.770993	23
38	.223606	12.38	.993832	.35	.229773	12.77	.770227	22
39	.224349	12.38	.993811	.37	.230539	12.72	.769461	21
40	9.225092	12.35	9.993789	.35	9.231302	12.72	0.768698	20
41	.225833	12.33	.993768	.37	.232065	12.68	.767935	19
42	.226573	12.30	.993746	.35	.232826	12.67	.767174	18
43	.227311	12.28	.993725	.37	.233586	12.65	.766414	17
44	.228048	12.27	.993703	.37	.234345	12.63	.765655	16
45	9.228784	12.23	9.993681	.35	9.235103	12.60	0.764897	15
46	.229518	12.23	.993660	.37	.235859	12.58	.764141	14
47	.230252	12.20	.993638	.37	.236614	12.57	.763386	13
48	.230984	12.18	.993616	.37	.237368	12.53	.762632	12
49	.231715	12.15	.993594	.37	.238120	12.53	.761880	11
50	9.232444	12.13	9.993572	.37	9.238872	12.50	0.761128	10
51	.233172	12.12	.993550	.37	.239622	12.48	.760378	9
52	.233899	12.10	.993528	.37	.240371	12.45	.759629	8
53	.234625	12.07	.993506	.37	.241118	12.45	.758882	7
54	.235349	12.07	.993484	.37	.241865	12.42	.758135	6
55	9.236073	12.03	9.993462	.37	9.242610	12.40	0.757390	5
56	.236795	12.00	.993440	.37	.243354	12.38	.756646	4
57	.237515	12.00	.993418	.37	.244097	12.37	.755903	3
58	.238235	11.97	.993396	.37	.244839	12.33	.755161	2
59	.238953	11.95	.993374	.37	.245579	12.33	.754421	1
60	9.239670		9.993351	.38	9.246319	12.33	0.753681	0
	Cos.	D. 1″.	Sin.	D. 1″.	Cot.	D. 1″.	Tan.	M.

M.	Sin.	D. 1''.	Cos.	D. 1''.	Tan.	D. 1''.	Cot.	
0	9.239670	11.93	9.993351	.37	9.246319	12.30	0.753681	60
1	.240386	11.92	.993329	.37	.247057	12.28	.752943	59
2	.241101	11.88	.993307	.37	.247794	12.27	.752206	58
3	.241814	11.87	.993284	.38	.248530	12.23	.751470	57
4	.242526	11.85	.993262	.37	.249264	12.23	.750736	56
5	9.243237	11.83	9.993240	.37	9.249998	12.23	0.750002	55
6	.243947	11.82	.993217	.38	.250730	12.20	.749270	54
7	.244656	11.78	.993195	.37	.251461	12.18	.748539	53
8	.245363	11.77	.993172	.38	.252191	12.17	.747809	52
9	.246069	11.77	.993149	.38	.252920	12.15	.747080	51
10	9.246775	11.72	9.993127	.37	9.253648	12.13	0.746352	50
11	.247478	11.72	.993104	.38	.254374	12.10	.745626	49
12	.248181	11.70	.993081	.38	.255100	12.10	.744900	48
13	.248883	11.67	.993059	.37	.255824	12.07	.744176	47
14	.249583	11.65	.993036	.38	.256547	12.05	.743453	46
15	9.250282	11.63	9.993013	.38	9.257269	12.03	0.742731	45
16	.250980	11.62	.992990	.38	.257990	12.02	.742010	44
17	.251677	11.60	.992967	.38	.258710	12.00	.741290	43
18	.252373	11.57	.992944	.38	.259429	11.98	.740571	42
19	.253067	11.57	.992921	.38	.260146	11.95	.739854	41
20	9.253761	11.53	9.992898	.38	9.260863	11.95	0.739137	40
21	.254453	11.52	.992875	.38	.261578	11.92	.738422	39
22	.255144	11.50	.992852	.38	.262292	11.90	.737708	38
23	.255834	11.48	.992829	.38	.263005	11.88	.736995	37
24	.256523	11.47	.992806	.38	.263717	11.87	.736283	36
25	9.257211	11.45	9.992783	.38	9.264428	11.85	0.735572	35
26	.257898	11.42	.992759	.40	.265138	11.83	.734862	34
27	.258583	11.42	.992736	.38	.265847	11.82	.734153	33
28	.259268	11.38	.992713	.38	.266555	11.80	.733445	32
29	.259951	11.37	.992690	.38	.267261	11.77	.732739	31
39	9.260633	11.35	9.992666	.40	9.267967	11.77	0.732033	30
31	.261314	11.33	.992643	.38	.268671	11.73	.731329	29
32	.261994	11.32	.992619	.40	.269375	11.73	.730625	28
33	.262673	11.30	.992596	.38	.270077	11.70	.729923	27
34	.263351	11.27	.992572	.40	.270779	11.70	.729221	26
35	9.264027	11.27	9.992549	.38	9.271479	11.67	0.728521	25
36	.264703	11.23	.992525	.40	.272178	11.65	.727822	24
37	.265377	11.23	.992501	.40	.272876	11.63	.727124	23
38	.266051	11.20	.992478	.38	.273573	11.62	.726427	22
39	.266723	11.20	.992454	.40	.274269	11.60	.725731	21
40	9.267395	11.17	9.992430	.40	9.274964	11.58	0.725036	20
41	.268065	11.15	.992406	.40	.275658	11.57	.724342	19
42	.268734	11.13	.992382	.40	.276351	11.55	.723649	18
43	.269402	11.12	.992359	.38	.277043	11.53	.722957	17
44	.270069	11.10	.992335	.40	.277734	11.52	.722266	16
45	9.270735	11.08	9.992311	.40	9.278424	11.50	0.721576	15
46	.271400	11.07	.992263	.40	.279113	11.48	.720887	14
47	.272064	11.03	.992263	.40	.279801	11.47	.720199	13
48	.272726	11.03	.992239	.42	.280488	1'.45	.719512	12
49	.273388	11.02	.992214	.40	.281174	11.43	.718826	11
50	9.274049	10.98	9.992190	.40	9.281858	11.40	0.718142	10
51	.274708	10.98	.992166	.40	.282542	11.40	.717458	9
52	.275367	10.97	.992142	.40	.283225	11.38	.716775	8
53	.276025	10.93	.992118	.42	.283907	11.37	.716093	7
54	.276681	10.93	.992093	.40	.284588	11.35	.715412	6
55	9.277337	10.90	9.992069	.42	9.285268	11.33	0.714732	5
56	.277991	10.90	.992044	.40	.285947	11.32	.714053	4
57	.278645	10.87	.992020	.40	.286624	11.28	.713376	3
58	.279297	10.85	.991996	.42	.287301	11.28	.712699	2
59	.279948	10.85	.991971	.40	.287977	11.27	.712023	1
60	9.280599		9.991947		9.288652	11.25	0.711348	0
	Cos.	D. 1''.	Sin.	D. 1''.	Cot.	D. 1''.	Tan.	M.

TABLE C—LOGARITHMIC SINES,

11°   168°

M.	Sin.	D. 1″.	Cos.	D. 1″.	Tan.	D. 1″.	Cot.	
0	9.280599	10.82	9.991947	.42	9.288652	11.23	0.711348	60
1	.281248	10.82	.991922	.42	.289326	11.22	.710674	59
2	.281897	10.78	.991897	.40	.289999	11.20	.710001	58
3	.282544	10.77	.991873	.42	.290671	11.18	.709329	57
4	.283190	10.77	.991848	.42	.291342	11.18	.708658	56
5	9.283836	10.73	9.991823	.40	9.292013	11.15	0.707987	55
6	.284480	10.73	.991799	.42	.292682	11.13	.707318	54
7	.285124	10.70	.991774	.42	.293350	11.12	.706650	53
8	.285766	10.70	.991749	.42	.294017	11.12	.705983	52
9	.286408	10.67	.991724	.42	.294684	11.08	.705316	51
10	9.287048	10.67	9.991699	.42	9.295349	11.07	0.704651	50
11	.287688	10.63	.991674	.42	.296013	11.07	.703987	49
12	.288326	10.63	.991649	.42	.296677	11.03	.703323	48
13	.288964	10.60	.991624	.42	.297339	11.03	.702661	47
14	.289600	10.60	.991599	.42	.298001	11.02	.701999	46
15	9.290236	10.57	9.991574	.42	9.298662	11.00	0.701338	45
16	.290870	10.57	.991549	.42	.299322	10.97	.700678	44
17	.291504	10.55	.991524	.43	.299980	10.97	.700020	43
18	.292137	10.52	.991498	.42	.300638	10.95	.699362	42
19	.292768	10.52	.991473	.42	.301295	10.93	.698705	41
20	9.293399	10.50	9.991448	.43	9.301951	10.93	0.698049	40
21	.294029	10.48	.991422	.42	.302607	10.90	.697393	39
22	.294658	10.47	.991397	.42	.303261	10.88	.696739	38
23	.295286	10.45	.991372	.43	.303914	10.88	.696086	37
24	.295913	10.43	.991346	.42	.304567	10.85	.695433	36
25	9.296539	10.42	9.991321	.43	9.305218	10.85	0.694782	35
26	.297164	10.40	.991295	.42	.305869	10.83	.694131	34
27	.297788	10.40	.991270	.43	.306519	10.82	.693481	33
28	.298412	10.37	.991244	.43	.307168	10.80	.692832	32
29	.299034	10.35	.991218	.42	.307816	10.78	.692184	31
30	9.299655	10.35	9.991193	.43	9.308463	10.77	0.691537	30
31	.300276	10.32	.991167	.43	.309109	10.75	.690891	29
32	.300895	10.32	.991141	.43	.309754	10.75	.690246	28
33	.301514	10.30	.991115	.42	.310399	10.72	.689601	27
34	.302132	10.27	.991090	.43	.311042	10.72	.688958	26
35	9.302748	10.27	9.991064	.43	9.311685	10.70	0.688315	25
36	.303364	10.25	.991038	.43	.312327	10.68	.687673	24
37	.303979	10.23	.991012	.43	.312968	10.67	.687032	23
38	.304593	10.23	.990986	.43	.313608	10.65	.686392	22
39	.305207	10.20	.990960	.43	.314247	10.63	.685753	21
40	9.305819	10.18	9.990934	.43	9.314885	10.63	0.685115	20
41	.306430	10.18	.990908	.43	.315523	10.60	.684477	19
42	.307041	10.15	.990882	.45	.316159	10.60	.683841	18
43	.307650	10.15	.990855	.43	.316795	10.58	.683205	17
44	.308259	10.13	.990829	.43	.317430	10.57	.682570	16
45	9.308867	10.12	9.990803	.43	9.318064	10.55	0.681936	15
46	.309474	10.10	.990777	.45	.318697	10.55	.681303	14
47	.310080	10.08	.990750	.43	.319330	10.52	.680670	13
48	.310685	10.07	.990724	.45	.319961	10.52	.680039	12
49	.311289	10.07	.990697	.45	.320592	10.50	.679408	11
50	9.311893	10.03	9.990671	.43	9.321222	10.48	0.678778	10
51	.312495	10.03	.990645	.45	.321851	10.47	.678149	9
52	.313097	10.02	.990618	.45	.322479	10.45	.677521	8
53	.313698	9.98	.990591	.43	.323106	10.45	.676894	7
54	.314297	10.00	.990565	.45	.323733	10.42	.676267	6
55	9.314897	9.97	9.990538	.45	9.324358	10.42	0.675642	5
56	.315495	9.95	.990511	.45	.324983	10.40	.675017	4
57	.316092	9.95	.990485	.43	.325607	10.40	.674393	3
58	.316689	9.92	.990458	.45	.326231	10.37	.673769	2
59	.317284	9.92	.990431	.45	.326853	10.37	.673147	1
60	9.317879		9.990404		9.327475		0.672525	0
	Cos.	D. 1″.	Sin.	D. 1″.	Cot.	D. 1″.	Tan.	M.

M.	Sin.	D. 1″.	Cos.	D. 1″.	Tan.	D. 1″.	Cot.	
0	9.317879		9.990404		9.327475		0.672525	60
1	.318473	9.90	.990378	.43	.328095	10.33	.671905	59
2	.319066	9.88	.990351	.45	.328715	10.33	.671285	58
3	.319658	9.87	.990324	.45	.329334	10.32	.670666	57
4	.320249	9.85	.990297	.45	.329953	10.32	.670047	56
5	9.320840	9.85	9.990270	.45	9.330570	10.28	0.669430	55
6	.321430	9.83	.990243	.45	.331187	10.28	.668813	54
7	.322019	9.82	.990215	.47	.331803	10.27	.668197	53
8	.322607	9.80	.990188	.45	.332418	10.25	.667582	52
9	.323194	9.78	.990161	.45	.333033	10.25	.666967	51
		9.77		.45		10.22		
10	9.323780	9.77	9.990134	.45	9.333646	10.22	0.666354	50
11	.324366	9.73	.990107	.47	.334259	10.20	.665741	49
12	.324950	9.73	.990079	.45	.334871	10.18	.665129	48
13	.325534	9.72	.990052	.47	.335482	10.18	.664518	47
14	.326117	9.72	.990025	.47	.336093	10.15	.663907	46
15	9.326700	9.68	9.989997	.45	9.336702	10.15	0.663298	45
16	.327281	9.68	.989970	.47	.337311	10.13	.662689	44
17	.327862	9.67	.989942	.45	.337919	10.13	.662081	43
18	.328442	9.65	.989915	.47	.338527	10.10	.661473	42
19	.329021	9.63	.989887	.45	.339133	10.10	.660867	41
20	9.329599	9.62	9.989860	.47	9.339739	10.08	0.660261	40
21	.330176	9.62	.989832	.47	.340344	10.07	.659656	39
22	.330753	9.60	.989804	.45	.340948	10.07	.659052	38
23	.331329	9.57	.989777	.47	.341552	10.05	.658448	37
24	.331903	9.58	.989749	.47	.342155	10.03	.657845	36
25	9.332478	9.55	9.989721	.47	9.342757	10.02	0.657243	35
26	.333051	9.55	.989693	.47	.343358	10.00	.656642	34
27	.333624	9.52	.989665	.47	.343958	10.00	.656042	33
28	.334195	9.53	.989637	.45	.344558	9.98	.655442	32
29	.334767	9.50	.989610	.47	.345157	9.97	.654843	31
30	9.335337	9.48	9.989582	.48	9.345755	9.97	0.654245	30
31	.335906	9.48	.989553	.47	.346353	9.93	.653647	29
32	.336475	9.47	.989525	.47	.346949	9.93	.653051	28
33	.337043	9.45	.989497	.47	.347545	9.93	.652455	27
34	.337610	9.43	.989469	.47	.348141	9.90	.651859	26
35	9.338176	9.43	9.989441	.47	9.348735	9.90	0.651265	25
36	.338742	9.42	.989413	.47	.349329	9.88	.650671	24
37	.339307	9.40	.989385	.48	.349922	9.87	.650078	23
38	.339871	9.38	.989356	.47	.350514	9.87	.649486	22
39	.340434	9.37	.989328	.47	.351106	9.85	.648894	21
40	9.340996	9.37	9.989300	.48	9.351697	9.83	0.648303	20
41	.341558	9.35	.989271	.47	.352287	9.82	.647713	19
42	.342119	9.33	.989243	.48	.352876	9.82	.647124	18
43	.342679	9.33	.989214	.47	.353465	9.80	.646535	17
44	.343239	9.30	.989186	.48	.354053	9.78	.645947	16
45	9.343797	9.30	9.989157	.48	9.354640	9.78	0.645360	15
46	.344355	9.28	.989128	.47	.355227	9.77	.644773	14
47	.344912	9.28	.989100	.48	.355813	9.75	.644187	13
48	.345469	9.25	.989071	.48	.356398	9.73	.643602	12
49	.346024	9.25	.989042	.47	.356982	9.73	.643018	11
50	9.346579	9.25	9.989014	.48	9.357566	9.72	0.642434	10
51	.347134	9.22	.988985	.48	.358149	9.70	.641851	9
52	.347687	9.22	.988956	.48	.358731	9.70	.641269	8
53	.348240	9.20	.988927	.48	.359313	9.67	.640687	7
54	.348792	9.18	.988898	.48	.359893	9.68	.640107	6
55	9.349343	9.17	9.988869	.48	9.360474	9.65	0.639526	5
56	.349893	9.17	.988840	.48	.361053	9.65	.638947	4
57	.350443	9.15	.998811	.48	.361632	9.63	.638368	3
58	.350992	9.13	.988782	.48	.362210	9.62	.637790	2
59	.351540	9.13	.988753	.48	.362787	9.62	.637213	1
60	9.352088		9.988724		9.363364		0.636636	0
	Cos.	D. 1″.	Sin.	D. 1″.	Cot.	D. 1″.	Tan.	M.

TABLE C—LOGARITHMIC SINES,

13°   166°

M.	Sin.	D. 1''.	Cos.	D. 1''.	Tan.	D. 1''.	Cot.	
0	9.352088	9.12	9.988724	.48	9.363364	9.60	0.636636	60
1	.352635	9.10	.988695	.48	.363940	9.58	.636060	59
2	.353181	9.08	.988666	.50	.364515	9.58	.635485	58
3	.353726	9.08	.988636	.48	.365090	9.57	.634910	57
4	.354271	9.07	.988607	.48	.365664	9.55	.634336	56
5	9.354815	9.05	9.988578	.48	9.366237	9.55	0.633763	55
6	.355358	9.05	.988548	.50	.366810	9.53	.633190	54
7	.355901	9.03	.988519	.48	.367382	9.52	.632618	53
8	.356443	9.02	.988489	.50	.367953	9.52	.632047	52
9	.356984	9.00	.988460	.48	.368524	9.50	.631476	51
10	9.357524	9.00	9.988430	.50	9.369094	9.48	0.630906	50
11	.358064	8.98	.988401	.48	.369663	9.48	.630337	49
12	.358603	8.97	.988371	.50	.370232	9.45	.629768	48
13	.359141	8.95	.988342	.48	.370799	9.47	.629201	47
14	.359678	8.95	.988312	.50	.371367	9.43	.628633	46
15	9.360215	8.95	9.988282	.50	9.371933	9.43	0.628067	45
16	.360752	8.92	.988252	.50	.372499	9.42	.627501	44
17	.361287	8.92	.988223	.48	.373064	9.42	.626936	43
18	.361822	8.90	.988193	.50	.373629	9.40	.626371	42
19	.362356	8.88	.988163	.50	.374193	9.38	.625807	41
20	9.362889	8.88	9.988133	.50	9.374756	9.38	0.625244	40
21	.363422	8.87	.988103	.50	.375319	9.37	.624681	39
22	.363954	8.85	.988073	.50	.375881	9.35	.624119	38
23	.364485	8.85	.988043	.50	.376442	9.35	.623558	37
24	.365016	8.83	.988013	.50	.377003	9.33	.622997	36
25	9.365546	8.82	9.987983	.50	9.377563	9.32	0.622437	35
26	.366075	8.82	.987953	.52	.378122	9.32	.621878	34
27	.366604	8.78	.987922	.50	.378681	9.30	.621319	33
28	.367131	8.80	.987892	.50	.379239	9.30	.620761	32
29	.367659	8.77	.987862	.50	.379797	9.28	.620203	31
30	9.368185	8.77	9.987832	.52	9.380354	9.27	0.619646	30
31	.368711	8.75	.987801	.50	.380910	9.27	.619090	29
32	.369236	8.75	.987771	.52	.381466	9.23	.618534	28
33	.369761	8.73	.987740	.50	.382020	9.25	.617980	27
34	.370285	8.72	.987710	.52	.382575	9.23	.617425	26
35	9.370808	8.70	9.987679	.50	9.383129	9.22	0.616871	25
36	.371330	8.70	.987649	.52	.383682	9.20	.616318	24
37	.371852	8.68	.987618	.50	.384234	9.20	.615766	23
38	.372373	8.68	.987588	.52	.384786	9.18	.615214	22
39	.372894	8.67	.987557	.52	.385337	9.18	.614663	21
40	9.373414	8.65	9.987526	.50	9.385888	9.17	0.614112	20
41	.373933	8.65	.987496	.52	.386438	9.15	.613562	19
42	.374452	8.63	.987465	.52	.386987	9.15	.613013	18
43	.374970	8.62	.987434	.52	.387536	9.13	.612464	17
44	.375487	8.60	.987403	.52	.388084	9.12	.611916	16
45	9.376003	8.60	9.987372	.52	9.388631	9.12	0.611369	15
46	.376519	8.60	.987341	.52	.389178	9.10	.610822	14
47	.377035	8.57	.987310	.52	.389724	9.10	.610276	13
48	.377549	8.57	.987279	.52	.390270	9.08	.609730	12
49	.378063	8.57	.987248	.52	.390815	9.08	.609185	11
50	9.378577	8.53	9.987217	.52	9.391360	9.05	0.608640	10
51	.379089	8.53	.987186	.52	.391903	9.07	.608097	9
52	.379601	8.53	.987155	.52	.392447	9.03	.607553	8
53	.380113	8.52	.987124	.53	.392989	9.03	.607011	7
54	.380624	8.50	.987092	.52	.393531	9.03	.606469	6
55	9.381134	8.48	9.987061	.52	9.394073	9.02	0.605927	5
56	.381643	8.48	.987030	.53	.394614	9.00	.605386	4
57	.382152	8.48	.986998	.52	.395154	9.00	.604846	3
58	.382661	8.45	.986967	.52	.395694	8.98	.604306	2
59	.383168	8.45	.986936	.53	.396233	8.97	.603767	1
60	9.383675		9.986904		9.396771		0.603229	0
	Cos.	D. 1''.	Sin.	D. 1''.	Cot.	D. 1''.	Tan.	M.

M.	Sin.	D. 1″.	Cos.	D. 1″.	Tan.	D. 1″.	Cot.	
0	9.383675	8.45	9.986904	.52	9.396771	8.97	0.603229	60
1	.384182	8.42	.986873	.53	.397309	8.95	.602691	59
2	.384687	8.42	.986841	.53	.397846	8.95	.602154	58
3	.385192	8.42	.986809	.52	.398383	8.93	.601617	57
4	.385697	8.40	.986778	.53	.398919	8.93	.601081	56
5	9.386201	8.38	9.986746	.53	9.399455	8.92	0.600545	55
6	.386704	8.38	.986714	.52	.399990	8.90	.600010	54
7	.387207	8.37	.986683	.53	.400524	8.90	.599476	53
8	.387709	8.35	.986651	.53	.401058	8.88	.598942	52
9	.388210	8.35	.986619	.53	.401591	8.88	.598409	51
10	9.388711	8.33	9.986587	.53	9.402124	8.87	0.597876	50
11	.389211	8.33	.986555	.53	.402656	8.85	.597344	49
12	.389711	8.32	.986523	.53	.403187	8.85	.596813	48
13	.390210	8.30	.986491	.53	.403718	8.85	.596282	47
14	.390708	8.30	.986459	.53	.404249	8.85	.595751	46
15	9.391206	8.28	9.986427	.53	9.404778	8.82	0.595222	45
16	.391703	8.27	.986395	.53	.405308	8.83	.594692	44
17	.392199	8.27	.986363	.53	.405836	8.80	.594164	43
18	.392695	8.27	.986331	.53	.406364	8.80	.593636	42
19	.393191	8.23	.986299	.55	.406892	8.80	.593108	41
20	9.393685	8.23	9.986266	.53	9.407419	8.78	0.592581	40
21	.394179	8.23	.986234	.53	.407945	8.77	.592055	39
22	.394673	8.22	.986202	.55	.408471	8.77	.591529	38
23	.395166	8.20	.986169	.53	.408996	8.75	.591004	37
24	.395658	8.20	.986137	.55	.409521	8.75	.590479	36
25	9.396150	8.18	9.986104	.53	9.410045	8.73	0.589955	35
26	.396641	8.18	.986072	.55	.410569	8.73	.589431	34
27	.397132	8.15	.986039	.53	.411092	8.72	.588908	33
28	.397621	8.17	.986007	.55	.411615	8.72	.588385	32
29	.398111	8.15	.985974	.53	.412137	8.70	.587863	31
30	9.398600	8.13	9.985942	.55	9.412658	8.68	0.587342	30
31	.399088	8.12	.985909	.55	.413179	8.68	.586821	29
32	.399575	8.12	.985876	.55	.413699	8.67	.586301	28
33	.400062	8.12	.985843	.53	.414219	8.67	.585781	27
34	.400549	8.10	.985811	.55	.414738	8.65	.585262	26
35	9.401035	8.08	9.985778	.55	9.415257	8.65	0.584743	25
36	.401520	8.08	.985745	.55	.415775	8.63	.584225	24
37	.402005	8.07	.985712	.55	.416293	8.63	.583707	23
38	.402489	8.05	.985679	.55	.416810	8.62	.583190	22
39	.402972	8.05	.985646	.55	.417326	8.60	.582674	21
40	9.403455	8.05	9.985613	.55	9.417842	8.60	0.582158	20
41	.403938	8.03	.985580	.55	.418358	8.60	.581642	19
42	.404420	8.02	.985547	.55	.418873	8.58	.581127	18
43	.404901	8.02	.985514	.57	.419387	8.57	.580613	17
44	.405382	8.00	.985480	.55	.419901	8.57	.580099	16
45	9.405862	7.98	9.985447	.55	9.420415	8.57	0.579585	15
46	.406341	7.98	.985414	.55	.420927	8.53	.579073	14
47	.406820	7.98	.985381	.55	.421440	8.55	.578560	13
48	.407299	7.97	.985347	.57	.421952	8.53	.578048	12
49	.407777	7.95	.985314	.55	.422463	8.52	.577537	11
50	9.408254	7.95	9.985280	.57	9.422974	8.52	0.577026	10
51	.408731	7.93	.985247	.55	.423484	8.50	.576516	9
52	.409207	7.92	.985213	.57	.423993	8.48	.576007	8
53	.409682	7.92	.985180	.55	.424503	8.50	.575497	7
54	.410157	7.92	.985146	.57	.425011	8.47	.574989	6
55	9.410632	7.90	9.985113	.55	9.425519	8.47	0.574481	5
56	.411106	7.88	.985079	.57	.426027	8.47	.573973	4
57	.411579	7.88	.985045	.57	.426534	8.45	.573466	3
58	.412052	7.87	.985011	.57	.427041	8.45	.572959	2
59	.412524	7.87	.984978	.55	.427547	8.43	.572453	1
60	9.412996		9.984914	.57	9.428052	8.42	0.571948	0
	Cos.	D. 1″.	Sin.	D. 1.″	Cot.	D. 1″.	Tan.	M.

TABLE C—LOGARITHMIC SINES,

15°   164°

M.	Sin.	D. 1".	Cos.	D. 1".	Tan.	D. 1".	Cot.	
0	9.412996	7.85	9.984944	.57	9.428052	8.43	0.571948	60
1	.413467	7.85	.984910	.57	.428558	8.40	.571442	59
2	.413938	7.83	.984876	.57	.429062	8.40	.570938	58
3	.414408	7.83	.984842	.57	.429566	8.40	.570434	57
4	.414878	7.82	.984808	.57	.430070	8.38	.569930	56
5	9.415347	7.80	9.984774	.57	9.430573	8.37	0.569427	55
6	.415815	7.80	.984740	.57	.431075	8.37	.568925	54
7	.416283	7.80	.984706	.57	.431577	8.37	.568423	53
8	.416751	7.77	.984672	.57	.432079	8.35	.567921	52
9	.417217	7.78	.984638	.58	.432580	8.33	.567420	51
10	9.417684	7.77	9.984603	.57	9.433080	8.33	0.566920	50
11	.418150	7.75	.984569	.57	.433580	8.33	.566420	49
12	.418615	7.73	.984535	.58	.434080	8.32	.565920	48
13	.419079	7.75	.984500	.57	.434579	8.32	.565421	47
14	.419544	7.72	.984466	.57	.435078	8.30	.564922	46
15	9.420007	7.72	9.984432	.58	9.435576	8.28	0.564424	45
16	.420470	7.72	.984397	.57	.436073	8.28	.563927	44
17	.420933	7.70	.984363	.58	.436570	8.28	.563430	43
18	.421395	7.70	.984328	.57	.437067	8.27	.562933	42
19	.421857	7.68	.984294	.58	.437563	8.27	.562437	41
20	9.422318	7.67	9.984259	.58	9.438059	8.25	0.561941	40
21	.422778	7.67	.984224	.57	.438554	8.23	.561446	39
22	.423238	7.65	.984190	.58	.439048	8.25	.560952	38
23	.423697	7.65	.984155	.58	.439543	8.22	.560457	37
24	.424156	7.65	.984120	.58	.440036	8.22	.559964	36
25	9.424615	7.63	9.984085	.58	9.440529	8.22	0.559471	35
26	.425073	7.62	.984050	.58	.441022	8.20	.558978	34
27	.425530	7.62	.984015	.58	.441514	8.20	.558486	33
28	.425987	7.60	.983981	.57	.442006	8.18	.557994	32
29	.426443	7.60	.983946	.58	.442497	8.18	.557503	31
30	9.426899	7.58	9.983911	.58	9.442988	8.18	0.557012	30
31	.427354	7.58	.983875	.60	.443479	8.15	.556521	29
32	.427809	7.57	.983840	.58	.443968	8.17	.556032	28
33	.428263	7.57	.983805	.58	.444458	8.15	.555542	27
34	.428717	7.55	.983770	.58	.444947	8.15	.555053	26
35	9.429170	7.55	9.983735	.58	9.445435	8.13	0.554565	25
36	.429623	7.53	.983700	.58	.445923	8.13	.554077	24
37	.430075	7.53	.983664	.60	.446411	8.13	.553589	23
38	.430527	7.52	.983629	.58	.446898	8.12	.553102	22
39	.430978	7.52	.983594	.58	.447384	8.10	.552616	21
40	9.431429	7.50	9.983558	.60	9.447870	8.10	0.552130	20
41	.431879	7.50	.983523	.58	.448356	8.10	.551644	19
42	.432329	7.48	.983487	.60	.448841	8.08	.551159	18
43	.432778	7.47	.983452	.58	.449326	8.08	.550674	17
44	.433226	7.48	.983416	.60	.449810	8.07	.550190	16
45	9.433675	7.45	9.983381	.58	9.450294	8.07	0.549706	15
46	.434122	7.45	.983345	.60	.450777	8.05	.549223	14
47	.434569	7.45	.983309	.60	.451260	8.05	.548740	13
48	.435016	7.43	.983273	.60	.451743	8.05	.548257	12
49	.435462	7.43	.983238	.58	.452225	8.03	.547775	11
50	9.435908	7.42	9.983202	.60	9.452706	8.02	0.547294	10
51	.436353	7.42	.983166	.60	.453187	8.02	.546813	9
52	.436798	7.40	.983130	.60	.453668	8.02	.546332	8
53	.437242	7.40	.983094	.60	.454148	8.00	.545852	7
54	.437686	7.38	.983058	.60	.454628	8.00	.545372	6
55	9.438129	7.38	9.983022	.60	9.455107	7.98	0.544893	5
56	.438572	7.37	.982986	.60	.455586	7.98	.544414	4
57	.439014	7.37	.982950	.60	.456064	7.97	.543936	3
58	.439456	7.35	.982914	.60	.456542	7.97	.543458	2
59	.439897	7.35	.982878	.60	.457019	7.95	.542981	1
60	9.440338		9.982842	.60	9.457496	7.95	0.542504	0
	Cos.	D. 1".	Sin.	D. 1".	Cot.	D. 1".	Tan.	M.

105°   74°

M.	Sin.	D. 1″.	Cos.	D. 1″.	Tan.	D. 1″.	Cot.	
0	9.440338	7.33	9.982842	.62	9.457496	7.95	0.542504	60
1	.440778	7.33	.982805	.60	.457973	7.93	.542027	59
2	.441218	7.33	.982769	.60	.458449	7.93	.541551	58
3	.441658	7.30	.982733	.62	.458925	7.92	.541075	57
4	.442096	7.32	.982696	.60	.459400	7.92	.540600	56
5	9.442535	7.30	9.982660	.60	9.459875	7.90	0.540125	55
6	.442973	7.28	.982624	.62	.460349	7.90	.539651	54
7	.443410	7.28	.982587	.60	.460823	7.90	.539177	53
8	.443847	7.28	.982551	.62	.461297	7.88	.538703	52
9	.444284	7.27	.982514	.62	.461770	7.87	.538230	51
10	9.444720	7.25	9.982477	.60	9.462242	7.88	0.537758	50
11	.445155	7.25	.982441	.62	.462715	7.85	.537285	49
12	.445590	7.25	.982404	.62	.463186	7.87	.536814	48
13	.446025	7.23	.982367	.60	.463658	7.83	.536342	47
14	.446459	7.23	.982331	.62	.464128	7.85	.535872	46
15	9.446893	7.22	9.982294	.62	9.464599	7.83	0.535401	45
16	.447326	7.22	.982257	.62	.465069	7.83	.534931	44
17	.447759	7.20	.982220	.62	.465539	7.82	.534461	43
18	.448191	7.20	.982183	.62	.466008	7.82	.533992	42
19	.448623	7.18	.982146	.62	.466477	7.80	.533523	41
20	9.449054	7.18	9.982109	.62	9.466945	7.80	0.533055	40
21	.449485	7.17	.982072	.62	.467413	7.78	.532587	39
22	.449915	7.17	.982035	.62	.467880	7.78	.532120	38
23	.450345	7.17	.981998	.62	.468347	7.78	.531653	37
24	.450775	7.15	.981961	.62	.468814	7.77	.531186	36
25	9.451204	7.13	9.981924	.63	9.469280	7.77	0.530720	35
26	.451632	7.13	.981886	.62	.469746	7.75	.530254	34
27	.452060	7.13	.981849	.62	.470211	7.75	.529789	33
28	.452488	7.12	.981812	.63	.470676	7.75	.529324	32
29	.452915	7.12	.981774	.62	.471141	7.73	.528859	31
30	9.453342	7.10	9.981737	.62	9.471605	7.73	0.528395	30
31	.453768	7.10	.981700	.63	.472069	7.72	.527931	29
32	.454194	7.08	.981662	.63	.472532	7.72	.527468	28
33	.454619	7.08	.981625	.62	.472995	7.70	.527005	27
34	.455044	7.08	.981587	.63	.473457	7.70	.526543	26
35	9.455469	7.07	9.981549	.62	9.473919	7.70	0.526081	25
36	.455893	7.05	.981512	.63	.474381	7.68	.525619	24
37	.456316	7.05	.981474	.63	.474842	7.68	.525158	23
38	.456739	7.05	.981436	.62	.475303	7.67	.524697	22
39	.457162	7.03	.981399	.63	.475763	7.67	.524237	21
40	9.457584	7.03	9.981361	.63	9.476223	7.67	0.523777	20
41	.458006	7.02	.981323	.63	.476683	7.65	.523317	19
42	.458427	7.02	.981285	.63	.477142	7.65	.522858	18
43	.458848	7.00	.981247	.63	.477601	7.63	.522399	17
44	.459268	7.00	.981209	.63	.478059	7.63	.521941	16
45	9.459688	7.00	9.981171	.63	9.478517	7.63	0.521483	15
46	.460108	6.98	.981133	.63	.478975	7.62	.521025	14
47	.460527	6.98	.981095	.63	.479432	7.62	.520568	13
48	.460946	6.97	.981057	.63	.479889	7.60	.520111	12
49	.461364	6.97	.981019	.63	.480345	7.60	.519655	11
50	9.461782	6.95	9.980981	.65	9.480801	7.60	0.519199	10
51	.462199	6.95	.980942	.63	.481257	7.58	.518743	9
52	.462616	6.93	.980904	.63	.481712	7.58	.518288	8
53	.463032	6.93	.980866	.65	.482167	7.57	.517833	7
54	.463448	6.93	.980827	.63	.482621	7.57	.517379	6
55	9.463864	6.92	9.980789	.65	9.483075	7.57	0.516925	5
56	.464279	6.92	.980750	.65	.483529	7.55	.516471	4
57	.464694	6.90	.980712	.63	.483982	7.55	.516018	3
58	.465108	6.90	.980673	.65	.484435	7.53	.515565	2
59	.465522	6.88	.980635	.63	.484887	7.53	.515113	1
60	9.465935		9.980596	.65	9.485339		0.514661	0
	Cos.	D. 1″.	Sin.	D. 1″.	Cot.	D. 1″.	Tan.	M.

TABLE C—LOGARITHMIC SINES,

17°   162°

M.	Sin.	D. 1″.	Cos.	D. 1″.	Tan.	D. 1″.	Cot.	
0	9.465935	6.88	9.980596	.63	9.485339	7.53	0.514661	60
1	.466348	6.88	.980558	.65	.485791	7.52	.514209	59
2	.466761	6.87	.980519	.65	.486242	7.52	.513758	58
3	.467173	6.87	.980480	.63	.486693	7.50	.513307	57
4	.467585	6.85	.980442	.65	.487143	7.50	.512857	56
5	9.467996	6.85	9.980403	.65	9.487593	7.50	0.512407	55
6	.468407	6.83	.980364	.65	.488043	7.48	.511957	54
7	.468817	6.83	.980325	.65	.488492	7.48	.511508	53
8	.469227	6.83	.980286	.65	.488941	7.48	.511059	52
9	.469637	6.82	.980247	.65	.489390	7.47	.510610	51
10	9.470046	6.82	9.980208	.65	9.489838	7.47	0.510162	50
11	.470455	6.80	.980169	.65	.490286	7.45	.509714	49
12	.470863	6.80	.980130	.65	.490733	7.45	.509267	48
13	.471271	6.80	.980091	.65	.491180	7.45	.508820	47
14	.471679	6.78	.980052	.67	.491627	7.45	.508373	46
15	9.472086	6.77	9.980012	.65	9.492073	7.43	0.507927	45
16	.472492	6.77	.979973	.65	.492519	7.43	.507481	44
17	.472898	6.77	.979934	.65	.492965	7.43	.507035	43
18	.473304	6.77	.979895	.67	.493910	7.42	.506590	42
19	.473710	6.75	.979855	.65	.493854	7.42	.506146	41
20	9.474115	6.73	9.979816	.67	9.494299	7.40	0.505701	40
21	.474519	6.73	.979776	.65	.494743	7.38	.505257	39
22	.474923	6.73	.979737	.67	.495186	7.40	.504814	38
23	.475327	6.72	.979697	.65	.495630	7.38	.504370	37
24	.475730	6.72	.979658	.67	.496073	7.37	.503927	36
25	9.476133	6.72	9.979618	.65	9.496515	7.37	0.503485	35
26	.476536	6.70	.979579	.67	.496957	7.37	.503043	34
27	.476938	6.70	.979539	.67	.497399	7.37	.502601	33
28	.477340	6.68	.979499	.67	.497841	7.35	.502159	32
29	.477741	6.68	979459	.65	.498282	7.33	.501718	31
30	9.478142	6.67	9.979420	.67	9.498722	7.35	0.501278	30
31	.478542	6.67	.979380	.67	.499163	7.33	.500837	29
32	.478942	6.67	.979340	.67	.499603	7.32	.500397	28
33	.479342	6.65	.979300	.67	.500042	7.32	.499958	27
34	.479741	6.65	.979260	.67	.500481	7.32	.499519	26
35	9.480140	6.65	9.979220	.67	9.500920	7.32	0.499080	25
36	.480539	6.63	.979180	.67	.501359	7.30	.498641	24
37	.480937	6.62	.979140	.67	.501797	7.30	.498203	23
38	.481334	6.62	.979100	.68	.502235	7.28	.497765	22
39	.481731	6.62	.979059	.67	.502672	7.28	.497328	21
40	9.482128	6.62	9.979019	.67	9.503109	7.28	0.496891	20
41	.482525	6.60	.978979	.67	.503546	7.27	.496454	19
42	.482921	6.58	.978939	.68	.503982	7.27	.496018	18
43	.483316	6.60	.978898	.67	.504418	7.27	.495582	17
44	.483712	6.58	.978858	.68	.504854	7.25	.495146	16
45	9.484107	6.57	9.978817	.67	9.505289	7.25	0.494711	15
46	.484501	6.57	.978777	.67	.505724	7.25	.494276	14
47	.484895	6.57	.978737	.68	.506159	7.23	.493841	13
48	.485289	6.55	.978696	.68	.506593	7.23	.493407	12
49	.485682	6.55	.978655	.67	.507027	7.22	.492973	11
50	9.486075	6.53	9.978615	.68	9.507460	7.22	0.492540	10
51	.486467	6.55	.978574	.68	.507893	7.22	.492107	9
52	.486860	6.52	.978533	.67	.508326	7.22	.491674	8
53	.487251	6.53	.978493	.68	.508759	7.20	.491241	7
54	.487643	6.52	.978452	.68	.509191	7.18	.490809	6
55	9.488034	6.50	9.978411	.68	9.509622	7.20	0.490378	5
56	.488424	6.50	.978370	.68	.510054	7.18	.489946	4
57	.488814	6.50	.978329	.68	.510485	7.18	.489515	3
58	.489204	6.48	.978288	.68	.510916	7.17	.489084	2
59	.489593	6.48	.978247	.68	.511346	7.17	.488654	1
60	9.489982		9.978206		9.511776		0.488224	0

	Cos.	D. 1″.	Sin.	D. 1″.	Cot.	D. 1″.	Tan.	M.

COSINES, TANGENTS, AND COTANGENTS

M.	Sin.	D. 1".	Cos.	D. 1".	Tan.	D. 1".	Cot.	
0	9.489982	6.48	9.978206	.68	9.511776	7.17	0.488224	60
1	.490371	6.47	.978165	.68	.512206	7.15	.487794	59
2	.490759	6.47	.978124	.68	.512635	7.15	.487365	58
3	.491147	6.47	.978083	.68	.513064	7.15	.486936	57
4	.491535	6.45	.978042	.68	.513493	7.13	.486507	56
5	9.491922	6.43	9.978001	.68	9.513921	7.13	0.486079	55
6	.492308	6.45	.977959	.70	.514349	7.13	.485651	54
7	.492695	6.43	.977918	.68	.514777	7.13	.485223	53
8	.493081	6.42	.977877	.68	.515204	7.12	.484796	52
9	.493466	6.42	.977835	.70	.515631	7.12	.484369	51
10	9.493851	6.42	9.977794	.68	9.516057	7.10	0.483943	50
11	.494236	6.42	.977752	.70	.516484	7.12	.483516	49
12	.494621	6.40	.977711	.68	.516910	7.10	.483090	48
13	.495005	6.38	.977669	.70	.517335	7.08	.482665	47
14	.495388	6.40	.977628	.68	.517761	7.10	.482239	46
15	9.495772	6.37	9.977586	.70	9.518186	7.08	0.481814	45
16	.496154	6.38	.977544	.70	.518610	7.07	.481390	44
17	.496537	6.37	.977503	.68	.519034	7.07	.480966	43
18	.496919	6.37	.977461	.70	.519458	7.07	.480542	42
19	.497301	6.35	.977419	.70	.519882	7.07	.480118	41
20	9.497682	6.37	9.977377	.70	9.520305	7.05	0.479695	40
21	.498064	6.33	.977335	.70	.520728	7.05	.479272	39
22	.498444	6.35	.977293	.70	.521151	7.05	.478849	38
23	.498825	6.32	.977251	.70	.521573	7.03	.478427	37
24	.499204	6.33	.977209	.70	.521995	7.03	.478005	36
25	9.499584	6.32	9.977167	.70	9.522417	7.03	0.477583	35
26	.499963	6.32	.977125	.70	.522838	7.02	.477162	34
27	.500342	6.32	.977083	.70	.523259	7.02	.476741	33
28	.500721	6.30	.977041	.70	.523680	7.02	.476320	32
29	.501099	6.28	.976999	.70	.524100	7.00	.475900	31
30	9.501476	6.30	9.976957	.72	9.524520	7.00	0.475480	30
31	.501854	6.28	.976914	.70	.524940	7.00	.475060	29
32	.502231	6.27	.976872	.70	.525359	6.98	.474641	28
33	.502607	6.28	.976830	.72	.525778	6.98	.474222	27
34	.502984	6.27	.976787	.70	.526197	6.98	.473803	26
35	9.503360	6.25	9.976745	.72	9.526615	6.97	0.473385	25
36	.503735	6.25	.976702	.70	.527033	6.97	.472967	24
37	.504110	6.25	.976660	.72	.527451	6.97	.472549	23
38	.504485	6.25	.976617	.72	.527868	6.95	.472132	22
39	.504860	6.23	.976574	.70	.528285	6.95	.471715	21
40	9.505234	6.23	9.976532	.72	9.528702	6.95	0.471298	20
41	.505608	6.22	.976489	.72	.529119	6.93	.470881	19
42	.505981	6.22	.976446	.72	.529535	6.93	.470465	18
43	.506354	6.22	.976404	.70	.529951	6.92	.470049	17
44	.506727	6.20	.976361	.72	.530366	6.92	.469634	16
45	9.507099	6.20	9.976318	.72	9.530781	6.92	0.469219	15
46	.507471	6.20	.976275	.72	.531196	6.92	.468804	14
47	.507843	6.18	.976232	.72	.531611	6.90	.468389	13
48	.508214	6.18	.976189	.72	.532025	6.90	.467975	12
49	.508585	6.18	.976146	.72	.532439	6.90	.467561	11
50	9.508956	6.17	9.976103	.72	9.532853	6.88	0.467147	10
51	.509326	6.17	.976060	.72	.533266	6.88	.466734	9
52	.509696	6.15	.976017	.72	.533679	6.88	.466321	8
53	.510065	6.15	.975974	.73	.534092	6.87	.465908	7
54	.510434	6.15	.975930	.72	.534504	6.87	.465496	6
55	9.510803	6.15	9.975887	.72	9.534916	6.87	0.465084	5
56	.511172	6.13	.975844	.73	.535328	6.85	.464672	4
57	.511540	6.12	.975800	.72	.535739	6.85	.464261	3
58	.511907	6.13	.975757	.72	.536150	6.85	.463850	2
59	.512275	6.12	.975714	.73	.536561	6.85	.463439	1
60	9.512642		9.975670		9.536972		0.463028	0
	Cos.	D. 1".	Sin.	D. 1".	Cot.	D. 1".	Tan.	M.

TABLE C—LOGARITHMIC SINES,

M.	Sin.	D. 1″.	Cos.	D. 1″.	Tan.	D. 1″.	Cot.	
0	9.512642	6.12	9.975670	.72	9.536972	6.83	0.463028	60
1	.513009	6.10	.975627	.73	.537382	6.83	.462618	59
2	.513375	6.10	.975583	.73	.537792	6.83	.462208	58
3	.513741	6.10	.975539	.72	.538202	6.82	.461798	57
4	.514107	6.08	.975496	.73	.538611	6.82	.461389	56
5	9.514472	6.08	9.975452	.73	9.539020	6.82	0.460980	55
6	.514837	6.08	.975408	.72	.539429	6.80	.460571	54
7	.515202	6.07	.975365	.73	.539837	6.80	.460163	53
8	.515566	6.07	.975321	.73	.540245	6.80	.459755	52
9	.515930	6.07	.975277	.73	.540653	6.80	.459347	51
10	9.516294	6.05	9.975233	.73	9.541061	6.78	0.458939	50
11	.516657	6.05	.975189	.73	.541468	6.78	.458532	49
12	.517020	6.03	.975145	.73	.541875	6.78	.458125	48
13	.517382	6.05	.975101	.73	.542281	6.77	.457719	47
14	.517745	6.03	.975057	.73	.542688	6.78	.457312	46
15	9.518107	6.02	9.975013	.73	9.543094	6.77	0.456906	45
16	.518468	6.02	.974969	.73	.543499	6.75	.456501	44
17	.518829	6.02	.974925	.73	.543905	6.77	.456095	43
18	.519190	6.02	.974880	.75	.544310	6.75	.455690	42
19	.519551	6.00	.974836	.73	.544715	6.75	.455285	41
20	9.519911	6.00	9.974792	.73	9.545119	6.73	0.454881	40
21	.520271	6.00	.974748	.75	.545524	6.75	.454476	39
22	.520631	5.98	.974703	.73	.545928	6.73	.454072	38
23	.520990	5.98	.974659	.75	.546331	6.72	.453669	37
24	.521349	5.97	.974614	.73	.546735	6.73	.453265	36
25	9.521707	5.98	9.974570	.75	9.547138	6.72	0.452862	35
26	.522066	5.97	.974525	.73	.547540	6.70	.452460	34
27	.522424	5.95	.974481	.75	.547943	6.72	.452057	33
28	.522781	5.95	.974436	.75	.548345	6.70	.451655	32
29	.523138	5.95	.974391	.73	.548747	6.70	.451253	31
30	9.523495	5.95	9.974347	.75	9.549149	6.70	0.450851	30
31	.523852	5.93	.974302	.75	.549550	6.68	.450450	29
32	.524208	5.93	.974257	.75	.549951	6.68	.450049	28
33	.524564	5.93	.974212	.75	.550352	6.68	.449648	27
34	.524920	5.92	.974167	.75	.550752	6.67	.449248	26
35	9.525275	5.92	9.974122	.75	9.551153	6.68	0.448847	25
36	.525630	5.30	.974077	.75	.551552	6.65	.448448	24
37	.525984	5.92	.974032	.75	.551952	6.67	.448048	23
38	.526339	5.90	.973987	.75	.552351	6.65	.447649	22
39	.526693	5.88	.973942	.75	.552750	6.65	.447250	21
40	9.527046	5.90	9.973897	.75	9.553149	6.65	0.446851	20
41	.527400	5.88	.973852	.75	.553548	6.63	.446452	19
42	.527753	5.87	.973807	.77	.553946	6.63	.446054	18
43	.528105	5.88	.973761	.75	.554344	6.62	.445656	17
44	.528458	5.87	.973716	.75	.554741	6.63	.445259	16
45	9.528810	5.85	9.973671	.77	9.555139	6.62	0.444861	15
46	.529161	5.87	.973625	.75	.555536	6.62	.444464	14
47	.529513	5.85	.973580	.75	.555933	6.62	.444067	13
48	.529864	5.85	.973535	.77	.556329	6.60	.443671	12
49	.530215	5.83	.973489	.75	.556725	6.60	.443275	11
50	9.530565	5.83	9.973444	.77	9.557121	6.60	0.442879	10
51	.530915	5.83	.973398	.77	.557517	6.60	.442483	9
52	.531265	5.82	.973352	.75	.557913	6.58	.442087	8
53	.531614	5.82	.973307	.77	.558308	6.58	.441692	7
54	.531963	5.82	.973261	.77	.558703	6.57	.441297	6
55	9.532312	5.82	9.973215	.77	9.559097	6.57	0.440903	5
56	.532661	5.80	.973169	.75	.559491	6.57	.440509	4
57	.533009	5.80	.973124	.77	.559885	6.57	.440115	3
58	.533357	5.78	.973078	.77	.560279	6.57	.439721	2
59	.533704	5.80	.973032	.77	.560673	6.55	.439327	1
60	9.534052		9.972986		9.561066		0.438934	0
	Cos.	D. 1″.	Sin.	D. 1″.	Cot.	D. 1″.	Tan.	M.

M.	Sin.	D. 1″.	Cos.	D. 1″.	Tan.	D. 1″.	Cot.	
0	9.534052	5.78	9.972986	.77	9.561066	6.55	0.438934	60
1	.534399	5.77	.972940	.77	.561459	6.53	.438541	59
2	.534745	5.78	.972894	.77	.561851	6.55	.438149	58
3	.535092	5.77	.972848	.77	.562244	6.55	.437756	57
4	.535438	5.75	.972802	.77	.562636	6.53	.437364	56
5	9.535783	5.77	9.972755	.78	9.563028	6.53	0.436972	55
6	.536129	5.75	.972709	.77	.563419	6.52	.436581	54
7	.536474	5.73	.972663	.77	.563811	6.53	.436189	53
8	.536818	5.75	.972617	.77	.564202	6.52	.435798	52
9	.537163	5.73	.972570	.78	.564593	6.52	.435407	51
10	9.537507	5.73	9.972524	.77	9.564983	6.50	0.435017	50
11	.527851	5.72	.972478	.77	.565373	6.50	.434627	49
12	.538194	5.73	.972431	.78	.565763	6.50	.434237	48
13	.538538	5.70	.972385	.77	.566153	6.48	.433847	47
14	.538880	5.72	.972338	.78	.566542	6.50	.433458	46
15	9.539223	5.70	9.972291	.78	9.566932	6.47	0.433068	45
16	.539565	5.70	.972245	.77	.567320	6.48	.432680	44
17	.539907	5.70	.972198	.78	.567709	6.48	.432291	43
18	.540249	5.68	.972151	.78	.568098	6.47	.431902	42
19	.540590	5.68	.972105	.77	.568486	6.45	.431514	41
20	9.540931	5.68	9.972058	.78	9.568873	6.47	0.431127	40
21	.541272	5.68	.972011	.78	.569261	6.45	.430739	39
22	.541613	5.67	.971964	.78	.569648	6.45	.430352	38
23	.541953	5.67	.971917	.78	.570035	6.45	.429965	37
24	.542293	5.65	.971870	.78	.570422	6.45	.429578	36
25	9.542632	5.65	9.971823	.78	9.570809	6.43	0.429191	35
26	.542971	5.65	.971776	.78	.571195	6.43	.428805	34
27	.543310	5.65	.971729	.78	.571581	6.43	.428419	33
28	.543649	5.63	.971682	.78	.571967	6.43	.428033	32
29	.543987	5.63	.971635	.78	.572352	6.42	.427648	31
30	9.544325	5.63	9.971588	.80	9.572738	6.43	0.427262	30
31	.544663	5.62	.971540	.78	.573123	6.42	.426877	29
32	.545000	5.63	.971493	.78	.573507	6.40	.426493	28
33	.545338	5.60	.971446	.80	.573892	6.42	.426108	27
34	.545674	5.62	.971398	.78	.574276	6.40	.425724	26
35	9.546011	5.60	9.971351	.80	9.574660	6.40	0.425340	25
36	.546347	5.60	.971303	.78	.575044	6.40	.424956	24
37	.546683	5.60	.971256	.80	.575427	6.38	.424573	23
38	.547019	5.58	.971208	.78	.575810	6.38	.424190	22
39	.547354	5.58	.971161	.80	.576193	6.38	.423807	21
40	9.547689	5.58	9.971113	.78	9.576576	6.38	0.423424	20
41	.548024	5.58	.971066	.80	.576959	6.37	.423041	19
42	.548359	5.57	.971018	.80	.577341	6.37	.422659	18
43	.548693	5.57	.970970	.80	.577723	6.35	.422277	17
44	.549027	5.55	.970922	.80	.578104	6.37	.421896	16
45	9.549360	5.55	9.970874	.78	9.578486	6.35	0.421514	15
46	.549693	5.55	.970827	.80	.578867	6.35	.421133	14
47	.550026	5.55	.970779	.80	.579248	6.35	.420752	13
48	.550359	5.55	.970731	.80	.579629	6.33	.420371	12
49	.550692	5.53	.970683	.80	.580009	6.33	.419991	11
50	9.551024	5.53	9.970635	.82	9.580389	6.33	0.419611	10
51	.551356	5.52	.970586	.80	.580769	6.33	.419231	9
52	.551687	5.52	.970538	.80	.581149	6.32	.418851	8
53	.552018	5.52	.970490	.80	.581528	6.32	.418472	7
54	.552349	5.52	.970442	.80	.581907	6.32	.418093	6
55	9.552680	5.50	9.970394	.82	9.582286	6.32	0.417714	5
56	.553010	5.52	.970345	.80	.582665	6.32	.417335	4
57	.553341	5.48	.970297	.80	.583044	6.30	.416956	3
58	.553670	5.50	.970249	.82	.583422	6.30	.416578	2
59	.554000	5.48	.970200	.80	.583800	6.30	.416200	1
60	9.554329		9.970152		9.584177	6.28	0.415823	0
	Cos.	D. 1″.	Sin.	D. 1″.	Cot.	D. 1″.	Tan.	M.

TABLE C—LOGARITHMIC SINES,

21° 158°

M.	Sin.	D. 1".	Cos.	D. 1".	Tan.	D. 1".	Cot.	
0	9.554329	5.48	9.970152	.82	9.584177	6.30	0.415823	60
1	.554658	5.48	.970103	.80	.584555	6.28	.415445	59
2	.554987	5.47	.970055	.82	.584932	6.28	.415068	58
3	.555315	5.47	.970006	.82	.585309	6.28	.414691	57
4	.555643	5.47	.969957	.80	.585686	6.27	.414314	56
5	9.555971	5.47	9.969909	.82	9.586062	6.28	0.413938	55
6	.556299	5.45	.969860	.82	.586439	6.27	.413561	54
7	.556626	5.45	.969811	.82	.586815	6.27	.413185	53
8	.556953	5.45	.969762	.80	.587190	6.27	.412810	52
9	.557280	5.43	.969714	.82	.587566	6.25	.412434	51
10	9.557606	5.43	9.969665	.82	9.587941	6.25	0.412059	50
11	.557932	5.43	.969616	.82	.588316	6.25	.411684	49
12	.558258	5.43	.969567	.82	.588691	6.25	.411309	48
13	.558583	5.42	.969518	.82	.589066	6.25	.410934	47
14	.558909	5.43	.969469	.82	.589440	6.23	.410560	46
15	9.559234	5.42	9.969420	.82	9.589814	6.23	0.410186	45
16	.559558	5.40	.969370	.83	.590188	6.23	.409812	44
17	.559883	5.42	.969321	.82	.590562	6.23	.409438	43
18	.560207	5.40	.969272	.82	.590935	6.22	.409065	42
19	.560531	5.40	.969223	.82	.591308	6.22	.408692	41
20	9.560855	5.40	9.969173	.83	9.591681	6.22	0.408319	40
21	.561178	5.38	.969124	.82	.592054	6.22	.407946	39
22	.561501	5.38	.969075	.82	.592426	6.20	.407574	38
23	.561824	5.38	.969025	.83	.592799	6.22	.407201	37
24	.562146	5.37	.968976	.82	.593171	6.20	.406829	36
25	9.562468	5.37	9.968926	.83	9.593542	6.20	0.406458	35
26	.562790	5.37	.968877	.82	.593914	6.18	.406086	34
27	.563112	5.37	.968827	.83	.594285	6.20	.405715	33
28	.563433	5.35	.968777	.83	.594656	6.18	.405344	32
29	.563755	5.37	.968728	.82	.595027	6.18	.404973	31
30	9.564075	5.33	9.968678	.83	9.595398	6.18	0.404602	30
31	.564396	5.35	.968628	.83	.595768	6.17	.404232	29
32	.564716	5.33	.968578	.83	.596138	6.17	.403862	28
33	.565036	5.33	.968528	.83	.596508	6.17	.403492	27
34	.565356	5.33	.968479	.82	.596878	6.17	.403122	26
35	9.565676	5.33	9.968429	.83	9.597247	6.15	0.402753	25
36	.565995	5.32	.968379	.83	.597616	6.15	.402384	24
37	.566314	5.32	.968329	.83	.597985	6.15	.402015	23
38	.566632	5.30	.968278	.85	.598354	6.15	.401646	22
39	.566951	5.32	.968228	.83	.598722	6.13	.401278	21
40	9.567269	5.30	9.968178	.83	9.599091	6.15	0.400909	20
41	.567587	5.30	.968128	.83	.599459	6.13	.400541	19
42	.567904	5.28	.968078	.83	.599827	6.13	.400173	18
43	.568222	5.30	.968027	.85	.600194	6.12	.399806	17
44	.568539	5.28	.967977	.83	.600562	6.13	.399438	16
45	9.568856	5.28	9.967927	.83	9.600929	6.12	0.399071	15
46	.569172	5.27	.967876	.85	.601296	6.12	.398704	14
47	.569488	5.27	.967826	.83	.601663	6.12	.398337	13
48	.569804	5.27	.967775	.85	.602029	6.12	.397971	12
49	.570120	5.27	.967725	.83	.602395	6.10	.397605	11
50	9.570435	5.25	9.967674	.85	9.602761	6.10	0.397239	10
51	.570751	5.27	.967624	.83	.603127	6.10	.396873	9
52	.571066	5.25	.967573	.85	.603493	6.10	.396507	8
53	.571380	5.23	.967522	.85	.603858	6.08	.396142	7
54	.571695	5.25	.967471	.85	.604223	6.08	.395777	6
55	9.572009	5.23	9.967421	.83	9.604588	6.08	0.395412	5
56	.572323	5.23	.967370	.85	.604953	6.08	.395047	4
57	.572636	5.22	.967319	.85	.605317	6.07	.394683	3
58	.572950	5.23	.967268	.85	.605682	6.08	.394318	2
59	.573263	5.22	.967217	.85	.606046	6.07	.393954	1
60	9.573575	5.20	9.967166	.85	9.606410	6.07	0.393590	0
	Cos.	D. 1".	Sin.	D. 1".	Cot.	D. 1".	Tan.	M.

111° 68°

COSINES, TANGENTS, AND COTANGENTS

M.	Sin.	D. 1".	Cos.	D. 1".	Tan.	D. 1".	Cot.	
0	9.573575	5.22	9.967166	.85	9.606410	6.05	0.393590	60
1	.573888	5.20	.967115	.85	.606773	6.07	.393227	59
2	.574200	5.20	.967064	.85	.607137	6.05	.392863	58
3	.574512	5.20	.967013	.87	.607500	6.05	.392500	57
4	.574824	5.20	.966961	.85	.607863	6.03	.392137	56
5	9.575136	5.18	9.966910	.85	9.608225	6.05	0.391775	55
6	.575447	5.18	.966859	.85	.608588	6.03	.391412	54
7	.575758	5.18	.966808	.87	.608950	6.03	.391050	53
8	.576069	5.17	.966756	.85	.609312	6.03	.390688	52
9	.576379	5.17	.966705	.87	.609674	6.03	.390326	51
10	9.576689	5.17	9.966653	.85	9.610036	6.02	0.389964	50
11	.576999	5.17	.966602	.87	.610397	6.03	.389603	49
12	.577309	5.15	.966550	.85	.610759	6.02	.389241	48
13	.577618	5.15	.966499	.87	.611120	6.00	.388880	47
14	.577927	5.15	.966447	.87	.611480	6.02	.388520	46
15	9.578236	5.15	9.966395	.85	9.611841	6.00	0.388159	45
16	.578545	5.13	.966344	.87	.612201	6.00	.387799	44
17	.578853	5.15	.966292	.87	.612561	6.00	.387439	43
18	.579162	5.13	.966240	.87	.612921	6.00	.387079	42
19	.579470	5.12	.966188	.87	.613281	6.00	.386719	41
20	9.579777	5.13	9.966136	.85	9.613641	5.98	0.386359	40
21	.580085	5.12	.966085	.87	.614000	5.98	.386000	39
22	.580392	5.12	.966033	.87	.614359	5.98	.385641	38
23	.580699	5.10	.965981	.87	.614718	5.98	.385282	37
24	.581005	5.12	.965929	.88	.615077	5.97	.384923	36
25	9.581312	5.10	9.965876	.87	9.615435	5.97	0.384565	35
26	.581618	5.10	.965824	.87	.615793	5.97	.384207	34
27	.581924	5.08	.965772	.87	.616151	5.97	.383849	33
28	.582229	5.10	.965720	.87	.616509	5.97	.383491	32
29	.582535	5.08	.965668	.88	.616867	5.95	.383133	31
30	9.582840	5.08	9.965615	.87	9.617224	5.97	0.382776	30
31	.583145	5.07	.965563	.87	.617582	5.95	.382418	29
32	.583449	5.08	.965511	.88	.617939	5.93	.382061	28
33	.583754	5.07	.965458	.87	.618295	5.95	.381705	27
34	.584058	5.05	.965406	.88	.618652	5.93	.381348	26
35	9.584361	5.07	9.965353	.87	9.619008	5.93	0.380992	25
36	.584665	5.05	.965301	.88	.619364	5.93	.380636	24
37	.584968	5.07	.965248	.88	.619720	5.93	.380280	23
38	.585272	5.03	.965195	.87	.620076	5.93	.379924	22
39	.585574	5.05	.965143	.88	.620432	5.92	.379568	21
40	9.585877	5.03	9.965090	.88	9.620787	5.92	0.379213	20
41	.586179	5.05	.965037	.88	.621142	5.92	.378858	19
42	.586482	5.02	.964984	.88	.621497	5.92	.378503	18
43	.586783	5.03	.964931	.88	.621852	5.92	.378148	17
44	.587085	5.02	.964879	.87	.622207	5.90	.377793	16
45	9.587386	5.03	9.964826	.88	9.622561	5.90	0.377439	15
46	.587688	5.02	.964773	.88	.622915	5.90	.377085	14
47	.587989	5.00	.964720	.88	.623269	5.90	.376731	13
48	.588289	5.02	.964666	.90	.623623	5.88	.376377	12
49	.588590	5.00	.964613	.88	.623976	5.90	.376024	11
50	9.588890	5.00	9.964560	.88	9.624330	5.88	0.375670	10
51	.589190	4.98	.964507	.88	.624683	5.88	.375317	9
52	.589489	5.00	.964454	.90	.625036	5.87	.374964	8
53	.589789	4.98	.964400	.88	.625388	5.88	.374612	7
54	.590088	4.98	.964347	.88	.625741	5.87	.374259	6
55	9.590387	4.98	9.964294	.90	9.626093	5.87	0.373907	5
56	.590686	4.97	.964240	.88	.626445	5.87	.373555	4
57	.590984	4.97	.964187	.90	.626797	5.87	.373203	3
58	.591282	4.97	.964133	.88	.627149	5.87	.372851	2
59	.591580	4.97	.964080	.90	.627501	5.85	.372499	1
60	9.591878		9.964026		9.627852		0.372148	0
	Cos.	D. 1".	Sin.	D. 1".	Cot.	D. 1".	Tan.	M.

M.	Sin.	D. 1″.	Cos.	D. 1″.	Tan.	D. 1″.	Cot.	
0	9.591878		9.964026		9.627852		0.372148	60
1	.592176	4.97	.963972	.90	.628203	5.85	.371797	59
2	.592473	4.95	.963919	.88	.628554	5.85	.371446	58
3	.592770	4.95	.963865	.90	.628905	5.85	.371095	57
4	.593067	4.95	.963811	.90	.629255	5.83	.370745	56
5	9.593363	4.93	9.963757	.90	9.629606	5.85	0.370394	55
6	.593659	4.93	.963704	.88	.629956	5.83	.370044	54
7	.593955	4.93	.963650	.90	.630306	5.83	.369694	53
8	.594251	4.93	.963596	.90	.630656	5.83	.369344	52
9	.594547	4.93	.963542	.90	.631005	5.82	.368995	51
10	9.594842	4.92	9.963488	.90	9.631355	5.83	0.368645	50
11	.595137	4.92	.963434	.90	.631704	5.82	.368296	49
12	.595432	4.92	.963379	.92	.632053	5.82	.367947	48
13	.595727	4.92	.963325	.90	.632402	5.82	.367598	47
14	.596021	4.90	.963271	.90	.632750	5.80	.367250	46
15	9.596315	4.90	9.963217	.90	9.633099	5.82	0.366901	45
16	.596609	4.90	.963163	.90	.633447	5.80	.366553	44
17	.596903	4.90	.963108	.92	.633795	5.80	.366205	43
18	.597196	4.88	.963054	.90	.634143	5.80	.365857	42
19	.597490	4.90	.962999	.92	.634490	5.78	.365510	41
20	9.597783	4.88	9.962945	.90	9.634838	5.80	0.365162	40
21	.598075	4.87	.962890	.92	.635185	5.78	.364815	39
22	.598368	4.88	.962836	.90	.635532	5.78	.364468	38
23	.598660	4.87	.962781	.92	.635879	5.78	.364121	37
24	.598952	4.87	.962727	.90	.636226	5.78	.363774	36
25	9.599244	4.87	9.962672	.92	9.636572	5.77	0.363428	35
26	.599536	4.87	.962617	.92	.636919	5.78	.363081	34
27	.599827	4.85	.962562	.90	.637265	5.77	.362735	33
28	.600118	4.85	.962508	.92	.637611	5.77	.362389	32
29	.600409	4.85	.962453	.92	.637956	5.75	.362044	31
30	9.600700	4.85	9.962398	.92	9.638302	5.77	0.361698	30
31	.600990	4.83	.962343	.92	.638647	5.75	.361353	29
32	.601280	4.83	.962288	.92	.638992	5.75	.361008	28
33	.601570	4.83	.962233	.92	.639337	5.75	.360663	27
34	.601860	4.83	.962178	.92	.639682	5.75	.360318	26
35	9.602150	4.83	9.962123	.92	9.640027	5.75	0.359973	25
36	.602439	4.82	.962067	.93	.640371	5.75	.359629	24
37	.602728	4.82	.962012	.92	.640716	5.73	.359284	23
38	.603017	4.82	.961957	.92	.641060	5.75	.358940	22
39	.603305	4.80	.961902	.92	.641404	5.73	.358596	21
40	9.603594	4.82	9.961846	.93	9.641747	5.73	0.358253	20
41	.603882	4.80	.961791	.92	.642091	5.73	.357909	19
42	.604170	4.80	.961735	.93	.642434	5.72	.357566	18
43	.604457	4.78	.961680	.92	.642777	5.72	.357223	17
44	.604745	4.80	.961624	.93	.643120	5.72	.356880	16
45	9.605032	4.78	9.961569	.92	9.643463	5.72	0.356537	15
46	.605319	4.78	.961513	.93	.643806	5.72	.356194	14
47	.605606	4.78	.961458	.92	.644148	5.70	.355852	13
48	.605892	4.77	.961402	.93	.644490	5.70	.355510	12
49	.606179	4.78	.961346	.93	.644832	5.70	.355168	11
50	9.606465	4.77	9.961290	.93	9.645174	5.70	0.354826	10
51	.606751	4.77	.961235	.92	.645516	5.70	.354484	9
52	.607036	4.75	.961179	.93	.645857	5.68	.354143	8
53	.607322	4.77	.961123	.93	.646199	5.70	.353801	7
54	.607607	4.75	.961067	.93	.646540	5.68	.353460	6
55	9.607892	4.75	9.961011	.93	9.646881	5.68	0.353119	5
56	.608177	4.75	.960955	.93	.647222	5.68	.352778	4
57	.608461	4.73	.960899	.93	.647562	5.67	.352438	3
58	.608745	4.73	.960843	.93	.647903	5.68	.352097	2
59	.609029	4.73	.960786	.95	.648243	5.67	.351757	1
60	9.609313	4.73	9.960730	.93	9.648583	5.67	0.351417	0
	Cos.	D. 1″.	Sin.	D. 1″.	Cot.	D. 1″.	Tan.	M.

COSINES, TANGENTS, AND COTANGENTS

24° / **155°**

M.	Sin.	D. 1″.	Cos.	D. 1″.	Tan.	D. 1″.	Cot.	
0	9.609313	4.73	9.960730	.93	9.648583	5.67	0.351417	60
1	.609597	4.72	.960674	.93	.648923	5.67	.351077	59
2	.609880	4.73	.960618	.93	.649263	5.67	.350737	58
3	.610164	4.72	.960561	.95	.649602	5.65	.350398	57
4	.610447	4.70	.960505	.93	.649942	5.67	.350058	56
5	9.610729	4.72	9.960448	.95	9.650281	5.65	0.349719	55
6	.611012	4.70	.960392	.93	.650620	5.65	.349380	54
7	.611294	4.70	.960335	.95	.650959	5.65	.349041	53
8	.611576	4.70	.960279	.93	.651297	5.63	.348703	52
9	.611858	4.70	.960222	.95	.651636	5.65	.348364	51
10	9.612140	4.70	9.960165	.95	9.651974	5.63	0.348026	50
11	.612421	4.68	.960109	.93	.652312	5.63	.347688	49
12	.612702	4.68	.960052	.95	.652650	5.63	.347350	48
13	.612983	4.68	.959995	.95	.652988	5.63	.347012	47
14	.613264	4.68	.959938	.95	.653326	5.63	.346674	46
15	9.613545	4.68	9.959882	.93	9.653663	5.62	0.346337	45
16	.613825	4.67	.959825	.95	.654000	5.62	.346000	44
17	.614105	4.67	.959768	.95	.654337	5.62	.345663	43
18	.614385	4.67	.959711	.95	.654674	5.62	.345326	42
19	.614665	4.67	.959654	.95	.655011	5.62	.344989	41
20	9.614944	4.65	9.959596	.97	9.655348	5.60	0.344652	40
21	.615223	4.65	.959539	.95	.655684	5.60	.344316	39
22	.615502	4.65	.959482	.95	.656020	5.60	.343980	38
23	.615781	4.65	.959425	.95	.656356	5.60	.343644	37
24	.616060	4.65	.959368	.95	.656692	5.60	.343308	36
25	9.616338	4.63	9.959310	.97	9.657028	5.60	0.342972	35
26	.616616	4.63	.959253	.95	.657364	5.58	.342636	34
27	.616894	4.63	.959195	.97	.657699	5.58	.342301	33
28	.617172	4.63	.959138	.95	.658034	5.58	.341966	32
29	.617450	4.62	.959080	.97	.658369	5.58	.341631	31
30	9.617727	4.62	9.959023	.95	9.658704	5.58	0.341296	30
31	.618004	4.62	.958965	.97	.659039	5.57	.340961	29
32	.618281	4.62	.958908	.95	.659373	5.58	.340627	28
33	.618558	4.60	.958850	.97	.659708	5.57	.340292	27
34	.618834	4.60	.958792	.97	.660042	5.57	.339958	26
35	9.619110	4.60	9.958734	.95	9.660376	5.57	0.339624	25
36	.619386	4.60	.958677	.97	.660710	5.55	.339290	24
37	.619662	4.60	.958619	.97	.661043	5.57	.338957	23
38	.619938	4.58	.958561	.97	.661377	5.55	.338623	22
39	.620213	4.58	.958503	.97	.661710	5.55	.338290	21
40	9.620488	4.58	9.958445	.97	9.662043	5.55	0.337957	20
41	.620763	4.58	.958387	.97	.662376	5.55	.337624	19
42	.621038	4.58	.958329	.97	.662709	5.55	.337291	18
43	.621313	4.57	.958271	.97	.663042	5.55	.336958	17
44	.621587	4.57	.958213	.98	.663375	5.53	.336625	16
45	9.621861	4.57	9.958154	.97	9.663707	5.53	0.336293	15
46	.622135	4.57	.958096	.97	.664039	5.53	.335961	14
47	.622409	4.55	.958038	.98	.664371	5.53	.335629	13
48	.622682	4.57	.957979	.97	.664703	5.53	.335297	12
49	.622956	4.55	.957921	.97	.665035	5.52	.334965	11
50	9.623229	4.55	9.957863	.98	9.665366	5.53	0.334634	10
51	.623502	4.53	.957804	.97	.665698	5.52	.334302	9
52	.623774	4.55	.957746	.98	.666029	5.52	.333971	8
53	.624047	4.53	.957687	.98	.666360	5.52	.333640	7
54	.624319	4.53	.957628	.97	.666691	5.50	.333309	6
55	9.624591	4.53	9.957570	.98	9.667021	5.52	0.332979	5
56	.624863	4.53	.957511	.98	.667352	5.50	.332648	4
57	.625135	4.52	.957452	.98	.667682	5.52	.332318	3
58	.625406	4.52	.957393	.98	.668013	5.50	.331987	2
59	.625677	4.52	.957335	.97	.668343	5.50	.331657	1
60	9.625948	4.52	9.957276	.98	9.668673	5.50	0.331327	0
	Cos.	D. 1″.	Sin.	D. 1″.	Cot.	D. 1″.	Tan.	M.

114° / **65°**

373

M.	Sin.	D. 1″.	Cos.	D. 1.″	Tan.	D. 1″.	Cot.	
0	9.625948	4.52	9.957276	.98	9.668673	5.48	0.331327	60
1	.626219	4.52	.957217	.98	.669002	5.50	.330998	59
2	.626490	4.50	.957158	.98	.669332	5.48	.330668	58
3	.626760	4.50	.957099	.98	.669661	5.50	.330339	57
4	.627030	4.50	.957040	.98	.669991	5.48	.330009	56
5	9.627300	4.50	9.956981	.98	9.670320	5.48	0.329680	55
6	.627570	4.50	.956921	1.00	.670649	5.48	.329351	54
7	.627840	4.48	.956862	.98	.670977	5.47	.329023	53
8	.628109	4.48	.956803	.98	.671306	5.48	.328694	52
9	.628378	4.48	.956744	.98	.671635	5.48	.328365	51
10	9.628647	4.48	9.956684	1.00	9.671963	5.47	0.328037	50
11	.628916	4.48	.956625	.98	.672291	5.47	.327709	49
12	.629185	4.48	.956566	.98	.672619	5.47	.327381	48
13	.629453	4.47	.956506	1.00	.672947	5.47	.327053	47
14	.629721	4.47	.956447	.98	.673274	5.45	.326726	46
15	9.629989	4.47	9.956387	1.00	9.673602	5.47	0.326398	45
16	.630257	4.47	.956327	1.00	.673929	5.45	.326071	44
17	.630524	4.45	.956268	.98	.674257	5.47	.325743	43
18	.630792	4.47	.956208	1.00	.674584	5.45	.325416	42
19	.631059	4.45	.956148	1.00	.674911	5.45	.325089	41
20	9.631326	4.45	9.956089	.98	9.675237	5.43	0.324763	40
21	.631593	4.45	.956029	1.00	.675564	5.45	.324436	39
22	.631859	4.43	.955969	1.00	.675890	5.43	.324110	38
23	.632125	4.43	.955909	1.00	.676217	5.45	.323783	37
24	.632392	4.45	.955849	1.00	.676543	5.43	.323457	36
25	9.632658	4.43	9.955789	1.00	9.676869	5.43	0.323131	35
26	.632923	4.42	.955729	1.00	.677194	5.43	.322806	34
27	.633189	4.43	.955669	1.00	.677520	5.42	.322480	33
28	.633454	4.42	.955609	1.00	.677846	5.43	.322154	32
29	.633719	4.42	.955548	1.02	.678171	5.43	.321829	31
30	9.633984	4.42	9.955488	1.00	9.678496	5.42	0.321504	30
31	.634249	4.42	.955428	1.00	.678821	5.42	.321179	29
32	.634514	4.42	.955368	1.00	.679146	5.42	.320854	28
33	.634778	4.40	.955307	1.02	.679471	5.42	.320529	27
34	.635042	4.40	.955247	1.00	.679795	5.42	.320205	26
35	9.635306	4.40	9.955186	1.02	9.680120	5.40	0.319880	25
36	.635570	4.40	.955126	1.00	.680444	5.40	.319556	24
37	.635834	4.40	.955065	1.02	.680768	5.40	.319232	23
38	.636097	4.38	.955005	1.00	.681092	5.40	.318908	22
39	.636360	4.38	.954944	1.02	.681416	5.40	.318584	21
40	9.636623	4.38	9.954883	1.02	9.681740	5.40	0.318260	20
41	.636886	4.38	.954823	1.00	.682063	5.38	.317937	19
42	.637148	4.37	.954762	1.02	.682387	5.40	.317613	18
43	.637411	4.38	.954701	1.02	.682710	5.38	.317290	17
44	.637673	4.37	.954640	1.02	.683033	5.38	.316967	16
45	9.637935	4.37	9.954579	1.02	9.683356	5.38	0.316644	15
46	.638197	4.37	.954518	1.02	.683679	5.38	.316321	14
47	.638458	4.35	.954457	1.02	.684001	5.37	.315999	13
48	.638720	4.37	.954396	1.02	.684324	5.38	.315676	12
49	.638981	4.35	.954335	1.02	.684646	5.37	.315354	11
50	9.639242	4.35	9.954274	1.02	9.684968	5.37	0.315032	10
51	.639503	4.35	.954213	1.02	.685290	5.37	.314710	9
52	.639764	4.33	.954152	1.03	.685612	5.37	.314388	8
53	.640024	4.33	.954090	1.02	.685934	5.35	.314066	7
54	.640284	4.33	.954029	1.02	.686255	5.37	.313745	6
55	9.640544	4.33	9.953968	1.03	9.686577	5.35	0.313423	5
56	.640804	4.33	.953906	1.02	.686898	5.35	.313102	4
57	.641064	4.33	.953845	1.03	.687219	5.35	.312781	3
58	.641324	4.32	.953783	1.02	.687540	5.35	.312460	2
59	.641583	4.32	.953722	1.03	.687861	5.35	.312139	1
60	9.641842		9.953660		9.688182		0.311818	0
	Cos.	D. 1″.	Sin.	D. 1″.	Cot.	D. 1″.	Tan.	M.

M.	Sin.	D. 1″.	Cos.	D. 1″.	Tan.	D. 1″.	Cot.	
0	9.641842	4.32	9.953660	1.02	9.688182	5.33	0.311818	60
1	.642101	4.32	.953599	1.03	.688502	5.35	.311498	59
2	.642360	4.30	.953537	1.03	.688823	5.33	.311177	58
3	.642618	4.32	.953475	1.03	.689143	5.33	.310857	57
4	.642877	4.30	.953413	1.02	.689463	5.33	.310537	56
5	9.643135	4.30	9.953352	1.03	9.689783	5.33	0.310217	55
6	.643393	4.28	.953290	1.03	.690103	5.33	.309897	54
7	.643650	4.30	.953228	1.03	.690423	5.32	.309577	53
8	.643908	4.28	.953166	1.03	.690742	5.33	.309258	52
9	.644165	4.30	.953104	1.03	.691062	5.32	.308938	51
10	9.644423	4.28	9.953042	1.03	9.691381	5.32	0.308619	50
11	.644680	4.27	.952980	1.03	.691700	5.32	.308300	49
12	.644936	4.28	.952918	1.05	.692019	5.32	.307981	48
13	.645193	4.28	.952855	1.03	.692338	5.30	.307662	47
14	.645450	4.27	.952793	1.03	.692656	5.32	.307344	46
15	9.645706	4.27	9.952731	1.03	9.692975	5.30	0.307025	45
16	.645962	4.27	.952669	1.05	.693293	5.32	.306707	44
17	.646218	4.27	.952606	1.03	.693612	5.30	.306388	43
18	.646474	4.25	.952544	1.05	.693930	5.30	.306070	42
19	.646729	4.25	.952481	1.03	.694248	5.30	.305752	41
20	9.646984	4.27	9.952419	1.05	9.694566	5.28	0.305434	40
21	.647240	4.23	.952356	1.03	.694883	5.30	.305117	39
22	.647494	4.25	.952294	1.05	.695201	5.28	.304799	38
23	.647749	4.25	.952231	1.05	.695518	5.30	.304482	37
24	.648004	4.23	.952168	1.03	.695836	5.28	.304164	36
25	9.648258	4.23	9.952106	1.05	9.696153	5.28	0.303847	35
26	.648512	4.23	.952043	1.05	.696470	5.28	.303530	34
27	.648766	4.23	.951980	1.05	.696787	5.28	.303213	33
28	.649020	4.23	.951917	1.05	.697103	5.27	.302897	32
29	.649274	4.22	.951854	1.05	.697420	5.28	.302580	31
30	9.649527	4.23	9.951791	1.05	9.697736	5.27	0.302264	30
31	.649781	4.22	.951728	1.05	.698053	5.27	.301947	29
32	.650034	4.22	.951665	1.05	.698369	5.27	.301631	28
33	.650287	4.22	.951602	1.05	.698685	5.27	.301315	27
34	.650539	4.20	.951539	1.05	.699001	5.25	.300999	26
35	9.650792	4.20	9.951476	1.07	9.699316	5.27	0.300684	25
36	.651044	4.22	.951412	1.05	.699632	5.25	.300368	24
37	.651297	4.20	.951349	1.05	.699947	5.27	.300053	23
38	.651549	4.18	.951286	1.07	.700263	5.25	.299737	22
39	.651800	4.20	.951222	1.05	.700578	5.25	.299422	21
40	9.652052	4.20	9.951159	1.05	9.700893	5.25	0.299107	20
41	.652304	4.18	.951096	1.07	.701208	5.25	.298792	19
42	.652555	4.18	.951032	1.07	.701523	5.23	.298477	18
43	.652806	4.18	.950968	1.05	.701837	5.25	.298163	17
44	.653057	4.18	.950905	1.07	.702152	5.23	.297848	16
45	9.653308	4.17	9.950841	1.05	9.702466	5.25	0.297534	15
46	.653558	4.17	.950778	1.07	.702781	5.23	.297219	14
47	.653808	4.18	.950714	1.07	.703095	5.23	.296905	13
48	.654059	4.17	.950650	1.07	.703409	5.22	.296591	12
49	.654309	4.15	.950586	1.07	.703722	5.23	.296278	11
50	9.654558	4.17	9.950522	1.07	9.704036	5.23	0.295964	10
51	.654808	4.17	.950458	1.07	.704350	5.22	.295650	9
52	.655058	4.15	.950394	1.07	.704663	5.22	.295337	8
53	.655307	4.15	.950330	1.07	.704976	5.23	.295024	7
54	.655556	4.15	.950266	1.07	.705290	5.22	.294710	6
55	9.655805	4.15	9.950202	1.07	9.705603	5.22	0.294397	5
56	.656054	4.13	.950138	1.07	.705916	5.20	.294084	4
57	.656302	4.15	.950074	1.07	.706228	5.22	.293772	3
58	.656551	4.13	.950010	1.08	.706541	5.22	.293459	2
59	.656799	4.13	.949945	1.07	.706854	5.20	.293146	1
60	9.657047		9.949881		9.707166		0.292834	0
	Cos.	D. 1″.	Sin.	D. 1″.	Cot.	D. 1″.	Tan.	M.

TABLE C—LOGARITHMIC SINES,
27° 152°

M.	Sin.	D. 1″.	Cos.	D. 1″.	Tan.	D. 1″.	Cot.	
0	9.657047	4.13	9.949881	1.08	9.707166	5.20	0.292834	60
1	.657295	4.12	.949816	1.07	.707478	5.20	.292522	59
2	.657542	4.13	.949752	1.07	.707790	5.20	.292210	58
3	.657790	4.12	.949688	1.08	.708102	5.20	.291898	57
4	.658037	4.12	.949623	1.08	.708414	5.20	.291586	56
5	9.658284	4.12	9.949558	1.07	9.708726	5.20	0.291274	55
6	.658531	4.12	.949494	1.08	.709037	5.18	.290963	54
7	.658778	4.12	.949429	1.08	.709349	5.20	.290651	53
8	.659025	4.10	.949364	1.07	.709660	5.18	.290340	52
9	.659271	4.10	.949300	1.08	.709971	5.18	.290029	51
10	9.659517	4.10	9.949235	1.08	9.710282	5.18	0.289718	50
11	.659763	4.10	.949170	1.08	.710593	5.18	.289407	49
12	.660009	4.10	.949105	1.08	.710904	5.18	.289096	48
13	.660255	4.10	.949040	1.08	.711215	5.18	.288785	47
14	.660501	4.08	.948975	1.08	.711525	5.17	.288475	46
15	9.660746	4.08	9.948910	1.08	9.711836	5.18	0.288164	45
16	.660991	4.08	.948845	1.08	.712146	5.17	.287854	44
17	.661236	4.08	.948780	1.08	.712456	5.17	.287544	43
18	.661481	4.08	.948715	1.08	.712766	5.17	.287234	42
19	.661726	4.07	.948650	1.10	.713076	5.17	.286924	41
20	9.661970	4.07	9.948584	1.08	9.713386	5.17	0.286614	40
21	.662214	4.08	.948519	1.08	.713696	5.17	.286304	39
22	.662459	4.07	.948454	1.10	.714005	5.15	.285995	38
23	.662703	4.05	.948388	1.08	.714314	5.17	.285686	37
24	.662946	4.07	.948323	1.10	.714624	5.15	.285376	36
25	9.663190	4.05	9.948257	1.08	9.714933	5.15	0.285067	35
26	.663433	4.07	.948192	1.10	.715242	5.15	.284758	34
27	.663677	4.05	.948126	1.10	.715551	5.15	.284449	33
28	.663920	4.05	.948060	1.08	.715860	5.13	.284140	32
29	.664163	4.05	.947995	1.10	.716168	5.15	.283832	31
30	9.664406	4.03	9.947929	1.10	9.716477	5.13	0.283523	30
31	.664648	4.05	.947863	1.10	.716785	5.13	.283215	29
32	.664891	4.03	.947797	1.10	.717093	5.13	.282907	28
33	.665133	4.03	.947731	1.10	.717401	5.13	.282599	27
34	.665375	4.03	.947665	1.08	.717709	5.13	.282291	26
35	9.665617	4.03	9.947600	1.12	9.718017	5.13	0.281983	25
36	.665859	4.02	.947533	1.10	.718325	5.13	.281675	24
37	.666100	4.03	.947467	1.10	.718633	5.12	.281367	23
38	.666342	4.02	.947401	1.10	.718940	5.13	.281060	22
39	.666583	4.02	.947335	1.10	.719248	5.12	.280752	21
40	9.666824	4.02	9.947269	1.10	9.719555	5.12	0.280445	20
41	.667065	4.00	.947203	1.12	.719862	5.12	.280138	19
42	.667305	4.02	.947136	1.10	.720169	5.12	.279831	18
43	.667546	4.00	.947070	1.10	.720476	5.12	.279524	17
44	.667786	4.02	.947004	1.12	.720783	5.10	.279217	16
45	9.668027	4.00	9.946937	1.10	9.721089	5.12	0.278911	15
46	.668267	3.98	.946871	1.12	.721396	5.10	.278604	14
47	.668506	4.00	.946804	1.10	.721702	5.10	.278298	13
48	.668746	4.00	.946738	1.12	.722009	5.12	.277991	12
49	.668986	3.98	.946671	1.12	.722315	5.10	.277685	11
50	9.669225	3.98	9.946604	1.10	9.722621	5.10	0.277379	10
51	.669464	3.98	.946538	1.12	.722927	5.10	.277073	9
52	.669703	3.98	.946471	1.12	.723232	5.08	.276768	8
53	.669942	3.98	.946404	1.12	.723538	5.10	.276462	7
54	.670181	3.97	.946337	1.12	.723844	5.08	.276156	6
55	9.670419	3.98	9.946270	1.12	9.724149	5.08	0.275851	5
56	.670658	3.97	.946203	1.12	.724454	5.08	.275546	4
57	.670896	3.97	.946136	1.12	.724760	5.10	.275240	3
58	.671134	3.97	.946069	1.12	.725065	5.08	.274935	2
59	.671372	3.95	.946002	1.12	.725370	5.08	.274630	1
60	9.671609		9.945935		9.725674	5.07	0.274326	0
	Cos.	D. 1″.	Sin.	D. 1″.	Cot.	D. 1″.	Tan.	M.

M.	Sin.	D. 1″.	Cos.	D. 1″.	Tan.	D. 1″.	Cot.	
0	9.671609	3.97	9.945935	1.12	9.725674	5.08	0.274326	60
1	.671847	3.95	.945868	1.13	.725979	5.08	.274021	59
2	.672084	3.95	.945800	1.12	.726284	5.07	.273716	58
3	.672321	3.95	.945733	1.12	.726588	5.07	.273412	57
4	.672558	3.95	.945666	1.13	.726892	5.08	.273108	56
5	9.672795	3.95	9.945598	1.12	9.727197	5.07	0.272803	55
6	.673032	3.93	.945531	1.12	.727501	5.07	.272499	54
7	.673268	3.95	.945464	1.13	.727805	5.07	.272195	53
8	.673505	3.93	.945396	1.13	.728109	5.05	.271891	52
9	.673741	3.93	.945328	1.12	.728412	5.07	.271588	51
10	9.673977	3.93	9.945261	1.13	9.728716	5.07	0.271284	50
11	.674213	3.92	.945193	1.13	.729020	5.05	.270980	49
12	.674448	3.93	.945125	1.12	.729323	5.05	.270677	48
13	.674684	3.92	.945058	1.13	.729626	5.05	.270374	47
14	.674919	3.93	.944990	1.13	.729929	5.05	.270071	46
15	9.675155	3.92	9.944922	1.13	9.730233	5.07	0.269767	45
16	.675390	3.90	.944854	1.13	.730535	5.03	.269465	44
17	.675624	3.92	.944786	1.13	.730838	5.05	.269162	43
18	.675859	3.92	.944718	1.13	.731141	5.05	.268859	42
19	.676094	3.90	.944650	1.13	.731444	5.03	.268556	41
20	9.676328	3.90	9.944582	1.13	9.731746	5.03	0.268254	40
21	.676562	3.90	.944514	1.13	.732048	5.05	.267952	39
22	.676796	3.90	.944446	1.15	.732351	5.03	.267649	38
23	.677030	3.90	.944377	1.13	.732653	5.03	.267347	37
24	.677264	3.90	.944309	1.13	.732955	5.03	.267045	36
25	9.677498	3.88	9.944241	1.15	9.733257	5.02	0.266743	35
26	.677731	3.88	.944172	1.13	.733558	5.03	.266442	34
27	.677964	3.88	.944104	1.13	.733860	5.03	.266140	33
28	.678197	3.88	.944036	1.15	.734162	5.02	.265838	32
29	.678430	3.88	.943967	1.13	.734463	5.02	.265537	31
30	9.678663	3.87	9.943899	1.15	9.734764	5.03	0.265236	30
31	.678895	3.88	.943830	1.15	.735066	5.02	.264934	29
32	.679128	3.87	.943761	1.13	.735367	5.02	.264633	28
33	.679360	3.87	.943693	1.15	.735668	5.02	.264332	27
34	.679592	3.87	.943624	1.15	.735969	5.00	.264031	26
35	9.679824	3.87	9.943555	1.15	9.736269	5.02	0.263731	25
36	.680056	3.87	.943486	1.15	.736570	5.00	.263430	24
37	.680288	3.85	.943417	1.15	.736870	5.02	.263130	23
38	.680519	3.85	.943348	1.15	.737171	5.00	.262829	22
39	.680750	3.87	.943279	1.15	.737471	5.00	.262529	21
40	9.680982	3.85	9.943210	1.15	9.737771	5.00	0.262229	20
41	.681213	3.83	.943141	1.15	.738071	5.00	.261929	19
42	.681443	2.85	.943072	1.15	.738371	5.00	.261629	18
43	.681674	3.85	.943003	1.15	.738671	5.00	.261329	17
44	.681905	3.83	.942934	1.17	.738971	5.00	.261029	16
45	9.682135	3.83	9.942864	1.15	9.739271	4.98	0.260729	15
46	.682365	3.83	.942795	1.15	.739570	5.00	.260430	14
47	.682595	3.83	.942726	1.17	.739870	4.98	.260130	13
48	.682825	3.83	.942656	1.15	.740169	4.98	.259831	12
49	.683055	3.82	.942587	1.17	.740468	4.98	.259532	11
50	9.683284	3.83	9.942517	1.15	9.740767	4.98	0.259233	10
51	.683514	3.82	.942448	1.17	.741066	4.98	.258934	9
52	.683743	3.82	.942378	1.17	.741365	4.98	.258635	8
53	.683972	3.82	.942308	1.15	.741664	4.97	.258336	7
54	.684201	3.82	.942239	1.17	.741962	4.98	.258038	6
55	9.684430	3.80	9.942169	1.17	9.742261	4.97	0.257739	5
56	.684658	3.82	.942099	1.17	.742559	4.98	.257441	4
57	.684887	3.80	.942029	1.17	.742858	4.97	.257142	3
58	.685115	3.80	.941959	1.17	.743156	4.97	.256844	2
59	.685343	3.80	.941889	1.17	.743454	4.97	.256546	1
60	9.685571		9.941819	1.17	9.743752		0.256248	0
	Cos.	D. 1″.	Sin.	D. 1″.	Cot.	D. 1″.	Tan.	M.

M.	Sin.	D. 1″.	Cos.	D. 1″.	Tan.	D. 1″.	Cot.	
0	9.685571		9.941819		9.743752		0.256248	60
1	.685799	3.80	.941749	1.17	.744050	4.97	.255950	59
2	.686027	3.80	.941679	1.17	.744348	4.97	.255652	58
3	.686254	3.78	.941609	1.17	.744645	4.95	.255355	57
4	.686482	3.80	.941539	1.17	.744943	4.97	.255057	56
5	9.686709	3.78	9.941469	1.17	9.745240	4.95	0.254760	55
6	.686936	3.78	.941398	1.18	.745538	4.97	.254462	54
7	.687163	3.78	.941328	1.17	.745835	4.95	.254165	53
8	.687389	3.77	.941258	1.17	.746132	4.95	.253868	52
9	.687616	3.78	.941187	1.18	.746429	4.95	.253571	51
10	9.687843	3.78	9.941117	1.17	9.746726	4.95	0.253274	50
11	.688069	3.77	.941046	1.18	.747023	4.95	.252977	49
12	.688295	3.77	.940975	1.18	.747319	4.93	.252681	48
13	.688521	3.77	.940905	1.17	.747616	4.95	.252384	47
14	.688747	3.77	.940834	1.18	.747913	4.95	.252087	46
15	9.688972	3.77	9.940763	1.18	9.748209	4.93	0.251791	45
16	.689198	3.75	.940693	1.17	.748505	4.93	.251495	44
17	.689423	3.75	.940622	1.18	.748801	4.93	.251199	43
18	.689648	3.75	.940551	1.18	.749097	4.93	.250903	42
19	.689873	3.75	.940480	1.18	.749393	4.93	.250607	41
20	9.690098	3.75	9.940409	1.18	9.749689	4.93	0.250311	40
21	.690323	3.75	.940338	1.18	.749985	4.93	.250015	39
22	.690548	3.75	.940267	1.18	.750281	4.93	.249719	38
23	.690772	3.73	.940196	1.18	.750576	4.92	.249424	37
24	.690996	3.73	.940125	1.18	.750872	4.93	.249128	36
25	9.691220	3.73	9.940054	1.20	9.751167	4.92	0.248833	35
26	.691444	3.73	.939982	1.18	.751462	4.92	.248538	34
27	.691668	3.73	.939911	1.18	.751757	4.92	.248243	33
28	.691892	3.73	.939840	1.18	.752052	4.92	.247948	32
29	.692115	3.72	.939768	1.20	.752347	4.92	.247653	31
30	9.692339	3.73	9.939697	1.18	9.752642	4.92	0.247358	30
31	.692562	3.72	.939625	1.20	.752937	4.92	.247063	29
32	.692785	3.72	.939554	1.18	.753231	4.90	.246769	28
33	.693008	3.72	.939482	1.20	.753526	4.92	.246474	27
34	.693231	3.72	.939410	1.20	.753820	4.90	.246180	26
35	9.693453	3.70	9.939339	1.18	9.754115	4.92	0.245885	25
36	.693676	3.72	.939267	1.20	.754409	4.90	.245591	24
37	.693898	3.70	.939195	1.20	.754703	4.90	.245297	23
38	.694120	3.70	.939123	1.20	.754997	4.90	.245003	22
39	.694342	3.70	.939052	1.18	.755291	4.90	.244709	21
40	9.694564	3.70	9.938980	1.20	9.755585	4.90	0.244415	20
41	.694786	3.70	.938908	1.20	.755878	4.90	.244122	19
42	.695007	3.68	.938836	1.20	.756172	4.88	.243828	18
43	.695229	3.70	.938763	1.22	.756465	4.90	.243535	17
44	.695450	3.68	.938691	1.20	.756759	4.90	.243241	16
45	9.695671	3.68	9.938619	1.20	9.757052	4.88	0.242948	15
46	.695892	3.68	.938547	1.20	.757345	4.88	.242655	14
47	.696113	3.68	.938475	1.20	.757638	4.88	.242362	13
48	.696334	3.68	.938402	1.22	.757931	4.88	.242069	12
49	.696554	3.67	.938330	1.20	.758224	4.88	.241776	11
50	9.696775	3.68	9.938258	1.20	9.758517	4.88	0.241483	10
51	.696995	3.67	.938185	1.22	.758810	4.88	.241190	9
52	.697215	3.67	.938113	1.20	.759102	4.87	.240898	8
53	.697435	3.67	.938040	1.22	.759395	4.87	.240605	7
54	.697654	3.65	.937967	1.22	.759687	4.87	.240313	6
55	9.697874	3.67	9.937895	1.20	9.759979	4.88	0.240021	5
56	.698094	3.67	.937822	1.22	.760272	4.87	.239728	4
57	.698313	3.65	.937749	1.22	.760564	4.87	.239436	3
58	.698532	3.65	.937676	1.22	.760856	4.87	239144	2
59	.698751	3.65	.937604	1.20	.761148	4.87	.238852	1
60	9.698970	3.65	9.937531	1.22	9.761439	4.85	0.238561	0
	Cos.	D. 1″.	Sin.	D. 1″.	Cot.	D. 1″.	Tan.	M.

M.	Sin.	D. 1".	Cos.	D. 1".	Tan.	D. 1".	Cot.	
0	9.698970	3.65	9.937531	1.22	9.761439	4.87	0.238561	60
1	.699189	3.63	.937458	1.22	.761731	4.87	.238269	59
2	.699407	3.65	.937385	1.22	.762023	4.85	.237977	58
3	.699626	3.63	.937312	1.23	.762314	4.87	.237686	57
4	.699844	3.63	.937238	1.22	.762606	4.87	.237394	56
5	9.700062	3.63	9.937165	1.22	9.762897	4.85	0.237103	55
6	.700280	3.63	.937092	1.22	.763188	4.85	.236812	54
7	.700498	3.63	.937019	1.22	.763479	4.85	.236521	53
8	.700716	3.62	.936946	1.23	.763770	4.85	.236230	52
9	.700933	3.63	.936872	1.22	.764061	4.85	.235939	51
10	9.701151	3.62	9.936799	1.23	9.764352	4.85	0.235648	50
11	.701368	3.62	.936725	1.22	.764643	4.83	.235357	49
12	.701585	3.62	.936652	1.23	.764933	4.85	.235067	48
13	.701802	3.62	.936578	1.22	.765224	4.83	.234776	47
14	.702019	3.62	.936505	1.23	.765514	4.85	.234486	46
15	9.702236	3.60	9.936431	1.23	9.765805	4.83	0.234195	45
16	.702452	3.62	.936357	1.22	.766095	4.83	.233905	44
17	.702669	3.60	.936284	1.23	.766385	4.83	.233615	43
18	.702885	3.60	.936210	1.23	.766675	4.83	.233325	42
19	.703101	3.60	.936136	1.23	.766965	4.83	.233035	41
20	9.703317	3.60	9.936062	1.23	9.767255	4.83	0.232745	40
21	.703533	3.60	.935988	1.23	.767545	4.82	.232455	39
22	.703749	3.58	.935914	1.23	.767834	4.83	.232166	38
23	.703964	3.58	.935840	1.23	.768124	4.83	.231876	37
24	.704179	3.60	.935766	1.23	.768414	4.82	.231586	36
25	9.704395	3.58	9.935692	1.23	9.768703	4.82	0.231297	35
26	.704610	3.58	.935618	1.25	.768992	4.82	.231008	34
27	.704825	3.58	.935543	1.23	.769281	4.82	.230719	33
28	.705040	3.57	.935469	1.23	.769571	4.83	.230429	32
29	.705254	3.58	.935395	1.25	.769860	4.82	.230140	31
30	9.705469	3.57	9.935320	1.23	9.770148	4.80	0.229852	30
31	.705683	3.58	.935246	1.25	.770437	4.82	.229563	29
32	.705898	3.57	.935171	1.23	.770726	4.82	.229274	28
33	.706112	3.57	.935097	1.25	.771015	4.80	.228985	27
34	.706326	3.57	.935022	1.23	.771303	4.82	.228697	26
35	9.706539	3.55	9.934948	1.25	9.771592	4.80	0.228408	25
36	.706753	3.57	.934873	1.25	.771880	4.80	.228120	24
37	.706967	3.55	.934798	1.25	.772168	4.82	.227832	23
38	.707180	3.55	.934723	1.23	.772457	4.80	.227543	22
39	.707393	3.55	.934649	1.25	.772745	4.80	.227255	21
40	9.707606	3.55	9.934574	1.25	9.773033	4.80	0.226967	20
41	.707819	3.55	.934499	1.25	.773321	4.80	.226679	19
42	.708032	3.55	.934424	1.25	.773608	4.78	.226392	18
43	.708245	3.55	.934349	1.25	.773896	4.80	.226104	17
44	.708458	3.53	.934274	1.25	.774184	4.78	.225816	16
45	9.708670	3.53	9.934199	1.27	9.774471	4.80	0.225529	15
46	.708882	3.53	.934123	1.25	.774759	4.78	.225241	14
47	.709094	3.53	.934048	1.25	.775046	4.78	.224954	13
48	.709306	3.53	.933973	1.25	.775333	4.80	.224667	12
49	.709518	3.53	.933898	1.27	.775621	4.78	.224379	11
50	9.709730	3.52	9.933822	1.25	9.775908	4.78	0.224092	10
51	.709941	3.53	.933747	1.27	.776195	4.78	.223805	9
52	.710153	3.52	.933671	1.25	.776482	4.77	.223518	8
53	.710364	3.52	.933596	1.27	.776768	4.78	.223232	7
54	.710575	3.52	.933520	1.25	.777055	4.78	.222945	6
55	9.710786	3.52	9.933445	1.27	9.777342	4.77	0.222658	5
56	.710997	3.52	.933369	1.27	.777628	4.78	.222372	4
57	.711208	3.52	.933293	1.27	.777915	4.77	.222085	3
58	.711419	3.50	.933217	1.27	.778201	4.77	.221799	2
59	.711629	3.50	.933141	1.25	.778488	4.78	.221512	1
60	9.711839		9.933066		9.778774	4.77	0.221226	0
	Cos.	D. 1".	Sin.	D. 1".	Cot.	D. 1".	Tan.	M.

TABLE C—LOGARITHMIC SINES,

31° 148°

M.	Sin.	D. 1".	Cos.	D. 1".	Tan.	D. 1".	Cot.	
0	9.711839	3.52	9.933066	1.27	9.778774	4.77	0.221226	60
1	.712050	3.50	.932990	1.27	.779060	4.77	.220940	59
2	.712260	3.48	.932914	1.27	.779346	4.77	.220654	58
3	.712469	3.50	.932838	1.27	.779632	4.77	.220368	57
4	.712679	3.50	.932762	1.27	.779918	4.77	.220082	56
5	9.712889	3.48	9.932685	1.28	9.780203	4.75	0.219797	55
6	.713098	3.50	.932609	1.27	.780489	4.77	.219511	54
7	.713308	3.48	.932533	1.27	.780775	4.77	.219225	53
8	.713517	3.48	.932457	1.28	.781060	4.77	.218940	52
9	.713726	3.48	.932380	1.27	.781346	4.75	.218654	51
10	9.713935	3.48	9.932304	1.27	9.781631	4.75	0.218369	50
11	.714144	3.47	.932228	1.28	.781916	4.75	.218084	49
12	.714352	3.48	.932151	1.27	.782201	4.75	.217799	48
13	.714561	3.47	.932075	1.28	.782486	4.75	.217514	47
14	.714769	3.48	.931998	1.28	.782771	4.75	.217229	46
15	9.714978	3.47	9.931921	1.27	9.783056	4.75	0.216944	45
16	.715186	3.47	.931845	1.28	.783341	4.75	.216659	44
17	.715394	3.47	.931768	1.28	.783626	4.73	.216374	43
18	.715602	3.45	.931691	1.28	.783910	4.73	.216090	42
19	.715809	3.47	.931614	1.28	.784195	4.73	.215805	41
20	9.716017	3.45	9.931537	1.28	9.784479	4.75	0.215521	40
21	.716224	3.47	.931460	1.28	.784764	4.73	.215236	39
22	.716432	3.45	.931383	1.28	.785048	4.73	.214952	38
23	.716639	3.45	.931306	1.28	.785332	4.73	.214668	37
24	.716846	3.45	.931229	1.28	.785616	4.73	.214384	36
25	9.717053	3.43	9.931152	1.28	9.785900	4.73	0.214100	35
26	.717259	3.45	.931075	1.28	.786184	4.73	.213816	34
27	.717466	3.45	.930998	1.28	.786468	4.73	.213532	33
28	.717673	3.43	.930921	1.28	.786752	4.73	.213248	32
29	.717879	3.43	.930843	1.30	.787036	4.72	.212964	31
30	9.718085	3.43	9.930766	1.28	9.787319	4.73	0.212681	30
31	.718291	3.43	.930688	1.30	.787603	4.72	.212397	29
32	.718497	3.43	.930611	1.28	.787886	4.73	.212114	28
33	.718703	3.43	.930533	1.30	.788170	4.72	.211830	27
34	.718909	3.42	.930456	1.28	.788453	4.72	.211547	26
35	9.719114	3.43	9.930378	1.30	9.788736	4.72	0.211264	25
36	.719320	3.42	.930300	1.30	.789019	4.72	.210981	24
37	.719525	3.42	.930223	1.28	.789302	4.72	.210698	23
38	.719730	3.42	.930145	1.30	.789585	4.72	.210415	22
39	.719935	3.42	.930067	1.30	.789868	4.72	.210132	21
40	9.720140	3.42	9.929989	1.30	9.790151	4.72	0.209849	20
41	.720345	3.40	.929911	1.30	.790434	4.70	.209566	19
42	.720549	3.42	.929833	1.30	.790716	4.72	.209284	18
43	.720754	3.40	.929755	1.30	.790999	4.70	.209001	17
44	.720958	3.40	.929677	1.30	.791281	4.70	.208719	16
45	9.721162	3.40	9.929599	1.30	9.791563	4.72	0.208437	15
46	.721366	3.40	.929521	1.32	.791846	4.70	.208154	14
47	.721570	3.40	.929442	1.30	.792128	4.70	.207872	13
48	.721774	3.40	.929364	1.30	.792410	4.70	.207590	12
49	.721978	3.38	.929286	1.32	.792692	4.70	.207308	11
50	9.722181	3.40	9.929207	1.30	9.792974	4.70	0.207026	10
51	.722385	3.38	.929129	1.32	.793256	4.70	.206744	9
52	.722588	3.38	.929050	1.30	.793538	4.68	.206462	8
53	.722791	3.38	.928972	1.32	.793819	4.70	.206181	7
54	.722994	3.38	.928893	1.30	.794101	4.68	.205899	6
55	9.723197	3.38	9.928815	1.32	9.794383	4.68	0.205617	5
56	.723400	3.38	.928736	1.32	.794664	4.70	.205336	4
57	.723603	3.37	.928657	1.32	.794946	4.68	.205054	3
58	.723805	3.37	.928578	1.32	.795227	4.68	.204773	2
59	.724007	3.38	.928499	1.32	.795508	4.68	.204492	1
60	9.724210		9.928420		9.795789		0.204211	0
	Cos.	D. 1".	Sin.	D. 1".	Cot.	D. 1".	Tan.	M.

M.	Sin.	D. 1″.	Cos.	D. 1″.	Tan.	D. 1″.	Cot.	
0	9.724210	3.37	9.928420	1.30	9.795789	4.68	0.204211	60
1	.724412	3.37	.928342	1.32	.796070	4.68	.203930	59
2	.724614	3.37	.928263	1.32	.796351	4.68	.203649	58
3	.724816	3.35	.928183	1.33	.796632	4.68	.203368	57
4	.725017	3.37	.928104	1.32	.796913	4.68	.203087	56
5	9.725219	3.35	9.928025	1.32	9.797194	4.68	0.202806	55
6	.725420	3.37	.927946	1.32	.797474	4.67	.202526	54
7	.725622	3.35	.927867	1.33	.797755	4.68	.202245	53
8	.725823	3.35	.927787	1.32	.798036	4.67	.201964	52
9	.726024	3.35	.927708	1.32	.798316	4.67	.201684	51
10	9.726225	3.35	9.927629	1.33	9.798596	4.68	0.201404	50
11	.726426	3.35	.927549	1.32	.798877	4.67	.201123	49
12	.726626	3.35	.927470	1.33	.799157	4.67	.200843	48
13	.726827	3.33	.927390	1.33	.799437	4.67	.200563	47
14	.727027	3.35	.927310	1.32	.799717	4.67	.200283	46
15	9.727228	3.33	9.927231	1.33	9.799997	4.67	0.200003	45
16	.727428	3.33	.927151	1.33	.800277	4.67	.199723	44
17	.727628	3.33	.927071	1.33	.800557	4.65	.199443	43
18	.727828	3.32	.926991	1.33	.800836	4.67	.199164	42
19	.728027	3.33	.926911	1.33	.801116	4.67	.198884	41
20	9.728227	3.33	9.926831	1.33	9.801396	4.65	0.198604	40
21	.728427	3.32	.926751	1.33	.801675	4.67	.198325	39
22	.728626	3.32	.926671	1.33	.801955	4.65	.198045	38
23	.728825	3.32	.926591	1.33	.802234	4.65	.197766	37
24	.729024	3.32	.926511	1.33	.802513	4.65	.197487	36
25	9.729223	3.32	9.926431	1.33	9.802792	4.67	0.197208	35
26	.729422	3.32	.926351	1.35	.803072	4.65	.196928	34
27	.729621	3.32	.926270	1.33	.803351	4.65	.196649	33
28	.729820	3.30	.926190	1.33	.803630	4.65	.196370	32
29	.730018	3.32	.926110	1.33	.803909	4.63	.196091	31
30	9.730217	3.30	9.926029	1.35	9.804187	4.65	0.195813	30
31	.730415	3.30	.925949	1.33	.804466	4.65	.195534	29
32	.730613	3.30	.925868	1.33	.804745	4.63	.195255	28
33	.730811	3.30	.925788	1.35	.805023	4.65	.194977	27
34	.731009	3.28	.925707	1.35	.805302	4.63	.194698	26
35	9.731206	3.30	9.925626	1.35	9.805580	4.65	0.194420	25
36	.731404	3.30	.925545	1.33	.805859	4.63	.194141	24
37	.731602	3.28	.925465	1.35	.806137	4.63	.193863	23
38	.731799	3.28	.925384	1.35	.806415	4.63	.193585	22
39	.731996	3.28	.925303	1.35	.806693	4.63	.193307	21
40	9.732193	3.28	9.925222	1.35	9.806971	4.63	0.193029	20
41	.732390	3.28	.925141	1.35	.807249	4.63	.192751	19
42	.732587	3.28	.925060	1.35	.807527	4.63	.192473	18
43	.732784	3.27	.924979	1.35	.807805	4.63	.192195	17
44	.732980	3.28	.924897	1.37	.808083	4.63	.191917	16
45	9.733177	3.27	9.924816	1.35	9.808361	4.62	0.191639	15
46	.733373	3.27	.924735	1.35	.808638	4.63	.191362	14
47	.733569	3.27	.924654	1.37	.808916	4.62	.191084	13
48	.733765	3.27	.924572	1.35	.809193	4.63	.190807	12
49	.733961	3.27	.924491	1.37	.809471	4.62	.190529	11
50	9.734157	3.27	9.924409	1.35	9.809748	4.62	0.190252	10
51	.734353	3.27	.924328	1.37	.810025	4.62	.189975	9
52	.734549	3.25	.924246	1.37	.810302	4.63	.189698	8
53	.734744	3.25	.924164	1.35	.810580	4.62	.189420	7
54	.734939	3.27	.924083	1.37	.810857	4.62	.189143	6
55	9.735135	3.25	9.924001	1.37	9.811134	4.60	0.188866	5
56	.735330	3.25	.923919	1.37	.811410	4.62	.188590	4
57	.735525	3.23	.923837	1.37	.811687	4.62	.188313	3
58	.735719	3.25	.923755	1.37	.811964	4.62	.188036	2
59	.735914	3.25	.923673	1.37	.812241	4.60	.187759	1
60	9.736109		9.923591		9.812517		0.187483	0
	Cos.	D. 1″.	Sin.	D. 1″.	Cot.	D. 1″.	Tan.	M.

TABLE C—LOGARITHMIC SINES,

33°   146°

M.	Sin.	D. 1".	Cos.	D. 1".	Tan.	D. 1".	Cot.	
0	9.736109	3.23	9.923591	1.37	9.812517	4.62	0.187483	60
1	.736303	3.25	.923509	1.37	.812794	4.60	.187206	59
2	.736498	3.23	.923427	1.37	.813070	4.62	.186930	58
3	.736692	3.23	.923345	1.37	.813347	4.60	.186653	57
4	.736886	3.23	.923263	1.37	.813623	4.60	.186377	56
5	9.737080	3.23	9.923181	1.38	9.813899	4.62	0.186101	55
6	.737274	3.22	.923098	1.37	.814176	4.60	.185824	54
7	.737467	3.23	.923016	1.38	.814452	4.60	.185548	53
8	.737661	3.23	.922933	1.37	.814728	4.60	.185272	52
9	.737855	3.22	.922851	1.38	.815004	4.60	.184996	51
10	9.738048	3.22	9.922768	1.37	9.815280	4.58	0.184720	50
11	.738241	3.22	.922686	1.38	.815555	4.60	.184445	49
12	.738434	3.22	.922603	1.38	.815831	4.60	.184169	48
13	.738627	3.22	.922520	1.37	.816107	4.58	.183893	47
14	.738820	3.22	.922438	1.38	.816382	4.60	.183618	46
15	9.739013	3.22	9.922355	1.38	9.816658	4.58	0.183342	45
16	.739206	3.20	.922272	1.38	.816933	4.60	.183067	44
17	.739398	3.20	.922189	1.38	.817209	4.58	.182791	43
18	.739590	3.22	.922106	1.38	.817484	4.58	.182516	42
19	.739783	3.20	.922023	1.38	.817759	4.60	.182241	41
20	9.739975	3.20	9.921940	1.38	9.818035	4.58	0.181965	40
21	.740167	3.20	.921857	1.38	.818310	4.58	.181690	39
22	.740359	3.18	.921774	1.38	.818585	4.58	.181415	38
23	.740550	3.20	.921691	1.40	.818860	4.58	.181140	37
24	.740742	3.20	.921607	1.38	.819135	4.58	.180865	36
25	9.740934	3.18	9.921524	1.38	9.819410	4.57	0.180590	35
26	.741125	3.18	.921441	1.40	.819684	4.58	.180316	34
27	.741316	3.20	.921357	1.38	.819959	4.58	.180041	33
28	.741508	3.18	.921274	1.40	.820234	4.57	.179766	32
29	.741699	3.17	.921190	1.38	.820508	4.58	.179492	31
30	9.741889	3.18	9.921107	1.40	9.820783	4.57	0.179217	30
31	.742080	3.18	.921023	1.40	.821057	4.58	.178943	29
32	.742271	3.18	.920939	1.38	.821332	4.57	.178668	28
33	.742462	3.17	.920856	1.40	.821606	4.57	.178394	27
34	.742652	3.17	.920772	1.40	.821880	4.57	.178120	26
35	9.742842	3.18	9.920688	1.40	9.822154	4.58	0.177846	25
36	.743033	3.17	.920604	1.40	.822429	4.57	.177571	24
37	.743223	3.17	.920520	1.40	.822703	4.57	.177297	23
38	.743413	3.15	.920436	1.40	.822977	4.57	.177023	22
39	.743602	3.17	.920352	1.40	.823251	4.55	.176749	21
40	9.743792	3.17	9.920268	1.40	9.823524	4.57	0.176476	20
41	.743982	3.15	.920184	1.42	.823798	4.57	.176202	19
42	.744171	3.17	.920099	1.40	.824072	4.55	.175928	18
43	.744361	3.15	.920015	1.40	.824345	4.57	.175655	17
44	.744550	3.15	.919931	1.42	.824619	4.57	.175381	16
45	9.744739	3.15	9.919846	1.40	9.824893	4.55	0.175107	15
46	.744928	3.15	.919762	1.42	.825166	4.55	.174834	14
47	.745117	3.15	.919677	1.40	.825439	4.57	.174561	13
48	.745306	3.13	.919593	1.42	.825713	4.55	.174287	12
49	.745494	3.15	.919508	1.40	.825986	4.55	.174014	11
50	9.745683	3.13	9.919424	1.42	9.826259	4.55	0.173741	10
51	.745871	3.15	.919339	1.42	.826532	4.55	.173468	9
52	.746060	3.13	.919254	1.42	.826805	4.55	.173195	8
53	.746248	3.13	.919169	1.40	.827078	4.55	.172922	7
54	.746436	3.13	.919085	1.42	.827351	4.55	.172649	6
55	9.746624	3.13	9.919000	1.42	9.827624	4.55	0.172376	5
56	.746812	3.12	.918915	1.42	.827897	4.55	.172103	4
57	.746999	3.13	.918830	1.42	.828170	4.53	.171830	3
58	.74 187	3.12	.918745	1.43	.828442	4.55	.171558	2
59	.74 '374	3.13	.918659	1.42	.828715	4.53	.171285	1
60	9.747562		9.918574		9.828987		0.171013	0
	Cos.	D. 1".	Sin.	D. 1".	Cot.	D. 1".	Tan.	M.

M.	Sin.	D. 1".	Cos.	D. 1".	Tan.	D. 1".	Cot.	
0	9.747562	3.12	9.918574	1.42	9.828987	4.55	0.171013	60
1	.747749	3.12	.918489	1.42	.829260	4.53	.170740	59
2	.747936	3.12	.918404	1.43	.829532	4.55	..170468	58
3	.748123	3.12	.918318	1.42	.829805	4.53	.170195	57
4	.748310	3.12	.918233	1.42	.830077	4.53	.169923	56
5	9.748497	3.10	9.918147	1.42	9.830349	4.53	0.169651	55
6	.748683	3.12	.918062	1.42	.830621	4.53	.169379	54
7	.748870	3.10	.917976	1.42	.830893	4.53	.169107	53
8	.749056	3.12	.917891	1.43	.831165	4.53	.168835	52
9	.749243	3.10	.917805	1.43	.831437	4.53	.168563	51
10	9.749429	3.10	9.917719	1.42	9.831709	4.53	0.168291	50
11	.749615	3.10	.917634	1.43	.831981	4.53	.168019	49
12	.749801	3.10	.917548	1.43	.832253	4.53	.167747	48
13	.749987	3.08	.917462	1.43	.832525	4.53	.167475	47
14	.750172	3.10	.917376	1.43	.832796	4.52	.167204	46
15	9.750358	3.08	9.917290	1.43	9.833068	4.53	0.166932	45
16	.750543	3.10	.917204	1.43	.833339	4.52	.166661	44
17	.750729	3.08	.917118	1.43	.833611	4.53	.166389	43
18	.750914	3.08	.917032	1.43	.833882	4.53	.166118	42
19	.751099	3.08	.916946	1.45	.834154	4.52	.165846	41
20	9.751284	3.08	9.916859	1.43	9.834425	4.52	0.165575	40
21	.751469	3.08	.916773	1.43	.834696	4.52	.165304	39
22	.751654	3.08	.916687	1.45	.834967	4.52	.165033	38
23	.751839	3.07	.916600	1.43	.835238	4.52	.164762	37
24	.752023	3.08	.916514	1.45	.835509	4.52	.164491	36
25	9.752208	3.07	9.916427	1.43	9.835780	4.52	0.164220	35
26	.752392	3.07	.916341	1.45	.836051	4.52	.163949	34
27	.752576	3.07	.916254	1.45	.836322	4.52	.163678	33
28	.752760	3.07	.916167	1.45	.836593	4.52	.163407	32
29	.752944	3.07	.916081	1.45	.836864	4.50	.163136	31
30	9.753128	3.07	9.915994	1.45	9.837134	4.52	0.162866	30
31	.753312	3.05	.915907	1.45	.837405	4.50	.162595	29
32	.753495	3.07	.915820	1.45	.837675	4.52	.162325	28
33	.753679	3.05	.915733	1.45	.837946	4.50	.162054	27
34	.753862	3.07	.915646	1.45	.838216	4.50	.161784	26
35	9.754046	3.05	9.915559	1.45	9.838487	4.52	0.161513	25
36	.754229	3.05	.915472	1.45	.838757	4.50	.161243	24
37	.754412	3.05	.915385	1.47	.839027	4.50	.160973	23
38	.754595	3.05	.915297	1.45	.839297	4.50	.160703	22
39	.754778	3.03	.915210	1.45	.839568	4.52	.160432	21
40	9.754960	3.05	9.915123	1.47	9.839838	4.50	0.160162	20
41	.755143	3.05	.915035	1.45	.840108	4.50	.159892	19
42	.755326	3.03	.914948	1.47	.840378	4.50	.159622	18
43	.755508	3.03	.914860	1.45	.840648	4.48	.159352	17
44	.755690	3.03	.914773	1.47	.840917	4.50	.159083	16
45	9.755872	3.03	9.914685	1.45	9.841187	4.50	0.158813	15
46	.756054	3.03	.914598	1.47	.841457	4.50	.158543	14
47	.756236	3.03	.914510	1.47	.841727	4.48	.158273	13
48	.756418	3.03	.914422	1.47	.841996	4.50	.158004	12
49	.756600	3.03	.914334	1.47	.842266	4.48	.157734	11
50	9.756782	3.02	9.914246	1.47	9.842535	4.50	0.157465	10
51	.756963	3.02	.914158	1.47	.842805	4.48	.157195	9
52	.757144	3.03	.914070	1.47	.843074	4.48	.156926	8
53	.757326	3.02	.913982	1.47	.843343	4.48	.156657	7
54	.757507	3.02	.913894	1.47	.843612	4.50	.156388	6
55	9.757688	3.02	9.913806	1.47	9.843882	4.48	0.156118	5
56	.757869	3.02	.913718	1.47	.844151	4.48	.155849	4
57	.758050	3.00	.913630	1.48	.844420	4.48	.155580	3
58	.758230	3.02	.913541	1.47	.844689	4.48	.155311	2
59	.758411	3.00	.913453	1.47	.844958	4.48	.155042	1
60	9.758591		9.913365		9.845227		0.154773	0
	Cos.	D. 1".	Sin.	D. 1".	Cot.	D. 1".	Tan.	M.

TABLE C—LOGARITHMIC SINES,

35° 144°

M.	Sin.	D. 1″.	Cos.	D. 1″.	Tan.	D. 1″.	Cot.	
0	9.758591	3.02	9.913365	1.48	9.845227	4.48	0.154773	60
1	.758772	3.00	.913276	1.48	.845496	4.47	.154504	59
2	.758952	3.00	.913187	1.47	.845764	4.48	.154236	58
3	.759132	3.00	.913099	1.48	.846033	4.48	.153967	57
4	.759312	3.00	.913010	1.47	.846302	4.47	.153698	56
5	9.759492	3.00	.912922	1.48	9.846570	4.48	0.153430	55
6	.759672	3.00	.912833	1.48	.846839	4.48	.153161	54
7	.759852	2.98	.912744	1.48	.847108	4.48	.152892	53
8	.760031	3.00	.912655	1.48	.847376	4.47	.152624	52
9	.760211	2.98	.912566	1.48	.847644	4.48	.152356	51
10	9.760390	2.98	9.912477	1.48	9.847913	4.47	0.152087	50
11	.760569	2.98	.912388	1.48	.848181	4.47	.151819	49
12	.760748	2.98	.912299	1.48	.848449	4.47	.151551	48
13	.760927	2.98	.912210	1.48	.848717	4.47	.151283	47
14	.761106	2.98	.912121	1.50	.848986	4.48	.151014	46
15	9.761285	2.98	9.912031	1.48	9.849254	4.47	0.150746	45
16	.761464	2.97	.911942	1.48	.849522	4.47	.150478	44
17	.761642	2.98	.911853	1.50	.849790	4.45	.150210	43
18	.761821	2.97	.911763	1.48	.850057	4.47	.149943	42
19	.761999	2.97	.911674	1.50	.850325	4.47	.149675	41
20	9.762177	2.98	9.911584	1.48	9.850593	4.47	0.149407	40
21	.762356	2.97	.911495	1.50	.850861	4.47	.149139	39
22	.762534	2.97	.911405	1.50	.851129	4.45	.148871	38
23	.762712	2.95	.911315	1.48	.851396	4.47	.148604	37
24	.762889	2.97	.911226	1.50	.851664	4.45	.148336	36
25	9.763067	2.97	9.911136	1.50	9.851931	4.47	0.148069	35
26	.763245	2.95	.911046	1.50	.852199	4.45	.147801	34
27	.763422	2.97	.910956	1.50	.852466	4.45	.147534	33
28	.763600	2.95	.910866	1.50	.852733	4.47	.147267	32
29	.763777	2.95	.910776	1.50	.853001	4.45	.146999	31
30	9.763954	2.95	9.910686	1.50	9.853268	4.45	0.146732	30
31	.764131	2.95	.910596	1.50	.853535	4.45	.146465	29
32	.764308	2.95	.910506	1.50	.853802	4.45	.146198	28
33	.764485	2.95	.910415	1.52	.854069	4.45	.145931	27
34	.764662	2.93	.910325	1.50	.854336	4.45	.145664	26
35	9.764838	2.95	9.910235	1.50	9.854603	4.45	0.145397	25
36	.765015	2.93	.910144	1.52	.854870	4.45	.145130	24
37	.765191	2.93	.910054	1.50	.855137	4.45	.144863	23
38	.765367	2.95	.909963	1.52	.855404	4.45	.144596	22
39	.765544	2.93	.909873	1.50	.855671	4.45	.144329	21
40	9.765720	2.93	9.909782	1.52	9.855938	4.43	0.144062	20
41	.765896	2.93	.909691	1.50	.856204	4.45	.143796	19
42	.766072	2.92	.909601	1.52	.856471	4.43	.143529	18
43	.766247	2.93	.909510	1.52	.856737	4.45	.143263	17
44	.766423	2.92	.909419	1.52	.857004	4.43	.142996	16
45	9.766598	2.93	9.909328	1.52	9.857270	4.45	0.142730	15
46	.766774	2.92	.909237	1.52	.857537	4.43	.142463	14
47	.766949	2.92	.909146	1.52	.857803	4.43	.142197	13
48	.767124	2.93	.909055	1.52	.858069	4.45	.141931	12
49	.767300	2.92	.908964	1.52	.858336	4.43	.141664	11
50	9.767475	2.90	9.908873	1.53	9.858602	4.43	0.141398	10
51	.767649	2.92	.908781	1.52	.858868	4.43	.141132	9
52	.767824	2.92	.908690	1.52	.859134	4.43	.140866	8
53	.767999	2.90	.908599	1.53	.859400	4.43	.140600	7
54	.768173	2.92	.908507	1.52	.859666	4.43	.140334	6
55	9.768348	2.90	9.908416	1.53	9.859932	4.43	0.140068	5
56	.768522	2.92	.908324	1.52	.860198	4.43	.139802	4
57	.768697	2.90	.908233	1.53	.860464	4.43	.139536	3
58	.768871	2.90	.908141	1.53	.860730	4.42	.139270	2
59	.769045	2.90	.908049	1.53	.860995	4.43	.139005	1
60	9.769219		9.907958	1.52	9.861261		0.138739	0
	Cos.	D. 1″.	Sin.	D. 1″.	Cot.	D. 1″.	Tan.	M.

M.	Sin.	D. 1″.	Cos.	D. 1″.	Tan.	D. 1″.	Cot.	
0	9.769219	2.90	9.907958	1.53	9.861261	4.43	0.138739	60
1	.769393	2.88	.907866	1.53	.861527	4.42	.138473	59
2	.769566	2.90	.907774	1.53	.861792	4.43	.138208	58
3	.769740	2.88	.907682	1.53	.862058	4.42	.137942	57
4	.769913	2.90	.907590	1.53	.862323	4.43	.137677	56
5	9.770087	2.88	9.907498	1.53	9.862589	4.42	0.137411	55
6	.770260	2.88	.907406	1.53	.862854	4.42	.137146	54
7	.770433	2.88	.907314	1.53	.863119	4.43	.136881	53
8	.770606	2.88	.907222	1.55	.863385	4.42	.136615	52
9	.770779	2.88	.907129	1.53	.863650	4.42	.136350	51
10	9.770952	2.88	9.907037	1.53	9.863915	4.42	0.136085	50
11	.771125	2.88	.906945	1.55	.864180	4.42	.135820	49
12	.771298	2.87	.906852	1.53	.864445	4.42	.135555	48
13	.771470	2.88	.906760	1.55	.864710	4.42	.135290	47
14	.771643	2.87	.906667	1.53	.864975	4.42	.135025	46
15	9.771815	2.87	9.906575	1.55	9.865240	4.42	0.134760	45
16	.771987	2.87	.906482	1.55	.865505	4.42	.134495	44
17	.772159	2.87	.906389	1.55	.865770	4.42	.134230	43
18	.772331	2.87	.906296	1.53	.866035	4.42	.133965	42
19	.772503	2.87	.906204	1.55	.866300	4.40	.133700	41
20	9.772675	2.87	9.906111	1.55	9.866564	4.42	0.133436	40
21	.772847	2.85	.906018	1.55	.866829	4.42	.133171	39
22	.773018	2.87	.905925	1.55	.867094	4.40	.132906	38
23	.773190	2.85	.905832	1.55	.867358	4.42	.132642	37
24	.773361	2.87	.905739	1.57	.867625	4.40	.132377	36
25	9.773533	2.85	9.905645	1.55	9.867887	4.42	0.132113	35
26	.773704	2.85	.905552	1.55	.868152	4.40	.131848	34
27	.773875	2.85	.905459	1.55	.868416	4.40	.131584	33
28	.774046	2.85	.905366	1.57	.868680	4.42	.131320	32
29	.774217	2.85	.905272	1.55	.868945	4.40	.131055	31
30	9.774388	2.83	9.905179	1.57	9.869209	4.40	0.130791	30
31	.774558	2.85	.905085	1.55	.869473	4.40	.130527	29
32	.774729	2.83	.904992	1.57	.869737	4.40	.130263	28
33	.774899	2.85	.904898	1.57	.870001	4.40	.129999	27
34	.775070	2.83	.904804	1.57	.870265	4.40	.129735	26
35	9.775240	2.83	9.904711	1.55	9.870529	4.40	0.129471	25
36	.775410	2.83	.904617	1.57	.870793	4.40	.129207	24
37	.775580	2.83	.904523	1.57	.871057	4.40	.128943	23
38	.775750	2.83	.904429	1.57	.871321	4.40	.128679	22
39	.775920	2.83	.904335	1.57	.871585	4.40	.128415	21
40	9.776090	2.82	9.904241	1.57	9.871849	4.38	0.128151	20
41	.776259	2.83	.904147	1.57	.872112	4.40	.127888	19
42	.776429	2.82	.904053	1.57	.872376	4.40	.127624	18
43	.776598	2.83	.903959	1.58	.872640	4.38	.127360	17
44	.776768	2.82	.903864	1.57	.872903	4.40	.127097	16
45	9.776937	2.82	9.903770	1.57	9.873167	4.38	0.126833	15
46	.777106	2.82	.903676	1.58	.873430	4.40	.126570	14
47	.777275	2.82	.903581	1.57	.873694	4.38	.126306	13
48	.777444	2.82	.903487	1.58	.873957	4.38	.126043	12
49	.777613	2.80	.903392	1.57	.874220	4.40	.125780	11
50	9.777781	2.82	9.903298	1.58	9.874484	4.38	0.125516	10
51	.777950	2.82	.903203	1.58	.874747	4.38	.125253	9
52	.778119	2.80	.903108	1.57	.875010	4.38	.124990	8
53	.778287	2.80	.903014	1.58	.875273	4.40	.124727	7
54	.778455	2.82	.902919	1.58	.875537	4.38	.124463	6
55	9.778624	2.80	9.902824	1.58	9.875800	4.38	0.124200	5
56	.778792	2.80	.902729	1.58	.876063	4.38	.123937	4
57	.778960	2.80	.902634	1.58	.876326	4.38	.123674	3
58	.779128	2.78	.902539	1.58	.876589	4.38	.123411	2
59	.779295	2.80	.902444	1.58	.876852	4.37	.123148	1
60	9.779463		9.902349		9.877114		0.122886	0
	Cos.	D. 1″.	Sin.	D. 1″.	Cot.	D. 1″.	Tan.	M.

M.	Sin.	D. 1″.	Cos.	D. 1″.	Tan.	D. 1″.	Cot.	
0	9.779463	2.80	9.902349	1.60	9.877114	4.38	0.122886	60
1	.779631	2.78	.902253	1.58	.877377	4.38	.122623	59
2	.779798	2.80	.902158	1.58	.877640	4.38	.122360	58
3	.779966	2.78	.902063	1.58	.877903	4.37	.122097	57
4	.780133	2.78	.901967	1.60	.878165	4.38	.121835	56
5	9.780300	2.78	9.901872	1.58	9.878428	4.38	0.121572	55
6	.780467	2.78	.901776	1.60	.878691	4.37	.121309	54
7	.780634	2.78	.901681	1.58	.878953	4.38	.121047	53
8	.780801	2.78	.901585	1.60	.879216	4.37	.120784	52
9	.780968	2.77	.901490	1.58	.879478	4.38	.120522	51
10	9.781134	2.78	9.901394	1.60	9.879741	4.37	0.120259	50
11	.781301	2.78	.901298	1.60	.880003	4.37	.119997	49
12	.781468	2.77	.901202	1.60	.880265	4.38	.119735	48
13	.781634	2.77	.901106	1.60	.880528	4.37	.119472	47
14	.781800	2.77	.901010	1.60	.880790	4.37	.119210	46
15	9.781966	2.77	9.900914	1.60	9.881052	4.37	0.118948	45
16	.782132	2.77	.900818	1.60	.881314	4.38	.118686	44
17	.782298	2.77	.900722	1.60	.881577	4.37	.118423	43
18	.782464	2.77	.900626	1.60	.881839	4.37	.118161	42
19	.782630	2.77	.900529	1.62	.882101	4.37	.117899	41
20	9.782796	2.75	9.900433	1.60	9.882363	4.37	0.117637	40
21	.782961	2.77	.900337	1.62	.882625	4.37	.117375	39
22	.783127	2.75	.900240	1.60	.882887	4.35	.117113	38
23	.783292	2.77	.900144	1.62	.883148	4.37	.116852	37
24	.783458	2.75	.900047	1.60	.883410	4.37	.116590	36
25	9.783623	2.75	9.899951	1.62	9.883672	4.37	0.116328	35
26	.783788	2.75	.899854	1.62	.883934	4.37	.116066	34
27	.783953	2.75	.899757	1.62	.884196	4.35	.115804	33
28	.784118	2.73	.899660	1.60	.884457	4.37	.115543	32
29	.784282	2.75	.899564	1.62	.884719	4.35	.115281	31
30	9.784447	2.75	9.899467	1.62	9.884980	4.37	0.115020	30
31	.784612	2.73	.899370	1.62	.885242	4.37	.114758	29
32	.784776	2.75	.899273	1.62	.885504	4.35	.114496	28
33	.784941	2.73	.899176	1.62	.885765	4.35	.114235	27
34	.785105	2.73	.899078	1.63	.886026	4.37	.113974	26
35	9.785269	2.73	9.898981	1.62	9.886288	4.35	0.113712	25
36	.785433	2.73	.898884	1.62	.886549	4.37	.113451	24
37	.785597	2.73	.898787	1.63	.886811	4.35	.113189	23
38	.785761	2.73	.898689	1.62	.887072	4.35	.112928	22
39	.785925	2.73	.898592	1.63	.887333	4.35	.112667	21
40	9.786089	2.72	9.898494	1.62	9.887594	4.35	0.112406	20
41	.786252	2.73	.898397	1.63	.887855	4.35	.112145	19
42	.786416	2.72	.898299	1.62	.888116	4.37	.111884	18
43	.786579	2.72	.898202	1.63	.888378	4.35	.111622	17
44	.786742	2.73	.898104	1.63	.888639	4.35	.111361	16
45	9.786906	2.72	9.898006	1.63	9.888900	4.35	0.111100	15
46	.787069	2.72	.897908	1.63	.889161	4.33	.110839	14
47	.787232	2.72	.897810	1.63	.889421	4.35	.110579	13
48	.787395	2.70	.897712	1.63	.889682	4.35	.110318	12
49	.787557	2.72	.897614	1.63	.889943	4.35	.110057	11
50	9.787720	2.72	9.897516	1.63	9.890204	4.35	0.109796	10
51	.787883	2.70	.897418	1.63	.890465	4.33	.109535	9
52	.788045	2.72	.897320	1.63	.890725	4.35	.109275	8
53	.788208	2.70	.897222	1.63	.890986	4.35	.109014	7
54	.788370	2.70	.897123	1.65	.891247	4.33	.108753	6
55	9.788532	2.70	9.897025	1.63	9.891507	4.35	0.108493	5
56	.788694	2.70	.896926	1.65	.891768	4.33	.108232	4
57	.788856	2.70	.896828	1.63	.892028	4.35	.107972	3
58	.789018	2.70	.896729	1.65	.892289	4.33	.107711	2
59	.789180	2.70	.896631	1.63	.892549	4.35	.107451	1
60	9.789342		9.896532	1.65	9.892810		0.107190	0
	Cos.	D. 1″.	Sin.	D. 1″.	Cot.	D. 1″.	Tan.	M.

M.	Sin.	D. 1″.	Cos.	D. 1″.	Tan.	D. 1″.	Cot.	
0	9.789342	2.70	9.896532	1.65	9.892810	4.33	0.107190	60
1	.789504	2.68	.896433	1.63	.893070	4.35	.106930	59
2	.789665	2.70	.896335	1.65	.893331	4.33	.106669	58
3	.789827	2.68	.896236	1.65	.893591	4.33	.106409	57
4	.789988	2.68	.896137	1.65	.893851	4.33	.106149	56
5	9.790149	2.68	9.896038	1.65	9.894111	4.35	0.105889	55
6	.790310	2.68	.895939	1.65	.894372	4.33	.105628	54
7	.790471	2.68	.895840	1.65	.894632	4.33	.105368	53
8	.790632	2.68	.895741	1.67	.894892	4.33	.105108	52
9	.790793	2.68	.895641	1.65	.895152	4.33	.104848	51
10	9.790954	2.68	9.895542	1.65	9.895412	4.33	0.104588	50
11	.791115	2.67	.895443	1.67	.895672	4.33	.104328	49
12	.791275	2.68	.895343	1.65	.895932	4.33	.104068	48
13	.791436	2.67	.895244	1.65	.896192	4.33	.103808	47
14	.791596	2.68	.895145	1.67	.896452	4.33	.103548	46
15	9.791757	2.67	9.895045	1.67	9.896712	4.32	0.103288	45
16	.791917	2.67	.894945	1.65	.896971	4.33	.103029	44
17	.792077	2.67	.894846	1.67	.897231	4.33	.102769	43
18	.792237	2.67	.894746	1.67	.897491	4.33	.102509	42
19	.792397	2.67	.894646	1.67	.897751	4.32	.102249	41
20	9.792557	2.65	9.894546	1.67	9.898010	4.33	0.101990	40
21	.792716	2.67	.894446	1.67	.898270	4.33	.101730	39
22	.792876	2.65	.894346	1.67	.898530	4.32	.101470	38
23	.793035	2.67	.894246	1.67	.898789	4.33	.101211	37
24	.793195	2.65	.894146	1.67	.899049	4.32	.100951	36
25	9.793354	2.67	9.894046	1.67	9.899308	4.33	0.100692	35
26	.793514	2.65	.893946	1.67	.899568	4.32	.100432	34
27	.793673	2.65	.893846	1.67	.899827	4.33	.100173	33
28	.793832	2.65	.893745	1.68	.900087	4.32	.099913	32
29	.793991	2.65	.893645	1.67	.900346	4.32	.099654	31
30	9.794150	2.63	9.893544	1.68	9.900605	4.32	0.099395	30
31	.794308	2.65	.893444	1.67	.900864	4.33	.099136	29
32	.794467	2.65	.893343	1.68	.901124	4.32	.098876	28
33	.794626	2.63	.893243	1.67	.901383	4.32	.098617	27
34	.794784	2.63	.893142	1.68	.901642	4.32	.098358	26
35	9.794942	2.65	9.893041	1.68	9.901901	4.32	0.098099	25
36	.795101	2.63	.892940	1.68	.902160	4.33	.097840	24
37	.795259	2.63	.892839	1.68	.902420	4.32	.097580	23
38	.795417	2.63	.892739	1.67	.902679	4.32	.097321	22
39	.795575	2.63	.892638	1.70	.902938	4.32	.097062	21
40	9.795733	2.63	9.892536	1.68	9.903197	4.32	0.096803	20
41	.795891	2.63	.892435	1.68	.903456	4.30	.096544	19
42	.796049	2.62	.892334	1.68	.903714	4.32	.096286	18
43	.796206	2.63	.892233	1.68	.903973	4.32	.096027	17
44	.796364	2.62	.892132	1.70	.904232	4.32	.095768	16
45	9.796521	2.63	9.892030	1.68	9.904491	4.32	0.095509	15
46	.796679	2.62	.891929	1.70	.904750	4.30	.095250	14
47	.796836	2.62	.891827	1.68	.905008	4.32	.094992	13
48	.796993	2.62	.891726	1.70	.905267	4.32	.094733	12
49	.797150	2.62	.891624	1.68	.905526	4.32	.094474	11
50	9.797307	2.62	9.891523	1.70	9.905785	4.30	0.094215	10
51	.797464	2.62	.891421	1.70	.906043	4.32	.093957	9
52	.797621	2.60	.891319	1.70	.906302	4.30	.093698	8
53	.797777	2.62	.891217	1.70	.906560	4.32	.093440	7
54	.797934	2.62	.891115	1.70	.906819	4.30	.093181	6
55	9.798091	2.60	9.891013	1.70	9.907077	4.32	0.092923	5
56	.798247	2.60	.890911	1.70	.907336	4.30	.092664	4
57	.798403	2.62	.890809	1.70	.907594	4.32	.092406	3
58	.798560	2.60	.890707	1.70	.907853	4.30	.092147	2
59	.798716	2.60	.890605	1.70	.908111	4.30	.091889	1
60	9.798872		9.890503	1.70	9.908369		0.091631	0
	Cos.	D. 1″.	Sin.	D. 1″.	Cot.	D. 1″.	Tan.	M.

M.	Sin.	D. 1″.	Cos.	D. 1″.	Tan.	D. 1″.	Cot.	
0	9.798872	2.60	9.890503	1.72	9.908369	4.32	0.091631	60
1	.799028	2.60	.890400	1.70	.908628	4.30	.091372	59
2	.799184	2.58	.890298	1.72	.908886	4.30	.091114	58
3	.799339	2.60	.890195	1.70	.909144	4.30	.090856	57
4	.799495	2.60	.890093	1.72	.909402	4.30	.090598	56
5	9.799651	2.58	9.889990	1.70	9.909660	4.30	0.090340	55
6	.799806	2.60	.889888	1.72	.909918	4.30	.090082	54
7	.799962	2.58	.889785	1.72	.910177	4.32	.089823	53
8	.800117	2.58	.889682	1.72	.910435	4.30	.089565	52
9	.800272	2.58	.889579	1.70	.910693	4.30	.089307	51
10	9.800427	2.58	9.889477	1.72	9.910951	4.30	0.089049	50
11	.800582	2.58	.889374	1.72	.911209	4.30	.088791	49
12	.800737	2.58	.889271	1.72	.911467	4.30	.088533	48
13	.800892	2.58	.889168	1.73	.911725	4.30	.088275	47
14	.801047	2.57	.889064	1.72	.911982	4.28	.088018	46
15	9.801201	2.58	9.888961	1.72	9.912240	4.30	0.087760	45
16	.801356	2.58	.888858	1.72	.912498	4.30	.087502	44
17	.801511	2.57	.888755	1.73	.912756	4.30	.087244	43
18	.801665	2.57	.888651	1.72	.913014	4.28	.086986	42
19	.801819	2.57	.888548	1.73	.913271	4.30	.086729	41
20	9.801973	2.58	9.888444	1.72	9.913529	4.30	0.086471	40
21	.802128	2.57	.888341	1.73	.913787	4.28	.086213	39
22	.802282	2.57	.888237	1.72	.914044	4.30	.085956	38
23	.802436	2.55	.888134	1.73	.914302	4.30	.085698	37
24	.802589	2.57	.888030	1.73	.914560	4.28	.085440	36
25	9.802743	2.57	9.887926	1.73	9.914817	4.30	0.085183	35
26	.802897	2.55	.887822	1.73	.915075	4.28	.084925	34
27	.803050	2.57	.887718	1.73	.915332	4.30	.084668	33
28	.803204	2.55	.887614	1.73	.915590	4.28	.084410	32
29	.803357	2.57	.887510	1.73	.915847	4.28	.084153	31
30	9.803511	2.55	9.887406	1.73	9.916104	4.30	0.083896	30
31	.803664	2.55	.887302	1.73	.916362	4.28	.083638	29
32	.803817	2.55	.887198	1.75	.916619	4.30	.083381	28
33	.803970	2.55	.887093	1.73	.916877	4.28	.083123	27
34	.804123	2.55	.886989	1.73	.917134	4.28	.082866	26
35	9.804276	2.55	9.886885	1.75	9.917391	4.28	0.082609	25
36	.804428	2.53	.886780	1.73	.917648	4.30	.082352	24
37	.804581	2.55	.886676	1.75	.917906	4.28	.082094	23
38	.804734	2.53	.886571	1.75	.918163	4.28	.081837	22
39	.804886	2.55	.886466	1.73	.918420	4.28	.081580	21
40	9.805039	2.53	9.886362	1.75	9.918677	4.28	0.081323	20
41	.805191	2.53	.886257	1.75	.918934	4.28	.081066	19
42	.805343	2.53	.886152	1.75	.919191	4.28	.080809	18
43	.805495	2.53	.886047	1.75	.919448	4.28	.080552	17
44	.805647	2.53	.885942	1.75	.919705	4.28	.080295	16
45	9.805799	2.53	9.885837	1.75	9.919962	4.28	0.080038	15
46	.805951	2.53	.885732	1.75	.920219	4.28	.079781	14
47	.806103	2.52	.885627	1.75	.920476	4.28	.079524	13
48	.806254	2.53	.885522	1.77	.920733	4.28	.079267	12
49	.806406	2.52	.885416	1.75	.920990	4.28	.079010	11
50	9.806557	2.53	9.885311	1.77	9.921247	4.27	0.078753	10
51	.806709	2.52	.885205	1.75	.921503	4.28	.078497	9
52	.806860	2.52	.885100	1.77	.921760	4.28	.078240	8
53	.807011	2.53	.884994	1.75	.922017	4.28	.077983	7
54	.807163	2.52	.884889	1.77	.922274	4.27	.077726	6
55	9.807314	2.52	9.884783	1.77	9.922530	4.28	0.077470	5
56	.807465	2.50	.884677	1.75	.922787	4.28	.077213	4
57	.807615	2.52	.884572	1.77	.923044	4.27	.076956	3
58	.807766	2.52	.884466	1.77	.923300	4.28	.076700	2
59	.807917	2.50	.884360	1.77	.923557	4.28	.076443	1
60	9.808067		9.884254	1.77	9.923814		0.076186	0
	Cos.	D. 1″.	Sin.	D. 1″.	Cot.	D. 1″.	Tan.	M.

M.	Sin.	D. 1″.	Cos.	D. 1″.	Tan.	D. 1″.	Cot.	
0	9.808067	2.52	9.884254	1.77	9.923814	4.27	0.076186	60
1	.808218	2.50	.884148	1.77	.924070	4.28	.075930	59
2	.808368	2.52	.884042	1.77	.924327	4.27	.075673	58
3	.808519	2.50	.883936	1.78	.924583	4.28	.075417	57
4	.808669	2.50	.883829	1.77	.924840	4.27	.075160	56
5	9.808819	2.50	9.883723	1.77	9.925096	4.27	0.074904	55
6	.808969	2.50	.883617	1.78	.925352	4.28	.074648	54
7	.809119	2.50	.883510	1.77	.925609	4.27	.074391	53
8	.809269	2.50	.883404	1.78	.925865	4.28	.074135	52
9	.809419	2.50	.883297	1.77	.926122	4.27	.073878	51
10	9.809569	2.48	9.883191	1.78	9.926378	4.27	0.073622	50
11	.809718	2.50	.883084	1.78	.926634	4.27	.073366	49
12	.809868	2.48	.882977	1.77	.926890	4.28	.073110	48
13	.810017	2.50	.882871	1.78	.927147	4.27	.072853	47
14	.810167	2.48	.882764	1.78	.927403	4.27	.072597	46
15	9.810316	2.48	9.882657	1.78	9.927659	4.27	0.072341	45
16	.810465	2.48	.882550	1.78	.927915	4.27	.072085	44
17	.810614	2.48	.882443	1.78	.928171	4.27	.071829	43
18	.810763	2.48	.882336	1.78	.928427	4.28	.071573	42
19	.810912	2.48	.882229	1.80	.928684	4.27	.071316	41
20	9.811061	2.48	9.882121	1.78	9.928940	4.27	0.071060	40
21	.811210	2.47	.882014	1.78	.929196	4.27	.070804	39
22	.811358	2.48	.881907	1.80	.929452	4.27	.070548	38
23	.811507	2.47	.881799	1.78	.929708	4.27	.070292	37
24	.811655	2.48	.881692	1.80	.929964	4.27	.070036	36
25	9.811804	2.47	9.881584	1.80	9.930220	4.25	0.069780	35
26	.811952	2.47	.881477	1.78	.930475	4.27	.069525	34
27	.812100	2.47	.881369	1.80	.930731	4.27	.069269	33
28	.812248	2.47	.881261	1.80	.930987	4.27	.069013	32
29	.812396	2.47	.881153	1.80	.931243	4.27	.068757	31
30	9.812544	2.47	9.881046	1.80	9.931499	4.27	0.068501	30
31	.812692	2.47	.880938	1.80	.931755	4.25	.068245	29
32	.812840	2.47	.880830	1.90	.932010	4.27	.067990	28
33	.812988	2.45	.880722	1.82	.932266	4.27	.067734	27
34	.813135	2.47	.880613	1.80	.932522	4.27	.067478	26
35	9.813283	2.45	9.880505	1.80	9.932778	4.25	0.067222	25
36	.813430	2.47	.880397	1.80	.933033	4.27	.066967	24
37	.813578	2.45	.880289	1.82	.933289	4.27	.066711	23
38	.813725	2.45	.880180	1.80	.933545	4.25	.066455	22
39	.813872	2.45	.880072	1.82	.933800	4.27	.066200	21
40	9.814019	2.45	9.879963	1.80	9.934056	4.25	0.065944	20
41	.814166	2.45	.879855	1.82	.934311	4.27	.065689	19
42	.814313	2.45	.879746	1.82	.934567	4.25	.065433	18
43	.814460	2.45	.879637	1.80	.934822	4.27	.065178	17
44	.814607	2.43	.879529	1.82	.935078	4.25	.064922	16
45	9.814753	2.45	9.879420	1.82	9.935333	4.25	0.064667	15
46	.814900	2.43	.879311	1.82	.935589	4.25	.064411	14
47	.815046	2.45	.879202	1.82	.935844	4.27	.064156	13
48	.815193	2.43	.879093	1.82	.936100	4.25	.063900	12
49	.815339	2.43	.878984	1.82	.936355	4.27	.063645	11
50	9.815485	2.45	9.878875	1.82	9.936611	4.25	0.063389	10
51	.815632	2.43	.878766	1.83	.936866	4.25	.063134	9
52	.815778	2.43	.878656	1.82	.937121	4.27	.062879	8
53	.815924	2.42	.878547	1.82	.937377	4.25	.062623	7
54	.816069	2.43	.878438	1.82	.937632	4.25	.062368	6
55	9.816215	2.43	9.878328	1.83	9.937887	4.25	0.062113	5
56	.816361	2.43	.878219	1.82	.938142	4.27	.061858	4
57	.816507	2.42	.878109	1.83	.938398	4.25	.061602	3
58	.816652	2.43	.877999	1.83	.938653	4.25	.061347	2
59	.816798	2.42	.877890	1.83	.938908	4.25	.061092	1
60	9.816943		9.877780		9.939163		0.060837	0
	Cos.	D. 1″.	Sin.	D. 1″.	Cot.	D. 1″.	Tan.	M.

TABLE C—LOGARITHMIC SINES,
41°

138°

M.	Sin.	D. 1″.	Cos.	D. 1″.	Tan.	D. 1″.	Cot.	
0	9.816943	2.42	9.877780	1.83	9.939163	4.25	0.060837	60
1	.817088	2.42	.877670	1.83	.939418	4.25	.060582	59
2	.817233	2.43	.877560	1.83	.939673	4.25	.060327	58
3	.817379	2.42	.877450	1.83	.939928	4.25	.060072	57
4	.817524	2.40	.877340	1.83	.940183	4.27	.059817	56
5	9.817668	2.42	9.877230	1.83	9.940439	4.25	0.059561	55
6	.817813	2.42	.877120	1.83	.940694	4.25	.059306	54
7	.817958	2.42	.877010	1.85	.940949	4.25	.059051	53
8	.818103	2.40	.876899	1.83	.941204	4.25	.058796	52
9	.818247	2.42	.876789	1.85	.941459	4.23	.058541	51
10	9.818392	2.40	9.876678	1.83	9.941713	4.25	0.058287	50
11	.818536	2.42	.876568	1.85	.941968	4.25	.058032	49
12	.818681	2.40	.876457	1.83	.942223	4.25	.057777	48
13	.818825	2.40	.876347	1.85	.942478	4.25	.057522	47
14	.818969	2.40	.876236	1.85	.942733	4.25	.057267	46
15	9.819113	2.40	9.876125	1.85	9.942988	4.25	0.057012	45
16	.819257	2.40	.876014	1.83	.943243	4.25	.056757	44
17	.819401	2.40	.875904	1.85	.943498	4.23	.056502	43
18	.819545	2.40	.875793	1.85	.943752	4.25	.056248	42
19	.819689	2.38	.875682	1.85	.944007	4.25	.055993	41
20	9.819832	2.40	9.875571	1.87	9.944262	4.25	0.055738	40
21	.819976	2.40	.875459	1.85	.944517	4.23	.055483	39
22	.820120	2.38	.875348	1.85	.944771	4.25	.055229	38
23	.820263	2.38	.875237	1.85	.945026	4.25	.054974	37
24	.820406	2.40	.875126	1.87	.945281	4.23	.054719	36
25	9.820550	2.38	9.875014	1.85	9.945535	4.25	0.054465	35
26	.820693	2.38	.874903	1.87	.945790	4.25	.054210	34
27	.820836	2.38	.874791	1.85	.946045	4.23	.053955	33
28	.820979	2.38	.874680	1.87	.946299	4.25	.053701	32
29	.821122	2.38	.874568	1.87	.946554	4.23	.053446	31
30	9.821265	2.37	9.874456	1.87	9.946808	4.25	0.053192	30
31	.821407	2.38	.874344	1.87	.947063	4.25	.052937	29
32	.821550	2.38	.874232	1.85	.947318	4.23	.052682	28
33	.821693	2.37	.874121	1.87	.947572	4.25	.052428	27
34	.821835	2.37	.874009	1.88	.947827	4.23	.052173	26
35	9.821977	2.38	9.873896	1.87	9.948081	4.23	0.051919	25
36	.822120	2.37	.873784	1.87	.948335	4.25	.051665	24
37	.822262	2.37	.873672	1.87	.948590	4.23	.051410	23
38	.822404	2.37	.873560	1.87	.948844	4.25	.051156	22
39	.822546	2.37	.873448	1.88	.949099	4.23	.050901	21
40	9.822688	2.37	9.873335	1.87	9.949353	4.25	0.050647	20
41	.822830	2.37	.873223	1.88	.949608	4.23	.050392	19
42	.822972	2.37	.873110	1.87	.949862	4.23	.050138	18
43	.823114	2.35	.872998	1.88	950116	4.25	.049884	17
44	.823255	2.37	.872885	1.88	.950371	4.23	.019629	16
45	9.823397	2.37	9.872772	1.88	9.950625	4.23	0.049375	15
46	.823539	2.35	.872659	1.87	.950879	4.23	.049121	14
47	.823680	2.35	.872547	1.88	.951133	4.25	.048867	13
48	.823821	2.37	.872434	1.88	.951388	4.23	.048612	12
49	.823963	2.35	.872321	1.88	.951642	4.23	.048358	11
50	9.824104	2.35	9.872208	1.88	9.951896	4.23	0.048104	10
51	.824245	2.35	.872095	1.90	.952150	4.25	.047850	9
52	.824386	2.35	.871981	1.88	.952405	4.23	.047595	8
53	.824527	2.35	.871868	1.88	.952659	4.23	.047341	7
54	.824668	2.33	.871755	1.90	.952913	4.23	.047087	6
55	9.824808	2.35	9.871641	1.88	9.953167	4.23	0.046833	5
56	.824949	2.35	.871528	1.90	.953421	4.23	.046579	4
57	.825090	2.33	.871414	1.90	.953675	4.23	.046325	3
58	.825230	2.35	.871301	1.88	.953929	4.23	.046071	2
59	.825371	2.33	.871187	1.90	.954183	4.23	.045817	1
60	9.825511		9.871073	1.90	9.954437		0.045563	0
	Cos.	D. 1″.	Sin.	D. 1″.	Cot.	D. 1″.	Tan.	M.

M.	Sin.	D. 1″.	Cos.	D. 1″.	Tan.	D. 1″.	Cot.	
0	9.825511	2.33	9.871073	1.88	9.954437	4.23	0.045563	60
1	.825651	2.33	.870960	1.90	.954691	4.25	.045309	59
2	.825791	2.33	.870846	1.90	.954946	4.23	.045054	58
3	.825931	2.33	.870732	1.90	.955200	4.23	.044800	57
4	.826071	2.33	.870618	1.90	.955454	4.23	.044546	56
5	9.826211	2.33	9.870504	1.90	9.955708	4.23	0.044292	55
6	.826351	2.33	.870390	1.90	.955961	4.22	.044039	54
7	.826491	2.33	.870276	1.90	.956215	4.23	.043785	53
8	.826631	2.32	.870161	1.92	.956469	4.23	.043531	52
9	.826770	2.33	.870047	1.90	.956723	4.23	.043277	51
10	9.826910	2.32	9.869933	1.90	9.956977	4.23	0.043023	50
11	.827049	2.33	.869818	1.92	.957231	4.23	.042769	49
12	.827189	2.32	.869704	1.90	.957485	4.23	.042515	48
13	.827328	2.32	.869589	1.92	.957739	4.23	.042261	47
14	.827467	2.32	.869474	1.92	.957993	4.23	.042007	46
15	9.827606	2.32	9.869360	1.90	9.958247	4.22	0.041753	45
16	.827745	2.32	.869245	1.92	.958500	4.23	.041500	44
17	.827884	2.32	.869130	1.92	.958754	4.23	.041246	43
18	.828023	2.32	.869015	1.92	.959008	4.23	.040992	42
19	.828162	2.32	.868900	1.92	.959262	4.23	.040738	41
20	9.828301	2.30	9.868785	1.92	9.959516	4.22	0.040484	40
21	.828439	2.32	.868670	1.92	.959769	4.23	.040231	39
22	.828578	2.30	.868555	1.92	.960023	4.23	.039977	38
23	.828716	2.32	.868440	1.93	.960277	4.22	.039723	37
24	.828855	2.30	.868324	1.92	.960530	4.23	.039470	36
25	9.828993	2.30	9.868209	1.93	9.960784	4.23	0.039216	35
26	.829131	2.30	.868093	1.92	.961038	4.23	.038962	34
27	.829269	2.30	.867978	1.93	.961292	4.23	.038708	33
28	.829407	2.30	.867862	1.92	.961545	4.22	.038455	32
29	.829545	2.30	.867747	1.93	.961799	4.23	.038201	31
30	9.829683	2.30	9.867631	1.93	9.962052	4.22	0.037948	30
31	.829821	2.30	.867515	1.93	.962306	4.23	.037694	29
32	.829959	2.30	.867399	1.93	.962560	4.22	.037440	28
33	.830097	2.28	.867283	1.93	.962813	4.23	.037187	27
34	.830234	2.30	.867167	1.93	.963067	4.22	.036933	26
35	9.830372	2.28	9.867051	1.93	9.963320	4.23	0.036680	25
36	.830509	2.28	.866935	1.93	.963574	4.23	.036426	24
37	.830646	2.30	.866819	1.93	.963828	4.22	.036172	23
38	.830784	2.28	.866703	1.95	.964081	4.23	.035919	22
39	.830921	2.28	.866586	1.93	.964335	4.22	.035665	21
40	9.831058	2.28	9.866470	1.95	9.964588	4.23	0.035412	20
41	.831195	2.28	.866353	1.93	.964842	4.22	.035158	19
42	.831332	2.28	.866237	1.95	.965095	4.23	.034905	18
43	.831469	2.28	.866120	1.93	.965349	4.22	.034651	17
44	.831606	2.27	.866004	1.95	.965602	4.22	.034398	16
45	9.831742	2.28	9.865887	1.95	9.965855	4.23	0.034145	15
46	.831879	2.27	.865770	1.95	.966109	4.22	.033891	14
47	.832015	2.28	.865653	1.95	.966362	4.23	.033638	13
48	.832152	2.27	.865536	1.95	.966616	4.22	.033384	12
49	.832288	2.28	.865419	1.95	.966869	4.23	.033131	11
50	9.832425	2.27	9.865302	1.95	9.967123	4.22	0.032877	10
51	.832561	2.27	.865185	1.95	.967376	4.22	.032624	9
52	.832697	2.27	.865068	1.97	.967629	4.23	.032371	8
53	.832833	2.27	.864950	1.95	.967883	4.22	.032117	7
54	.832969	2.27	.864833	1.95	.968136	4.22	.031864	6
55	9.833105	2.27	9.864716	1.97	9.968389	4.23	0.031611	5
56	.833241	2.27	.864598	1.95	.968643	4.22	.031357	4
57	.833377	2.25	.864481	1.97	.968896	4.22	.031104	3
58	.833512	2.27	.864363	1.97	.969149	4.23	.030851	2
59	.833648	2.25	.864245	1.97	.969403	4.22	.030597	1
60	9.833783		9.864127	1.97	9.969656		0.030344	0
	Cos.	D. 1″.	Sin.	D. 1″.	Cot.	D. 1″.	Tan.	M.

M.	Sin.	D. 1″.	Cos.	D. 1″.	Tan.	D. 1″.	Cot.	
0	9.833783	2.27	9.864127	1.95	9.969656	4.22	0.030344	60
1	.833919	2.25	.864010	1.97	.969909	4.22	.030091	59
2	.834054	2.25	.863892	1.97	.970162	4.23	.029838	58
3	.834189	2.27	.863774	1.97	.970416	4.22	.029584	57
4	.834325	2.25	.863656	1.97	.970669	4.22	.029331	56
5	9.834460	2.25	9.863538	1.98	9.970922	4.22	0.029078	55
6	.834595	2.25	.863419	1.97	.971175	4.23	.028825	54
7	.834730	2.25	.863301	1.97	.971429	4.22	.028571	53
8	.834865	2.23	.863183	1.98	.971682	4.22	.028318	52
9	.834999	2.25	.863064	1.97	.971935	4.22	.028065	51
10	9.835134	2.25	9.862946	1.98	9.972188	4.22	0.027812	50
11	.835269	2.23	.862827	1.97	.972441	4.23	.027559	49
12	.835403	2.25	.862709	1.98	.972695	4.22	.027305	48
13	.835538	2.23	.862590	1.98	.972948	4.22	.027052	47
14	.835672	2.25	.862471	1.97	.973201	4.22	.026799	46
15	9.835807	2.23	9.862353	1.98	9.973454	4.22	0.026546	45
16	.835941	2.23	.862234	1.98	.973707	4.22	.026293	44
17	.836075	2.23	.862115	1.98	.973960	4.22	.026040	43
18	.836209	2.23	.861996	1.98	.974213	4.22	.025787	42
19	.836343	2.23	.861877	1.98	.974466	4.23	.025534	41
20	9.836477	2.23	9.861758	2.00	9.974720	4.22	0.025280	40
21	.836611	2.23	.861638	1.98	.974973	4.22	.025027	39
22	.836745	2.23	.861519	1.98	.975226	4.22	.024774	38
23	.836878	2.23	.861400	2.00	.975479	4.22	.024521	37
24	.837012	2.23	.861280	1.98	.975732	4.22	.024268	36
25	9.837146	2.22	9.861161	2.00	9.975985	4.22	0.024015	35
26	.837279	2.22	.861041	1.98	.976238	4.22	.023762	34
27	.837412	2.23	.860922	2.00	.976491	4.22	.023509	33
28	.837546	2.22	.860802	2.00	.976744	4.22	.023256	32
29	.837679	2.22	.860682	2.00	.976997	4.22	.023003	31
30	9.837812	2.22	9.860562	2.00	9.977250	4.22	0.022750	30
31	.837945	2.22	.860442	2.00	.977503	4.22	.022497	29
32	.838078	2.22	.860322	2.00	.977756	4.22	.022244	28
33	.838211	2.22	.860202	2.00	.978009	4.22	.021991	27
34	.838344	2.22	.860082	2.00	.978262	4.22	.021738	26
35	9.838477	2.22	9.859962	2.00	9.978515	4.22	0.021485	25
36	.838610	2.20	.859842	2.02	.978768	4.22	.021232	24
37	.838742	2.22	.859721	2.00	.979021	4.22	.020979	23
38	.838875	2.20	.859601	2.02	.979274	4.22	.020726	22
39	.839007	2.22	.859480	2.00	.979527	4.22	.020473	21
40	9.839140	2.20	9.859360	2.02	9.979780	4.22	0.020220	20
41	.839272	2.20	.859239	2.00	.980033	4.22	.019967	19
42	.839404	2.20	.859119	2.02	.980286	4.20	.019714	18
43	.839536	2.20	.858998	2.02	.980538	4.22	.019462	17
44	.839668	2.20	.858877	2.02	.980791	4.22	.019209	16
45	9.839800	2.20	9.858756	2.02	9.981044	4.22	0.018956	15
46	.839932	2.20	.858635	2.02	.981297	4.22	.018703	14
47	.840064	2.20	.858514	2.02	.981550	4.22	.018450	13
48	.840196	2.20	.858393	2.02	.981803	4.22	.018197	12
49	.840328	2.18	.858272	2.02	.982056	4.22	.017944	11
50	9.840459	2.20	9.858151	2.03	9.982309	4.22	0.017691	10
51	.840591	2.18	.858029	2.02	.982562	4.20	.017438	9
52	.840722	2.20	.857908	2.03	.982814	4.22	.017186	8
53	.840854	2.18	.857786	2.02	.983067	4.22	.016933	7
54	.840985	2.18	.857665	2.03	.983320	4.22	.016680	6
55	9.841116	2.18	9.857543	2.02	9.983573	4.22	0.016427	5
56	.841247	2.18	.857422	2.03	.983826	4.22	.016174	4
57	.841378	2.18	.857300	2.03	.984079	4.22	.015921	3
58	.841509	2.18	.857178	2.03	.984332	4.20	.015668	2
59	.841640	2.18	.857056	2.03	.984584	4.22	.015416	1
60	9.841771		9.856934		9.984837		0.015163	0
	Cos.	D. 1″.	Sin.	D. 1″.	Cot.	D. 1″.	Tan.	M.

M.	Sin.	D. 1".	Cos.	D. 1".	Tan.	D. 1".	Cot.	
0	9.841771	2.18	9.856934	2.03	9.984837	4.22	0.015163	60
1	.841902	2.18	.856812	2.03	.985090	4.22	.014910	59
2	.842033	2.17	.856690	2.03	.985343	4.22	.014657	58
3	.842163	2.18	.856568	2.03	.985596	4.22	.014404	57
4	.842294	2.17	.856446	2.03	.985848	4.20	.014152	56
5	9.842424	2.18	9.856323	2.05	9.986101	4.22	0.013899	55
6	.842555	2.17	.856201	2.03	.986354	4.22	.013646	54
7	.842685	2.17	.856078	2.05	.986607	4.22	.013393	53
8	.842815	2.18	.855956	2.03	.986860	4.20	.013140	52
9	.842946	2.17	.855833	2.05	.987112	4.22	.012888	51
10	9.843076	2.17	9.855711	2.03	9.987365	4.22	0.012635	50
11	.843206	2.17	.855588	2.05	.987618	4.22	.012382	49
12	.843336	2.17	.855465	2.05	.987871	4.20	.012129	48
13	.843466	2.17	.855342	2.05	.988123	4.22	.011877	47
14	.843595	2.15	.855219	2.05	.988376	4.22	.011624	46
15	9.843725	2.17	9.855096	2.05	9.988629	4.22	0.011371	45
16	.843855	2.17	.854973	2.05	.988882	4.22	.011118	44
17	.843984	2.15	.854850	2.05	.989134	4.22	.010866	43
18	.844114	2.17	.854727	2.05	.989387	4.22	.010613	42
19	.844243	2.15	.854603	2.07	.989640	4.22	.010360	41
20	9.844372	2.15	9.854480	2.05	9.989893	4.20	0.010107	40
21	.844502	2.17	.854356	2.07	.990145	4.22	.009855	39
22	.844631	2.15	.854233	2.05	.990398	4.22	.009602	38
23	.844760	2.15	.854109	2.07	.990651	4.20	.009349	37
24	.844889	2.15	.853986	2.05	.990903	4.22	.009097	36
25	9.845018	2.15	9.853862	2.07	9.991156	4.20	0.008844	35
26	.845147	2.15	.853738	2.07	.991409	4.22	.008591	34
27	.845276	2.15	.853614	2.07	.991662	4.20	.008338	33
28	.845405	2.13	.853490	2.07	.991914	4.22	.008086	32
29	.845533	2.15	.853366	2.07	.992167	4.22	.007833	31
30	9.845662	2.13	9.853242	2.07	9.992420	4.20	0.007580	30
31	.845790	2.15	.853118	2.07	.992672	4.22	.007328	29
32	.845919	2.13	.852994	2.08	.992925	4.22	.007075	28
33	.846047	2.13	.852869	2.07	.993178	4.22	.006822	27
34	.846175	2.13	.852745	2.08	.993431	4.20	.006569	26
35	9.846304	2.15	9.852620	2.07	9.993683	4.22	0.006317	25
36	.846432	2.13	.852496	2.08	.993936	4.22	.006064	24
37	.846560	2.13	.852371	2.07	.994189	4.20	.005811	23
38	.846688	2.13	.852247	2.08	.994441	4.22	.005559	22
39	.846816	2.13	.852122	2.08	.994694	4.22	.005306	21
40	9.846944	2.12	9.851997	2.08	9.994947	4.20	0.005053	20
41	.847071	2.13	.851872	2.08	.995199	4.22	.004801	19
42	.847199	2.13	.851747	2.08	.995452	4.22	.004548	18
43	.847327	2.12	.851622	2.08	.995705	4.20	.004295	17
44	.847454	2.13	.851497	2.08	.995957	4.22	.004043	16
45	9.847582	2.12	9.851372	2.08	9.996210	4.22	0.003790	15
46	.847709	2.12	.851246	2.10	.996463	4.20	.003537	14
47	.847836	2.13	.851121	2.08	.996715	4.22	.003285	13
48	.847964	2.12	.850996	2.08	.996968	4.22	.003032	12
49	.848091	2.12	.850870	2.10	.997221	4.20	.002779	11
50	9.848218	2.12	9.850745	2.08	9.997473	4.22	0.002527	10
51	.848345	2.12	.850619	2.10	.997726	4.22	.002274	9
52	.848472	2.12	.850493	2.10	.997979	4.20	.002021	8
53	.848599	2.12	.850368	2.08	.998231	4.22	.001769	7
54	.848726	2.10	.850242	2.10	.998484	4.22	.001516	6
55	9.848852	2.12	9.850116	2.10	9.998737	4.20	0.001263	5
56	.848979	2.12	.849990	2.10	.998989	4.22	.001011	4
57	.849106	2.10	.849864	2.10	.999242	4.22	.000758	3
58	.849232	2.12	.849738	2.12	.999495	4.20	.000505	2
59	.849359	2.10	.849611	2.10	.999747	4.22	.000253	1
60	9.849485		9.849485		0.000000		0.000000	0
	Cos.	D. 1".	Sin.	D. 1".	Cot.	D. 1".	Tan.	M.

TABLE D—AUXILIARY TABLE FOR LOGARITHMIC SINES

		0°			1°			2°		
M.	S.	Sin.	Tan.	S.	Sin.	Tan.	S.	Sin.	Tan.	M.
		4.68			4.68			4.68		
0	0	5575	5575	3600	5553	5619	7200	5487	5751	0
1	60	5575	5575	3660	5552	5620	7260	5485	5754	1
2	120	5575	5575	3720	5551	5622	7320	5484	5757	2
3	180	5575	5575	3780	5551	5623	7380	5482	5760	3
4	240	5575	5575	3840	5550	5625	7440	5481	5763	4
5	300	5575	5575	3900	5549	5627	7500	5479	5766	5
6	360	5575	5575	3960	5548	5628	7560	5478	5769	6
7	420	5575	5575	4020	5547	5630	7620	5476	5773	7
8	480	5574	5576	4080	5547	5632	7680	5475	5776	8
9	540	5574	5576	4140	5546	5633	7740	5473	5779	9
10	600	5574	5576	4200	5545	5635	7800	5471	5782	10
11	660	5574	5576	4260	5544	5637	7860	5470	5785	11
12	720	5574	5577	4320	5543	5638	7920	5468	5788	12
13	780	5574	5577	4380	5542	5640	7980	5467	5792	13
14	840	5574	5577	4440	5541	5642	8040	5465	5795	14
15	900	5573	5578	4500	5540	5644	8100	5463	5798	15
16	960	5573	5578	4560	5539	5646	8160	5462	5802	16
17	1020	5573	5578	4620	5539	5648	8220	5460	5805	17
18	1080	5573	5579	4680	5538	5649	8280	5458	5808	18
19	1140	5573	5579	4740	5537	5651	8340	5457	5812	19
20	1200	5572	5580	4800	5536	5653	8400	5455	5815	20
21	1260	5572	5580	4860	5535	5655	8460	5453	5818	21
22	1320	5572	5581	4920	5534	5657	8520	5451	5822	22
23	1380	5572	5581	4980	5533	5659	8580	5450	5825	23
24	1440	5571	5582	5040	5532	5661	8640	5448	5829	24
25	1500	5571	5583	5100	5531	5663	8700	5446	5833	25
26	1560	5571	5583	5160	5530	5665	8760	5444	5836	26
27	1620	5570	5584	5220	5529	5668	8820	5443	5840	27
28	1680	5570	5584	5280	5527	5670	8880	5441	5843	28
29	1740	5570	5585	5340	5526	5672	8940	5439	5847	29
30	1800	5569	5586	5400	5525	5674	9000	5437	5851	30
31	1860	5569	5587	5460	5524	5676	9060	5435	5854	31
32	1920	5569	5587	5520	5523	5679	9120	5433	5858	32
33	1980	5568	5588	5580	5522	5681	9180	5431	5862	33
34	2040	5568	5589	5640	5521	5683	9240	5430	5866	34
35	2100	5567	5590	5700	5520	5685	9300	5428	5869	35
36	2160	5567	5591	5760	5518	5688	9360	5426	5873	36
37	2220	5566	5592	5820	5517	5690	9420	5424	5877	37
38	2280	5566	5593	5880	5516	5693	9480	5422	5881	38
39	2340	5566	5593	5940	5515	5695	9540	5420	5885	39
40	2400	5565	5594	6000	5514	5697	9600	5418	5889	40
41	2460	5565	5595	6060	5512	5700	9660	5416	5893	41
42	2520	5564	5596	6120	5511	5702	9720	5414	5897	42
43	2580	5564	5598	6180	5510	5705	9780	5412	5900	43
44	2640	5563	5599	6240	5509	5707	9840	5410	5905	44
45	2700	5562	5600	6300	5507	5710	9900	5408	5909	45
46	2760	5562	5601	6360	5506	5713	9960	5406	5913	46
47	2820	5561	5602	6420	5505	5715	10020	5404	5917	47
48	2880	5561	5603	6480	5503	5718	10080	5402	5921	48
49	2940	5560	5604	6540	5502	5720	10140	5400	5925	49
50	3000	5560	5605	6600	5501	5723	10200	5398	5929	50
51	3060	5559	5607	6660	5499	5726	10260	5396	5933	51
52	3120	5558	5608	6720	5498	5729	10320	5394	5937	52
53	3180	5558	5609	6780	5497	5731	10380	5392	5942	53
54	3240	5557	5611	6840	5495	5734	10440	5389	5946	54
55	3300	5556	5612	6900	5494	5737	10500	5387	5950	55
56	3360	5556	5613	6960	5492	5740	10560	5385	5955	56
57	3420	5555	5615	7020	5491	5743	10620	5383	5959	57
58	3480	5554	5616	7080	5490	5745	10680	5381	5963	58
59	3540	5554	5618	7140	5488	5748	10740	5379	5968	59
60	3600	5553	5619	7200	5487	5751	10800	5376	5972	60
M.	S.	Sin.	Tan.	S.	Sin.	Tan.	S.	Sin.	Tan.	M.

	3°			4°			5°			
M.	S.	Sin.	Tan.	S.	Sin.	Tan.	S.	Sin.	Tan.	M.
		4.68			4.68			4.68		
0	10800	5376	5972	14400	5222	6281	18000	5024	6679	0
1	10860	5374	5976	14460	5219	6287	18060	5020	6687	1
2	10920	5372	5981	14520	5216	6293	18120	5016	6694	2
3	10980	5370	5985	14580	5213	6299	18180	5012	6702	3
4	11040	5367	5990	14640	5210	6305	18240	5009	6709	4
5	11100	5365	5994	14700	5207	6311	18300	5005	6716	5
6	11160	5363	5999	14760	5204	6317	18360	5001	6724	6
7	11220	5361	6004	14820	5201	6323	18420	4997	6732	7
8	11280	5358	6008	14880	5198	6329	18480	4994	6739	8
9	11340	5356	6013	14940	5195	6335	18540	4990	6747	9
10	11400	5354	6017	15000	5192	6341	18600	4986	6754	10
11	11460	5351	6022	15060	5189	6348	18660	4982	6762	11
12	11520	5349	6027	15120	5186	6354	18720	4978	6770	12
13	11580	5347	6031	15180	5183	6360	18780	4975	6777	13
14	11640	5344	6036	15240	5180	6366	18840	4971	6785	14
15	11700	5342	6041	15300	5177	6372	18900	4967	6793	15
16	11760	5340	6046	15360	5173	6379	18960	4963	6800	16
17	11820	5337	6051	15420	5170	6385	19020	4959	6808	17
18	11880	5335	6055	15480	5167	6391	19080	4955	6816	18
19	11940	5332	6060	15540	5164	6398	19140	4951	6824	19
20	12000	5330	6065	15600	5161	6404	19200	4948	6832	20
21	12060	5327	6070	15660	5158	6410	19260	4944	6840	21
22	12120	5325	6075	15720	5154	6417	19320	4940	6848	22
23	12180	5322	6080	15780	5151	6423	19380	4936	6855	23
24	12240	5320	6085	15840	5148	6430	19440	4932	6863	24
25	12300	5317	6090	15900	5145	6436	19500	4928	6871	25
26	12360	5315	6095	15960	5141	6443	19560	4924	6879	26
27	12420	5312	6100	16020	5138	6449	19620	4920	6887	27
28	12480	5310	6105	16080	5135	6456	19680	4916	6896	28
29	12540	5307	6110	16140	5132	6463	19740	4912	6904	29
30	12600	5305	6116	16200	5128	6469	19800	4908	6912	30
31	12660	5302	6121	16260	5125	6476	19860	4904	6920	31
32	12720	5300	6126	16320	5122	6482	19920	4900	6928	32
33	12780	5297	6131	16380	5118	6489	19980	4895	6936	33
34	12840	5294	6136	16440	5115	6496	20040	4891	6944	34
35	12900	5292	6142	16500	5112	6503	20100	4887	6953	35
36	12960	5289	6147	16560	5108	6509	20160	4883	6961	36
37	13020	5286	6152	16620	5105	6516	20220	4880	6969	37
38	13080	5284	6158	16680	5101	6523	20280	4875	6977	38
39	13140	5281	6163	16740	5098	6530	20340	4871	6986	39
40	13200	5278	6168	16800	5095	6537	20400	4867	6994	40
41	13260	5276	6174	16860	5091	6544	20460	4862	7003	41
42	13320	5273	6179	16920	5088	6551	20520	4858	7011	42
43	13380	5270	6185	16980	5084	6557	20580	4854	7019	43
44	13440	5268	6190	17040	5081	6564	20640	4850	7028	44
45	13500	5265	6196	17100	5077	6571	20700	4846	7036	45
46	13560	5262	6201	17160	5074	6578	20760	4841	7045	46
47	13620	5259	6207	17220	5070	6585	20820	4837	7053	47
48	13680	5256	6212	17280	5067	6593	20880	4833	7062	48
49	13740	5254	6218	17340	5063	6600	20940	4829	7070	49
50	13800	5251	6224	17400	5060	6607	21000	4824	7079	50
51	13860	5248	6229	17460	5056	6614	21060	4820	7088	51
52	13920	5245	6235	17520	5053	6621	21120	4816	7096	52
53	13980	5242	6241	17580	5049	6628	21180	4811	7105	53
54	14040	5239	6246	17640	5045	6635	21240	4807	7114	54
55	14100	5237	6252	17700	5042	6643	21300	4803	7122	55
56	14160	5234	6258	17760	5038	6650	21360	4798	7131	56
57	14220	5231	6264	17820	5034	6657	21420	4794	7140	57
58	14280	5228	6269	17880	5031	6665	21480	4790	7149	58
59	14340	5225	6275	17940	5027	6672	21540	4785	7158	59
60	14400	5222	6281	18000	5024	6679	21600	4781	7166	60
M.	S.	Sin.	Tan.	S.	Sin.	Tan.	S.	Sin.	Tan.	M.

USE OF AUXILIARY TABLE D FOR LOGARITHMIC SINES AND TANGENTS OF SMALL ANGLES

Frequently the usual methods of interpolation are not sufficiently exact for determining the logarithmic sines, tangents, and cotangents of small angles. It is then necessary to apply a method based on the fact that the natural sines and tangents of small angles vary almost directly with the angles. Thus, $\dfrac{\sin 0° \ 15' \ 24''}{\sin 0° \ 15' \ 00''} = \dfrac{0° \ 15' \ 24''}{0° \ 15' \ 00''} = \dfrac{924''}{900''}$, and $\sin 0° \ 15' \ 24''$

$= 924 \times \dfrac{\sin 0° \ 15' \ 00''}{900}$. If logarithms of both sides of the equation are taken, log sin 0° 15' 24" = log 924 + (log sin 0° 15' 00" − log 900).

In Table D on pages 590 and 591, the values of log sin $\propto$ −log $\propto$ (in seconds) and of log tan $\propto$ −log $\propto$ (in seconds) are given for various values of $\propto$ in the columns headed sin and tan, respectively. To obtain the logarithmic sine or the logarithmic tangent of a small angle, add the logarithm of the angle (expressed in seconds) to the value taken from the table for the nearest minute. When the logarithmic sine or tangent is known and the angle is required, first determine the approximate angle from Table C. Subtract the value found in the auxiliary table from the given logarithmic sine or logarithmic tangent. The result is the logarithm of the required angle, expressed in seconds. Logarithmic cotangents of small angles may be obtained from the relation, log cot $\propto$ = 10 − log tan $\propto$.

EXAMPLES

To find log sin 0° 15' 24" (=924"). From Table D,

$$\log \left(\frac{\sin 0° \ 15'}{900} \right) = 4.685573$$

$$\log 924 = 2.965672$$

log sin 0° 15' 24" = 7.651245

To find log tan 1° 12' 47" (=4367"). From Table D,

$$\log \left(\frac{\tan 1° \ 13'}{4380} \right) = 4.685640$$

$$\log 4367 = 3.640183$$

log tan 1° 12' 47" = 8.325823

To find angle when log sin = 8.442414 From Table C the approximate angle is 1° 35'

$$\log \sin \propto \ = 8.442414$$

From Table D,

$$\log \left(\frac{\sin 1° \ 35'}{5700} \right) = 4.685520$$

$$\log \propto '' = 3.756894$$

$\propto = 5713'' = 1° \ 35' \ 13''$

To find angle when log tan = 8.206747 From Table C the approximate angle is 0° 55'

$$\log \tan \propto \ = 8.206747$$

From Table D,

$$\log \left(\frac{\tan 0° \ 55'}{3300} \right) = 4.685612$$

$$\log \propto '' = 3.521135$$

$\propto = 3320'' = 0° \ 55' \ 20''$

′	0°		1°		2°		3°		4°		′
	Sine	Cosine	Sine	Cosine	Sine	Cosine	Sine	Cosine	Sine	Cosine	
0	.00000	1.	.01745	.99985	.03490	.99939	.05234	.99863	.06976	.99756	60
1	.00029	1.	.01774	.99984	.03519	.99938	.05263	.99861	.07005	.99754	59
2	.00058	1.	.01803	.99984	.03548	.99937	.05292	.99860	.07034	.99752	58
3	.00087	1.	.01832	.99983	.03577	.99936	.05321	.99858	.07063	.99750	57
4	.00116	1.	.01862	.99983	.03606	.99935	.05350	.99857	.07092	.99748	56
5	.00145	1.	.01891	.99982	.03635	.99934	.05379	.99855	.07121	.99746	55
6	.00175	1.	.01920	.99982	.03664	.99933	.05408	.99854	.07150	.99744	54
7	.00204	1.	.01949	.99981	.03693	.99932	.05437	.99852	.07179	.99742	53
8	.00233	1.	.01978	.99980	.03723	.99931	.05466	.99851	.07208	.99740	52
9	.00262	1.	.02007	.99980	.03752	.99930	.05495	.99849	.07237	.99738	51
10	.00291	1.	.02036	.99979	.03781	.99929	.05524	.99847	.07266	.99736	50
11	.00320	.99999	.02065	.99979	.03810	.99927	.05553	.99846	.07295	.99734	49
12	.00349	.99999	.02094	.99978	.03839	.99926	.05582	.99844	.07324	.99731	48
13	.00378	.99999	.02123	.99977	.03868	.99925	.05611	.99842	.07353	.99729	47
14	.00407	.99999	.02152	.99977	.03897	.99924	.05640	.99841	.07382	.99727	46
15	.00436	.99999	.02181	.99976	.03926	.99923	.05669	.99839	.07411	.99725	45
16	.00465	.99999	.02211	.99976	.03955	.99923	.05698	.99838	.07440	.99723	44
17	.00495	.99999	.02240	.99975	.03984	.99921	.05727	.99836	.07469	.99721	43
18	.00524	.99999	.02269	.99974	.04013	.99919	.05756	.99834	.07498	.99719	42
19	.00553	.99998	.02298	.99974	.04042	.99918	.05785	.99833	.07527	.99716	41
20	.00582	.99998	.02327	.99973	.04071	.99917	.05814	.99831	.07556	.99714	40
21	.00611	.99998	.02356	.99972	.04100	.99916	.05844	.99829	.07585	.99712	39
22	.00640	.99998	.02385	.99972	.04129	.99915	.05873	.99827	.07614	.99710	38
23	.00669	.99998	.02414	.99971	.04159	.99913	.05902	.99826	.07643	.99708	37
24	.00698	.99998	.02443	.99970	.04188	.99912	.05931	.99824	.07672	.99705	36
25	.00727	.99997	.02472	.99969	.04217	.99911	.05960	.99822	.07701	.99703	35
26	.00756	.99997	.02501	.99969	.04246	.99910	.05989	.99821	.07730	.99701	34
27	.00785	.99997	.02530	.99968	.04275	.99909	.06018	.99819	.07759	.99699	33
28	.00814	.99997	.02560	.99967	.04304	.99907	.06047	.99817	.07788	.99696	32
29	.00844	.99996	.02589	.99966	.04333	.99906	.06076	.99815	.07817	.99694	31
30	.00873	.99996	.02618	.99966	.04362	.99905	.06105	.99813	.07846	.99692	30
31	.00902	.99996	.02647	.99965	.04391	.99904	.06134	.99812	.07875	.99689	29
32	.00931	.99996	.02676	.99964	.04420	.99902	.06163	.99810	.07904	.99687	28
33	.00960	.99995	.02705	.99963	.04449	.99901	.06192	.99808	.07933	.99685	27
34	.00989	.99995	.02734	.99963	.04478	.99900	.06221	.99806	.07962	.99683	26
35	.01018	.99995	.02763	.99962	.04507	.99898	.06250	.99804	.07991	.99680	25
36	.01047	.99994	.02792	.99961	.04536	.99897	.06279	.99803	.08020	.99678	24
37	.01076	.99994	.02821	.99960	.04565	.99896	.06308	.99801	.08049	.99676	23
38	.01105	.99994	.02850	.99959	.04594	.99894	.06337	.99799	.08078	.99673	22
39	.01134	.99994	.02879	.99959	.04623	.99893	.06366	.99797	.08107	.99671	21
40	.01164	.99993	.02908	.99958	.04653	.99892	.06395	.99795	.08136	.99668	20
41	.01193	.99993	.02938	.99957	.04682	.99890	.06424	.99793	.08165	.99666	19
42	.01222	.99993	.02967	.99956	.04711	.99889	.06453	.99792	.08194	.99664	18
43	.01251	.99992	.02996	.99955	.04740	.99888	.06482	.99790	.08223	.99661	17
44	.01280	.99992	.03025	.99954	.04769	.99886	.06511	.99788	.08252	.99659	16
45	.01309	.99991	.03054	.99953	.04798	.99885	.06540	.99786	.08281	.99657	15
46	.01338	.99991	.03083	.99952	.04827	.99883	.06569	.99784	.08310	.99654	14
47	.01367	.99991	.03112	.99952	.04856	.99882	.06598	.99782	.08339	.99652	13
48	.01396	.99990	.03141	.99951	.04885	.99881	.06627	.99780	.08368	.99649	12
49	.01425	.99990	.03170	.99950	.04914	.99879	.06656	.99778	.08397	.99647	11
50	.01454	.99989	.03199	.99949	.04943	.99878	.06685	.99776	.08426	.99644	10
51	.01483	.99989	.03228	.99948	.04972	.99876	.06714	.99774	.08455	.99642	9
52	.01513	.99989	.03257	.99947	.05001	.99875	.06743	.99772	.08484	.99639	8
53	.01542	.99988	.03286	.99946	.05030	.99873	.06773	.99770	.08513	.99637	7
54	.01571	.99988	.03316	.99945	.05059	.99872	.06802	.99768	.08542	.99635	6
55	.01600	.99987	.03345	.99944	.05088	.99870	.06831	.99766	.08571	.99632	5
56	.01629	.99987	.03374	.99943	.05117	.99869	.06860	.99764	.08600	.99630	4
57	.01658	.99986	.03403	.99942	.05146	.99867	.06889	.99762	.08629	.99627	3
58	.01687	.99986	.03432	.99941	.05175	.99866	.06918	.99760	.08658	.99625	2
59	.01716	.99985	.03461	.99940	.05205	.99864	.06947	.99758	.08687	.99622	1
60	.01745	.99985	.03490	.99939	.05234	.99863	.06976	.99756	.08716	.99619	0
′	Cosine	Sine	Cosine	Sine	Cosine	Sine	Cosine	Sine	Cosine	Sine	′
	89°		88°		87°		86°		85°		

TABLE E.—NATURAL SINES AND COSINES

′	5° Sine	5° Cosine	6° Sine	6° Cosine	7° Sine	7° Cosine	8° Sine	8° Cosine	9° Sine	9° Cosine	′
0	.08716	.99619	.10453	.99452	.12187	.99255	.13917	.99027	.15643	.98769	60
1	.08745	.99617	.10482	.99449	.12216	.99251	.13946	.99023	.15672	.98764	59
2	.08774	.99614	.10511	.99446	.12245	.99248	.13975	.99019	.15701	.98760	58
3	.08803	.99612	.10540	.99443	.12274	.99244	.14004	.99015	.15730	.98755	57
4	.08831	.99609	.10569	.99440	.12302	.99240	.14033	.99011	.15758	.98751	56
5	.08860	.99607	.10597	.99437	.12331	.99237	.14061	.99006	.15787	.98746	55
6	.08889	.99604	.10626	.99434	.12360	.99233	.14090	.99002	.15816	.98741	54
7	.08918	.99602	.10655	.99431	.12389	.99230	.14119	.98998	.15845	.98737	53
8	.08947	.99599	.10684	.99428	.12418	.99226	.14148	.98994	.15873	.98732	52
9	.08976	.99596	.10713	.99424	.12447	.99222	.14177	.98990	.15902	.98728	51
10	.09005	.99594	.10742	.99421	.12476	.99219	.14205	.98986	.15931	.98723	50
11	.09034	.99591	.10771	.99418	.12504	.99215	.14234	.98982	.15959	.98718	49
12	.09063	.99588	.10800	.99415	.12533	.99211	.14263	.98978	.15988	.98714	48
13	.09092	.99586	.10829	.99412	.12562	.99208	.14292	.98973	.16017	.98709	47
14	.09121	.99583	.10858	.99409	.12591	.99204	.14320	.98969	.16046	.98704	46
15	.09150	.99580	.10887	.99406	.12620	.99200	.14349	.98965	.16074	.98700	45
16	.09179	.99578	.10916	.99402	.12649	.99197	.14378	.98961	.16103	.98695	44
17	.09208	.99575	.10945	.99399	.12678	.99193	.14407	.98957	.16132	.98690	43
18	.09237	.99572	.10973	.99396	.12706	.99189	.14436	.98953	.16160	.98686	42
19	.09266	.99570	.11002	.99393	.12735	.99186	.14464	.98948	.16189	.98681	41
20	.09295	.99567	.11031	.99390	.12764	.99182	.14493	.98944	.16218	.98676	40
21	.09324	.99564	.11060	.99386	.12793	.99178	.14522	.98940	.16246	.98671	39
22	.09353	.99562	.11089	.99383	.12822	.99175	.14551	.98936	.16275	.98667	38
23	.09382	.99559	.11118	.99380	.12851	.99171	.14580	.98931	.16304	.98662	37
24	.09411	.99556	.11147	.99377	.12880	.99167	.14608	.98927	.16333	.98657	36
25	.09440	.99553	.11176	.99374	.12908	.99163	.14637	.98923	.16361	.98652	35
26	.09469	.99551	.11205	.99370	.12937	.99160	.14666	.98919	.16390	.98648	34
27	.09498	.99548	.11234	.99367	.12966	.99156	.14695	.98914	.16419	.98643	33
28	.09527	.99545	.11263	.99364	.12995	.99152	.14723	.98910	.16447	.98638	32
29	.09556	.99542	.11291	.99360	.13024	.99148	.14752	.98906	.16476	.98633	31
30	.09585	.99540	.11320	.99357	.13053	.99144	.14781	.98902	.16505	.98629	30
31	.09614	.99537	.11349	.99354	.13081	.99141	.14810	.98897	.16533	.98624	29
32	.09642	.99534	.11378	.99351	.13110	.99137	.14838	.98893	.16562	.98619	28
33	.09671	.99531	.11407	.99347	.13139	.99133	.14867	.98889	.16591	.98614	27
34	.09700	.99528	.11436	.99344	.13168	.99129	.14896	.98884	.16620	.98609	26
35	.09729	.99526	.11465	.99341	.13197	.99125	.14925	.98880	.16648	.98604	25
36	.09758	.99523	.11494	.99337	.13226	.99122	.14954	.98876	.16677	.98600	24
37	.09787	.99520	.11523	.99334	.13254	.99118	.14982	.98871	.16706	.98595	23
38	.09816	.99517	.11552	.99331	.13283	.99114	.15011	.98867	.16734	.98590	22
39	.09845	.99514	.11580	.99327	.13312	.99110	.15040	.98863	.16763	.98585	21
40	.09874	.99511	.11609	.99324	.13341	.99106	.15069	.98858	.16792	.98580	20
41	.09903	.99508	.11638	.99320	.13370	.99102	.15097	.98854	.16820	.98575	19
42	.09932	.99506	.11667	.99317	.13399	.99098	.15126	.98849	.16849	.98570	18
43	.09961	.99503	.11696	.99314	.13427	.99094	.15155	.98845	.16878	.98565	17
44	.09990	.99500	.11725	.99310	.13456	.99091	.15184	.98841	.16906	.98561	16
45	.10019	.99497	.11754	.99307	.13485	.99087	.15212	.98836	.16935	.98556	15
46	.10048	.99494	.11783	.99303	.13514	.99083	.15241	.98832	.16964	.98551	14
47	.10077	.99491	.11812	.99300	.13543	.99079	.15270	.98827	.16992	.98546	13
48	.10106	.99488	.11840	.99297	.13572	.99075	.15299	.98823	.17021	.98541	12
49	.10135	.99485	.11869	.99293	.13600	.99071	.15327	.98818	.17050	.98536	11
50	.10164	.99482	.11898	.99290	.13629	.99067	.15356	.98814	.17078	.98531	10
51	.10192	.99479	.11927	.99286	.13658	.99063	.15385	.98809	.17107	.98526	9
52	.10221	.99476	.11956	.99283	.13687	.99059	.15414	.98805	.17136	.98521	8
53	.10250	.99473	.11985	.99279	.13716	.99055	.15442	.98800	.17164	.98516	7
54	.10279	.99470	.12014	.99276	.13744	.99051	.15471	.98796	.17193	.98511	6
55	.10308	.99467	.12043	.99272	.13773	.99047	.15500	.98791	.17222	.98506	5
56	.10337	.99464	.12071	.99269	.13802	.99043	.15529	.98787	.17250	.98501	4
57	.10366	.99461	.12100	.99265	.13831	.99039	.15557	.98782	.17279	.98496	3
58	.10395	.99458	.12129	.99262	.13860	.99035	.15586	.98778	.17308	.98491	2
59	.10424	.99455	.12158	.99258	.13889	.99031	.15615	.98773	.17336	.98486	1
60	.10453	.99452	.12187	.99255	.13917	.99027	.15643	.98769	.17365	.98481	0
′	Cosine	Sine	Cosine	Sine	Cosine	Sine	Cosine	Sine	Cosine	Sine	′
	84°		83°		82°		81°		80°		

TABLE E.—NATURAL SINES AND COSINES

′	10° Sine	10° Cosine	11° Sine	11° Cosine	12° Sine	12° Cosine	13° Sine	13° Cosine	14° Sine	14° Cosine	′
0	.17365	.98481	.19081	.98163	.20791	.97815	.22495	.97437	.24192	.97030	60
1	.17393	.98476	.19109	.98157	.20820	.97809	.22523	.97430	.24220	.97023	59
2	.17422	.98471	.19138	.98152	.20848	.97803	.22552	.97424	.24249	.97015	58
3	.17451	.98466	.19167	.98146	.20877	.97797	.22580	.97417	.24277	.97008	57
4	.17479	.98461	.19195	.98140	.20905	.97791	.22608	.97411	.24305	.97001	56
5	.17508	.98455	.19224	.98135	.20933	.97784	.22637	.97404	.24333	.96994	55
6	.17537	.98450	.19252	.98129	.20962	.97778	.22665	.97398	.24362	.96987	54
7	.17565	.98445	.19281	.98124	.20990	.97772	.22693	.97391	.24390	.96980	53
8	.17594	.98440	.19309	.98118	.21019	.97766	.22722	.97384	.24418	.96973	52
9	.17623	.98435	.19338	.98112	.21047	.97760	.22750	.97378	.24446	.96966	51
10	.17651	.98430	.19366	.98107	.21076	.97754	.22778	.97371	.24474	.96959	50
11	.17680	.98425	.19395	.98101	.21104	.97748	.22807	.97365	.24503	.96952	49
12	.17708	.98420	.19423	.98096	.21132	.97742	.22835	.97358	.24531	.96945	48
13	.17737	.98414	.19452	.98090	.21161	.97735	.22863	.97351	.24559	.96937	47
14	.17766	.98409	.19481	.98084	.21189	.97729	.22892	.97345	.24587	.96930	46
15	.17794	.98404	.19509	.98079	.21218	.97723	.22920	.97338	.24615	.96923	45
16	.17823	.98399	.19538	.98073	.21246	.97717	.22948	.97331	.24644	.96916	44
17	.17852	.98394	.19566	.98067	.21275	.97711	.22977	.97325	.24672	.96909	43
18	.17880	.98389	.19595	.98061	.21303	.97705	.23005	.97318	.24700	.96902	42
19	.17909	.98383	.19623	.98056	.21331	.97698	.23033	.97311	.24728	.96894	41
20	.17937	.98378	.19652	.98050	.21360	.97692	.23062	.97304	.24756	.96887	40
21	.17966	.98373	.19680	.98044	.21388	.97686	.23090	.97298	.24784	.96880	39
22	.17995	.98368	.19709	.98039	.21417	.97680	.23118	.97291	.24813	.96873	38
23	.18023	.98362	.19737	.98033	.21445	.97673	.23146	.97284	.24841	.96866	37
24	.18052	.98357	.19766	.98027	.21474	.97667	.23175	.97278	.24869	.96858	36
25	.18081	.98352	.19794	.98021	.21502	.97661	.23203	.97271	.24897	.96851	35
26	.18109	.98347	.19823	.98016	.21530	.97655	.23231	.97264	.24925	.96844	34
27	.18138	.98341	.19851	.98010	.21559	.97648	.23260	.97257	.24954	.96837	33
28	.18166	.98336	.19880	.98004	.21587	.97642	.23288	.97251	.24982	.96829	32
29	.18195	.98331	.19908	.97998	.21616	.97636	.23316	.97244	.25010	.96822	31
30	.18224	.98325	.19937	.97992	.21644	.97630	.23345	.97237	.25038	.96815	30
31	.18252	.98320	.19965	.97987	.21672	.97623	.23373	.97230	.25066	.96807	29
32	.18281	.98315	.19994	.97981	.21701	.97617	.23401	.97223	.25094	.96800	28
33	.18309	.98310	.20022	.97975	.21729	.97611	.23429	.97217	.25122	.96793	27
34	.18338	.98304	.20051	.97969	.21758	.97604	.23458	.97210	.25151	.96786	26
35	.18367	.98299	.20079	.97963	.21786	.97598	.23486	.97203	.25179	.96778	25
36	.18395	.98294	.20108	.97958	.21814	.97592	.23514	.97196	.25207	.96771	24
37	.18424	.98288	.20136	.97952	.21843	.97585	.23542	.97189	.25235	.96764	23
38	.18452	.98283	.20165	.97946	.21871	.97579	.23571	.97182	.25263	.96756	22
39	.18481	.98277	.20193	.97940	.21899	.97573	.23599	.97176	.25291	.96749	21
40	.18509	.98272	.20222	.97934	.21928	.97566	.23627	.97169	.25320	.96742	20
41	.18538	.98267	.20250	.97928	.21956	.97560	.23656	.97162	.25348	.96734	19
42	.18567	.98261	.20279	.97922	.21985	.97553	.23684	.97155	.25376	.96727	18
43	.18595	.98256	.20307	.97916	.22013	.97547	.23712	.97148	.25404	.96719	17
44	.18624	.98250	.20336	.97910	.22041	.97541	.23740	.97141	.25432	.96712	16
45	.18652	.98245	.20364	.97905	.22070	.97534	.23769	.97134	.25460	.96705	15
46	.18681	.98240	.20393	.97899	.22098	.97528	.23797	.97127	.25488	.96697	14
47	.18710	.98234	.20421	.97893	.22126	.97521	.23825	.97120	.25516	.96690	13
48	.18738	.98229	.20450	.97887	.22155	.97515	.23853	.97113	.25545	.96682	12
49	.18767	.98223	.20478	.97881	.22183	.97508	.23882	.97106	.25573	.96675	11
50	.18795	.98218	.20507	.97875	.22212	.97502	.23910	.97100	.25601	.96667	10
51	.18824	.98212	.20535	.97869	.22240	.97496	.23938	.97093	.25629	.96660	9
52	.18852	.98207	.20563	.97863	.22268	.97489	.23966	.97086	.25657	.96653	8
53	.18881	.98201	.20592	.97857	.22297	.97483	.23995	.97079	.25685	.96645	7
54	.18910	.98196	.20620	.97851	.22325	.97476	.24023	.97072	.25713	.96638	6
55	.18938	.98190	.20649	.97845	.22353	.97470	.24051	.97065	.25741	.96630	5
56	.18967	.98185	.20677	.97839	.22382	.97463	.24079	.97058	.25769	.96623	4
57	.18995	.98179	.20706	.97833	.22410	.97457	.24108	.97051	.25798	.96615	3
58	.19024	.98174	.20734	.97827	.22438	.97450	.24136	.97044	.25826	.96608	2
59	.19052	.98168	.20763	.97821	.22467	.97444	.24164	.97037	.25854	.96600	1
60	.19081	.98163	.20791	.97815	.22495	.97437	.24192	.97030	.25882	.96593	0
′	Cosine	Sine	Cosine	Sine	Cosine	Sine	Cosine	Sine	Cosine	Sine	′
	79°		78°		77°		76°		75°		

TABLE E.—NATURAL SINES AND COSINES

′	15°		16°		17°		18°		19°		′
	Sine	Cosine	Sine	Cosine	Sine	Cosine	Sine	Cosine	Sine	Cosine	
0	.25882	.96593	.27564	.96126	.29237	.95630	.30902	.95106	.32557	.94552	60
1	.25910	.96585	.27592	.96118	.29265	.95622	.30929	.95097	.32584	.94542	59
2	.25938	.96578	.27620	.96110	.29293	.95613	.30957	.95088	.32612	.94533	58
3	.25966	.96570	.27648	.96102	.29321	.95605	.30985	.95079	.32639	.94523	57
4	.25994	.96562	.27676	.96094	.29348	.95596	.31012	.95070	.32667	.94514	56
5	.26022	.96555	.27704	.96086	.29376	.95588	.31040	.95061	.32694	.94504	55
6	.26050	.96547	.27731	.96078	.29404	.95579	.31068	.95052	.32722	.94495	54
7	.26079	.96540	.27759	.96070	.29432	.95571	.31095	.95043	.32749	.94485	53
8	.26107	.96532	.27787	.96062	.29460	.95562	.31123	.95033	.32777	.94476	52
9	.26135	.96524	.27815	.96054	.29487	.95554	.31151	.95024	.32804	.94466	51
10	.26163	.96517	.27843	.96046	.29515	.95545	.31178	.95015	.32832	.94457	50
11	.26191	.96509	.27871	.96037	.29543	.95536	.31206	.95006	.32859	.94447	49
12	.26219	.96502	.27899	.96029	.29571	.95528	.31233	.94997	.32887	.94438	48
13	.26247	.96494	.27927	.96021	.29599	.95519	.31261	.94988	.32914	.94428	47
14	.26275	.96486	.27955	.96013	.29626	.95511	.31289	.94979	.32942	.94418	46
15	.26303	.96479	.27983	.96005	.29654	.95502	.31316	.94970	.32969	.94409	45
16	.26331	.96471	.28011	.95997	.29682	.95493	.31344	.94961	.32997	.94399	44
17	.26359	.96463	.28039	.95989	.29710	.95485	.31372	.94952	.33024	.94390	43
18	.26387	.96456	.28067	.95981	.29737	.95476	.31399	.94943	.33051	.94380	42
19	.26415	.96448	.28095	.95972	.29765	.95467	.31427	.94933	.33079	.94370	41
20	.26443	.96440	.28123	.95964	.29793	.95459	.31454	.94924	.33106	.94361	40
21	.26471	.96433	.28150	.95956	.29821	.95450	.31482	.94915	.33134	.94351	39
22	.26500	.96425	.28178	.95948	.29849	.95441	.31510	.94906	.33161	.94342	38
23	.26528	.96417	.28206	.95940	.29876	.95433	.31537	.94897	.33189	.94332	37
24	.26556	.96410	.28234	.95931	.29904	.95424	.31565	.94888	.33216	.94322	36
25	.26584	.96402	.28262	.95923	.29932	.95415	.31593	.94878	.33244	.94313	35
26	.26612	.96394	.28290	.95915	.29960	.95407	.31620	.94869	.33271	.94303	34
27	.26640	.96386	.28318	.95907	.29987	.95398	.31648	.94860	.33298	.94293	33
28	.26668	.96379	.28346	.95898	.30015	.95389	.31675	.94851	.33326	.94284	32
29	.26696	.96371	.28374	.95890	.30043	.95380	.31703	.94842	.33353	.94274	31
30	.26724	.96363	.28402	.95882	.30071	.95372	.31730	.94832	.33381	.94264	30
31	.26752	.96355	.28429	.95874	.30098	.95363	.31758	.94823	.33408	.94254	29
32	.26780	.96347	.28457	.95865	.30126	.95354	.31786	.94814	.33436	.94245	28
33	.26808	.96340	.28485	.95857	.30154	.95345	.31813	.94805	.33463	.94235	27
34	.26836	.96332	.28513	.95849	.30182	.95337	.31841	.94795	.33490	.94225	26
35	.26864	.96324	.28541	.95841	.30209	.95328	.31868	.94786	.33518	.94215	25
36	.26892	.96316	.28569	.95832	.30237	.95319	.31896	.94777	.33545	.94206	24
37	.26920	.96308	.28597	.95824	.30265	.95310	.31923	.94768	.33573	.94196	23
38	.26948	.96301	.28625	.95816	.30292	.95301	.31951	.94758	.33600	.94186	22
39	.26976	.96293	.28652	.95807	.30320	.95293	.31979	.94749	.33627	.94176	21
40	.27004	.96285	.28680	.95799	.30348	.95284	.32006	.94740	.33655	.94167	20
41	.27032	.96277	.28708	.95791	.30376	.95275	.32034	.94730	.33682	.94157	19
42	.27060	.96269	.28736	.95782	.30403	.95266	.32061	.94721	.33710	.94147	18
43	.27088	.96261	.28764	.95774	.30431	.95257	.32089	.94712	.33737	.94137	17
44	.27116	.96253	.28792	.95766	.30459	.95248	.32116	.94702	.33764	.94127	16
45	.27144	.96246	.28820	.95757	.30486	.95240	.32144	.94693	.33792	.94118	15
46	.27172	.96238	.28847	.95749	.30514	.95231	.32171	.94684	.33819	.94108	14
47	.27200	.96230	.28875	.95740	.30542	.95222	.32199	.94674	.33846	.94098	13
48	.27228	.96222	.28903	.95732	.30570	.95213	.32227	.94665	.33874	.94088	12
49	.27256	.96214	.28931	.95724	.30597	.95204	.32254	.94656	.33901	.94078	11
50	.27284	.96206	.28959	.95715	.30625	.95195	.32282	.94646	.33929	.94068	10
51	.27312	.96198	.28987	.95707	.30653	.95186	.32309	.94637	.33956	.94058	9
52	.27340	.96190	.29015	.95698	.30680	.95177	.32337	.94627	.33983	.94049	8
53	.27368	.96182	.29042	.95690	.30708	.95168	.32364	.94618	.34011	.94039	7
54	.27396	.96174	.29070	.95681	.30736	.95159	.32392	.94609	.34038	.94029	6
55	.27424	.96166	.29098	.95673	.30763	.95150	.32419	.94599	.34065	.94019	5
56	.27452	.96158	.29126	.95664	.30791	.95142	.32447	.94590	.34093	.94009	4
57	.27480	.96150	.29154	.95656	.30819	.95133	.32474	.94580	.34120	.93999	3
58	.27508	.96142	.29182	.95647	.30846	.95124	.32502	.94571	.34147	.93989	2
59	.27536	.96134	.29209	.95639	.30874	.95115	.32529	.94561	.34175	.93979	1
60	.27564	.96126	.29237	.95630	.30902	.95106	.32557	.94552	.34202	.93969	0
′	Cosine	Sine	Cosine	Sine	Cosine	Sine	Cosine	Sine	Cosine	Sine	′
	74°		73°		72°		71°		70°		

400

TABLE E.—NATURAL SINES AND COSINES

′	20° Sine	20° Cosine	21° Sine	21° Cosine	22° Sine	22° Cosine	23° Sine	23° Cosine	24° Sine	24° Cosine	′
0	.34202	.93969	.35837	.93358	.37461	.92718	.39073	.92050	.40674	.91355	60
1	.34229	.93959	.35864	.93348	.37488	.92707	.39100	.92039	.40700	.91343	59
2	.34257	.93949	.35891	.93337	.37515	.92697	.39127	.92028	.40727	.91331	58
3	.34284	.93939	.35918	.93327	.37542	.92686	.39153	.92016	.40753	.91319	57
4	.34311	.93929	.35945	.93316	.37569	.92675	.39180	.92005	.40780	.91307	56
5	.34339	.93919	.35973	.93306	.37595	.92664	.39207	.91994	.40806	.91295	55
6	.34366	.93909	.36000	.93295	.37622	.92653	.39234	.91982	.40833	.91283	54
7	.34393	.93899	.36027	.93285	.37649	.92642	.39260	.91971	.40860	.91272	53
8	.34421	.93889	.36054	.93274	.37676	.92631	.39287	.91959	.40886	.91260	52
9	.34448	.93879	.36081	.93264	.37703	.92620	.39314	.91948	.40913	.91248	51
10	.34475	.93869	.36108	.93253	.37730	.92609	.39341	.91936	.40939	.91236	50
11	.34503	.93859	.36135	.93243	.37757	.92598	.39367	.91925	.40966	.91224	49
12	.34530	.93849	.36162	.93232	.37784	.92587	.39394	.91914	.40992	.91212	48
13	.34557	.93839	.36190	.93222	.37811	.92576	.39421	.91902	.41019	.91200	47
14	.34584	.93829	.36217	.93211	.37838	.92565	.39448	.91891	.41045	.91188	46
15	.34612	.93819	.36244	.93201	.37865	.92554	.39474	.91879	.41072	.91176	45
16	.34639	.93809	.36271	.93190	.37892	.92543	.39501	.91868	.41098	.91164	44
17	.34666	.93799	.36298	.93180	.37919	.92532	.39528	.91856	.41125	.91152	43
18	.34694	.93789	.36325	.93169	.37946	.92521	.39555	.91845	.41151	.91140	42
19	.34721	.93779	.36352	.93159	.37973	.92510	.39581	.91833	.41178	.91128	41
20	.34748	.93769	.36379	.93148	.37999	.92499	.39608	.91822	.41204	.91116	40
21	.34775	.93759	.36406	.93137	.38026	.92488	.39635	.91810	.41231	.91104	39
22	.34803	.93748	.36434	.93127	.38053	.92477	.39661	.91799	.41257	.91092	38
23	.34830	.93738	.36461	.93116	.38080	.92466	.39688	.0.2787	.41284	.91080	37
24	.34857	.93728	.36488	.93106	.38107	.92455	.39715	.91775	.41310	.91068	36
25	.34884	.93718	.36515	.93095	.38134	.92444	.39741	.91764	.41337	.91056	35
26	.34912	.93708	.36542	.93084	.38161	.92432	.39768	.91752	.41363	.91044	34
27	.34939	.93698	.36569	.93074	.38188	.92421	.39795	.91741	.41390	.91032	33
28	.34966	.93688	.36596	.93063	.38215	.92410	.39822	.91729	.41416	.91020	32
29	.34993	.93677	.36623	.93052	.38241	.92399	.39848	.91718	.41443	.91008	31
30	.35021	.93667	.36650	.93042	.38268	.92388	.39875	.91706	.41469	.90996	30
31	.35048	.93657	.36677	.93031	.38295	.92377	.39902	.91694	.41496	.90984	29
32	.35075	.93647	.36704	.93020	.38322	.92366	.39928	.91683	.41522	.90972	28
33	.35102	.93637	.36731	.93010	.38349	.92355	.39955	.91671	.41549	.90960	27
34	.35130	.93626	.36758	.92999	.38376	.92343	.39982	.91660	.41575	.90948	26
35	.35157	.93616	.36785	.92988	.38403	.92332	.40008	.91648	.41602	.90936	25
36	.35184	.93606	.36812	.92978	.38430	.92321	.40035	.91636	.41628	.90924	24
37	.35211	.93596	.36839	.92967	.38456	.92310	.40062	.91625	.41655	.90911	23
38	.35239	.93585	.36867	.92956	.38483	.92299	.40088	.91613	.41681	.90899	22
39	.35266	.93575	.36894	.92945	.38510	.92287	.40115	.91601	.41707	.90887	21
40	.35293	.93565	.36921	.92935	.38537	.92276	.40141	.91590	.41734	.90875	20
41	.35320	.93555	.36948	.92924	.38564	.92265	.40168	.91578	.41760	.90863	19
42	.35347	.93544	.36975	.92913	.38591	.92254	.40195	.91566	.41787	.90851	18
43	.35375	.93534	.37002	.92902	.38617	.92243	.40221	.91555	.41813	.90839	17
44	.35402	.93524	.37029	.92892	.38644	.92231	.40248	.91543	.41840	.90826	16
45	.35429	.93514	.37056	.92881	.38671	.92220	.40275	.91531	.41866	.90814	15
46	.35456	.93503	.37083	.92870	.38698	.92209	.40301	.91519	.41892	.90802	14
47	.35484	.93493	.37110	.92859	.38725	.92198	.40328	.91508	.41919	.90790	13
48	.35511	.93483	.37137	.92849	.38752	.92186	.40355	.91496	.41945	.90778	12
49	.35538	.93472	.37164	.92838	.38778	.92175	.40381	.91484	.41972	.90766	11
50	.35565	.93462	.37191	.92827	.38805	.92164	.40408	.91472	.41998	.90753	10
51	.35592	.93452	.37218	.92816	.38832	.92152	.40434	.91461	.42024	.90741	9
52	.35619	.93441	.37245	.92805	.38859	.92141	.40461	.91449	.42051	.90729	8
53	.35647	.93431	.37272	.92794	.38886	.92130	.40488	.91437	.42077	.90717	7
54	.35674	.93420	.37299	.92784	.38912	.92119	.40514	.91425	.42104	.90704	6
55	.35701	.93410	.37326	.92773	.38939	.92107	.40541	.91414	.42130	.90692	5
56	.35728	.93400	.37353	.92762	.38966	.92096	.40567	.91402	.42156	.90680	4
57	.35755	.93389	.37380	.92751	.38993	.92085	.40594	.91390	.42183	.90668	3
58	.35782	.93379	.37407	.92740	.39020	.92073	.40621	.91378	.42209	.90655	2
59	.35810	.93368	.37434	.92729	.39046	.92062	.40647	.91366	.42235	.90643	1
60	.35837	.93358	.37461	.92718	.39073	.92050	.40674	.91355	.42262	.90631	0
′	Cosine	Sine	Cosine	Sine	Cosine	Sine	Cosine	Sine	Cosine	Sine	′
	69°		68°		67°		66°		65°		

401

′	25°		26°		27°		28°		29°		′
	Sine	Cosine	Sine	Cosine	Sine	Cosine	Sine	Cosine	Sine	Cosine	
0	.42262	.90631	.43837	.89879	.45399	.89101	.46947	.88295	.48481	.87462	60
1	.42288	.90618	.43863	.89867	.45425	.89087	.46973	.88281	.48506	.87448	59
2	.42315	.90606	.43889	.89854	.45451	.89074	.46999	.88267	.48532	.87434	58
3	.42341	.90594	.43916	.89841	.45477	.89061	.47024	.88254	.48557	.87420	57
4	.42367	.90582	.43942	.89828	.45503	.89048	.47050	.88240	.48583	.87406	56
5	.42394	.90569	.43968	.89816	.45529	.89035	.47076	.88226	.48608	.87391	55
6	.42420	.90557	.43994	.89803	.45554	.89021	.47101	.88213	.48634	.87377	54
7	.42446	.90545	.44020	.89790	.45580	.89008	.47127	.88199	.48659	.87363	53
8	.42473	.90532	.44046	.89777	.45606	.88995	.47153	.88185	.48684	.87349	52
9	.42499	.90520	.44072	.89764	.45632	.88981	.47178	.88172	.48710	.87335	51
10	.42525	.90507	.44098	.89752	.45658	.88968	.47204	.88158	.48735	.87331	50
11	.42552	.90495	.44124	.89739	.45684	.88955	.47229	.88144	.48761	.87306	49
12	.42578	.90483	.44151	.89726	.45710	.88942	.47255	.88130	.48786	.87292	48
13	.42604	.90470	.44177	.89713	.45736	.88928	.47281	.88117	.48811	.87278	47
14	.42631	.90458	.44203	.89700	.45762	.88915	.47306	.88103	.48837	.87264	46
15	.42657	.90446	.44229	.89687	.45787	.88902	.47332	.88089	.48862	.87250	45
16	.42683	.90433	.44255	.89674	.45813	.88888	.47358	.88075	.48888	.87235	44
17	.42709	.90421	.44281	.89662	.45839	.88875	.47383	.88062	.48913	.87221	43
18	.42736	.90408	.44307	.89649	.45865	.88862	.47409	.88048	.48938	.87207	42
19	.42762	.90396	.44333	.89636	.45891	.88848	.47434	.88034	.48964	.87193	41
20	.42788	.90383	.44359	.89623	.45917	.88835	.47460	.88020	.48989	.87178	40
21	.42815	.90371	.44385	.89610	.45942	.88822	.47486	.88006	.49014	.87164	39
22	.42841	.90358	.44411	.89597	.45968	.88808	.47511	.87993	.49040	.87150	38
23	.42867	.90346	.44437	.89584	.45994	.88795	.47537	.87979	.49065	.87136	37
24	.42894	.90334	.44464	.89571	.46020	.88782	.47562	.87965	.49090	.87121	36
25	.42920	.90321	.44490	.89558	.46046	.88768	.47588	.87951	.49116	.87107	35
26	.42946	.90309	.44516	.89545	.46072	.88755	.47614	.87937	.49141	.87093	34
27	.42972	.90296	.44542	.89532	.46097	.88741	.47639	.87923	.49166	.87079	33
28	.42999	.90284	.44568	.89519	.46123	.88728	.47665	.87909	.49192	.87064	32
29	.43025	.90271	.44594	.89506	.46149	.88715	.47690	.87896	.49217	.87050	31
30	.43051	.90259	.44620	.89493	.46175	.88701	.47716	.87882	.49242	.87036	30
31	.43077	.90246	.44646	.89480	.46201	.88688	.47741	.87868	.49268	.87021	29
32	.43104	.90233	.44672	.89467	.46226	.88674	.47767	.87854	.49293	.87007	28
33	.43130	.90221	.44698	.89454	.46252	.88661	.47793	.87840	.49318	.86993	27
34	.43156	.90208	.44724	.89441	.46278	.88647	.47818	.87826	.49344	.86978	26
35	.43182	.90196	.44750	.89428	.46304	.88634	.47844	.87812	.49369	.86964	25
36	.43209	.90183	.44776	.89415	.46330	.88620	.47869	.87798	.49394	.86949	24
37	.43235	.90171	.44802	.89402	.46355	.88607	.47895	.87784	.49419	.86935	23
38	.43261	.90158	.44828	.89389	.46381	.88593	.47920	.87770	.49445	.86921	22
39	.43287	.90146	.44854	.89376	.46407	.88580	.47946	.87756	.49470	.86906	21
40	.43313	.90133	.44880	.89363	.46433	.88566	.47971	.87743	.49495	.86892	20
41	.43340	.90120	.44906	.89350	.46458	.88553	.47997	.87729	.49521	.86878	19
42	.43366	.90108	.44932	.89337	.46484	.88539	.48022	.87715	.49546	.86863	18
43	.43392	.90095	.44958	.89324	.46510	.88526	.48048	.87701	.49571	.86849	17
44	.43418	.90082	.44984	.89311	.46536	.88512	.48073	.87687	.49596	.86834	16
45	.43445	.90070	.45010	.89298	.46561	.88499	.48099	.87673	.49622	.86820	15
46	.43471	.90057	.45036	.89285	.46587	.88485	.48124	.87659	.49647	.86805	14
47	.43497	.90045	.45062	.89272	.46613	.88472	.48150	.87645	.49672	.86791	13
48	.43523	.90032	.45088	.89259	.46639	.88458	.48175	.87631	.49697	.86777	12
49	.43549	.90019	.45114	.89245	.46664	.88445	.48201	.87617	.49723	.86762	11
50	.43575	.90007	.45140	.89232	.46690	.88431	.48226	.87603	.49748	.86748	10
51	.43602	.89994	.45166	.89219	.46716	.88417	.48252	.87589	.49773	.86733	9
52	.43628	.89981	.45192	.89206	.46742	.88404	.48277	.87575	.49798	.86719	8
53	.43654	.89968	.45218	.89193	.46767	.88390	.48303	.87561	.49824	.86704	7
54	.43680	.89956	.45243	.89180	.46793	.88377	.48328	.87546	.49849	.86690	6
55	.43706	.89943	.45269	.89167	.46819	.88363	.48354	.87532	.49874	.86675	5
56	.43733	.89930	.45295	.89153	.46844	.88349	.48379	.87518	.49899	.86661	4
57	.43759	.89918	.45321	.89140	.46870	.88336	.48405	.87504	.49924	.86646	3
58	.43785	.89905	.45347	.89127	.46896	.88322	.48430	.87490	.49950	.86632	2
59	.43811	.89892	.45373	.89114	.46921	.88308	.48456	.87476	.49975	.86617	1
60	.43837	.89879	.45399	.89101	.46947	.88295	.48481	.87462	.50000	.86603	0
′	Cosine	Sine	Cosine	Sine	Cosine	Sine	Cosine	Sine	Cosine	Sine	′
	64°		63°		62°		61°		60°		

TABLE E.—NATURAL SINES AND COSINES

′	30° Sine	30° Cosine	31° Sine	31° Cosine	32° Sine	32° Cosine	33° Sine	33° Cosine	34° Sine	34° Cosine	′
0	.50000	.86603	.51504	.85717	.52992	.84805	.54464	.83867	.55919	.82904	60
1	.50025	.86588	.51529	.85702	.53017	.84789	.54488	.83851	.55943	.82887	59
2	.50050	.86573	.51554	.85687	.53041	.84774	.54513	.83835	.55968	.82871	58
3	.50076	.86559	.51579	.85672	.53066	.84759	.54537	.83819	.55992	.82855	57
4	.50101	.86544	.51604	.85657	.53091	.84743	.54561	.838c4	.56016	.82839	56
5	.50126	.86530	.51628	.85642	.53115	.84728	.54586	.83788	.56040	.82822	55
6	.50151	.86515	.51653	.85627	.53140	.84712	.54610	.83772	.56064	.82806	54
7	.50176	.86501	.51678	.85612	.53164	.84697	.54635	.83756	.56088	.82790	53
8	.50201	.86486	.51703	.85597	.53189	.84681	.54659	.83740	.56112	.82773	52
9	.50227	.86471	.51728	.85582	.53214	.84666	.54683	.83724	.56136	.82757	51
10	.50252	.86457	.51753	.85567	.53238	.84650	.54708	.83708	.56160	.82741	50
11	.50277	.86442	.51778	.85551	.53263	.84635	.54732	.83692	.56184	.82724	49
12	.50302	.86427	.51803	.85536	.53288	.84619	.54756	.83676	.56208	.82708	48
13	.50327	.86413	.51828	.85521	.53312	.84604	.54781	.83660	.56232	.82692	47
14	.50352	.86398	.51852	.85506	.53337	.84588	.54805	.83645	.56256	.82675	46
15	.50377	.86384	.51877	.85491	.53361	.84573	.54829	.83629	.56280	.82659	45
16	.50403	.86369	.51902	.85476	.53386	.84557	.54854	.83613	.56305	.82643	44
17	.50428	.86354	.51927	.85461	.53411	.84542	.54878	.83597	.56329	.82626	43
18	.50453	.86340	.51952	.85446	.53435	.84526	.54902	.83581	.56353	.82610	42
19	.50478	.86325	.51977	.85431	.53460	.84511	.54927	.83565	.56377	.82593	41
20	.50503	.86310	.52002	.85416	.53484	.84495	.54951	.83549	.56401	.82577	40
21	.50528	.86295	.52026	.85401	.53509	.84480	.54975	.83533	.56425	.82561	39
22	.50553	.86281	.52051	.85385	.53534	.84464	.54999	.83517	.56449	.82544	38
23	.50578	.86266	.52076	.85370	.53558	.84448	.55024	.83501	.56473	.82528	37
24	.50603	.86251	.52101	.85355	.53583	.84433	.55048	.83485	.56497	.82511	36
25	.50628	.86237	.52126	.85340	.53607	.84417	.55072	.83469	.56521	.82495	35
26	.50654	.86222	.52151	.85325	.53632	.84402	.55097	.83453	.56545	.82478	34
27	.50679	.86207	.52175	.85310	.53656	.84386	.55121	.83437	.56569	.82462	33
28	.50704	.86192	.52200	.85294	.53681	.84370	.55145	.83421	.56593	.82446	32
29	.50729	.86178	.52225	.85279	.53705	.84355	.55169	.83405	.56617	.82429	31
30	.50754	.86163	.52250	.85264	.53730	.84339	.55194	.83389	.56641	.82413	30
31	.50779	.86148	.52275	.85249	.53754	.84324	.55218	.83373	.56665	.82396	29
32	.50804	.86133	.52299	.85234	.53779	.84308	.55242	.83356	.56689	.82380	28
33	.50829	.86119	.52324	.85218	.53804	.84292	.55266	.83340	.56713	.82363	27
34	.50854	.86104	.52349	.85203	.53828	.84277	.55291	.83324	.56736	.82347	26
35	.50879	.86089	.52374	.85188	.53853	.84261	.55315	.83308	.56760	.82330	25
36	.50904	.86074	.52399	.85173	.53877	.84245	.55339	.83292	.56784	.82314	24
37	.50929	.86059	.52423	.85157	.53902	.84230	.55363	.83276	.56808	.82297	23
38	.50954	.86045	.52448	.85142	.53926	.84214	.55388	.83260	.56832	.82281	22
39	.50979	.86030	.52473	.85127	.53951	.84198	.55412	.83244	.56856	.82264	21
40	.51004	.86015	.52498	.85112	.53975	.84182	.55436	.83228	.56880	.82248	20
41	.51029	.86000	.52522	.85096	.54000	.84167	.55460	.83212	.56904	.82231	19
42	.51054	.85985	.52547	.85081	.54024	.84151	.55484	.83195	.56928	.82214	18
43	.51079	.85970	.52572	.85066	.54049	.84135	.55509	.83179	.56952	.82198	17
44	.51104	.85956	.52597	.85051	.54073	.84120	.55533	.83163	.56976	.82181	16
45	.51129	.85941	.52621	.85035	.54097	.84104	.55557	.83147	.57000	.82165	15
46	.51154	.85926	.52646	.85020	.54122	.84088	.55581	.83131	.57024	.82148	14
47	.51179	.85911	.52671	.85005	.54146	.84072	.55605	.83115	.57047	.82132	13
48	.51204	.85896	.52696	.84989	.54171	.84057	.55630	.83098	.57071	.82115	12
49	.51229	.85881	.52720	.84974	.54195	.84041	.55654	.83082	.57095	.82098	11
50	.51254	.85866	.52745	.84959	.54220	.84025	.55678	.83066	.57119	.82082	10
51	.51279	.85851	.52770	.84943	.54244	.84009	.55702	.83050	.57143	.82065	9
52	.51304	.85836	.52794	.84928	.54269	.83994	.55726	.83034	.57167	.82048	8
53	.51329	.85821	.52819	.84913	.54293	.83978	.55750	.83017	.57191	.82032	7
54	.51354	.85806	.52844	.84897	.54317	.83962	.55775	.83001	.57215	.82015	6
55	.51379	.85792	.52869	.84882	.54342	.83946	.55799	.82985	.57238	.81999	5
56	.51404	.85777	.52893	.84866	.54366	.83930	.55823	.82969	.57262	.81982	4
57	.51429	.85762	.52918	.84851	.54391	.83915	.55847	.82953	.57286	.81965	3
58	.51454	.85747	.52943	.84836	.54415	.83899	.55871	.82936	.57310	.81949	2
59	.51479	.85732	.52967	.84820	.54440	.83883	.55895	.82920	.57334	.81932	1
60	.51504	.85717	.52992	.84805	.54464	.83867	.55919	.82904	.57358	.81915	0
′	Cosine	Sine	Cosine	Sine	Cosine	Sine	Cosine	Sine	Cosine	Sine	′
	59°		58°		57°		56°		55°		

TABLE E.—NATURAL SINES AND COSINES

′	35° Sine	35° Cosine	36° Sine	36° Cosine	37° Sine	37° Cosine	38° Sine	38° Cosine	39° Sine	39° Cosine	′
0	.57358	.81915	.58779	.80902	.60182	.79864	.61566	.78801	.62932	.77715	60
1	.57381	.81899	.58802	.80885	.60205	.79846	.61589	.78783	.62955	.77696	59
2	.57405	.81882	.58826	.80867	.60228	.79829	.61612	.78765	.62977	.77678	58
3	.57429	.81865	.58849	.80850	.60251	.79811	.61635	.78747	.63000	.77660	57
4	.57453	.81848	.58873	.80833	.60274	.79793	.61658	.78729	.63022	.77641	56
5	.57477	.81832	.58896	.80816	.60298	.79776	.61681	.78711	.63045	.77623	55
6	.57501	.81815	.58920	.80799	.60321	.79758	.61704	.78694	.63068	.77605	54
7	.57524	.81798	.58943	.80782	.60344	.79741	.61726	.78676	.63090	.77586	53
8	.57548	.81782	.58967	.80765	.60367	.79723	.61749	.78658	.63113	.77568	52
9	.57572	.81765	.58990	.80748	.60390	.79706	.61772	.78640	.63135	.77550	51
10	.57596	.81748	.59014	.80730	.60414	.79688	.61795	.78622	.63158	.77531	50
11	.57619	.81731	.59037	.80713	.60437	.79671	.61818	.78604	.63180	.77513	49
12	.57643	.81714	.59061	.80696	.60460	.79653	.61841	.78586	.63203	.77494	48
13	.57667	.81698	.59084	.80679	.60483	.79635	.61864	.78568	.63225	.77476	47
14	.57691	.81681	.59108	.80662	.60506	.79618	.61887	.78550	.63248	.77458	46
15	.57715	.81664	.59131	.80644	.60529	.79600	.61909	.78532	.63271	.77439	45
16	.57738	.81647	.59154	.80627	.60553	.79583	.61932	.78514	.63293	.77421	44
17	.57762	.81631	.59178	.80610	.60576	.79565	.61955	.78496	.63316	.77402	43
18	.57786	.81614	.59201	.80593	.60599	.79547	.61978	.78478	.63338	.77384	42
19	.57810	.81597	.59225	.80576	.60622	.79530	.62001	.78460	.63361	.77366	41
20	.57833	.81580	.59248	.80558	.60645	.79512	.62024	.78442	.63383	.77347	40
21	.57857	.81563	.59272	.80541	.60668	.79494	.62046	.78424	.63406	.77329	39
22	.57881	.81546	.59295	.80524	.60691	.79477	.62069	.78405	.63428	.77310	38
23	.57904	.81530	.59318	.80507	.60714	.79459	.62092	.78387	.63451	.77292	37
24	.57928	.81513	.59342	.80489	.60738	.79441	.62115	.78369	.63473	.77273	36
25	.57952	.81496	.59365	.80472	.60761	.79424	.62138	.78351	.63496	.77255	35
26	.57976	.81479	.59389	.80455	.60784	.79406	.62160	.78333	.63518	.77236	34
27	.57999	.81462	.59412	.80438	.60807	.79388	.62183	.78315	.63540	.77218	33
28	.58023	.81445	.59436	.80420	.60830	.79371	.62206	.78297	.63563	.77199	32
29	.58047	.81428	.59459	.80403	.60853	.79353	.62229	.78279	.63585	.77181	31
30	.58070	.81412	.59482	.80386	.60876	.79335	.62251	.78261	.63608	.77162	30
31	.58094	.81395	.59506	.80368	.60899	.79318	.62274	.78243	.63630	.77144	29
32	.58118	.81378	.59529	.80351	.60922	.79300	.62297	.78225	.63653	.77125	28
33	.58141	.81361	.59552	.80334	.60945	.79282	.62320	.78206	.63675	.77107	27
34	.58165	.81344	.59576	.80316	.60968	.79264	.62342	.78188	.63698	.77088	26
35	.58189	.81327	.59599	.80299	.60991	.79247	.62365	.78170	.63720	.77070	25
36	.58212	.81310	.59622	.80282	.61015	.79229	.62388	.78152	.63742	.77051	24
37	.58236	.81293	.59646	.80264	.61038	.79211	.62411	.78134	.63765	.77033	23
38	.58260	.81276	.59669	.80247	.61061	.79193	.62433	.78116	.63787	.77014	22
39	.58283	.81259	.59693	.80230	.61084	.79176	.62456	.78098	.63810	.76996	21
40	.58307	.81242	.59716	.80212	.61107	.79158	.62479	.78079	.63832	.76977	20
41	.58330	.81225	.59739	.80195	.61130	.79140	.62502	.78061	.63854	.76959	19
42	.58354	.81208	.59763	.80178	.61153	.79122	.62524	.78043	.63877	.76940	18
43	.58378	.81191	.59786	.80160	.61176	.79105	.62547	.78025	.63899	.76921	17
44	.58401	.81174	.59809	.80143	.61199	.79087	.62570	.78007	.63922	.76903	16
45	.58425	.81157	.59832	.80125	.61222	.79069	.62592	.77988	.63944	.76884	15
46	.58449	.81140	.59856	.80108	.61245	.79051	.62615	.77970	.63966	.76866	14
47	.58472	.81123	.59879	.80091	.61268	.79033	.62638	.77952	.63989	.76847	13
48	.58496	.81106	.59902	.80073	.61291	.79016	.62660	.77934	.64011	.76828	12
49	.58519	.81089	.59926	.80056	.61314	.78998	.62683	.77916	.64033	.76810	11
50	.58543	.81072	.59949	.80038	.61337	.78980	.62706	.77897	.64056	.76791	10
51	.58567	.81055	.59972	.80021	.61360	.78962	.62728	.77879	.64078	.76772	9
52	.58590	.81038	.59995	.80003	.61383	.78944	.62751	.77861	.64100	.76754	8
53	.58614	.81021	.60019	.79986	.61406	.78926	.62774	.77843	.64123	.76735	7
54	.58637	.81004	.60042	.79968	.61429	.78908	.62796	.77824	.64145	.76717	6
55	.58661	.80987	.60065	.79951	.61451	.78891	.62819	.77806	.64167	.76698	5
56	.58684	.80970	.60089	.79934	.61474	.78873	.62842	.77788	.64190	.76679	4
57	.58708	.80953	.60112	.79916	.61497	.78855	.62864	.77769	.64212	.76661	3
58	.58731	.80936	.60135	.79899	.61520	.78837	.62887	.77751	.64234	.76642	2
59	.58755	.80919	.60158	.79881	.61543	.78819	.62909	.77733	.64256	.76623	1
60	.58779	.80902	.60182	.79864	.61566	.78801	.62932	.77715	.64279	.76604	0
′	Cosine	Sine	Cosine	Sine	Cosine	Sine	Cosine	Sine	Cosine	Sine	′
	54°		53°		52°		51°		50°		

TABLE E.—NATURAL SINES AND COSINES

′	40° Sine	40° Cosine	41° Sine	41° Cosine	42° Sine	42° Cosine	43° Sine	43° Cosine	44° Sine	44° Cosine	′
0	.64279	.76604	.65606	.75471	.66913	.74314	.68200	.73135	.69466	.71934	60
1	.64301	.76586	.65628	.75452	.66935	.74295	.68221	.73116	.69487	.71914	59
2	.64323	.76567	.65650	.75433	.66956	.74276	.68242	.73096	.69508	.71894	58
3	.64346	.76548	.65672	.75414	.66978	.74256	.68264	.73076	.69529	.71873	57
4	.64368	.76530	.65694	.75395	.66999	.74237	.68285	.73056	.69549	.71853	56
5	.64390	.76511	.65716	.75375	.67021	.74217	.68306	.73036	.69570	.71833	55
6	.64412	.76492	.65738	.75356	.67043	.74198	.68327	.73016	.69591	.71813	54
7	.64435	.76473	.65759	.75337	.67064	.74178	.68349	.72996	.69612	.71792	53
8	.64457	.76455	.65781	.75318	.67086	.74159	.68370	.72976	.69633	.71772	52
9	.64479	.76436	.65803	.75299	.67107	.74139	.68391	.72957	.69654	.71752	51
10	.64501	.76417	.65825	.75280	.67129	.74120	.68412	.72937	.69675	.71732	50
11	.64524	.76398	.65847	.75261	.67151	.74100	.68434	.72917	.69696	.71711	49
12	.64546	.76380	.65869	.75241	.67172	.74080	.68455	.72897	.69717	.71691	48
13	.64568	.76361	.65891	.75222	.67194	.74061	.68476	.72877	.69737	.71671	47
14	.64590	.76342	.65913	.75203	.67215	.74041	.68497	.72857	.69758	.71650	46
15	.64612	.76323	.65935	.75184	.67237	.74022	.68518	.72837	.69779	.71630	45
16	.64635	.76304	.65956	.75165	.67258	.74002	.68539	.72817	.69800	.71610	44
17	.64657	.76286	.65978	.75146	.67280	.73983	.68561	.72797	.69821	.71590	43
18	.64679	.76267	.66000	.75126	.67301	.73963	.68582	.72777	.69842	.71569	42
19	.64701	.76248	.66022	.75107	.67323	.73944	.68603	.72757	.69862	.71549	41
20	.64723	.76229	.66044	.75088	.67344	.73924	.68624	.72737	.69883	.71529	40
21	.64746	.76210	.66066	.75069	.67366	.73904	.68645	.72717	.69904	.71508	39
22	.64768	.76192	.66088	.75050	.67387	.73885	.68666	.72697	.69925	.71488	38
23	.64790	.76173	.66109	.75030	.67409	.73865	.68688	.72677	.69946	.71468	37
24	.64812	.76154	.66131	.75011	.67430	.73846	.68709	.72657	.69966	.71447	36
25	.64834	.76135	.66153	.74992	.67452	.73826	.68730	.72637	.69987	.71427	35
26	.64856	.76116	.66175	.74973	.67473	.73806	.68751	.72617	.70008	.71407	34
27	.64878	.76097	.66197	.74953	.67495	.73787	.68772	.72597	.70029	.71386	33
28	.64901	.76078	.66218	.74934	.67516	.73767	.68793	.72577	.70049	.71366	32
29	.64923	.76059	.66240	.74915	.67538	.73747	.68814	.72557	.70070	.71345	31
30	.64945	.76041	.66262	.74896	.67559	.73728	.68835	.72537	.70091	.71325	30
31	.64967	.76022	.66284	.74876	.67580	.73708	.68857	.72517	.70112	.71305	29
32	.64989	.76003	.66306	.74857	.67602	.73688	.68878	.72497	.70132	.71284	28
33	.65011	.75984	.66327	.74838	.67623	.73669	.68899	.72477	.70153	.71264	27
34	.65033	.75965	.66349	.74818	.67645	.73649	.68920	.72457	.70174	.71243	26
35	.65055	.75946	.66371	.74799	.67666	.73629	.68941	.72437	.70195	.71223	25
36	.65077	.75927	.66393	.74780	.67688	.73610	.68962	.72417	.70215	.71203	24
37	.65100	.75908	.66414	.74760	.67709	.73590	.68983	.72397	.70236	.71182	23
38	.65122	.75889	.66436	.74741	.67730	.73570	.69004	.72377	.70257	.71162	22
39	.65144	.75870	.66458	.74722	.67752	.73551	.69025	.72357	.70277	.71141	21
40	.65166	.75851	.66480	.74703	.67773	.73531	.69046	.72337	.70298	.71121	20
41	.65188	.75832	.66501	.74683	.67795	.73511	.69067	.72317	.70319	.71100	19
42	.65210	.75813	.66523	.74664	.67816	.73491	.69088	.72297	.70339	.71080	18
43	.65232	.75794	.66545	.74644	.67837	.73472	.69109	.72277	.70360	.71059	17
44	.65254	.75775	.66566	.74625	.67859	.73452	.69130	.72257	.70381	.71039	16
45	.65276	.75756	.66588	.74606	.67880	.73432	.69151	.72236	.70401	.71019	15
46	.65298	.75738	66610	.74586	.67901	.73413	.69172	.72216	.70422	.70998	14
47	.65320	.75719	.66632	.74567	.67923	.73393	.69193	.72196	.70443	.70978	13
48	.65342	.75700	.66653	.74548	.67944	.73373	.69214	.72176	.70463	.70957	12
49	.65364	.75680	.66675	.74528	.67965	.73353	.69235	.72156	.70484	.70937	11
50	.65386	.75661	.66697	.74509	.67987	.73333	.69256	.72136	.70505	.70916	10
51	.65408	.75642	.66718	.74489	.68008	.73314	.69277	.72116	.70525	.70896	9
52	.65430	.75623	.66740	.74470	.68029	.73294	.69298	.72095	.70546	.70875	8
53	.65452	.75604	.66762	.74451	.68051	.73274	.69319	.72075	.70567	.70855	7
54	.65474	.75585	.66783	.74431	.68072	.73254	.69340	.72055	.70587	.70834	6
55	.65496	.75566	.66805	.74412	.68093	.73234	.69361	.72035	.70608	.70813	5
56	.65518	.75547	.66827	.74392	.68115	.73215	.69382	.72015	.70628	.70793	4
57	.65540	.75528	.66848	.74373	.68136	.73195	.69403	.71995	.70649	.70772	3
58	.65562	.75509	.66870	.74353	.68157	.73175	.69424	.71974	.70670	.70752	2
59	.65584	.75490	.66891	.74334	.68179	.73155	.69445	.71954	.70690	.70731	1
60	.65606	.75471	.66913	.74314	.68200	.73135	.69466	.71934	.70711	.70711	0
′	Cosine	Sine	Cosine	Sine	Cosine	Sine	Cosine	Sine	Cosine	Sine	′
	49°		48°		47°		46°		45°		

′	0° Tang	0° Cotang	1° Tang	1° Cotang	2° Tang	2° Cotang	3° Tang	3° Cotang	4° Tang	4° Cotang	′
0	.00000	Infinite	.01746	57.2900	.03492	28.6363	.05241	19.0811	.06993	14.3007	60
1	.00029	3437.75	.01775	56.3506	.03521	28.3994	.05270	18.9755	.07022	14.2411	59
2	.00058	1718.87	.01804	55.4415	.03550	28.1664	.05299	18.8711	.07051	14.1821	58
3	.00087	1145.92	.01833	54.5613	.03579	27.9372	.05328	18.7678	.07080	14.1235	57
4	.00116	859.436	.01862	53.7086	.03609	27.7117	.05357	18.6656	.07110	14.0655	56
5	.00145	687.549	.01891	52.8821	.03638	27.4899	.05387	18.5645	.07139	14.0079	55
6	.00175	572.957	.01920	52.0807	.03667	27.2715	.05416	18.4645	.07168	13.9507	54
7	.00204	491.106	.01949	51.3032	.03696	27.0566	.05445	18.3655	.07197	13.8940	53
8	.00233	429.718	.01978	50.5485	.03725	26.8450	.05474	18.2677	.07227	13.8378	52
9	.00262	381.971	.02007	49.8157	.03754	26.6367	.05503	18.1708	.07256	13.7821	51
10	.00291	343.774	.02036	49.1039	.03783	26.4316	.05533	18.0750	.07285	13.7267	50
11	.00320	312.521	.02066	48.4121	.03812	26.2296	.05562	17.9802	.07314	13.6719	49
12	.00349	286.478	.02095	47.7395	.03842	26.0307	.05591	17.8863	.07344	13.6174	48
13	.00378	264.441	.02124	47.0853	.03871	25.8348	.05620	17.7934	.07373	13.5634	47
14	.00407	245.552	.02153	46.4489	.03900	25.6418	.05649	17.7015	.07402	13.5098	46
15	.00436	229.182	.02182	45.8294	.03929	25.4517	.05678	17.6106	.07431	13.4566	45
16	.00465	214.858	.02211	45.2261	.03958	25.2644	.05708	17.5205	.07461	13.4039	44
17	.00495	202.219	.02240	44.6386	.03987	25.0798	.05737	17.4314	.07490	13.3515	43
18	.00524	190.984	.02269	44.0661	.04016	24.8978	.05766	17.3432	.07519	13.2996	42
19	.00553	180.932	.02298	43.5081	.04046	24.7185	.05795	17.2558	.07548	13.2480	41
20	.00582	171.885	.02328	42.9641	.04075	24.5418	.05824	17.1693	.07578	13.1969	40
21	.00611	163.700	.02357	42.4335	.04104	24.3675	.05854	17.0837	.07607	13.1461	39
22	.00640	156.259	.02386	41.9158	.04133	24.1957	.05883	16.9990	.07636	13.0958	38
23	.00669	149.465	.02415	41.4106	.04162	24.0263	.05912	16.9150	.07665	13.0458	37
24	.00698	143.237	.02444	40.9174	.04191	23.8593	.05941	16.8319	.07695	12.9962	36
25	.00727	137.507	.02473	40.4358	.04220	23.6945	.05970	16.7496	.07724	12.9469	35
26	.00756	132.219	.02502	39.9655	.04250	23.5321	.05999	16.6681	.07753	12.8981	34
27	.00785	127.321	.02531	39.5059	.04279	23.3718	.06029	16.5874	.07782	12.8496	33
28	.00815	122.774	.02560	39.0568	.04308	23.2137	.06058	16.5075	.07812	12.8014	32
29	.00844	118.540	.02589	38.6177	.04337	23.0577	.06087	16.4283	.07841	12.7536	31
30	.00873	114.589	.02619	38.1885	.04366	22.9038	.06116	16.3499	.07870	12.7062	30
31	.00902	110.892	.02648	37.7686	.04395	22.7519	.06145	16.2722	.07899	12.6591	29
32	.00931	107.426	.02677	37.3579	.04424	22.6020	.06175	16.1952	.07929	12.6124	28
33	.00960	104.171	.02706	36.9560	.04454	22.4541	.06204	16.1190	.07958	12.5660	27
34	.00989	101.107	.02735	36.5627	.04483	22.3081	.06233	16.0435	.07987	12.5199	26
35	.01018	98.2179	.02764	36.1776	.04512	22.1640	.06262	15.9687	.08017	12.4742	25
36	.01047	95.4895	.02793	35.8006	.04541	22.0217	.06291	15.8945	.08046	12.4288	24
37	.01076	92.9085	.02822	35.4313	.04570	21.8813	.06321	15.8211	.08075	12.3838	23
38	.01105	90.4633	.02851	35.0695	.04599	21.7426	.06350	15.7483	.08104	12.3390	22
39	.01135	88.1436	.02881	34.7151	.04628	21.6056	.06379	15.6762	.08134	12.2946	21
40	.01164	85.9398	.02910	34.3678	.04658	21.4704	.06408	15.6048	.08163	12.2505	20
41	.01193	83.8435	.02939	34.0273	.04687	21.3369	.06437	15.5340	.08192	12.2067	19
42	.01222	81.8470	.02968	33.6935	.04716	21.2049	.06467	15.4638	.08221	12.1632	18
43	.01251	79.9434	.02997	33.3662	.04745	21.0747	.06496	15.3943	.08251	12.1201	17
44	.01280	78.1263	.03026	33.0452	.04774	20.9460	.06525	15.3254	.08280	12.0772	16
45	.01309	76.3900	.03055	32.7303	.04803	20.8188	.06554	15.2571	.08309	12.0346	15
46	.01338	74.7292	.03084	32.4213	.04833	20.6932	.06584	15.1893	.08339	11.9923	14
47	.01367	73.1390	.03114	32.1181	.04862	20.5691	.06613	15.1222	.08368	11.9504	13
48	.01396	71.6151	.03143	31.8205	.04891	20.4465	.06642	15.0557	.08397	11.9087	12
49	.01425	70.1533	.03172	31.5284	.04920	20.3253	.06671	14.9898	.08427	11.8673	11
50	.01455	68.7501	.03201	31.2416	.04949	20.2056	.06700	14.9244	.08456	11.8262	10
51	.01484	67.4019	.03230	30.9599	.04978	20.0872	.06730	14.8596	.08485	11.7853	9
52	.01513	66.1055	.03259	30.6833	.05007	19.9702	.06759	14.7954	.08514	11.7448	8
53	.01542	64.8580	.03288	30.4116	.05037	19.8546	.06788	14.7317	.08544	11.7045	7
54	.01571	63.6567	.03317	30.1446	.05066	19.7403	.06817	14.6685	.08573	11.6645	6
55	.01600	62.4992	.03346	29.8823	.05095	19.6273	.06847	14.6059	.08602	11.6248	5
56	.01629	61.3829	.03376	29.6245	.05124	19.5156	.06876	14.5438	.08632	11.5853	4
57	.01658	60.3058	.03405	29.3711	.05153	19.4051	.06905	14.4823	.08661	11.5461	3
58	.01687	59.2659	.03434	29.1220	.05182	19.2959	.06934	14.4212	.08690	11.5072	2
59	.01716	58.2612	.03463	28.8771	.05212	19.1879	.06963	14.3607	.08720	11.4685	1
60	.01746	57.2900	.03492	28.6363	.05241	19.0811	.06993	14.3007	.08749	11.4301	0
′	Cotang	Tang	Cotang	Tang	Cotang	Tang	Cotang	Tang	Cotang	Tang	′
	89°		88°		87°		86°		85°		

′	5° Tang	Cotang	6° Tang	Cotang	7° Tang	Cotang	8° Tang	Cotang	9° Tang	Cotang	′
0	.08749	11.4301	.10510	9.51436	.12278	8.14435	.14054	7.11537	.15838	6.31375	60
1	.08778	11.3919	.10540	9.48781	.12308	8.12481	.14084	7.10038	.15868	6.30189	59
2	.08807	11.3540	.10569	9.46141	.12338	8.10536	.14113	7.08546	.15898	6.29007	58
3	.08837	11.3163	.10599	9.43515	.12367	8.08600	.14143	7.07059	.15928	6.27829	57
4	.08866	11.2789	.10628	9.40904	.12397	8.06674	.14173	7.05579	.15958	6.26655	56
5	.08895	11.2417	.10657	9.38307	.12426	8.04756	.14202	7.04105	.15988	6.25486	55
6	.08925	11.2048	.10687	9.35724	.12456	8.02848	.14232	7.02637	.16017	6.24321	54
7	.08954	11.1681	.10716	9.33155	.12485	8.00948	.14262	7.01174	.16047	6.23160	53
8	.08983	11.1316	.10746	9.30599	.12515	7.99058	.14291	6.99718	.16077	6.22003	52
9	.09013	11.0954	.10775	9.28058	.12544	7.97176	.14321	6.98268	.16107	6.20851	51
10	.09042	11.0594	.10805	9.25530	.12574	7.95302	.14351	6.96823	.16137	6.19703	50
11	.09071	11.0237	.10834	9.23016	.12603	7.93438	.14381	6.95385	.16167	6.18559	49
12	.09101	10.9882	.10863	9.20516	.12633	7.91582	.14410	6.93952	.16196	6.17419	48
13	.09130	10.9529	.10893	9.18028	.12662	7.89734	.14440	6.92525	.16226	6.16283	47
14	.09159	10.9178	.10922	9.15554	.12692	7.87895	.14470	6.91104	.16256	6.15151	46
15	.09189	10.8829	.10952	9.13093	.12722	7.86064	.14499	6.89688	.16286	6.14023	45
16	.09218	10.8483	.10981	9.10646	.12751	7.84242	.14529	6.88278	.16316	6.12899	44
17	.09247	10.8139	.11011	9.08211	.12781	7.82428	.14559	6.86874	.16346	6.11779	43
18	.09277	10.7797	.11040	9.05789	.12810	7.80622	.14588	6.85475	.16376	6.10664	42
19	.09306	10.7457	.11070	9.03379	.12840	7.78825	.14618	6.84082	.16405	6.09552	41
20	.09335	10.7119	.11099	9.00983	.12869	7.77035	.14648	6.82694	.16435	6.08444	40
21	.09365	10.6783	.11128	8.98598	.12899	7.75254	.14678	6.81312	.16465	6.07340	39
22	.09394	10.6450	.11158	8.96227	.12929	7.73480	.14707	6.79936	.16495	6.06240	38
23	.09423	10.6118	.11187	8.93867	.12958	7.71715	.14737	6.78564	.16525	6.05143	37
24	.09453	10.5789	.11217	8.91520	.12988	7.69957	.14767	6.77199	.16555	6.04051	36
25	.09482	10.5462	.11246	8.89185	.13017	7.68208	.14796	6.75838	.16585	6.02962	35
26	.09511	10.5136	.11276	8.86862	.13047	7.66466	.14826	6.74483	.16615	6.01878	34
27	.09541	10.4813	.11305	8.84551	.13076	7.64732	.14856	6.73133	.16645	6.00797	33
28	.09570	10.4491	.11335	8.82252	.13106	7.63005	.14886	6.71789	.16674	5.99720	32
29	.09600	10.4172	.11364	8.79964	.13136	7.61287	.14915	6.70450	.16704	5.98646	31
30	.09629	10.3854	.11394	8.77689	.13165	7.59575	.14945	6.69116	.16734	5.97576	30
31	.09658	10.3538	.11423	8.75425	.13195	7.57872	.14975	6.67787	.16764	5.96510	29
32	.09688	10.3224	.11452	8.73172	.13224	7.56176	.15005	6.66463	.16794	5.95448	28
33	.09717	10.2913	.11482	8.70931	.13254	7.54487	.15034	6.65144	.16824	5.94390	27
34	.09746	10.2602	.11511	8.68701	.13284	7.52806	.15064	6.63831	.16854	5.93335	26
35	.09776	10.2294	.11541	8.66482	.13313	7.51132	.15094	6.62523	.16884	5.92283	25
36	.09805	10.1988	.11570	8.64275	.13343	7.49465	.15124	6.61219	.16914	5.91236	24
37	.09834	10.1683	.11600	8.62078	.13372	7.47806	.15153	6.59921	.16944	5.90191	23
38	.09864	10.1381	.11629	8.59893	.13402	7.46154	.15183	6.58627	.16974	5.89151	22
39	.09893	10.1080	.11659	8.57718	.13432	7.44509	.15213	6.57339	.17004	5.88114	21
40	.09923	10.0780	.11688	8.55555	.13461	7.42871	.15243	6.56055	.17033	5.87080	20
41	.09952	10.0483	.11718	8.53402	.13491	7.41240	.15272	6.54777	.17063	5.86051	19
42	.09981	10.0187	.11747	8.51259	.13521	7.39616	.15302	6.53503	.17093	5.85024	18
43	.10011	9.98931	.11777	8.49128	.13550	7.37999	.15332	6.52234	.17123	5.84001	17
44	.10040	9.96007	.11806	8.47007	.13580	7.36389	.15362	6.50970	.17153	5.82982	16
45	.10069	9.93101	.11836	8.44896	.13609	7.34786	.15391	6.49710	.17183	5.81966	15
46	.10099	9.90211	.11865	8.42795	.13639	7.33190	.15421	6.48456	.17213	5.80953	14
47	.10128	9.87338	.11895	8.40705	.13669	7.31600	.15451	6.47206	.17243	5.79944	13
48	.10158	9.84482	.11924	8.38625	.13698	7.30018	.15481	6.45961	.17273	5.78938	12
49	.10187	9.81641	.11954	8.36555	.13728	7.28442	.15511	6.44720	.17303	5.77936	11
50	.10216	9.78817	.11983	8.34496	.13758	7.26873	.15540	6.43484	.17333	5.76937	10
51	.10246	9.76009	.12013	8.32446	.13787	7.25310	.15570	6.42253	.17363	5.75941	9
52	.10275	9.73217	.12042	8.30406	.13817	7.23754	.15600	6.41026	.17393	5.74949	8
53	.10305	9.70441	.12072	8.28376	.13846	7.22204	.15630	6.39804	.17423	5.73960	7
54	.10334	9.67680	.12101	8.26355	.13876	7.20661	.15660	6.38587	.17453	5.72974	6
55	.10363	9.64935	.12131	8.24345	.13906	7.19125	.15689	6.37374	.17483	5.71992	5
56	.10393	9.62205	.12160	8.22344	.13935	7.17594	.15719	6.36165	.17513	5.71013	4
57	.10422	9.59490	.12190	8.20352	.13965	7.16071	.15749	6.34961	.17543	5.70037	3
58	.10452	9.56791	.12219	8.18370	.13995	7.14553	.15779	6.33761	.17573	5.69064	2
59	.10481	9.54106	.12249	8.16398	.14024	7.13042	.15809	6.32566	.17603	5.68094	1
60	.10510	9.51436	.12278	8.14435	.14054	7.11537	.15838	6.31375	.17633	5.67128	0
′	Cotang	Tang	Cotang	Tang	Cotang	Tang	Cotang	Tang	Cotang	Tang	′
	84°		83°		82°		81°		80°		

TABLE F.—NATURAL TANGENTS AND COTANGENTS

′	10° Tang	Cotang	11° Tang	Cotang	12° Tang	Cotang	13° Tang	Cotang	14° Tang	Cotang	′
0	.17633	5.67128	.19438	5.14455	.21256	4.70463	.23087	4.33148	.24933	4.01078	60
1	.17663	5.66165	.19468	5.13658	.21286	4.69791	.23117	4.32573	.24964	4.00582	59
2	.17693	5.65205	.19498	5.12862	.21316	4.69121	.23148	4.32001	.24995	4.00086	58
3	.17723	5.64248	.19529	5.12069	.21347	4.68452	.23179	4.31430	.25026	3.99592	57
4	.17753	5.63295	.19559	5.11279	.21377	4.67786	.23209	4.30860	.25056	3.99099	56
5	.17783	5.62344	.19589	5.10490	.21408	4.67121	.23240	4.30291	.25087	3.98607	55
6	.17813	5.61397	.19619	5.09704	.21438	4.66458	.23271	4.29724	.25118	3.98117	54
7	.17843	5.60452	.19649	5.08921	.21469	4.65797	.23301	4.29159	.25149	3.97627	53
8	.17873	5.59511	.19680	5.08139	.21499	4.65138	.23332	4.28595	.25180	3.97139	52
9	.17903	5.58573	.19710	5.07360	.21529	4.64480	.23363	4.28032	.25211	3.96651	51
10	.17933	5.57638	.19740	5.06584	.21560	4.63825	.23393	4.27471	.25242	3.96165	50
11	.17963	5.56706	.19770	5.05809	.21590	4.63171	.23424	4.26911	.25273	3.95680	49
12	.17993	5.55777	.19801	5.05037	.21621	4.62518	.23455	4.26352	.25304	3.95196	48
13	.18023	5.54851	.19831	5.04267	.21651	4.61868	.23485	4.25795	.25335	3.94713	47
14	.18053	5.53927	.19861	5.03499	.21682	4.61219	.23516	4.25239	.25366	3.94232	46
15	.18083	5.53007	.19891	5.02734	.21712	4.60572	.23547	4.24685	.25397	3.93751	45
16	.18113	5.52090	.19921	5.01971	.21743	4.59927	.23578	4.24132	.25428	3.93271	44
17	.18143	5.51176	.19952	5.01210	.21773	4.59283	.23608	4.23580	.25459	3.92793	43
18	.18173	5.50264	.19982	5.00451	.21804	4.58641	.23639	4.23030	.25490	3.92316	42
19	.18203	5.49356	.20012	4.99695	.21834	4.58001	.23670	4.22481	.25521	3.91839	41
20	.18233	5.48451	.20042	4.98940	.21864	4.57363	.23700	4.21933	.25552	3.91364	40
21	.18263	5.47548	.20073	4.98188	.21895	4.56726	.23731	4.21387	.25583	3.90890	39
22	.18293	5.46648	.20103	4.97438	.21925	4.56091	.23762	4.20842	.25614	3.90417	38
23	.18323	5.45751	.20133	4.96690	.21956	4.55458	.23793	4.20298	.25645	3.89945	37
24	.18353	5.44857	.20164	4.95945	.21986	4.54826	.23823	4.19756	.25676	3.89474	36
25	.18384	5.43966	.20194	4.95201	.22017	4.54196	.23854	4.19215	.25707	3.89004	35
26	.18414	5.43077	.20224	4.94460	.22047	4.53568	.23885	4.18675	.25738	3.88536	34
27	.18444	5.42192	.20254	4.93721	.22078	4.52941	.23916	4.18137	.25769	3.88068	33
28	.18474	5.41309	.20285	4.92984	.22108	4.52316	.23946	4.17600	.25800	3.87601	32
29	.18504	5.40429	.20315	4.92249	.22139	4.51693	.23977	4.17064	.25831	3.87136	31
30	.18534	5.39552	.20345	4.91516	.22169	4.51071	.24008	4.16530	.25862	3.86671	30
31	.18564	5.38677	.20376	4.90785	.22200	4.50451	.24039	4.15997	.25893	3.86208	29
32	.18594	5.37805	.20406	4.90056	.22231	4.49832	.24069	4.15465	.25924	3.85745	28
33	.18624	5.36936	.20436	4.89330	.22261	4.49215	.24100	4.14934	.25955	3.85284	27
34	.18654	5.36070	.20466	4.88605	.22292	4.48600	.24131	4.14405	.25986	3.84824	26
35	.18684	5.35206	.20497	4.87882	.22322	4.47986	.24162	4.13877	.26017	3.84364	25
36	.18714	5.34345	.20527	4.87162	.22353	4.47374	.24193	4.13350	.26048	3.83906	24
37	.18745	5.33487	.20557	4.86444	.22383	4.46764	.24223	4.12825	.26079	3.83449	23
38	.18775	5.32631	.20588	4.85727	.22414	4.46155	.24254	4.12301	.26110	3.82992	22
39	.18805	5.31778	.20618	4.85013	.22444	4.45548	.24285	4.11778	.26141	3.82537	21
40	.18835	5.30928	.20648	4.84300	.22475	4.44942	.24316	4.11256	.26172	3.82083	20
41	.18865	5.30080	.20679	4.83590	.22505	4.44338	.24347	4.10736	.26203	3.81630	19
42	.18895	5.29235	.20709	4.82882	.22536	4.43735	.24377	4.10216	.26235	3.81177	18
43	.18925	5.28393	.20739	4.82175	.22567	4.43134	.24408	4.09699	.26266	3.80726	17
44	.18955	5.27553	.20770	4.81471	.22597	4.42534	.24439	4.09182	.26297	3.80276	16
45	.18986	5.26715	.20800	4.80769	.22628	4.41936	.24470	4.08666	.26328	3.79827	15
46	.19016	5.25880	.20830	4.80068	.22658	4.41340	.24501	4.08152	.26359	3.79378	14
47	.19046	5.25048	.20861	4.79370	.22689	4.40745	.24532	4.07639	.26390	3.78931	13
48	.19076	5.24218	.20891	4.78673	.22719	4.40152	.24562	4.07127	.26421	3.78485	12
49	.19106	5.23391	.20921	4.77978	.22750	4.39560	.24593	4.06616	.26452	3.78040	11
50	.19136	5.22566	.20952	4.77286	.22781	4.38969	.24624	4.06107	.26483	3.77595	10
51	.19166	5.21744	.20982	4.76595	.22811	4.38381	.24655	4.05599	.26515	3.77152	9
52	.19197	5.20925	.21013	4.75906	.22842	4.37793	.24686	4.05092	.26546	3.76709	8
53	.19227	5.20107	.21043	4.75219	.22872	4.37207	.24717	4.04586	.26577	3.76268	7
54	.19257	5.19293	.21073	4.74534	.22903	4.36623	.24747	4.04081	.26608	3.75828	6
55	.19287	5.18480	.21104	4.73851	.22934	4.36040	.24778	4.03578	.26639	3.75388	5
56	.19317	5.17671	.21134	4.73170	.22964	4.35459	.24809	4.03076	.26670	3.74950	4
57	.19347	5.16863	.21164	4.72490	.22995	4.34879	.24840	4.02574	.26701	3.74512	3
58	.19378	5.16058	.21195	4.71813	.23026	4.34300	.24871	4.02074	.26733	3.74075	2
59	.19408	5.15256	.21225	4.71137	.23056	4.33723	.24902	4.01576	.26764	3.73640	1
60	.19438	5.14455	.21256	4.70463	.23087	4.33148	.24933	4.01078	.26795	3.73205	0
′	Cotang	Tang	Cotang	Tang	Cotang	Tang	Cotang	Tang	Cotang	Tang	′
	79°		78°		77°		76°		75°		

408

TABLE F.—NATURAL TANGENTS AND COTANGENTS

′	15° Tang	15° Cotang	16° Tang	16° Cotang	17° Tang	17° Cotang	18° Tang	18° Cotang	19° Tang	19° Cotang	′
0	.26795	3.73205	.28675	3.48741	.30573	3.27085	.32492	3.07768	.34433	2.90421	60
1	.26826	3.72771	.28706	3.48359	.30605	3.26745	.32524	3.07464	.34465	2.90147	59
2	.26857	3.72338	.28738	3.47977	.30637	3.26406	.32556	3.07160	.34498	2.89873	58
3	.26888	3.71907	.28769	3.47596	.30669	3.26067	.32588	3.06857	.34530	2.89600	57
4	.26920	3.71476	.28800	3.47216	.30700	3.25729	.32621	3.06554	.34563	2.89327	56
5	.26951	3.71046	.28832	3.46837	.30732	3.25392	.32653	3.06252	.34596	2.89055	55
6	.26982	3.70616	.28864	3.46458	.30764	3.25055	.32685	3.05950	.34628	2.88783	54
7	.27013	3.70188	.28895	3.46080	.30796	3.24719	.32717	3.05649	.34661	2.88511	53
8	.27044	3.69761	.28927	3.45703	.30828	3.24383	.32749	3.05349	.34693	2.88240	52
9	.27076	3.69335	.28958	3.45327	.30860	3.24049	.32782	3.05049	.34726	2.87970	51
10	.27107	3.68909	.28990	3.44951	.30891	3.23714	.32814	3.04749	.34758	2.87700	50
11	.27138	3.68485	.29021	3.44576	.30923	3.23381	.32846	3.04450	.34791	2.87430	49
12	.27169	3.68061	.29053	3.44202	.30955	3.23048	.32878	3.04152	.34824	2.87161	48
13	.27201	3.67638	.29084	3.43829	.30987	3.22715	.32911	3.03854	.34856	2.86892	47
14	.27232	3.67217	.29116	3.43456	.31019	3.22384	.32943	3.03556	.34889	2.86624	46
15	.27263	3.66796	.29147	3.43084	.31051	3.22053	.32975	3.03260	.34922	2.86356	45
16	.27294	3.66376	.29179	3.42713	.31083	3.21722	.33007	3.02963	.34954	2.86089	44
17	.27326	3.65957	.29210	3.42343	.31115	3.21392	.33040	3.02667	.34987	2.85822	43
18	.27357	3.65538	.29242	3.41973	.31147	3.21063	.33072	3.02372	.35020	2.85555	42
19	.27388	3.65121	.29274	3.41604	.31178	3.20734	.33104	3.02077	.35052	2.85289	41
20	.27419	3.64705	.29305	3.41236	.31210	3.20406	.33136	3.01783	.35085	2.85023	40
21	.27451	3.64289	.29337	3.40869	.31242	3.20079	.33169	3.01489	.35118	2.84758	39
22	.27482	3.63874	.29368	3.40502	.31274	3.19752	.33201	3.01196	.35150	2.84494	38
23	.27513	3.63461	.29400	3.40136	.31306	3.19426	.33233	3.00903	.35183	2.84229	37
24	.27545	3.63048	.29432	3.39771	.31338	3.19100	.33266	3.00611	.35216	2.83965	36
25	.27576	3.62636	.29463	3.39406	.31370	3.18775	.33298	3.00319	.35248	2.83702	35
26	.27607	3.62224	.29495	3.39042	.31402	3.18451	.33330	3.00028	.35281	2.83439	34
27	.27638	3.61814	.29526	3.38679	.31434	3.18127	.33363	2.99738	.35314	2.83176	33
28	.27670	3.61405	.29558	3.38317	.31466	3.17804	.33395	2.99447	.35346	2.82914	32
29	.27701	3.60996	.29590	3.37955	.31498	3.17481	.33427	2.99158	.35379	2.82653	31
30	.27732	3.60588	.29621	3.37594	.31530	3.17159	.33460	2.98868	.35412	2.82391	30
31	.27764	3.60181	.29653	3.37234	.31562	3.16838	.33492	2.98580	.35445	2.82130	29
32	.27795	3.59775	.29685	3.36875	.31594	3.16517	.33524	2.98292	.35477	2.81870	28
33	.27826	3.59370	.29716	3.36516	.31626	3.16197	.33557	2.98004	.35510	2.81610	27
34	.27858	3.58966	.29748	3.36158	.31658	3.15877	.33589	2.97717	.35543	2.81350	26
35	.27889	3.58562	.29780	3.35800	.31690	3.15558	.33621	2.97430	.35576	2.81091	25
36	.27921	3.58160	.29811	3.35443	.31722	3.15240	.33654	2.97144	.35608	2.80833	24
37	.27952	3.57758	.29843	3.35087	.31754	3.14922	.33686	2.96858	.35641	2.80574	23
38	.27983	3.57357	.29875	3.34732	.31786	3.14605	.33718	2.96573	.35674	2.80316	22
39	.28015	3.56957	.29906	3.34377	.31818	3.14288	.33751	2.96288	.35707	2.80059	21
40	.28046	3.56557	.29938	3.34023	.31850	3.13972	.33783	2.96004	.35740	2.79802	20
41	.28077	3.56159	.29970	3.33670	.31882	3.13656	.33816	2.95721	.35772	2.79545	19
42	.28109	3.55761	.30001	3.33317	.31914	3.13341	.33848	2.95437	.35805	2.79289	18
43	.28140	3.55364	.30033	3.32965	.31946	3.13027	.33881	2.95155	.35838	2.79033	17
44	.28172	3.54968	.30065	3.32614	.31978	3.12713	.33913	2.94872	.35871	2.78778	16
45	.28203	3.54573	.30097	3.32264	.32010	3.12400	.33945	2.94591	.35904	2.78523	15
46	.28234	3.54179	.30128	3.31914	.32042	3.12087	.33978	2.94309	.35937	2.78269	14
47	.28266	3.53785	.30160	3.31565	.32074	3.11775	.34010	2.94028	.35969	2.78014	13
48	.28297	3.53393	.30192	3.31216	.32106	3.11464	.34043	2.93748	.36002	2.77761	12
49	.28329	3.53001	.30224	3.30868	.32139	3.11153	.34075	2.93468	.36035	2.77507	11
50	.28360	3.52609	.30255	3.30521	.32171	3.10842	.34108	2.93189	.36068	2.77254	10
51	.28391	3.52219	.30287	3.30174	.32203	3.10532	.34140	2.92910	.36101	2.77002	9
52	.28423	3.51829	.30319	3.29829	.32235	3.10223	.34173	2.92632	.36134	2.76750	8
53	.28454	3.51441	.30351	3.29483	.32267	3.09914	.34205	2.92354	.36167	2.76498	7
54	.28486	3.51053	.30382	3.29139	.32299	3.09606	.34238	2.92076	.36199	2.76247	6
55	.28517	3.50666	.30414	3.28795	.32331	3.09298	.34270	2.91799	.36232	2.75996	5
56	.28549	3.50279	.30446	3.28452	.32363	3.08991	.34303	2.91523	.36265	2.75746	4
57	.28580	3.49894	.30478	3.28109	.32396	3.08685	.34335	2.91246	.36298	2.75496	3
58	.28612	3.49509	.30509	3.27767	.32428	3.08379	.34368	2.90971	.36331	2.75246	2
59	.28643	3.49125	.30541	3.27426	.32460	3.08073	.34400	2.90696	.36364	2.74997	1
60	.28675	3.48741	.30573	3.27085	.32492	3.07768	.34433	2.90421	.36397	2.74748	0
′	Cotang	Tang	Cotang	Tang	Cotang	Tang	Cotang	Tang	Cotang	Tang	′
	74°		73°		72°		71°		70°		

TABLE F.—NATURAL TANGENTS AND COTANGENTS

′	20° Tang	Cotang	21° Tang	Cotang	22° Tang	Cotang	23° Tang	Cotang	24° Tang	Cotang	′
0	.36397	2.74748	.38386	2.60509	.40403	2.47509	.42447	2.35585	.44523	2.24604	60
1	.36430	2.74499	.38420	2.60283	.40436	2.47302	.42482	2.35395	.44558	2.24428	59
2	.36463	2.74251	.38453	2.60057	.40470	2.47095	.42516	2.35205	.44593	2.24252	58
3	.36496	2.74004	.38487	2.59831	.40504	2.46888	.42551	2.35015	.44627	2.24077	57
4	.36529	2.73756	.38520	2.59606	.40538	2.46682	.42585	2.34825	.44662	2.23902	56
5	.36562	2.73509	.38553	2.59381	.40572	2.46476	.42619	2.34636	.44697	2.23727	55
6	.36595	2.73263	.38587	2.59156	.40606	2.46270	.42654	2.34447	.44732	2.23553	54
7	.36628	2.73017	.38620	2.58932	.40640	2.46065	.42688	2.34258	.44767	2.23378	53
8	.36661	2.72771	.38654	2.58708	.40674	2.45860	.42722	2.34069	.44802	2.23204	52
9	.36694	2.72526	.38687	2.58484	.40707	2.45655	.42757	2.33881	.44837	2.23030	51
10	.36727	2.72281	.38721	2.58261	.40741	2.45451	.42791	2.33693	.44872	2.22857	50
11	.36760	2.72036	.38754	2.58038	.40775	2.45246	.42826	2.33505	.44907	2.22683	49
12	.36793	2.71792	.38787	2.57815	.40809	2.45043	.42860	2.33317	.44942	2.22510	48
13	.36826	2.71548	.38821	2.57593	.40843	2.44839	.42894	2.33130	.44977	2.22337	47
14	.36859	2.71305	.38854	2.57371	.40877	2.44636	.42929	2.32943	.45012	2.22164	46
15	.36892	2.71062	.38888	2.57150	.40911	2.44433	.42963	2.32756	.45047	2.21992	45
16	.36925	2.70819	.38921	2.56928	.40945	2.44230	.42998	2.32570	.45082	2.21819	44
17	.36958	2.70577	.38955	2.56707	.40979	2.44027	.43032	2.32383	.45117	2.21647	43
18	.36991	2.70335	.38988	2.56487	.41013	2.43825	.43067	2.32197	.45152	2.21475	42
19	.37024	2.70094	.39022	2.56266	.41047	2.43623	.43101	2.32012	.45187	2.21304	41
20	.37057	2.69853	.39055	2.56046	.41081	2.43422	.43136	2.31826	.45222	2.21132	40
21	.37090	2.69612	.39089	2.55827	.41115	2.43220	.43170	2.31641	.45257	2.20961	39
22	.37123	2.69371	.39122	2.55608	.41149	2.43019	.43205	2.31456	.45292	2.20790	38
23	.37157	2.69131	.39156	2.55389	.41183	2.42819	.43230	2.31271	.45327	2.20619	37
24	.37190	2.68892	.39190	2.55170	.41217	2.42618	.43274	2.31086	.45362	2.20449	36
25	.37223	2.68653	.39223	2.54952	.41251	2.42418	.43308	2.30902	.45397	2.20278	35
26	.37256	2.68414	.39257	2.54734	.41285	2.42218	.43343	2.30718	.45432	2.20108	34
27	.37289	2.68175	.39290	2.54516	.41319	2.42019	.43378	2.30534	.45467	2.19938	33
28	.37322	2.67937	.39324	2.54299	.41353	2.41819	.43412	2.30351	.45502	2.19769	32
29	.37355	2.67700	.39357	2.54082	.41387	2.41620	.43447	2.30167	.45538	2.19599	31
30	.37388	2.67462	.39391	2.53865	.41421	2.41421	.43481	2.29984	.45573	2.19430	30
31	.37422	2.67225	.39425	2.53648	.41455	2.41223	.43516	2.29801	.45608	2.19261	29
32	.37455	2.66989	.39458	2.53432	.41490	2.41025	.43550	2.29619	.45643	2.19092	28
33	.37488	2.66752	.39492	2.53217	.41524	2.40827	.43585	2.29437	.45678	2.18923	27
34	.37521	2.66516	.39526	2.53001	.41558	2.40629	.43620	2.29254	.45713	2.18755	26
35	.37554	2.66281	.39559	2.52786	.41592	2.40432	.43654	2.29073	.45748	2.18587	25
36	.37588	2.66046	.39593	2.52571	.41626	2.40235	.43689	2.28891	.45784	2.18419	24
37	.37621	2.65811	.39626	2.52357	.41660	2.40038	.43724	2.28710	.45819	2.18251	23
38	.37654	2.65576	.39660	2.52142	.41694	2.39841	.43758	2.28528	.45854	2.18084	22
39	.37687	2.65342	.39694	2.51929	.41728	2.39645	.43793	2.28348	.45889	2.17916	21
40	.37720	2.65109	.39727	2.51715	.41763	2.39449	.43828	2.28167	.45924	2.17749	20
41	.37754	2.64875	.39761	2.51502	.41797	2.39253	.43862	2.27987	.45960	2.17582	19
42	.37787	2.64642	.39795	2.51289	.41831	2.39058	.43897	2.27806	.45995	2.17416	18
43	.37820	2.64410	.39829	2.51076	.41865	2.38863	.43932	2.27626	.46030	2.17249	17
44	.37853	2.64177	.39862	2.50864	.41899	2.38668	.43966	2.27447	.46065	2.17083	16
45	.37887	2.63945	.39896	2.50652	.41933	2.38473	.44001	2.27267	.46101	2.16917	15
46	.37920	2.63714	.39930	2.50440	.41968	2.38279	.44036	2.27088	.46136	2.16751	14
47	.37953	2.63483	.39963	2.50229	.42002	2.38084	.44071	2.26909	.46171	2.16585	13
48	.37986	2.63252	.39997	2.50018	.42036	2.37891	.44105	2.26730	.46206	2.16420	12
49	.38020	2.63021	.40031	2.49807	.42070	2.37697	.44140	2.26552	.46242	2.16255	11
50	.38053	2.62791	.40065	2.49597	.42105	2.37504	.44175	2.26374	.46277	2.16090	10
51	.38086	2.62561	.40098	2.49386	.42139	2.37311	.44210	2.26196	.46312	2.15925	9
52	.38120	2.62332	.40132	2.49177	.42173	2.37118	.44244	2.26018	.46348	2.15760	8
53	.38153	2.62103	.40166	2.48967	.42207	2.36925	.44279	2.25840	.46383	2.15596	7
54	.38186	2.61874	.40200	2.48758	.42242	2.36733	.44314	2.25663	.46418	2.15432	6
55	.38220	2.61646	.40234	2.48549	.42276	2.36541	.44349	2.25486	.46454	2.15268	5
56	.38253	2.61418	.40267	2.48340	.42310	2.36349	.44384	2.25309	.46489	2.15104	4
57	.38286	2.61190	.40301	2.48132	.42345	2.36158	.44418	2.25132	.46525	2.14940	3
58	.38320	2.60963	.40335	2.47924	.42379	2.35967	.44453	2.24956	.46560	2.14777	2
59	.38353	2.60736	.40369	2.47716	.42413	2.35776	.44488	2.24780	.46595	2.14614	1
60	.38386	2.60509	.40403	2.47509	.42447	2.35585	.44523	2.24604	.46631	2.14451	0
′	Cotang	Tang	Cotang	Tang	Cotang	Tang	Cotang	Tang	Cotang	Tang	′
	69°		68°		67°		66°		65°		

TABLE F.—NATURAL TANGENTS AND COTANGENTS

′	25° Tang	25° Cotang	26° Tang	26° Cotang	27° Tang	27° Cotang	28° Tang	28° Cotang	29° Tang	29° Cotang	′
0	.46631	2.14451	.48773	2.05030	.50953	1.96261	.53171	1.88073	.55431	1.80405	60
1	.46666	2.14288	.48809	2.04879	.50989	1.96120	.53208	1.87941	.55469	1.80281	59
2	.46702	2.14125	.48845	2.04728	.51026	1.95979	.53246	1.87809	.55507	1.80158	58
3	.46737	2.13963	.48881	2.04577	.51063	1.95838	.53283	1.87677	.55545	1.80034	57
4	.46772	2.13801	.48917	2.04426	.51099	1.95698	.53320	1.87546	.55583	1.79911	56
5	.46808	2.13639	.48953	2.04276	.51136	1.95557	.53358	1.87415	.55621	1.79788	55
6	.46843	2.13477	.48989	2.04125	.51173	1.95417	.53395	1.87283	.55659	1.79665	54
7	.46879	2.13316	.49026	2.03975	.51209	1.95277	.53432	1.87152	.55697	1.79542	53
8	.46914	2.13154	.49062	2.03825	.51246	1.95137	.53470	1.87021	.55736	1.79419	52
9	.46950	2.12993	.49098	2.03675	.51283	1.94997	.53507	1.86891	.55774	1.79296	51
10	.46985	2.12832	.49134	2.03526	.51319	1.94858	.53545	1.86760	.55812	1.79174	50
11	.47021	2.12671	.49170	2.03376	.51356	1.94718	.53582	1.86630	.55850	1.79051	49
12	.47056	2.12511	.49206	2.03227	.51393	1.94579	.53620	1.86499	.55888	1.78929	48
13	.47092	2.12350	.49242	2.03078	.51430	1.94440	.53657	1.86369	.55926	1.78807	47
14	.47128	2.12190	.49278	2.02929	.51467	1.94301	.53694	1.86239	.55964	1.78685	46
15	.47163	2.12030	.49315	2.02780	.51503	1.94162	.53732	1.86109	.56003	1.78563	45
16	.47199	2.11871	.49351	2.02631	.51540	1.94023	.53769	1.85979	.56041	1.78441	44
17	.47234	2.11711	.49387	2.02483	.51577	1.93885	.53807	1.85850	.56079	1.78319	43
18	.47270	2.11552	.49423	2.02335	.51614	1.93746	.53844	1.85720	.56117	1.78198	42
19	.47305	2.11392	.49459	2.02187	.51651	1.93608	.53882	1.85591	.56156	1.78077	41
20	.47341	2.11233	.49495	2.02039	.51688	1.93470	.53920	1.85462	.56194	1.77955	40
21	.47377	2.11075	.49532	2.01891	.51724	1.93332	.53957	1.85333	.56232	1.77834	39
22	.47412	2.10916	.49568	2.01743	.51761	1.93195	.53995	1.85204	.56270	1.77713	38
23	.47448	2.10758	.49604	2.01596	.51798	1.93057	.54032	1.85075	.56309	1.77592	37
24	.47483	2.10600	.49640	2.01449	.51835	1.92920	.54070	1.84946	.56347	1.77471	36
25	.47519	2.10442	.49677	2.01302	.51872	1.92782	.54107	1.84818	.56385	1.77351	35
26	.47555	2.10284	.49713	2.01155	.51909	1.92645	.54145	1.84689	.56424	1.77230	34
27	.47590	2.10126	.49749	2.01008	.51946	1.92508	.54183	1.84561	.56462	1.77110	33
28	.47626	2.09969	.49786	2.00862	.51983	1.92371	.54220	1.84433	.56501	1.76990	32
29	.47662	2.09811	.49822	2.00715	.52020	1.92235	.54258	1.84305	.56539	1.76869	31
30	.47698	2.09654	.49858	2.00569	.52057	1.92098	.54296	1.84177	.56577	1.76749	30
31	.47733	2.09498	.49894	2.00423	.52094	1.91962	.54333	1.84049	.56616	1.76629	29
32	.47769	2.09341	.49931	2.00277	.52131	1.91826	.54371	1.83922	.56654	1.76510	28
33	.47805	2.09184	.49967	2.00131	.52168	1.91690	.54409	1.83794	.56693	1.76390	27
34	.47840	2.09028	.50004	1.99986	.52205	1.91554	.54446	1.83667	.56731	1.76271	26
35	.47876	2.08872	.50040	1.99841	.52242	1.91418	.54484	1.83540	.56769	1.76151	25
36	.47912	2.08716	.50076	1.99695	.52279	1.91282	.54522	1.83413	.56808	1.76032	24
37	.47948	2.08560	.50113	1.99550	.52316	1.91147	.54560	1.83286	.56846	1.75913	23
38	.47984	2.08405	.50149	1.99406	.52353	1.91012	.54597	1.83159	.56885	1.75794	22
39	.48019	2.08250	.50185	1.99261	.52390	1.90876	.54635	1.83033	.56923	1.75675	21
40	.48055	2.08094	.50222	1.99116	.52427	1.90741	.54673	1.82906	.56962	1.75556	20
41	.48091	2.07939	.50258	1.98972	.52464	1.90607	.54711	1.82780	.57000	1.75437	19
42	.48127	2.07785	.50295	1.98828	.52501	1.90472	.54748	1.82654	.57039	1.75319	18
43	.48163	2.07630	.50331	1.98684	.52538	1.90337	.54786	1.82528	.57078	1.75200	17
44	.48198	2.07476	.50368	1.98540	.52575	1.90203	.54824	1.82402	.57116	1.75082	16
45	.48234	2.07321	.50404	1.98396	.52613	1.90069	.54862	1.82276	.57155	1.74964	15
46	.48270	2.07167	.50441	1.98253	.52650	1.89935	.54900	1.82150	.57193	1.74846	14
47	.48306	2.07014	.50477	1.98110	.52687	1.89801	.54938	1.82025	.57232	1.74728	13
48	.48342	2.06860	.50514	1.97966	.52724	1.89667	.54975	1.81899	.57271	1.74610	12
49	.48378	2.06706	.50550	1.97823	.52761	1.89533	.55013	1.81774	.57309	1.74492	11
50	.48414	2.06553	.50587	1.97681	.52798	1.89400	.55051	1.81649	.57348	1.74375	10
51	.48450	2.06400	.50623	1.97538	.52836	1.89266	.55089	1.81524	.57386	1.74257	9
52	.48486	2.06247	.50660	1.97395	.52873	1.89133	.55127	1.81399	.57425	1.74140	8
53	.48521	2.06094	.50696	1.97253	.52910	1.89000	.55165	1.81274	.57464	1.74022	7
54	.48557	2.05942	.50733	1.97111	.52947	1.88867	.55203	1.81150	.57503	1.73905	6
55	.48593	2.05790	.50769	1.96969	.52985	1.88734	.55241	1.81025	.57541	1.73788	5
56	.48629	2.05637	.50806	1.96827	.53022	1.88602	.55279	1.80901	.57580	1.73671	4
57	.48665	2.05485	.50843	1.96685	.53059	1.88469	.55317	1.80777	.57619	1.73555	3
58	.48701	2.05333	.50879	1.96544	.53096	1.88337	.55355	1.80653	.57657	1.73438	2
59	.48737	2.05182	.50916	1.96402	.53134	1.88205	.55393	1.80529	.57696	1.73321	1
60	.48773	2.05030	.50953	1.96261	.53171	1.88073	.55431	1.80405	.57735	1.73205	0
′	Cotang	Tang	Cotang	Tang	Cotang	Tang	Cotang	Tang	Cotang	Tang	′
	64°		63°		62°		61°		60°		

′	30°		31°		32°		33°		34°		′
	Tang	Cotang	Tang	Cotang	Tang	Cotang	Tang	Cotang	Tang	Cotang	
0	.57735	1.73205	.60086	1.66428	.62487	1.60033	.64941	1.53986	.67451	1.48256	60
1	.57774	1.73089	.60126	1.66318	.62527	1.59930	.64982	1.53888	.67493	1.48163	59
2	.57813	1.72973	.60165	1.66209	.62568	1.59826	.65024	1.53791	.67536	1.48070	58
3	.57851	1.72857	.60205	1.66099	.62608	1.59723	.65065	1.53693	.67578	1.47977	57
4	.57890	1.72741	.60245	1.65990	.62649	1.59620	.65106	1.53595	.67620	1.47885	56
5	.57929	1.72625	.60284	1.65881	.62689	1.59517	.65148	1.53497	.67663	1.47792	55
6	.57968	1.72509	.60324	1.65772	.62730	1.59414	.65189	1.53400	.67705	1.47699	54
7	.58007	1.72393	.60364	1.65663	.62770	1.59311	.65231	1.53302	.67748	1.47607	53
8	.58046	1.72278	.60403	1.65554	.62811	1.59208	.65272	1.53205	.67790	1.47514	52
9	.58085	1.72163	.60443	1.65445	.62852	1.59105	.65314	1.53107	.67832	1.47422	51
10	.58124	1.72047	.60483	1.65337	.62892	1.59002	.65355	1.53010	.67875	1.47330	50
11	.58162	1.71932	.60522	1.65228	.62933	1.58900	.65397	1.52913	.67917	1.47238	49
12	.58201	1.71817	.60562	1.65120	.62973	1.58797	.65438	1.52816	.67960	1.47146	48
13	.58240	1.71702	.60602	1.65011	.63014	1.58695	.65480	1.52719	.68002	1.47053	47
14	.58279	1.71588	.60642	1.64903	.63055	1.58593	.65521	1.52622	.68045	1.46962	46
15	.58318	1.71473	.60681	1.64795	.63095	1.58490	.65563	1.52525	.68088	1.46870	45
16	.58357	1.71358	.60721	1.64687	.63136	1.58388	.65604	1.52429	.68130	1.46778	44
17	.58396	1.71244	.60761	1.64579	.63177	1.58286	.65646	1.52332	.68173	1.46686	43
18	.58435	1.71129	.60801	1.64471	.63217	1.58184	.65688	1.52235	.68215	1.46595	42
19	.58474	1.71015	.60841	1.64363	.63258	1.58083	.65729	1.52139	.68258	1.46503	41
20	.58513	1.70901	.60881	1.64256	.63299	1.57981	.65771	1.52043	.68301	1.46411	40
21	.58552	1.70787	.60921	1.64148	.63340	1.57879	.65813	1.51946	.68343	1.46320	39
22	.58591	1.70673	.60960	1.64041	.63380	1.57778	.65854	1.51850	.68386	1.46229	38
23	.58631	1.70560	.61000	1.63934	.63421	1.57676	.65896	1.51754	.68429	1.46137	37
24	.58670	1.70446	.61040	1.63826	.63462	1.57575	.65938	1.51658	.68471	1.46046	36
25	.58709	1.70332	.61080	1.63719	.63503	1.57474	.65980	1.51562	.68514	1.45955	35
26	.58748	1.70219	.61120	1.63612	.63544	1.57372	.66021	1.51466	.68557	1.45864	34
27	.58787	1.70106	.61160	1.63505	.63584	1.57271	.66063	1.51370	.68600	1.45773	33
28	.58826	1.69992	.61200	1.63398	.63625	1.57170	.66105	1.51275	.68642	1.45682	32
29	.58865	1.69879	.61240	1.63292	.63666	1.57069	.66147	1.51179	.68685	1.45592	31
30	.58905	1.69766	.61280	1.63185	.63707	1.56969	.66189	1.51084	.68728	1.45501	30
31	.58944	1.69653	.61320	1.63079	.63748	1.56868	.66230	1.50988	.68771	1.45410	29
32	.58983	1.69541	.61360	1.62972	.63789	1.56767	.66272	1.50893	.68814	1.45320	28
33	.59022	1.69428	.61400	1.62866	.63830	1.56667	.66314	1.50797	.68857	1.45229	27
34	.59061	1.69316	.61440	1.62760	.63871	1.56566	.66356	1.50702	.68900	1.45139	26
35	.59101	1.69203	.61480	1.62654	.63912	1.56466	.66398	1.50607	.68942	1.45049	25
36	.59140	1.69091	.61520	1.62548	.63953	1.56366	.66440	1.50512	.68985	1.44958	24
37	.59179	1.68979	.61561	1.62442	.63994	1.56265	.66482	1.50417	.69028	1.44868	23
38	.59218	1.68866	.61601	1.62336	.64035	1.56165	.66524	1.50322	.69071	1.44778	22
39	.59258	1.68754	.61641	1.62230	.64076	1.56065	.66566	1.50228	.69114	1.44688	21
40	.59297	1.68643	.61681	1.62125	.64117	1.55966	.66608	1.50133	.69157	1.44598	20
41	.59336	1.68531	.61721	1.62019	.64158	1.55866	.66650	1.50038	.69200	1.44508	19
42	.59376	1.68419	.61761	1.61914	.64199	1.55766	.66662	1.49944	.69243	1.44418	18
43	.59415	1.68308	.61801	1.61808	.64240	1.55666	.66734	1.49849	.69286	1.44329	17
44	.59454	1.68196	.61842	1.61703	.64281	1.55567	.66776	1.49755	.69329	1.44239	16
45	.59494	1.68085	.61882	1.61598	.64322	1.55467	.66818	1.49661	.69372	1.44149	15
46	.59533	1.67974	.61922	1.61493	.64363	1.55368	.66860	1.49566	.69416	1.44060	14
47	.59573	1.67863	.61962	1.61388	.64404	1.55269	.66902	1.49472	.69459	1.43970	13
48	.59612	1.67752	.62003	1.61283	.64446	1.55170	.66944	1.49378	.69502	1.43881	12
49	.59651	1.67641	.62043	1.61179	.64487	1.55071	.66986	1.49284	.69545	1.43792	11
50	.59691	1.67530	.62083	1.61074	.64528	1.54972	.67028	1.49190	.69588	1.43703	10
51	.59730	1.67419	.62124	1.60970	.64569	1.54873	.67071	1.49097	.69631	1.43614	9
52	.59770	1.67309	.62164	1.60865	.64610	1.54774	.67113	1.49003	.69675	1.43525	8
53	.59809	1.67198	.62204	1.60761	.64652	1.54675	.67155	1.48909	.69718	1.43436	7
54	.59849	1.67088	.62245	1.60657	.64693	1.54576	.67197	1.48816	.69761	1.43347	6
55	.59888	1.66978	.62285	1.60553	.64734	1.54478	.67239	1.48722	.69804	1.43258	5
56	.59928	1.66867	.62325	1.60449	.64775	1.54379	.67282	1.48629	.69847	1.43169	4
57	.59967	1.66757	.62366	1.60345	.64817	1.54281	.67324	1.48536	.69891	1.43080	3
58	.60007	1.66647	.62406	1.60241	.64858	1.54183	.67366	1.48442	.69934	1.42992	2
59	.60046	1.66538	.62446	1.60137	.64899	1.54085	.67409	1.48349	.69977	1.42903	1
60	.60086	1.66428	.62487	1.60033	.64941	1.53986	.67451	1.48256	.70021	1.42815	0
′	Cotang	Tang	Cotang	Tang	Cotang	Tang	Cotang	Tang	Cotang	Tang	′
	59°		58°		57°		56°		55°		

TABLE F.—NATURAL TANGENTS AND COTANGENTS

′	35° Tang	Cotang	36° Tang	Cotang	37° Tang	Cotang	38° Tang	Cotang	39° Tang	Cotang	′
0	.70021	1.42815	.72654	1.37638	.75355	1.32704	.78129	1.27994	.80978	1.23490	60
1	.70064	1.42726	.72699	1.37554	.75401	1.32624	.78175	1.27917	.81027	1.23416	59
2	.70107	1.42638	.72743	1.37470	.75447	1.32544	.78222	1.27841	.81075	1.23343	58
3	.70151	1.42550	.72788	1.37386	.75492	1.32464	.78269	1.27764	.81123	1.23270	57
4	.70194	1.42462	.72832	1.37302	.75538	1.32384	.78316	1.27688	.81171	1.23196	56
5	.70238	1.42374	.72877	1.37218	.75584	1.32304	.78363	1.27611	.81220	1.23123	55
6	.70281	1.42286	.72921	1.37134	.75629	1.32224	.78410	1.27535	.81268	1.23050	54
7	.70325	1.42198	.72966	1.37050	.75675	1.32144	.78457	1.27458	.81316	1.22977	53
8	.70368	1.42110	.73010	1.36967	.75721	1.32064	.78504	1.27382	.81364	1.22904	52
9	.70412	1.42022	.73055	1.36883	.75767	1.31984	.78551	1.27306	.81413	1.22831	51
10	.70455	1.41934	.73100	1.36800	.75812	1.31904	.78598	1.27230	.81461	1.22758	50
11	.70499	1.41847	.73144	1.36716	.75858	1.31825	.78645	1.27153	.81510	1.22685	49
12	.70542	1.41759	.73189	1.36633	.75904	1.31745	.78692	1.27077	.81558	1.22612	48
13	.70586	1.41672	.73234	1.36549	.75950	1.31666	.78739	1.27001	.81606	1.22539	47
14	.70629	1.41584	.73278	1.36466	.75996	1.31586	.78786	1.26925	.81655	1.22467	46
15	.70673	1.41497	.73323	1.36383	.76042	1.31507	.78834	1.26849	.81703	1.22394	45
16	.70717	1.41409	.73368	1.36300	.76088	1.31427	.78881	1.26774	.81752	1.22321	44
17	.70760	1.41322	.73413	1.36217	.76134	1.31348	.78928	1.26698	.81800	1.22249	43
18	.70804	1.41235	.73457	1.36134	.76180	1.31269	.78975	1.26622	.81849	1.22176	42
19	.70848	1.41148	.73502	1.36051	.76226	1.31190	.79022	1.26546	.81898	1.22104	41
20	.70891	1.41061	.73547	1.35968	.76272	1.31110	.79070	1.26471	.81946	1.22031	40
21	.70935	1.40974	.73592	1.35885	.76318	1.31031	.79117	1.26395	.81995	1.21959	39
22	.70979	1.40887	.73637	1.35802	.76364	1.30952	.79164	1.26319	.82044	1.21886	38
23	.71023	1.40800	.73681	1.35719	.76410	1.30873	.79212	1.26244	.82092	1.21814	37
24	.71066	1.40714	.73726	1.35637	.76456	1.30795	.79259	1.26169	.82141	1.21742	36
25	.71110	1.40627	.73771	1.35554	.76502	1.30716	.79306	1.26093	.82190	1.21670	35
26	.71154	1.40540	.73816	1.35472	.76548	1.30637	.79354	1.26018	.82238	1.21598	34
27	.71198	1.40454	.73861	1.35389	.76594	1.30558	.79401	1.25943	.82287	1.21526	33
28	.71242	1.40367	.73906	1.35307	.76640	1.30480	.79449	1.25867	.82336	1.21454	32
29	.71285	1.40281	.73951	1.35224	.76686	1.30401	.79496	1.25792	.82385	1.21382	31
30	.71329	1.40195	.73996	1.35142	.76733	1.30323	.79544	1.25717	.82434	1.21310	30
31	.71373	1.40109	.74041	1.35060	.76779	1.30244	.79591	1.25642	.82483	1.21238	29
32	.71417	1.40022	.74086	1.34978	.76825	1.30166	.79639	1.25567	.82531	1.21166	28
33	.71461	1.39936	.74131	1.34896	.76871	1.30087	.79686	1.25492	.82580	1.21094	27
34	.71505	1.39850	.74176	1.34814	.76918	1.30009	.79734	1.25417	.82629	1.21023	26
35	.71549	1.39764	.74221	1.34732	.76964	1.29931	.79781	1.25343	.82678	1.20951	25
36	.71593	1.39679	.74267	1.34650	.77010	1.29853	.79829	1.25268	.82727	1.20879	24
37	.71637	1.39593	.74312	1.34568	.77057	1.29775	.79877	1.25193	.82776	1.20808	23
38	.71681	1.39507	.74357	1.34487	.77103	1.29696	.79924	1.25118	.82825	1.20736	22
39	.71725	1.39421	.74402	1.34405	.77149	1.29618	.79972	1.25044	.82874	1.20665	21
40	.71769	1.39336	.74447	1.34323	.77196	1.29541	.80020	1.24969	.82923	1.20593	20
41	.71813	1.39250	.74492	1.34242	.77242	1.29463	.80067	1.24895	.82972	1.20522	19
42	.71857	1.39165	.74538	1.34160	.77289	1.29385	.80115	1.24820	.83022	1.20451	18
43	.71901	1.39079	.74583	1.34079	.77335	1.29307	.80163	1.24746	.83071	1.20379	17
44	.71946	1.38994	.74628	1.33998	.77382	1.29229	.80211	1.24672	.83120	1.20308	16
45	.71990	1.38909	.74674	1.33916	.77428	1.29152	.80258	1.24597	.83169	1.20237	15
46	.72034	1.38824	.74719	1.33835	.77475	1.29074	.80306	1.24523	.83218	1.20166	14
47	.72078	1.38738	.74764	1.33754	.77521	1.28997	.80354	1.24449	.83268	1.20095	13
48	.72122	1.38653	.74810	1.33673	.77568	1.28919	.80402	1.24375	.83317	1.20024	12
49	.72167	1.38568	.74855	1.33592	.77615	1.28842	.80450	1.24301	.83366	1.19953	11
50	.72211	1.38484	.74900	1.33511	.77661	1.28764	.80498	1.24227	.83415	1.19882	10
51	.72255	1.38399	.74946	1.33430	.77708	1.28687	.80546	1.24153	.83465	1.19811	9
52	.72299	1.38314	.74991	1.33349	.77754	1.28610	.80594	1.24079	.83514	1.19740	8
53	.72344	1.38229	.75037	1.33268	.77801	1.28533	.80642	1.24005	.83564	1.19669	7
54	.72388	1.38145	.75082	1.33187	.77848	1.28456	.80690	1.23931	.83613	1.19599	6
55	.72432	1.38060	.75128	1.33107	.77895	1.28379	.80738	1.23858	.83662	1.19528	5
56	.72477	1.37976	.75173	1.33026	.77941	1.28302	.80786	1.23784	.83712	1.19457	4
57	.72521	1.37891	.75219	1.32946	.77988	1.28225	.80834	1.23710	.83761	1.19387	3
58	.72565	1.37807	.75264	1.32865	.78035	1.28148	.80882	1.23637	.83811	1.19316	2
59	.72610	1.37722	.75310	1.32785	.78082	1.28071	.80930	1.23563	.83860	1.19246	1
60	.72654	1.37638	.75355	1.32704	.78129	1.27994	.80978	1.23490	.83910	1.19175	0

′	Cotang	Tang	Cotang	Tang	Cotang	Tang	Cotang	Tang	Cotang	Tang	′
	54°		53°		52°		51°		50°		

413

TABLE F.—NATURAL TANGENTS AND COTANGENTS

,	40°		41°		42°		43°		44°		,
	Tang	Cotang	Tang	Cotang	Tang	Cotang	Tang	Cotang	Tang	Cotang	
0	.83910	1.19175	.86929	1.15037	.90040	1.11061	.93252	1.07237	.96569	1.03553	60
1	.83960	1.19105	.86980	1.14969	.90093	1.10996	.93306	1.07174	.96625	1.03493	59
2	.84009	1.19035	.87031	1.14902	.90146	1.10931	.93360	1.07112	.96681	1.03433	58
3	.84059	1.18964	.87082	1.14834	.90199	1.10867	.93415	1.07049	.96738	1.03372	57
4	.84108	1.18894	.87133	1.14767	.90251	1.10802	.93469	1.06987	.96794	1.03312	56
5	.84158	1.18824	.87184	1.14699	.90304	1.10737	.93524	1.06925	.96850	1.03252	55
6	.84208	1.18754	.87236	1.14632	.90357	1.10672	.93578	1.06862	.96907	1.03192	54
7	.84258	1.18684	.87287	1.14565	.90410	1.10607	.93633	1.06800	.96963	1.03132	53
8	.84307	1.18614	.87338	1.14498	.90463	1.10543	.93688	1.06738	.97020	1.03072	52
9	.84357	1.18544	.87389	1.14430	.90516	1.10478	.93742	1.06676	.97076	1.03012	51
10	.84407	1.18474	.87441	1.14363	.90569	1.10414	.93797	1.06613	.97133	1.02952	50
11	.84457	1.18404	.87492	1.14296	.90621	1.10349	.93852	1.06551	.97189	1.02892	49
12	.84507	1.18334	.87543	1.14229	.90674	1.10285	.93906	1.06489	.97246	1.02832	48
13	.84556	1.18264	.87595	1.14162	.90727	1.10220	.93961	1.06427	.97302	1.02772	47
14	.84606	1.18194	.87646	1.14095	.90781	1.10156	.94016	1.06365	.97359	1.02713	46
15	.84656	1.18125	.87698	1.14028	.90834	1.10091	.94071	1.06303	.97416	1.02653	45
16	.84706	1.18055	.87749	1.13961	.90887	1.10027	.94125	1.06241	.97472	1.02593	44
17	.84756	1.17986	.87801	1.13894	.90940	1.09963	.94180	1.06179	.97529	1.02533	43
18	.84806	1.17916	.87852	1.13828	.90993	1.09899	.94235	1.06117	.97586	1.02474	42
19	.84856	1.17846	.87904	1.13761	.91046	1.09834	.94290	1.06056	.97643	1.02414	41
20	.84906	1.17777	.87955	1.13694	.91099	1.09770	.94345	1.05994	.97700	1.02355	40
21	.84956	1.17708	.88007	1.13627	.91153	1.09706	.94400	1.05932	.97756	1.02295	39
22	.85006	1.17638	.88059	1.13561	.91206	1.09642	.94455	1.05870	.97813	1.02236	38
23	.85057	1.17569	.88110	1.13494	.91259	1.09578	.94510	1.05809	.97870	1.02176	37
24	.85107	1.17500	.88162	1.13428	.91313	1.09514	.94565	1.05747	.97927	1.02117	36
25	.85157	1.17430	.88214	1.13361	.91366	1.09450	.94620	1.05685	.97984	1.02057	35
26	.85207	1.17361	.88265	1.13295	.91419	1.09386	.94676	1.05624	.98041	1.01998	34
27	.85257	1.17292	.88317	1.13228	.91473	1.09322	.94731	1.05562	.98098	1.01939	33
28	.85308	1.17223	.88369	1.13162	.91526	1.09258	.94786	1.05501	.98155	1.01879	32
29	.85358	1.17154	.88421	1.13096	.91580	1.09195	.94841	1.05439	.98213	1.01820	31
30	.85408	1.17085	.88473	1.13029	.91633	1.09131	.94896	1.05378	.98270	1.01761	30
31	.85458	1.17016	.88524	1.12963	.91687	1.09067	.94952	1.05317	.98327	1.01702	29
32	.85509	1.16947	.88576	1.12897	.91740	1.09003	.95007	1.05255	.98384	1.01642	28
33	.85559	1.16878	.88628	1.12831	.91794	1.08940	.95062	1.05194	.98441	1.01583	27
34	.85609	1.16809	.88680	1.12765	.91847	1.08876	.95118	1.05133	.98499	1.01524	26
35	.85660	1.16741	.88732	1.12699	.91901	1.08813	.95173	1.05072	.98556	1.01465	25
36	.85710	1.16672	.88784	1.12633	.91955	1.08749	.95229	1.05010	.98613	1.01406	24
37	.85761	1.16603	.88836	1.12567	.92008	1.08686	.95284	1.04949	.98671	1.01347	23
38	.85811	1.16535	.88888	1.12501	.92062	1.08622	.95340	1.04888	.98728	1.01288	22
39	.85862	1.16466	.88940	1.12435	.92116	1.08559	.95395	1.04827	.98786	1.01229	21
40	.85912	1.16398	.88992	1.12369	.92170	1.08496	.95451	1.04766	.98843	1.01170	20
41	.85963	1.16329	.89045	1.12303	92224	1.08432	.95506	1.04705	.98901	1.01112	19
42	.86014	1.16261	.89097	1.12238	.92277	1.08369	.95562	1.04644	.98958	1.01053	18
43	.86064	1.16192	.89149	1.12172	.92331	1.08306	.95618	1.04583	.99016	1.00994	17
44	.86115	1.16124	.89201	1.12106	.92383	1.08243	.95673	1.04522	.99073	1.00935	16
45	.86166	1.16056	.89253	1.12041	.92439	1.08179	.95729	1.04461	.99131	1.00876	15
46	.86216	1.15987	.89306	1.11975	.92493	1.08116	.95785	1.04401	.99189	1.00818	14
47	.86267	1.15919	.89358	1.11909	.92547	1.08053	.95841	1.04340	.99247	1.00759	13
48	.86318	1.15851	.89410	1.11844	.92601	1.07990	.95897	1.04279	.99304	1.00701	12
49	.86368	1.15783	.89463	1.11778	.92655	1.07927	.95952	1.04218	.99362	1.00642	11
50	.86419	1.15715	.89515	1.11713	.92709	1.07864	.96008	1.04158	.99420	1.00583	10
51	.86470	1.15647	.89567	1.11648	.92763	1.07801	.96064	1.04097	.99478	1.00525	9
52	.86521	1.15579	.89620	1.11582	.92817	1.07738	.96120	1.04036	.99536	1.00467	8
53	.86572	1.15511	.89672	1.11517	.92872	1.07676	.96176	1.03976	.99594	1.00408	7
54	.86623	1.15443	.89725	1.11452	.92926	1.07613	.96232	1.03915	.99652	1.00350	6
55	.86674	1.15375	.89777	1.11387	.92980	1.07550	.96288	1.03855	.99710	1.00291	5
56	.86725	1.15308	.89830	1.11321	.93034	1.07487	.96344	1.03794	.99768	1.00233	4
57	.86776	1.15240	.89883	1.11256	.93088	1.07425	.96400	1.03734	.99826	1.00175	3
58	.86827	1.15172	.89935	1.11191	.93143	1.07362	.96457	1.03674	.99884	1.00116	2
59	.86878	1.15104	.89988	1.11126	.93197	1.07299	.96513	1.03613	.99942	1.00058	1
60	.86929	1.15037	.90040	1.11061	.93252	1.07237	.96569	1.03553	1.00000	1.00000	0
,	Cotang	Tang	Cotang	Tang	Cotang	Tang	Cotang	Tang	Cotang	Tang	,
	49°		48°		47°		46°		45°		

TABLE G—LENGTHS OF CIRCULAR ARCS FOR RADIUS=1

Deg.	Length	Deg.	Length	Min.	Length	Sec.	Length
1	0.017 45 329	61	1.064 65 084	1	.000 29 089	1	.000 00 485
2	.034 90 659	62	.082 10 414	2	0 58 178	2	00 970
3	.052 35 988	63	.099 55 743	3	0 87 266	3	01 454
4	.069 81 317	64	.117 01 072	4	1 16 355	4	01 939
5	0.087 26 646	65	1.134 46 401	5	.001 45 444	5	.000 02 424
6	.104 71 976	66	.151 91 731	6	1 74 533	6	02 909
7	.122 17 305	67	.169 37 060	7	2 03 622	7	03 394
8	.139 62 634	68	.186 82 389	8	2 32 711	8	03 879
9	.157 07 963	69	.204 27 718	9	2 61 799	9	04 363
10	0.174 53 293	70	1.221 73 048	10	.002 90 888	10	.000 04 848
11	.191 98 622	71	.239 18 377	11	3 19 977	11	05 333
12	.209 43 951	72	.256 63 706	12	3 49 066	12	05 818
13	.226 89 280	73	.274 09 035	13	3 78 155	13	06 303
14	.244 34 610	74	.291 54 365	14	4 07 243	14	06 787
15	0.261 79 939	75	1.308 99 694	15	.004 36 332	15	.000 07 272
16	.279 25 268	76	.326 45 023	16	4 65 421	16	07 757
17	.296 70 597	77	.343 90 352	17	4 94 510	17	08 242
18	.314 15 927	78	.361 35 682	18	5 23 599	18	08 727
19	.331 61 256	79	.378 81 011	19	5 52 688	19	09 211
20	0.349 06 585	80	1.396 26 340	20	.005 81 776	20	.000 09 696
21	.366 51 914	81	.413 71 669	21	6 10 865	21	10 181
22	.383 97 244	82	.431 16 999	22	6 39 954	22	10 666
23	.401 42 573	83	.448 62 328	23	6 69 043	23	11 151
24	.418 87 902	84	.466 07 657	24	6 98 132	24	11 636
25	0.436 33 231	85	1.483 52 986	25	.007 27 221	25	.000 12 120
26	.453 78 561	86	.500 98 316	26	7 56 309	26	12 605
27	.471 23 890	87	.518 43 645	27	7 85 398	27	13 090
28	.488 69 219	88	.535 88 974	28	8 14 487	28	13 575
29	.506 14 548	89	.553 34 303	29	8 43 576	29	14 060
30	0.523 59 878	90	1.570 79 633	30	.008 72 665	30	.000 14 544
31	.541 05 207	91	.588 24 962	31	9 01 753	31	15 029
32	.558 50 536	92	.605 70 291	32	9 30 842	32	15 514
33	.575 95 865	93	.623 15 620	33	9 59 931	33	15 999
34	.593 41 195	94	.640 60 950	34	9 89 020	34	16 484
35	0.610 86 524	95	1.658 06 279	35	.010 18 109	35	.000 16 969
36	.628 31 853	96	.675 51 608	36	10 47 198	36	17 453
37	.645 77 182	97	.692 96 937	37	10 76 286	37	17 938
38	.663 22 512	98	.710 42 267	38	11 05 375	38	18 423
39	.680 67 841	99	.727 87 596	39	11 34 464	39	18 908
40	0.698 13 170	100	1.745 32 925	40	.011 63 553	40	.000 19 393
41	.715 58 499	101	.762 78 254	41	11 92 642	41	19 877
42	.733 03 829	102	.780 23 584	42	12 21 730	42	20 362
43	.750 49 158	103	.797 68 913	43	12 50 819	43	20 847
44	.767 94 487	104	.815 14 242	44	12 79 908	44	21 332
45	0.785 39 816	105	1.832 59 571	45	.013 08 997	45	.000 21 817
46	.802 85 146	106	.850 04 901	46	13 38 086	46	22 301
47	.820 30 475	107	.867 50 230	47	13 67 175	47	22 786
48	.837 75 804	108	.884 95 559	48	13 96 263	48	23 271
49	.855 21 133	109	.902 40 888	49	14 25 352	49	23 756
50	0.872 66 463	110	1.919 86 218	50	.014 54 441	50	.000 24 241
51	.890 11 792	111	.937 31 547	51	14 83 530	51	24 726
52	.907 57 121	112	.954 76 876	52	15 12 619	52	25 210
53	.925 02 450	113	.972 22 205	53	15 41 708	53	25 695
54	.942 47 780	114	.989 67 535	54	15 70 796	54	26 180
55	0.959 93 109	115	2.007 12 864	55	.015 99 885	55	.000 26 665
56	0.977 38 438	116	.024 58 193	56	16 28 974	56	27 150
57	0.994 83 767	117	.042 03 522	57	16 58 063	57	27 634
58	1.012 29 097	118	.059 48 852	58	16 87 152	58	28 119
59	1.029 74 426	119	.076 94 181	59	17 16 240	59	28 604
60	1.047 19 755	120	.094 39 510	60	17 45 329	60	29 089

TABLE H.—TRIGONOMETRIC FORMULAS FOR THE SOLUTION OF RIGHT TRIANGLES

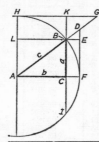

Let A = angle BAC = arc BF, and let radius AF = AB = AH = 1. Then,

sin $A = BC$	csc $A = AG$
cos $A = AC$	sec $A = AD$
tan $A = DF$	cot $A = HG$
vers $A = CF = BE$	covers $A = BK = LH$
exsec $A = BD$	coexsec $A = BG$
chord $A = BF$	chord 2 $A = BI = 2\ BC$

In the right-angled triangle ABC, let $AB = c$, $BC = a$, $CA = b$. Then,

1. $\sin A = \dfrac{a}{c}$

2. $\cos A = \dfrac{b}{c}$

3. $\tan A = \dfrac{a}{b}$

4. $\cot A = \dfrac{b}{a}$

5. $\sec A = \dfrac{c}{b}$

6. $\csc A = \dfrac{c}{a}$

7. vers $A = 1 - \cos A = \dfrac{c-b}{c} = $ covers B

8. exsec $A = \sec A - 1 = \dfrac{c-b}{b} = $ coexsec B

9. covers $A = \dfrac{c-a}{c} = $ vers B

10. coexsec $A = \dfrac{c-a}{a} = $ exsec B

11. $a = c \sin A = b \tan A$

12. $b = c \cos A = a \cot A$

13. $c = \dfrac{a}{\sin A} = \dfrac{b}{\cos A}$

14. $a = c \cos B = b \cot B$

15. $b = c \sin B = a \tan B$

16. $c = \dfrac{a}{\cos B} = \dfrac{b}{\sin B}$

17. $a = \sqrt{c^2 - b^2} = \sqrt{(c-b)(c+b)}$

18. $b = \sqrt{c^2 - a^2} = \sqrt{(c-a)(c+a)}$

19. $c = \sqrt{a^2 + b^2}$

20. $C = 90° = A + B$

21. Area $= \frac{1}{2}ab$

TABLE I.—TRIGONOMETRIC FORMULAS FOR THE SOLUTION OF OBLIQUE TRIANGLES

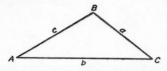

No.	Given	Sought	Formula
22	A, B, a	C, b, c	$C = 180° - (A+B)$ $b = \dfrac{a}{\sin A} \times \sin B$ $c = \dfrac{a}{\sin A} \times \sin (A+B) = \dfrac{a}{\sin A} \times \sin C$
		Area	$\text{Area} = \tfrac{1}{2}ab \sin C = \dfrac{a^2 \sin B \sin C}{2 \sin A}$
23	A, a, b	B, C, c	$\sin B = \dfrac{\sin A}{a} \times b$ $C = 180° - (A+B)$ $c = \dfrac{a}{\sin A} \times \sin C$
		Area	$\text{Area} = \tfrac{1}{2}ab \sin C$
24	$C, a, b,$	c	$c = \sqrt{a^2 + b^2 - 2ab \cos C}$
25		$\tfrac{1}{2}(A+B)$	$\tfrac{1}{2}(A+B) = 90° - \tfrac{1}{2}C$
26		$\tfrac{1}{2}(A-B)$	$\tan \tfrac{1}{2}(A-B) = \dfrac{a-b}{a+b} \times \tan \tfrac{1}{2}(A+B)$
27		A, B	$A = \tfrac{1}{2}(A+B) + \tfrac{1}{2}(A-B)$ $B = \tfrac{1}{2}(A+B) - \tfrac{1}{2}(A-B)$
28		c	$c = (a+b) \times \dfrac{\cos \tfrac{1}{2}(A+B)}{\cos \tfrac{1}{2}(A-B)} = (a-b) \times \dfrac{\sin \tfrac{1}{2}(A+B)}{\sin \tfrac{1}{2}(A-B)}$
29		Area	$\text{Area} = \tfrac{1}{2}ab \sin C$
30	a, b, c	A	Let $s = \dfrac{a+b+c}{2}$
31			$\sin \tfrac{1}{2} A = \sqrt{\dfrac{(s-b)(s-c)}{bc}}$ $\cos \tfrac{1}{2} A = \sqrt{\dfrac{s(s-a)}{bc}}$ $\tan \tfrac{1}{2} A = \sqrt{\dfrac{(s-b)(s-c)}{s(s-a)}}$
32			$\sin A = \dfrac{2\sqrt{s(s-a)(s-b)(s-c)}}{bc}$ $\cos A = \dfrac{b^2 + c^2 - a^2}{2bc}$
33		Area	$\text{Area} = \sqrt{s(s-a)(s-b)(s-c)}$

INDEX

INDEX